PATHWAYS TO
PREGNANCY & PARTURITION

3RD EDITION

P.L. SENGER, Ph.D.

Emeritus Professor
Washington State University
Pullman, Washington 99164-6332 USA

Current Conceptions, Inc.

8045 NW Grubstake Way
Redmond, OR 97756

Website: www.currentconceptions.com
E-mail: cciadmin@currentconceptions.com

ISBN 0-9657648-3-4

3rd Edition
Phillip L. Senger, Author

Printed in the United States of America by: Innovative Technologies in Print (www.itpofusa.com)

First Edition, 1997
First Revised Edition, 1999
Second Edition, 2003
Second Revised Edition, 2005

Additional copies may be ordered from:

Current Conceptions, Inc.
8045 NW Grubstake Way
Redmond, OR 97756
www.currentconceptions.com

Phone: 541-526-5803
FAX: 541-316-1653
Email: cciadmin@currentconceptions.com

Cover art: Glenn Burleigh (www.creativejunipersource.com)
Cover design: Jill DelSordi
Specimen photograpy: Henry Moore, Jr.
Cover photography: Angela C. Oki
Pre-press layout: Angela C. Oki
Art and Graphics: Sonja Gerard, Oei Graphics, Bellevue,WA (sgerard@oeigraphics.com)
        Jill DelSordi, White Window Studios, Seattle, WA (www.whitewindowstudios.com)

Cover Art

The image on the cover was sculpted from 12 different wooden pieces from Western Juniper trees. The sculpture is symbolic of the male reproductive tract of ungulates. The artist is Glenn Burleigh of Powell Butte, Oregon where he specializes in artistic creations from the Western Juniper (his work can be viewed at www.creativejunipersource.com).

Western Juniper trees (*Juniperus occidentalis*), like the ones in the photo below, are common in the high desert of Central Oregon. The species is drought hardy, very slow growing and long-lived. It is common for these trees in this ecosytem to live up to 400 years. Records indicate that one individual of the Juniper subspecies in California is over 3,000 years old.

DEDICATION

*To paraphrase Hodding Carter, there are two lasting benefits
we can give our students, children and other people we associate with.*
"One is roots and the other is wings."

This book is dedicated to Dr. R.G. (Dick) Saacke and his wife, Ann, a couple who have been models for countless students, fellow educators/professionals, friends and their own children in emphasizing the importance of uncompromising commitment to high standards and values (**roots**). At the same time, they have always encouraged others to fly and to enjoy their journey (**wings**).

Ann Saacke and Dr. R.G. Saacke

THE AUTHOR

P. L. (Phil) Senger grew up in Cary, North Carolina and received his B.S. in Zoology from North Carolina State University. He was awarded the M.S. and Ph.D. in reproductive physiology from Virginia Polytechnic Institute and State University. He has been Professor of Animal Sciences at Washington State University and Penn State University where his primary teaching responsibilities included animal physiology and reproductive physiology. He has authored over 200 scientific, educational and popular press papers. Dr. Senger is currently President of Current Conceptions, Inc.

Dr. Senger has over 30 years of experience conducting research and teaching students, and clientele about reproductive physiology. He is the recipient of six teaching awards, including the *American Society of Animal Science Distinguished Teaching Award* in 1998 and the Marion E. Smith Faculty Achievement Award in 2005. He has received two national awards for research in reproductive physiology. Dr. Senger has been a frequent speaker, columnist and author about animal reproduction to clientele throughout the world.

PREFACE

The ultimate goal of **Pathways to Pregnancy and Parturition - 3rd Edition** is to enable people to understand the principles of reproductive physiology. This discipline is a visual one and requires images of anatomical structures and physiologic processes. Good visual imaging makes learning easier, less time consuming and the knowledge is retained longer. We have made every effort to make this book a good investment in visual understanding.

As students, when you listen to lectures, read and study the content, we hope that this book will help you draw pictures of the concepts in your minds. In this context, the comment *"if you can't draw a picture of it, you probably don't understand it"* made by Larry M. Lee (B.S., M.S., Engineering) should serve as an educational mantra in your pursuit of understanding, regardless of the subject matter.

Third Edition of **Pathways to Pregnancy and Parturition** is not an expanded one. It remains approximately the same length as 2nd Revised Edition. It continues to reflect our philosophy that science textbooks should focus on the essential concepts without unessential detail, build a logical flow of information and refrain from becoming "information dumps" that overwhelm students and instructors alike.

KNOWLEDGE & KNOW-HOW

The reproductive physiologists listed below are known for their excellence in research <u>AND</u> their excellence in teaching. These individuals made valuable contributions to the educational mission of this book by serving as reviewers of one or more chapters.

C. A. Bagnell (Rutgers University)

J. G. Berardinelli (Montana State University)

P. J. Chenoweth (Charles Sturt University, Australia)

E. K. Inskeep (West Virginia University)

J. S. Jorgensen (University of Wisconsin-Madison)

J. W. Knight (Virginia Tech)

M. C. Lucy (University of Missouri)

A. L. Macrina (Penn State University)

T. L. Ott (Penn State University)

J. E. Parks (Cornell University)

J. J. Parrish (University of Wisconsin-Madison)

J. L. Pate (Penn State University)

J. K. Pru (Washington State University)

G. D. Smith (University of Michigan)

A. Tibary (Washington State University)

R. R. Wilborn (Auburn University)

KNOWLEDGE & KNOW-HOW

Several Baccalaureate and Veterinary students contributed significantly and are presented below.

Cerissa K. Blair - BS, Animal Sciences, Washington State University, 2002.
She assisted in the development of Figure 4-11 (inguinal hernia) in cooperation with the Washington State University Student Swine Cooperative.

Rebecca L. Cody - BS, Animal Sciences, Washington State University, 1998, DVM, Washington State University 2002.
Figures 3-9 and 3-10 were produced as part of a Washington State University Honors College Thesis entitled, "Intravascular Polymerization as a Method of Observing Countercurrent Exchange Systems in Bovine Reproductive Tracts," 1998. The project was sponsored by Current Conceptions, Inc., Pullman, WA.

Christina M. Davis - BS, Animal Sciences, Washington State University, 2002.
Figures 15-4 through 15-8 were produced as part of a Washington State University Honors College Thesis entitled, "A Full-Color Photographic Description of Postpartum Uterine Involution in the Dairy Cow," 2002. The project was sponsored by Current Conceptions, Inc., Pullman, WA.

Sarah Bobbitt - BS, Animal Sciences, University of Idaho, 2006. The 3-D model describing the relationship between Sertoli cells and developing germ cells.

Brian R. Voortman - BS, Animal Sciences, Washington State University, 1998. DVM, Washington State University 2002. Assisted in the preparation of placental specimens and vascular casting.

The following individuals provided valuable technical assistance.

S.R. Fenimore - Radiology Technician, College of Veterinary Medicine, Washington State University

P.L. Johnson - Instructional Lab Supervisor, College of Veterinary Medicine, Washington State University

V.L. Mitzimberg - Technician Supervisor, College of Veterinary Medicine, Washington State University

B.A. Toms - Project Manager, Innovative Technologies in Print

TABLE OF CONTENTS

Introduction to
REPRODUCTION

TAKE HOME MESSAGE

Reproduction is a sequence of events beginning with development of the reproductive system in the embryo. After the animal is born, it must grow and achieve puberty by acquiring the ability to produce fertile gametes. This ability must be accompanied by reproductive behavior and copulation. After copulation, the sperm and egg meet, fertilization occurs and development of the preattachment embryo follows. The conceptus attaches to the uterus by a specialized organ called the placenta. It allows the conceptus to grow and develop to term. The fully developed fetus is born and the female giving birth to it must lactate to provide nourishment for the neonate. During or after lactation the dam must reestablish cyclicity before she can become pregnant again. Knowledge and understanding of the reproductive process will become increasingly important as the human population continues to grow and resources become increasingly scarce.

Welcome to the exciting and fascinating subject of reproductive physiology. Among the many scientific subjects in the natural sciences, knowledge about reproductive physiology commands interest even among those who have no scientific inclination at all. In its broadest sense, the subject of reproductive physiology carries with it interest, imagination, expectation, emotion and an intrinsic desire to know more. The average person on the street could care less about Boyle's Law, Beer's Law, the periodic table or the phylogenetic organization of plant and animal kingdoms. But, mention copulation, ejaculation, spermatozoa, pregnancy, the uterus, fertilization, embryo development or any of the myriad terms associated with reproduction and most people will be interested. Almost without exception, everyone wants to know more about the reproductive process, whether it relates to humans, food-producing animals, their pet or just for the sake of having more knowledge.

Reproductive Science Consists of Several Subspecialities

The field of reproductive science is a subspecialty of the physiology discipline. In its broadest context, reproductive science can be defined as the study of reproductive processes regardless of species. In the field of Animal Sciences, reproductive physiology is a general term used to describe a field of study that deals primarily with reproduction in food-producing animals. The terms andrology, gynecology, theriogenology and obstetrics all imply a clinical application associated with reproductive function in humans and animals. **Andrology** is a branch of reproductive physiology that deals specifically with the study and treatment of male animals including humans. **Gynecology** is a branch of reproductive physiology and medicine that deals specifically with reproductive issues in women. **Theriogenology** is a branch of veterinary medicine that focuses on the reproductive system in animals. **Obstetrics** is a branch of reproductive physiology, veterinary medicine and/or human medicine that specializes in the female before, during and after parturition.

Reproductive science is one of the most relevant specialties in all of biology. There is a wide breadth of applications and opportunities in the field of reproductive physiology that range from animal production, clinical, educational and research applications (See Figure 1-1). Also, pharmaceutical companies manufacture and market hundreds of hormones and drugs that manipulate reproductive functions in humans and animals. These corporations provide significant research, technology transfer and marketing opportunities for those with training in reproductive physiology.

Figure 1-1. Opportunities in Reproductive Physiology

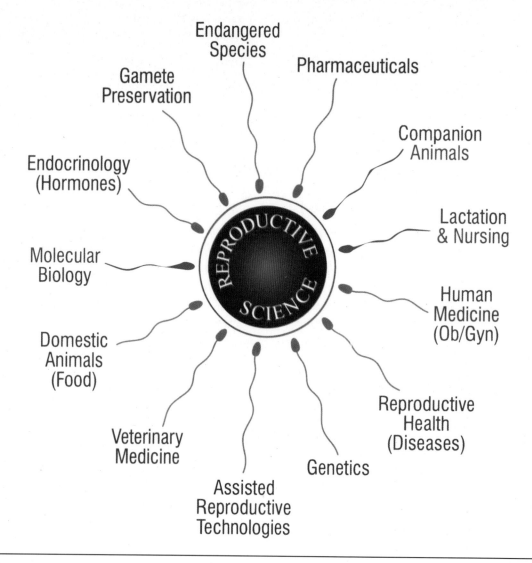

You Should Have Some Knowledge About the Historical Development of Reproductive Physiology

> *The study of reproductive physiology started with Aristotle around 2350 years ago. But, most of our knowledge has been generated during the past 100 years.*

Aristotle provided the first recorded information on how he thought the reproductive system functioned in his book entitled *Generation of Animals*. He believed that the fetus arose from menstrual blood. He had no way of observing spermatozoa in the ejaculate or the beginnings of embryo development. Therefore, he concluded, based on the observation that menstruation did not occur during pregnancy that the fetus was derived from menstrual blood. He also proposed that the conversion of menstrual blood to a fetus was initiated by seminal fluid deposited in the female during copulation. Aristotle thought that semen was derived from all parts of the body and that the testes were simply pendular weights that kept the transport ducts (the ductus deferens) from becoming kinked or plugged with seminal fluid. Considering that Aristotle had no research tools whatsoever, his speculations were quite reasonable.

The next major observation in reproductive physiology, occurring almost 2,000 years later, was made by Fallopius, who described the oviducts. The name **Fallopian tube** reflects his discovery. A student of Fallopius, Coiter, discovered the **corpus luteum** in 1573. It wasn't until almost 100 years later that a scientist named Regnier de Graaf described the antral follicle that has been named the **Graafian follicle** in honor of his discovery. De Graaf killed female rabbits at half-hour intervals after they had copulated. He discovered that the number of "scar-like" wounds on the surface of the ovaries (we now know these to be ovulation sites) usually corresponded with the number of embryos in the uterus of the rabbit. However, de Graaf thought that the entire follicle was the egg.

A major technological breakthrough in the study of reproductive physiology was made by a Dutch scientist named van Leeuwenhoek, who developed a simple microscope. A medical student suggested to van Leeuwenhoek that semen might contain living cells. Using his microscope, van Leeuwenhoek observed semen and discovered that it contained small particles that moved about. He referred to these particles as "animalcules". While the first "animalcules" were observed in semen from a man afflicted with a venereal disease, van Leeuwenhoek found that similar "animalcules" were present in semen from males of many species and published a paper on his observations in 1677. The discovery that semen contained "animalcules" (spermatozoa) led to an outburst of speculation regarding their function. The most widely accepted speculation of the day was that the "animalcules" contained fully formed individuals within their cellular confines. In other words, the sperm head was thought to contain a microscopic, yet fully formed individual.

The father of modern artificial insemination was an Italian priest named Spallanzani. He showed that one drop of dog semen diluted with 25 pounds of fluid retained its ability to fertilize. Using the dog, he performed the first artificial insemination.

The fertilization process was not described until it was discovered that follicles contained ova and were precursors to the early embryo. A scientist named Dumas collected bodies about 1 mm in diameter from rabbit follicles. This discovery led Dumas to conclude that the "animalcules," now called spermatozoa, were responsible for uniting with the ovum and producing an embryo. Using rabbits, he demonstrated in 1825 that spermatozoa were the fertilizing agents. This early description of fertilization marked the beginning of modern reproductive physiology. Over 2,000 years elapsed from the original conjectures of Aristotle until it was understood that spermatozoa from the male were required to fertilize ova from the female. The major historical events leading to development of the modern discipline of reproductive physiology are presented in Figure 1-2.

The era of modern reproductive physiology that followed can be characterized as an "explosion of knowledge." While it is common knowledge today, recognition that the gonads produce steroid hormones that alter the function of the reproductive tissues and that the anterior pituitary controls the function of the gonads were major milestones of discovery. The understanding that females experience reproductive cyclicity and that they ovulate with predictable frequency continued the explosion of knowledge. Development of the radioimmunoassay for the measurement of hormones enabled the precise description of hormonal profiles in both the male and female. These discoveries opened the door for the development of methods for artificial manipulation of reproductive processes. In the 1940's and 1950's, understanding spermatozoal physiology and how these cells function in test-tube environments led to successful artificial insemination in several species. It wasn't until the 1960's that it was understood that prostaglandin $F_{2\alpha}$ regulated the length of the estrous cycle in most mammalian females. The discovery that natural prostaglandin $F_{2\alpha}$ caused destruction of the corpus luteum made it possible to manipulate and alter estrous cycles and to control the time of ovulation. Such application is now commonplace in dairy and beef enterprises throughout the world.

> *Improvement in reproductive rate is a major goal in food animal production because a 3% increase would result in:*
> * *1 million more beef calves/year*
> * *3.2 million more pigs/year*
> * *3.7 million more gallons of milk/year*

Once a certain fundamental level of understanding had been achieved, reproductive physiologists began to develop ways to perturb or to manipulate reproductive events within the animal. Such manipulations are a major goal in reproductive physiology research today. Techniques for enhancing reproduction are important when one considers that animal-derived food products are based on the ability of the species to reproduce. Small improvements in reproductive rate have profound positive effects on overall efficiency of production. For example, litter size in swine is an important characteristic that is a function of ovulation rate, fertilization rate and number of live pigs born. In dairy cows, failure to produce one calf every 13-14 months results in compromised milk production. In beef cattle, the reproducing cow is the fundamental production unit. Production of less than one calf per year reduces the efficiency of the beef herd. In sheep, the ability to give birth to twins and to nurse these individuals to weaning significantly improves production.

Figure 1-2. The History of Reproductive Physiology

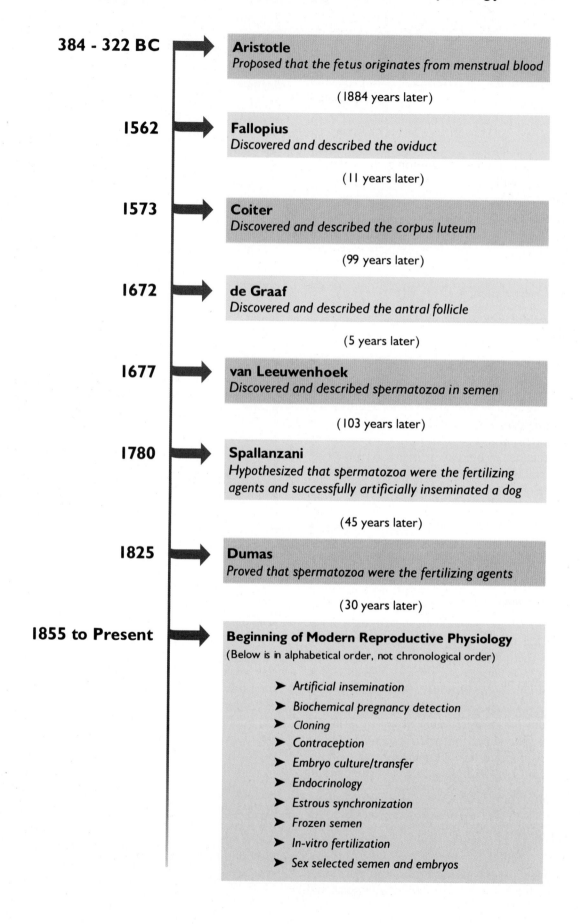

384 - 322 BC

Aristotle
Proposed that the fetus originates from menstrual blood

(1884 years later)

1562

Fallopius
Discovered and described the oviduct

(11 years later)

1573

Coiter
Discovered and described the corpus luteum

(99 years later)

1672

de Graaf
Discovered and described the antral follicle

(5 years later)

1677

van Leeuwenhoek
Discovered and described spermatozoa in semen

(103 years later)

1780

Spallanzani
Hypothesized that spermatozoa were the fertilizing agents and successfully artificially inseminated a dog

(45 years later)

1825

Dumas
Proved that spermatozoa were the fertilizing agents

(30 years later)

1855 to Present

Beginning of Modern Reproductive Physiology
(Below is in alphabetical order, not chronological order)

➤ *Artificial insemination*
➤ *Biochemical pregnancy detection*
➤ *Cloning*
➤ *Contraception*
➤ *Embryo culture/transfer*
➤ *Endocrinology*
➤ *Estrous synchronization*
➤ *Frozen semen*
➤ *In-vitro fertilization*
➤ *Sex selected semen and embryos*

Any factor that improves reproductive performance even slightly has the potential of having a large impact on the efficiency of food animal production. For example, there are approximately 35 million beef cows in the American beef herd. If the overall reproductive rate could be improved by only 3%, an additional 1.05 million beef calves would be born in one year. In swine, a 3% increase in pigs weaned would translate into an increase of 3.2 million pigs per year in the national swine herd. In the American dairy herd, a 3% increase in pregnancy rate would translate into an additional 3.7 million gallons of milk per year. There will always be a need for managers of food animal enterprises, their veterinarians and related agribusiness service personnel to have a strong understanding of reproductive physiology, because proper application of new technology will require this knowledge.

> ### The Global Population Crisis means that:
>
> - *in the time it takes you to read this sentence, 24 people will be added to the earth's population*
>
> - *within an hour, the number will reach 12,000*
>
> - *by day's end it will be 288,000*
>
> - *before you go to bed two nights from now, the net growth in the human population will be enough to fill a city the size of San Francisco*

There will be an increasing demand in the future for the development of new techniques to limit rather than enhance reproductive function. The human population must be controlled so that overpopulation does not erode worldwide resources and quality of life. Elimination of costly wastes associated with overpopulation of pets must be accomplished. In addition, methods to control the population growth of vermin and insects through reproductive manipulation will be needed as environmental concerns preclude the use of chemical control. The above needs will become more urgent with time. Therefore, there will be an increasing need for understanding the reproductive processes in more and more species.

> ### The global challenge is to:
>
> - *decrease the rate of human population growth*
>
> - *increase reproduction efficiency in food-producing animals*
>
> - *educate the public about the importance of managing reproductive function in all species*

In addition to basic scientific understanding, better educational techniques must be developed to disseminate knowledge regarding reproductive processes so that individuals without specialized training can appreciate and apply techniques that will improve the quality of life in both humans and animals. Basic knowledge and understanding are the prerequisites for the solution to any problem. It is the intent of this book to provide this basic knowledge about reproductive physiology so that current and future problems in the field can be solved.

How to Make This Book Work for You

Pathways to Pregnancy and Parturition is intended to help you develop a solid scientific understanding of the principles of reproduction in domestic animals and humans. Further, it is intended to help you become fluent in the language of the subject matter. If you develop this fluency, you will enjoy a lifetime of understanding that will enable you to adapt successfully to new knowledge and technology that will affect reproduction in animals as well as humans.

> ### Pathways to Pregnancy and Parturition includes the following aids to learning:
> - *sequence maps*
> - *take-home messages*
> - *fact boxes*
> - *bolded words*

As you use ***Pathways to Pregnancy and Parturition***, you will encounter a "**Sequence Map**" at the beginning of each chapter (See Figure 1-3). In the "sequence map," each major event is represented by a sphere positioned along the pathway. A sign, reading "**You Are Here**" lets you know exactly where the

Figure 1-3. Sequence Map of Reproductive Events

The male and female have a common sequence of developmental events until after copulation. After copulation the female bears all of the responsibility for gestation, parturition, lactation and postpartum uterine repair. The arrow on the male pathway indicates his departure from the sequence after copulation. The sign "**You are here**" indicates where the chapter you are about to read fits in the sequence of reproductive events.

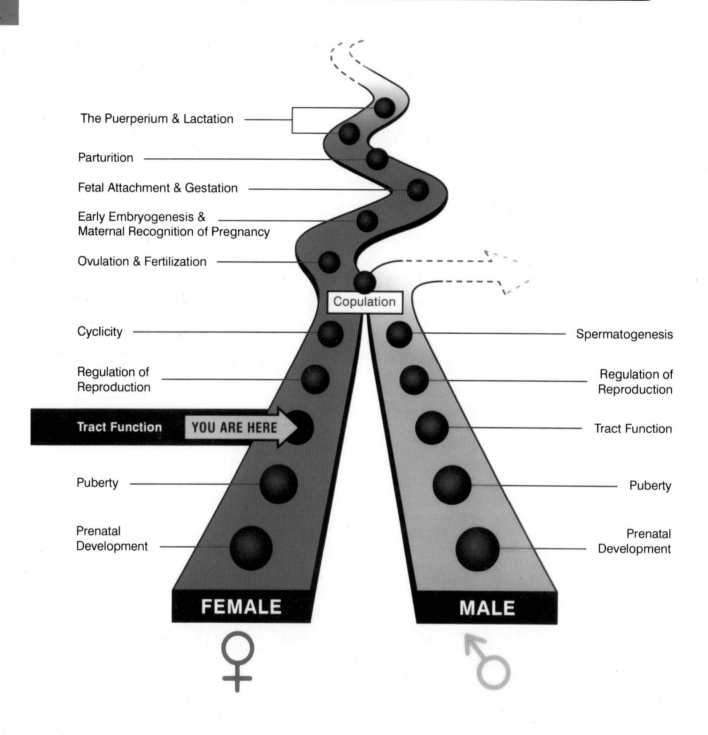

The Puerperium & Lactation

Parturition

Fetal Attachment & Gestation

Early Embryogenesis & Maternal Recognition of Pregnancy

Ovulation & Fertilization

Copulation

Cyclicity — Spermatogenesis

Regulation of Reproduction — Regulation of Reproduction

Tract Function — YOU ARE HERE — Tract Function

Puberty — Puberty

Prenatal Development — Prenatal Development

FEMALE   MALE

chapter you are about to read and where each particular chapter fits in the overall sequence of reproductive events. Each event in the "sequence map" has one or more chapters dedicated to it.

As you read the chapters in this book you will encounter several features that are intended to make learning and understanding easy. The text of each chapter begins with a **"Take-Home Message"**. This feature provides you with the main points of the chapter before you engage the details. The "Take-Home Message" should establish some questions in your mind that will then be answered later in the chapter. It is also intended as a study guide, highlighting the main points of each chapter.

Fact Boxes are included throughout each chapter to give you a "quick read," to highlight important points, terms and/or sequences and to allow you to regroup your thoughts as you read the text.

Many words and terms in this textbook are in **bold print**. They are the important key words, learn their definitions. You should understand them, know how to pronounce them, know how to spell them and be able to use them correctly in a discussion or in writing. In addition to the explanations appearing in the text, these terms are also defined in the glossary at the end of the book.

At the end of each chapter is a short section called **"Key References"**. Important sources containing additional, in-depth information about the subject of the chapter are provided. In general, these are scientific review papers that will provide detail beyond what is presented in the chapter.

There are some remarkable reproductive phenomena throughout the animal kingdom. The section entitled "**Further Phenomena for Fertility**" is intended to present some of the interesting facts, observations and even myths relating to the topic of each chapter. This section will give species other than domestic animals a place to shine and will provide you with plenty of opportunities to amaze (and even teach) your friends and family about phenomena that go beyond the science.

"Prenatal Development" (Chapter 4)

Sex of the embryo is determined at the time of fertilization. However, the development of a male or a female reproductive tract and the anterior and posterior pituitary occurs later, during development of the embryo.

"Acquisition of Puberty" (Chapter 6)

After the animal is born, it enters a period of growth and development that precedes the development of reproductive function. After a critical body size is reached, the hypothalamus and pituitary begin to secrete hormones, the animal enters puberty and the reproductive system gains full function.

"Tract Function" (Chapters 2 and 3)

Complete anatomical structure and function of the male and female reproductive tract are required before successful reproduction can take place. Knowledge of the function and structure of the reproductive organs is essential for complete understanding.

"Regulation of Reproduction" (Chapter 5)

After the animal reaches puberty, the reproductive system is regulated precisely by an intricate interplay of hormones secreted by the anterior pituitary and the gonads (ovaries and testes). This interplay of hormones results in cyclicity in the female and spermatogenesis in the male.

"Cyclicity" (Chapters 7, 8 and 9)

The female must exhibit estrous cycles. An estrous cycle is characterized as a repeated sequence of events, usually beginning with behavioral estrus (heat) and ending with a subsequent behavioral estrus several weeks later. The estrous cycle consists of a follicular phase and a luteal phase.

"Spermatogenesis" (Chapter 10)

After puberty, the male acquires the ability to produce large quantities of spermatozoa. These spermatozoa are produced on a continual basis in most males. Control of spermatogenesis is under the influence of pituitary hormones. Males are capable of producing between 1 and 25 billion spermatozoa per day.

"Reproductive Behavior and Copulation" (Chapter 11)

One of the characteristics associated with the acquisition of full reproductive potential is the display of reproductive behavior culminating in copulation and deposition of sperm into the female reproductive tract. The physiologic regulation of reproductive behavior is one of the most interesting, yet poorly understood components of reproductive physiology.

"Ovulation and Fertilization" (Chapter 12)

In most species, ovulation occurs after copulation. Fertilization then occurs and is the result of a series of cellular changes in the sperm and the oocyte within the female reproductive tract.

"Early Embryogenesis and Maternal Recognition of Pregnancy" (Chapter 13)

After fertilization, the embryo begins to develop and sends biochemical signals to the dam, physiologically "notifying" her that she is pregnant. Failure of these signals to be sent or recognized results in the termination of pregnancy.

"Placentation and the Endocrinology of Gestation and Parturition" (Chapter 14)

If successful maternal recognition of pregnancy occurs, then the fetus will attach to the uterus, forming a placenta that controls the exchange of nutrients and gases between the fetus and the dam. This transient organ (the placenta) also secretes hormones important for successful gestation. Successful birth (parturition) concludes the series of reproductive events. Parturition is a carefully orchestrated interplay of endocrine and muscular events.

"The Puerperium and Lactation" (Chapter 15)

Immediately after parturition, the female will begin to **lactate**. The purpose of lactation is to provide the neonatal animal with nutrition to grow and develop until it is weaned. Coincident with lactation is a period called the **puerperium**. During this period, uterine involution occurs along with return to cyclicity. Involution of the uterus is a dramatic reduction in size of the uterus and repair of the endometrial epithelium. Generally, the postpartum female does not become pregnant a second time until uterine involution is complete. Factors that alter the rate of uterine involution impact reproductive performance.

"Reproductive Physiology- The Human Factor" (Chapter 16)

The human reproductive process is unique in a number of ways. The menstrual cycle, while similar in concept to the estrous cycle has several unique features. Hormonal contraception is a widely used intervention that is not well understood by its users. Assisted reproductive technologies provide opportunities for infertile couples to become pregnant and have children. Long life expectancies are characterized by profound physiologic changes associated with menopause and andropause. This chapter will discuss the physiologic basis for these unique aspects of human reproduction.

Key References

The "Further Phenomena For Fertility" section at the end of each chapter contains a variety of information from widely scattered sources. The references below were the source for some of the information. They also contain many additional interesting concepts about reproduction in humans and a variety of other species.

Diamond, J.M. 1997. *Why Sex is Fun? The Evolution of Human Sexuality*. Basic Books. New York. ISBN 0-465-03127-7.

Judson, O. 2002. *Dr. Tatiana's Sex Advice to All Creation*. Metropolitan Books. New York. ISBN 0-8050-6331-5.

Low, B.S. 2000. *Why Sex Matters- A Darwinian Look at Human Behavior*. Princeton University Press. Princeton, NJ. ISBN 0-691-02895-8.

Panati, C. 1998. *Sexy Origins and Intimate Things*. Penguin Books. New York. ISBN 0-14027-1449.

Windybank, S. 1991. *Wild Sex - Way Beyond the Birds and the Bees*. St. Martin Press. New York. ISBN 0-312-08336-x.

1

CHAPTER 2

The Organization & Function of the
MALE REPRODUCTIVE TRACT

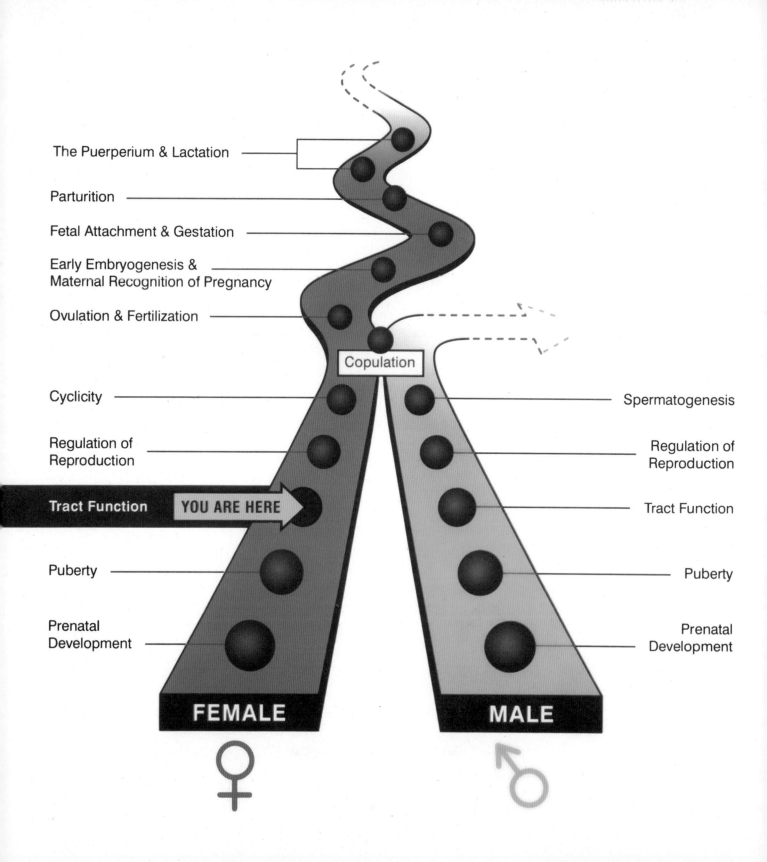

The Puerperium & Lactation

Parturition

Fetal Attachment & Gestation

Early Embryogenesis &
Maternal Recognition of Pregnancy

Ovulation & Fertilization

Copulation

Cyclicity

Regulation of
Reproduction

Tract Function

YOU ARE HERE

Puberty

Prenatal
Development

FEMALE

Spermatogenesis

Regulation of
Reproduction

Tract Function

Puberty

Prenatal
Development

MALE

Take Home Message

The female reproductive tract includes the ovaries, oviducts, uterus, cervix, vagina and the external genitalia. The ovaries produce gametes and a variety of hormones that act upon other parts of the reproductive tract. The oviducts provide the optimal environment for fertilization and preattachment development of the embryo. The uterus provides the environment for sperm transport, early embryogenesis and the site for attachment of the conceptus. The cervix is a barrier that secretes mucus during estrus and produces a cervical seal during pregnancy. The vagina is the copulatory organ and produces lubricating mucus during the time of estrus. Each tubular part of the tract has an outer serosal layer that is continuous with the peritoneum, a muscularis consisting of a longitudinal and circular layer of smooth muscle, a submucosal layer and a mucosal layer lining the lumen of each organ, that secretes substances vita lto the function of each region.

The major structures of the female reproductive tract include the **ovaries** (the female gonads), **oviducts, uterus, cervix, vagina** and **external genitalia**. As you will see later in the chapter, each of these organs may be subdivided into components that represent specific anatomical regions. These components usually have specific names. In all domestic species, the reproductive tract lies directly beneath the rectum and is separated from it by the **rectogenital pouch** (See Figures 2-3, 2-4, 2-6 and 2-8). In the cow, mare, and camel this fortuitous anatomical relationship provides the opportunity for manual palpation (manipulation per rectum) and/or ultrasonic examination of the female reproductive tract to: 1) diagnose the ovarian status of the female; 2) diagnose pregnancy by determining the presence or absence of a fetus or of fetal membranes located within the uterus; 3) manipulate the tract for insertion of an artificial insemination syringe; 4) recover embryos using nonsurgical techniques and 5) identify reproductive tract abnormalities. The rectum of the ewe, bitch and queen is too small for the human arm/hand to be inserted and thus palpation per rectum cannot be performed in these females. In large gilts and sows, pregnancy can be ascertained by palpating the uterine artery after 40 or more days of gestation. Pregnant animals have a high degree of arterial tone and fremitus (vibration).

> *The female tract is a series of tubes. Each tube is organized in concentric layers called the:*
> - *serosa (outer)*
> - *muscularis*
> - *submucosa*
> - *mucosa (inner)*

In its simplest form, the female reproductive tract can be considered as a series of interconnected tubes. Each of these tubes has distinct anatomical features. Thus, each tubular component can be identified easily. The tubular components of the female tract are the oviducts, uterus, cervix and vagina. Each component of the reproductive tract is characterized by having four distinct concentric layers. If you were to observe a cross-section of any one of the tubular components of the female reproductive tract you would see that the cross-section is composed of similar layers across all regions of the tract. These components are the **serosa, muscularis, submucosa** and **mucosa** (See Figure 2-1). The outer **serosal** coating is a single-cell layer of squamous (flattened) cells that simply cover the surface of the reproductive tract. The **muscularis** is usually a double layer of smooth muscle consisting of an outer longitudinal layer and an inner circular layer. The purpose of the muscularis is to provide the tubular components with the ability to contract. Such contractions are important for the transport of secretory products, gametes (spermatozoa and ova) and early embryos to the appropriate location within the tract. The muscularis of the uterus is also important in expulsion of the fetus and fetal membranes during parturition.

Immediately beneath the muscularis is the **submucosa**. The submucosa is a layer of varying thickness (depending on the specific anatomical region of the tract). This region houses blood vessels, nerves and lymphatics. It also serves as a supporting tissue for the mucosal layer. The lumen in all the parts of the reproductive tract is lined with a secretory layer of epithelium known as the **mucosa**. Each part of the female reproductive tract is lined by a different type of mucosal epithelium. Each type of mucosal epithelium performs a different function depending on the region of the tract in which it is located. For example, the oviduct is lined with a mixture of ciliated and nonciliated simple columnar epithelium. The cells produce fluids and also move materials along the oviduct because of ciliary action (See Figure 2-12). The posterior vagina is lined with stratified squamous epithelium (See Figure 2-22) that provides the organ with protection during copulation.

> *The reproductive tract is surrounded by the peritoneum that is continuous with the broad ligament.*

In the conceptus, the reproductive tract develops in a **retroperitoneal** position (behind the peritoneum). The peritoneum is the connective tissue lining of the abdominal cavity and completely surrounds or covers the reproductive tract. During embryonic development the tract grows and begins to push against the peritoneum. As the tract continues to grow it becomes completely surrounded by the peritoneum. A portion of the peritoneum eventually fuses to form a double layered connective tissue sheet that supports and suspends the ovaries, oviduct, uterus, cervix and the anterior vagina (See Figure 2-2 and 2-3) This suspensory tissue is called the **broad ligament** and can be seen *in situ* (in its normal place or its place of origin) in Figure 2-3. It consists of several anatomical components that support the various organs of the female tract. The broad ligament houses the vascular supply, the lymphatic drainage and nerves.

> *Components of the broad ligament are the:*
> - *mesovarium*
> - *mesosalpinx*
> - *mesometrium*

The anterior (**cranial**) portion of the broad ligament attaches to and supports the ovary. This component is called the **mesovarium**. The mesovarium houses the blood and lymphatic vessels and nerves that supply the ovary and forms the **hilus** (See Figure 2-11) of the ovary. An additional supportive ligament for the ovary is also present in most species. This ligament is the **utero-ovarian ligament** (See Figure 2-13) and, as the name implies, it attaches the ovary to the uterus. The utero-ovarian ligament is sometimes called the **proper ligament of the ovary** and is not actually part of the broad ligament.

The **oviduct (salpinx)** is surrounded and supported by a thin, serous part of the broad ligament known as the **mesosalpinx**. A serous membrane is a smooth transparent surface that either covers, lines, or attaches to an organ. This delicate subdivision of the broad ligament not only supports the oviducts but serves as a **bursa**-like pouch that surrounds the ovary. The mesosalpinx helps to orient the infundibulum so that ova released at ovulation have a high probability of being directed into the oviduct. The nature and orientation of the mesosalpinx and the infundibulum in the cow, ewe, mare, sow, bitch and queen can be observed in Figures 2-13 and 2-14. In the bitch, the mesosalpinx completely encloses the ovary forming a nearly complete ovarian bursa that hides the ovary from direct view (See Figure 2-14)

The **mesometrium** is the largest and most conspicuous part of the broad ligament. It supports the **uterine horns (cornua)** and the body of the uterus. The dorsal portion of the mesometrium is continuous with the dorsal peritoneum and thus the uterus literally "hangs" from the dorsal body wall (See Figures 2-2 and 2-3).

Figure 2-1. Typical Tubular Structure of the Female Tract

The lumen is lined with epithelium called mucosa, that is supported by the submucosa. Typically, the muscularis is composed of an inner layer of circular smooth muscle and an outer longitudinal layer of smooth muscle. The serosa is the connective tissue covering the tract.

2

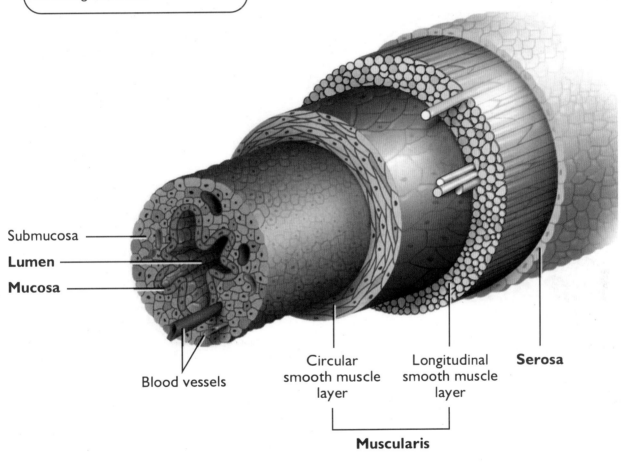

Submucosa

Lumen

Mucosa

Blood vessels

Circular
smooth muscle
layer

Longitudinal
smooth muscle
layer

Serosa

Muscularis

Figure 2-2.   Embryonic Development of the Broad Ligament

A

The uterine horns (UH) and the rectum (R) develop dorsal to the peritoneum. Development "behind" the peritoneum is called retroperitoneal.

B

As development advances, the uterine horn and rectum push into the body cavity (arrows in B) and eventually become completely surrounded by a layer of peritoneum (C).

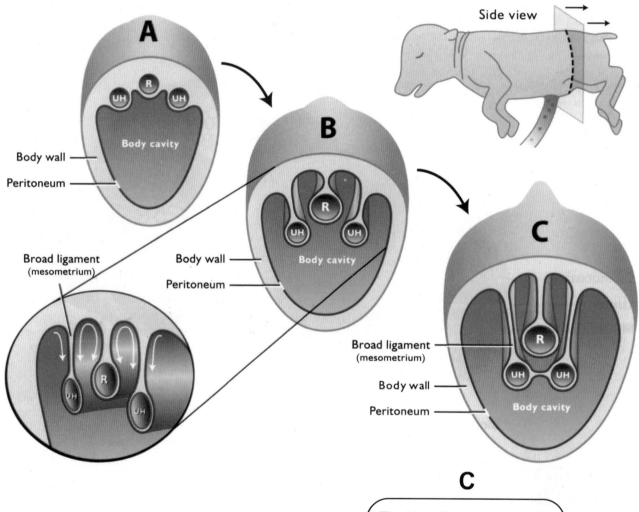

C

The broad ligament consists of two layers of peritoneum that "sandwich" the tract between them. Each layer of peritoneum is continuous with the peritoneal lining of the body cavity.

Figure 2-3. Caudal View of the Reproductive Tract
(Reproductive tracts *in situ*)

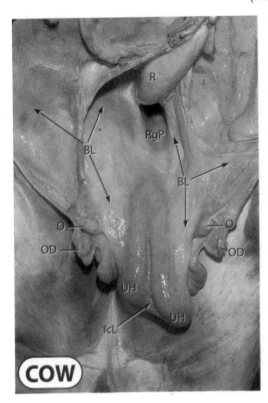

COW

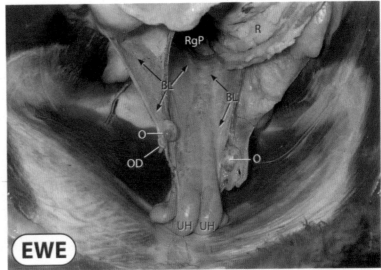

EWE

The intestines have been removed so that the reproductive tract is in full view. The tract is suspended by the broad ligament that is attached dorsally and is continuous with the peritoneum.

BL	=	Broad Ligament
CX	=	Cervix
IcL	=	Intercornual Ligament (Dorsal IcL seen here, Ventral IcL out of view.)
O	=	Ovary
OD	=	Oviduct
R	=	Rectum
RgP	=	Rectogenital Pouch
UH	=	Uterine Horn

(Photo of mare courtesy of O.J. Ginther)

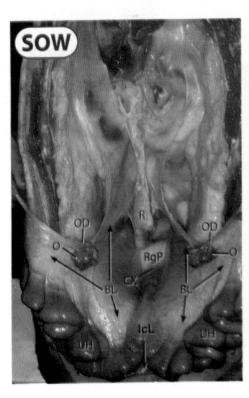

SOW

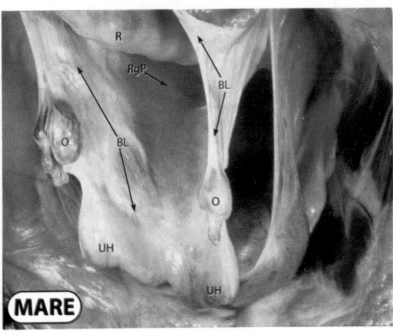

MARE

Figure 2-4. Lateral/Dorsal View of Cow

Ruminant (Cow)

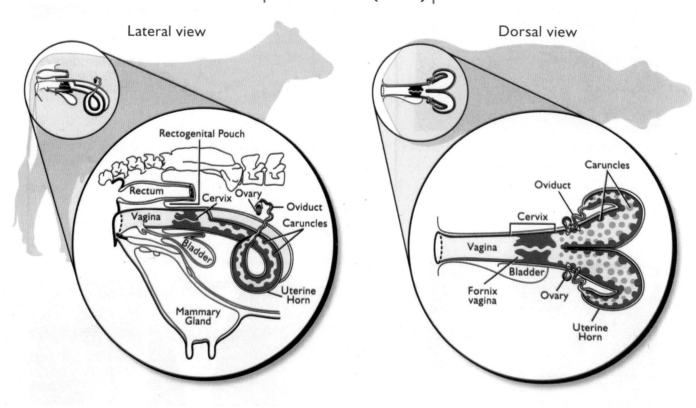

Lateral view

Dorsal view

Figure 2-5. Dorsal View of Excised Reproductive Tracts

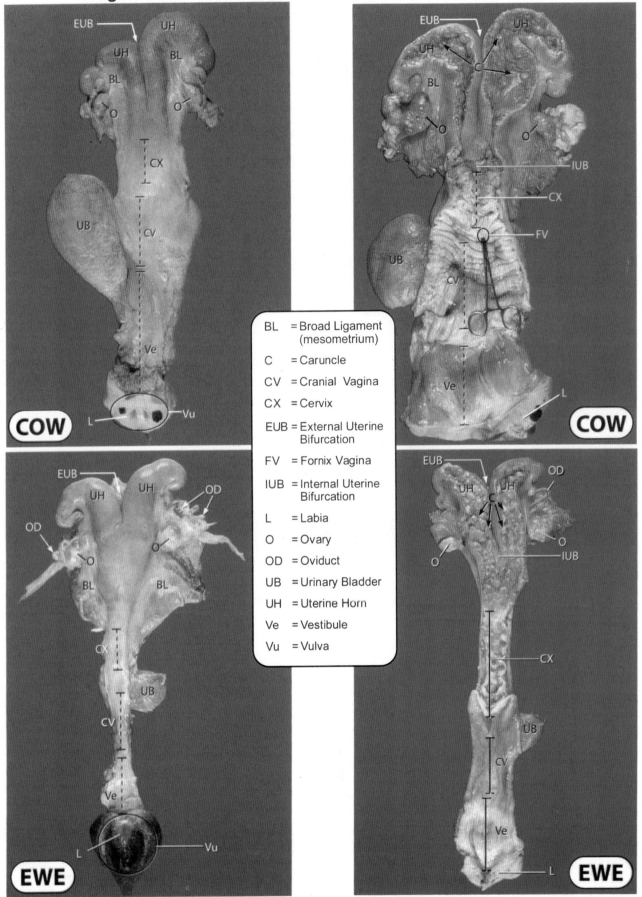

BL	= Broad Ligament (mesometrium)
C	= Caruncle
CV	= Cranial Vagina
CX	= Cervix
EUB	= External Uterine Bifurcation
FV	= Fornix Vagina
IUB	= Internal Uterine Bifurcation
L	= Labia
O	= Ovary
OD	= Oviduct
UB	= Urinary Bladder
UH	= Uterine Horn
Ve	= Vestibule
Vu	= Vulva

Figure 2-6. Lateral/Dorsal View of Sow and Mare

┤ **Sow** ├

Lateral view

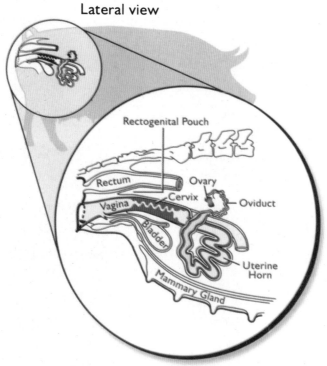

Dorsal view

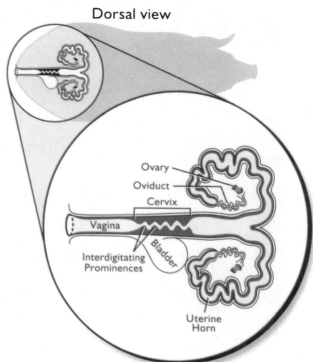

┤ **Mare** ├

Lateral view

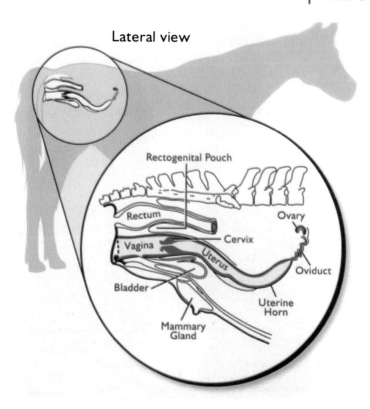

Dorsal view

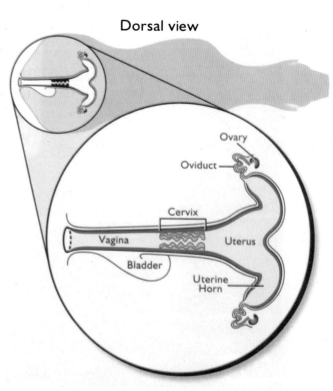

Figure 2-7. Dorsal View of Excised Reproductive Tracts

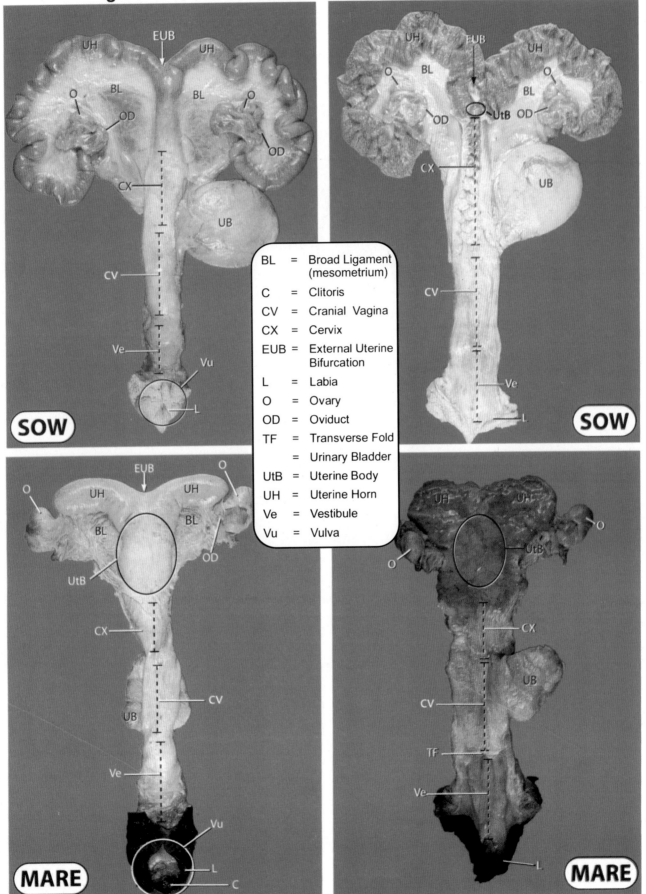

BL	=	Broad Ligament (mesometrium)
C	=	Clitoris
CV	=	Cranial Vagina
CX	=	Cervix
EUB	=	External Uterine Bifurcation
L	=	Labia
O	=	Ovary
OD	=	Oviduct
TF	=	Transverse Fold
	=	Urinary Bladder
UtB	=	Uterine Body
UH	=	Uterine Horn
Ve	=	Vestibule
Vu	=	Vulva

2

Figure 2-8 Lateral/Dorsal View of Bitch and Queen

| Bitch |

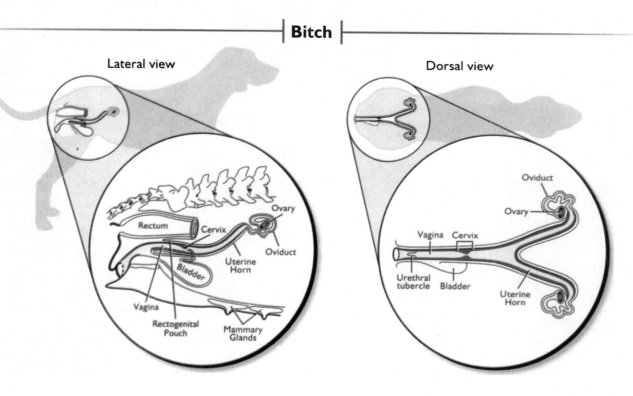

| Queen |

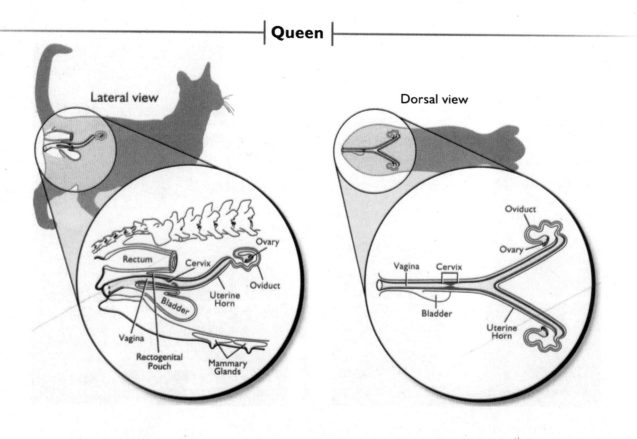

Figure 2-9. Dorsal View of Excised Reproductive Tracts

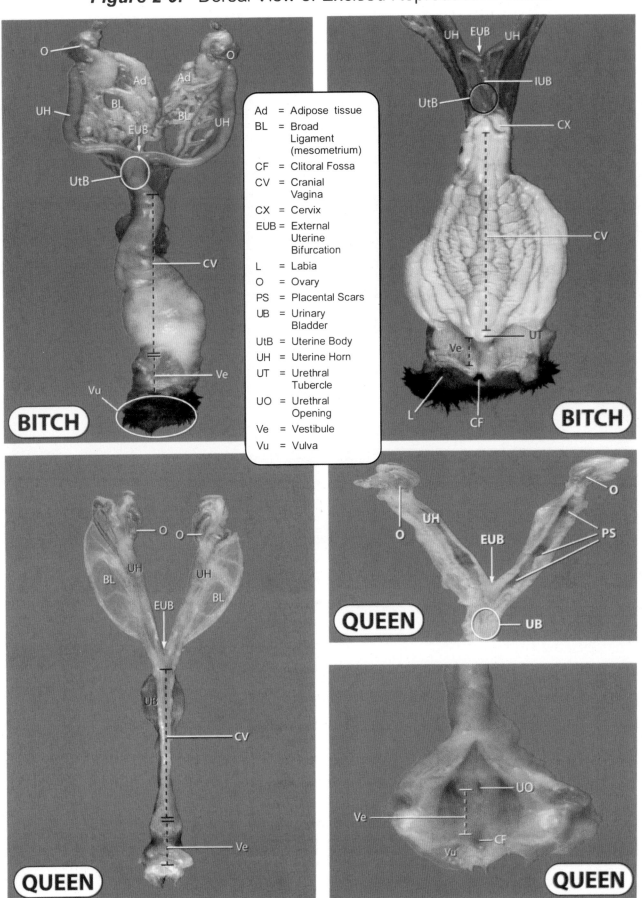

2

Ad = Adipose tissue
BL = Broad Ligament (mesometrium)
CF = Clitoral Fossa
CV = Cranial Vagina
CX = Cervix
EUB = External Uterine Bifurcation
L = Labia
O = Ovary
PS = Placental Scars
UB = Urinary Bladder
UtB = Uterine Body
UH = Uterine Horn
UT = Urethral Tubercle
UO = Urethral Opening
Ve = Vestibule
Vu = Vulva

Figure 2-10a. Radiographs of Excised Reproductive Tracts
(The uterine artery was infused with radiopaque contrast medium so that the blood supply to the uterus çan be visualized. The lumen of the tract can be visualized because it was infused with air.)

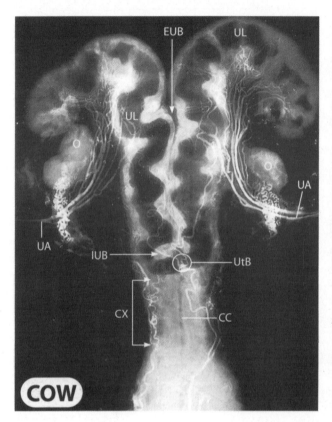

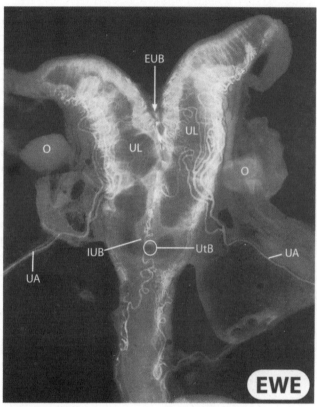

CC	= Cervical Canal
CX	= Cervix
EUB	= External Uterine Bifurcation
IUB	= Internal Uterine Bifurcation
O	= Ovary
UA	= Uterine Artery
UL	= Uterine Lumen
UtB	= Uterine Body

Figure 2-10b. Radiographs of Excised Reproductive Tracts
(The uterine artery was infused with radiopaque contrast medium so that the blood supply to the uterus can be visualized. The lumen of the tract can be visualized because it was infused with air.)

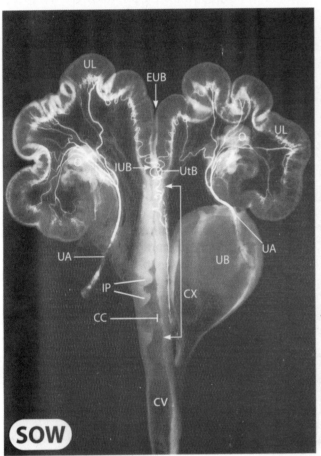

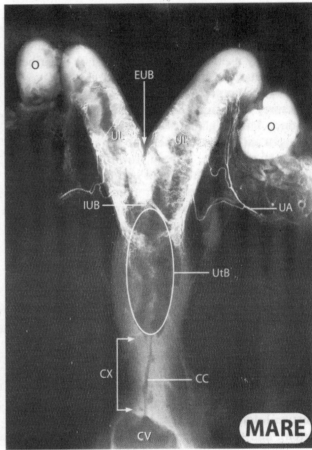

CC	= Cervical Canal
CV	= Cranial Vagina
CX	= Cervix
EUB	= External Uterine Bifurcation
IP	= Interdigitating Prominences
IUB	= Internal Uterine Bifurcation
O	= Ovary
UA	= Uterine Artery
UB	= Urinary Bladder
UL	= Uterine Lumen
UtB	= Uterine Body

Structures on the Ovary Undergo Constant Change

No other organ in the female body undergoes such a predictable and dramatic series of changes in such a short period of time as the ovary. For example, within a three to four week period ovulation occurs and antral **follicles** are transformed completely into a functional **corpus luteum** that produces progesterone. Later (2-3 weeks) the corpus luteum is destroyed, new follicles develop and produce large quantities of estrogen, ovulation occurs again and a complete ovarian cycle has occurred. This not only causes profound physiologic and behavioral changes in the female, but also causes profound morphologic changes in the ovary itself. These changes will be described in more detail in Chapters 7, 8, 9 and 11.

The **ovary** is an ovoid relatively dense structure, the primary functions of which are to produce female gametes (ova) and the hormones **estrogen** and **progesterone**. The corpus luteum also produces **oxytocin**, **relaxin**, **inhibin** and **activin**. Details about these hormones and their actions will be presented in subsequent chapters. In Figure 2-11, all of the ovarian structures of importance can be visualized. The ovary is composed of an outer connective tissue surface called the **tunica albuginea**. The tunica albuginea is covered by a single layer of cuboidal cells called the germinal epithelium. This layer has no function relating to production of the germinal cells and is thus erroneously named. Beneath the tunica albuginea is a zone referred to as the **ovarian cortex**. Generally (the mare is the exception), the ovarian cortex houses the population of oocytes. Cells surrounding oocytes will develop and produce follicles that will mature and eventually ovulate. The ovarian cortex also houses the functional **corpus luteum**, abbreviated **CL** (plural = **corpora lutea**), and the degenerating corpora lutea known as **corpora albicantia** (singular = corpus albicans). Corpora lutea ("yellow bodies") are relatively large, conspicuous structures that produce progesterone. Corpora albicantia can readily be observed on ovaries of most species. The word "albicans" is derived from the word "albino," that implies a white color. Corpora albicantia appear as white, scar-like structures and represent corpora lutea in various stages of degeneration from previous estrous cycles. Their white appearance is due to the increasing ratio of connective tissue (that appears white like a tendon) to secretory tissue. Thus, as the CL degenerates it undergoes a gradual color transition from an orange/yellow structure to a white scar-like structure. A good example of a corpus albicans can be seen in Figure 2-13 (sow).

The central part of the ovary is called the **ovarian medulla**. The medulla houses the vascula-ture, nerves and the lymphatics and is composed of relatively dense connective tissue.

Morphologically, the ovaries of the mare present several important exceptions to the information presented above. First, the ovarian medulla and cortex are reversed (cortex inside, medulla outside) when compared to other species. Second, ovulation occurs at only one location in the mare's ovary, while it occurs at random locations in the ovaries of the other mammals. Ovulation in the mare occurs in a specific anatomical location called the **ovulation fossa** (See Figure 2-13). Third, follicles can be palpated per rectum in the mare, but corpora lutea cannot. This is because corpora lutea do not protrude significantly from the ovarian surface but tend to penetrate into the ovarian tissue.

The ovaries of most females are relatively dense, turgid structures that can be distinguished tactilely from other tissues in the immediate anatomical vicinity in some species using palpation per rectum. By inserting the arm into the rectum (cow, mare, camel), the ovaries can be palpated by carefully manipulating the cranial portion of the tract. Determination of ovarian functional status can be made by identifying various structures (CL or follicles) on the ovaries. Utilization of an ultrasound probe inserted into the rectum allows detailed characteristics of ovarian structures in the cow and the mare to be observed. Recent use of this technology (See Chapter 8) has enabled a greater understanding of follicular growth patterns.

The primary ovarian structures are:

- *primary follicles*
- *secondary follicles*
- *antral follicles*
- *corpora lutea*
- *corpora albicantia*

Within any region of the ovarian cortex, one can encounter several different types of **ovarian follicles** (See Figure 2-11). The various types of ovarian follicles represent different stages of follicular development and maturity. The process whereby immature follicles develop into more advanced follicles and become candidates for ovulation is referred to as **folliculogenesis** (See Chapter 8 for details).

There are four types of follicles present within the ovary. **Primordial follicles** that are microscopic, are the most immature and are the smallest encountered in the ovarian cortex. The oocyte (egg) within the primordial follicle is surrounded by a single layer of flattened (squamous) cells (See Figure 2-11). The

Figure 2-11. The Major Structures of the Ovary

In general, all types of follicles are present within the ovary at any point in time. However, developing and functional corpora lutea may or may not be present depending on the stage of the estrous cycle. With the exception of the mare, development (and regression) of all ovarian structures occurs at random locations within the ovary.

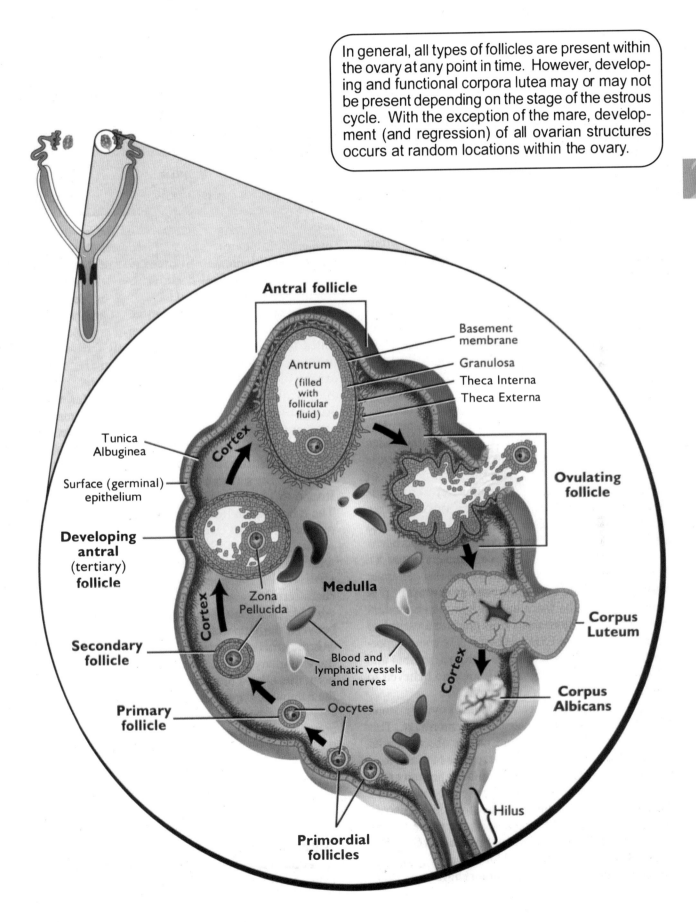

Antral follicle

Basement membrane

Antrum (filled with follicular fluid)

Granulosa
Theca Interna
Theca Externa

Tunica Albuginea

Cortex

Ovulating follicle

Surface (germinal) epithelium

Developing antral (tertiary) follicle

Cortex

Zona Pellucida

Medulla

Corpus Luteum

Secondary follicle

Blood and lymphatic vessels and nerves

Cortex

Corpus Albicans

Primary follicle

Oocytes

Hilus

Primordial follicles

primordial follicle will develop into a slightly more advanced follicle called the **primary follicle**. The primary follicle is characterized by having an oocyte that is surrounded by a single layer of cuboidal (cube-like) epithelium or follicular cells (See Figure 2-11). Females are born with a lifetime's supply of primordial and primary follicles. Primary follicles do not divide into other primary follicles. Instead, they either develop into a more advanced secondary follicle or they degenerate. A **secondary follicle**, also microscopic, is characterized as having two or more layers of follicle cells, but without an **antrum** or cavity (See Figure 2-11). In general, the oocyte within a secondary follicle is characterized as being surrounded by a relatively thick translucent layer called the **zona pellucida**. An **antral follicle** is characterized by a fluid-filled cavity called the antrum. The fluid within the antrum is called **follicular fluid**. Sometimes the antral follicle is referred to as a **tertiary follicle**. When the tertiary follicle becomes a dominant preovulatory follicle, it is sometimes called a **Graafian follicle**. Some antral follicles can be observed with the naked eye on the surface of the ovaries. They appear as blister-like structures that vary in size from less than 1 mm to several centimeters (See Figure 2-13). The sizes of these follicles vary depending on their stage of development or regression and upon species.

Antral follicles consist of three distinct layers. These layers are the **theca externa,** the **theca interna** and the **granulosal cell layer** (See Figure 2-11). The theca externa is composed primarily of loose connective tissue that completely surrounds and supports the follicle. The layer just beneath the theca externa is the theca interna. Cells of the theca interna are responsible for the production of androgens under the influence of LH (See Chapters 5 and 8). Beneath the theca interna is the granulosal cell layer (sometimes called the **membrana granulosa**). It is separated from the theca interna by a thin basement membrane. The granulosal cells produce a variety of materials and have FSH receptors. The most important products of these cells are estrogen, inhibin and follicular fluid. Granulosal cells are also believed to govern the maturation of the oocyte.

When dominant antral follicles ovulate, small blood vessels rupture, causing local hemorrhage. This small amount of bloody tissue can be observed with the naked eye. In addition to the rupture of these small blood vessels, the loss of fluid from the antrum of the follicle causes the follicle to collapse into many folds. Because of this in-folding (a type of implosion), some of the granulosal and thecal layers are pushed to the apex of the follicle. This small protrusion of tissue, coupled with the rupture of blood vessels, yields a structure called the **corpus hemorrhagicum**. After

the formation of the corpus hemorrhagicum ("bloody body"), the cells of the theca interna and the granulosal cells differentiate into luteal cells to form a corpus luteum. A detailed, full-color photographic presentation of corpora lutea formation as it relates to progesterone production during the estrous cycle is presented in Chapter 9. The corpus luteum produces progesterone and is essential for the maintenance of pregnancy.

> *The oviduct consists of the:*
> * *infundibulum*
> * *ampulla*
> * *isthmus*

A schematic illustration of the oviduct is presented in Figure 2-12. The **infundibulum** is the terminal end (cranial or ovarian end) of the oviduct and consists of a funnel-shaped opening. This funnel-like opening forms a pocket that "captures" the newly ovulated oocyte. The surface of the infundibulum is covered with many velvety, finger-like projections called **fimbriae**. The fimbriae greatly increase the surface area of the infundibulum and cause it to glide or slip over the entire surface of the ovary near the time of ovulation. Such an action maximizes the chance that the oocyte will be "captured" after ovulation and transported through an opening called the **ostium** into the ampulla of the oviduct. The relationship of the infundibulum to the ovary is presented in Figures 2-13 and 2-14. The surface area of the infundibulum ranges from 6 to 10 cm^2 in sheep to 20 to 30 cm^2 in cattle. The infundibulum leads directly into a thick portion of oviduct called the **ampulla**. The ampulla occupies one-half or more of the oviductal length and merges with the isthmus of the oviduct. The ampulla has a relatively large diameter, with the internal portions characterized by many fern-like mucosal folds with ciliated epithelium (See Figure 2-12). The junction between the ampulla and the isthmus (**ampullary-isthmic junction**) is generally ill-defined. In the mare, the ampullary-isthmic junction serves as a control point that allows only fertilized oocytes to pass into the isthmus and eventually into the uterus.

The **isthmus** is smaller in diameter than the ampulla. It is connected directly to the uterus and the point of juncture is called the **uterotubal junction**. The isthmus has a thicker muscular wall than the ampulla and has fewer mucosal folds (See Figure 2-12).

The primary function of the smooth muscle layer (muscularis) of the oviduct is to transport newly ovulated oocytes and spermatozoa to the site of fertilization (the ampulla). Gamete transport by the oviduct requires that spermatozoa and ova move in

Figure 2-12.   The Oviduct and its Components

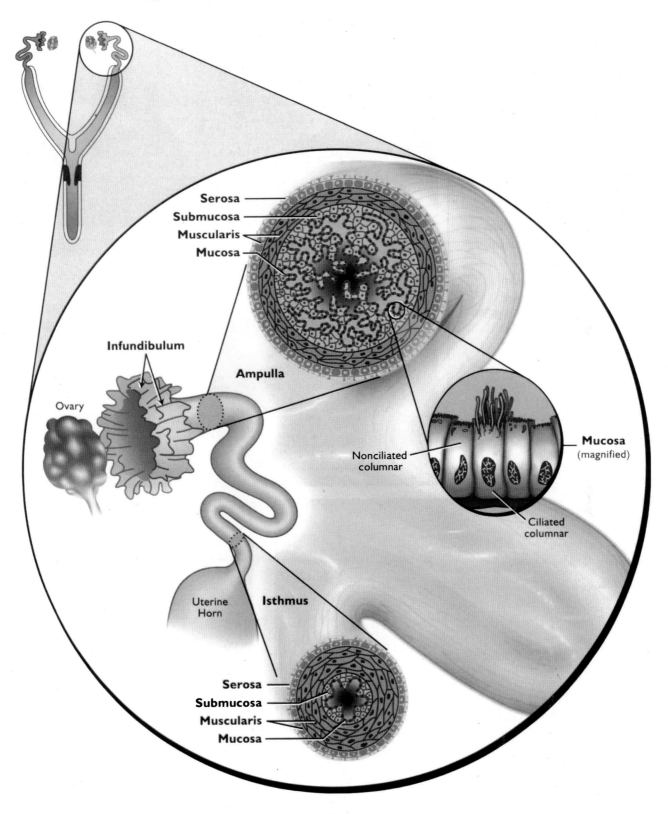

Serosa
Submucosa
Muscularis
Mucosa

Infundibulum

Ovary

Ampulla

Nonciliated
columnar

Mucosa
(magnified)

Ciliated
columnar

Uterine
Horn   **Isthmus**

Serosa
Submucosa
Muscularis
Mucosa

Figure 2-13. The Relationship of the Mesosalpinx to the Oviduct

Relationship of the meso-salpinx to the oviduct in the cow, ewe, sow and mare. The infundibulum is a delicate membrane-like component of the oviduct that is in close apposition to the ovary. Arrows indicate the direction of oocyte/embryo transport within the oviduct toward the uterus.

AF	=	Antral Follicle
CA	=	Corpus Albicans
CL	=	Corpus Luteum
H	=	Hilus
If	=	Infundibulum
M(OB)	=	Mesosalpinx forming an ovarian bursa
Ms	=	Mesosalpinx
O	=	Ovary
OD	=	Oviduct
OF	=	Ovulation Fossa
UH	=	Uterine Horn
UL	=	Uterine Lumen
UOL	=	Utero-Ovarian Ligament

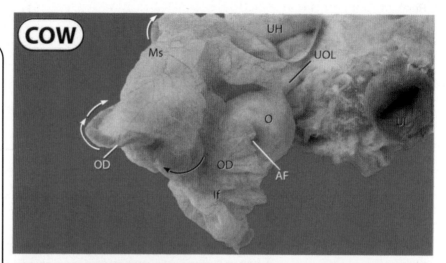

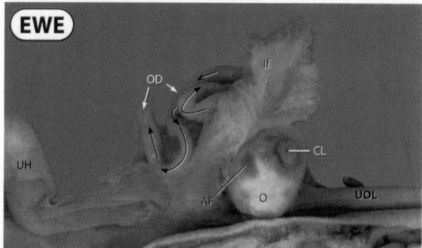

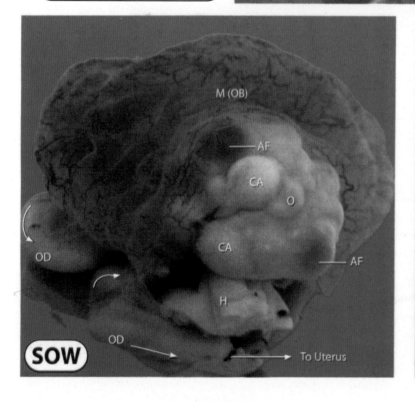

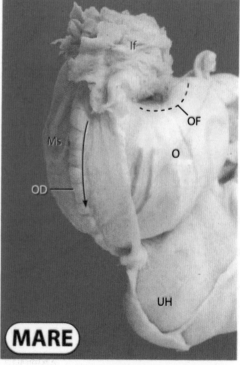

Figure 2-14. The Realationship of the Mesosalpinx to the Oviduct

Relationship of the meso-salpinx to the oviduct in the queen and bitch. The infundibulum is a delicate membrane-like component of the oviduct that is in close apposition to the ovary. Arrows indicate the direction of oocyte/embryo transport within the oviduct toward the uterus.

Ad	Adipose
BL	Broad Ligament
C(OB) =	Cavity - Ovarian Bursa
If =	Infundibulum
Ms =	Mesosalpinx
Ms(OB) =	Mesosalpinx - Ovarian Bursa
O =	Ovary
OB =	Ovarian Bursa
OD =	Oviduct
UH =	Uterine Horn

The red appearance of the bottom specimen (bitch) is due to retention of blood. The photos were taken immediately after ovariectomy.

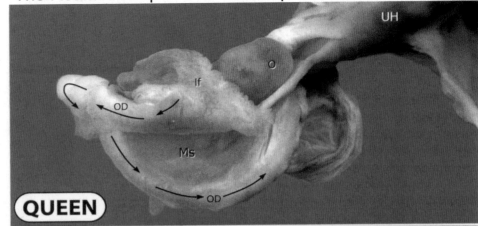

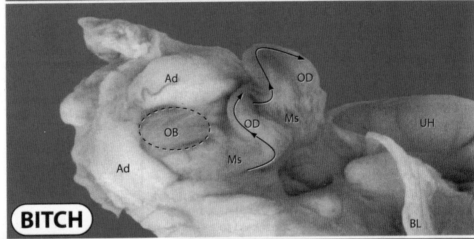

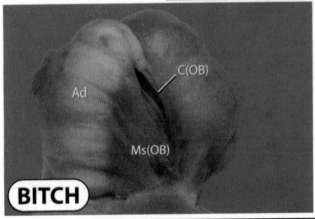

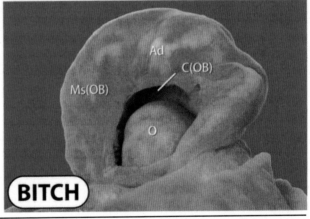

opposite directions so that they encounter each other in the ampulla. The mechanisms controlling gamete transport by the oviduct are not well understood.

The mucosa of the oviduct secretes substances that provide the optimum environment for the free-floating, unfertilized oocyte. It also sustains spermatozoal function until the oocyte arrives after ovulation. There is increasing evidence that the epithelium of the oviduct produces substances that facilitate the fertilizing capability of spermatozoa. After fertilization, the newly formed zygote must reside in the oviduct for a few days before it enters the uterus. Thus, the composition of the fluid secreted by the cells lining the oviduct is important for providing a suitable environ-

ment for the development of the early embryo.

In the cow, the **uterotubal junction** (often called the UTJ) is believed to regulate the movement of the embryo into the uterus. Under conditions of high estradiol, the uterotubal junction forms a "kink" (like a kink in a hose), thus blocking movement of embryos. As estradiol levels decrease, this kink straightens out; the lumen of the isthmus is no longer blocked by the kink and embryos can enter the uterine lumen with relative ease. In other species, the oviduct attaches to the uterus without an obvious kink-like anatomical constriction. In swine, constriction of the uterotubal junction serves as a major barrier to sperm transport and prevents excessive numbers of spermatozoa from reaching the ampulla. Such blockage is believed to be important in the prevention of polyspermy in swine.

The Uterus is the Organ of Pregnancy

The uterus connects the oviducts to the cervix. In most mammals, the uterus consists of two **uterine horns** or **cornua**. The degree to which the uterine horns are developed constitutes the basis for classification of mammalian uteri.

Among mammals there are three distinct anatomical types of uteri (See Figure 2-15). The first of these is a **duplex uterus,** characterized as having two cervical canals that separate each uterine horn into distinct compartments. There are two types of duplex uteri. The first is characterized by having a single vaginal canal opening to the exterior. On the interior it bifurcates (splits) into two vaginas and two cervices. Marsupials have this type of uterus. In the opossum, this interesting female anatomical configuration is accommodated by the forked penis of the male. It is believed that after intromission, the male opossum deposits semen in each of the two sides of the reproductive tract simultaneously. The second, less complex type of duplex uterus is found in the rabbit. In this type of duplex uterus, there are two uterine horns and two distinct cervical canals connected to a single vaginal canal. Therefore, in species like the rabbit it is possible to artificially inseminate the female into one horn with sperm from one male and to artificially inseminate the contralateral (opposite) horn with semen from another male; the offspring will represent two genetic types. The rabbit is an excellent animal to use for the study of various experimental seminal or embryo treatments, because transuterine migration of the gametes or embryos is not likely to occur.

The **bicornuate uterus** is characterized by having two uterine horns and a small uterine body. The length of the uterine horns is dependent on the degree of fusion between the paramesonephric ducts in the developing female fetus (See Chapter 4 for details). In species where there is a high degree of fusion (mare) there are short uterine horns and a relatively large uterine body. When a moderate degree of fusion occurs, uterine horns of intermediate length result (cow, ewe and goat). And, when little fusion takes place between adjacent paramesonephric ducts, long uterine horns result (sow, bitch and queen). In all types of bicornuate uteri, the uterus opens into the vagina through a single cervical canal. An **internal** and **external uterine bifurcation** of the horns can be distinguished in the bicornuate uterus (See Figures 2-5, 2-7 and 2-9).

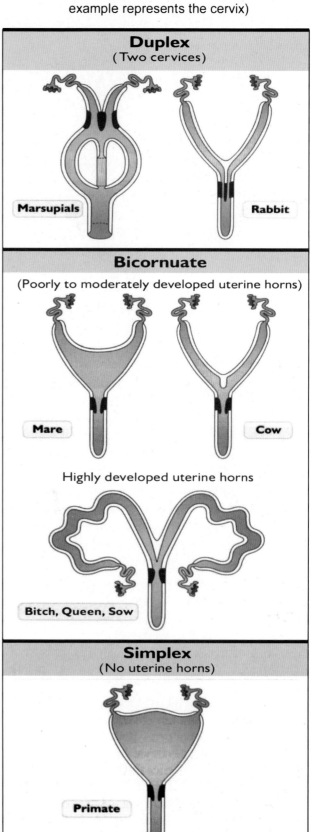

Figure 2-15. Types of Uteri Found in Mammals

(The solid brown area in each example represents the cervix)

Duplex
(Two cervices)

Marsupials   Rabbit

Bicornuate

(Poorly to moderately developed uterine horns)

Mare   Cow

Highly developed uterine horns

Bitch, Queen, Sow

Simplex
(No uterine horns)

Primate

In your readings outside of this book you will encounter the term "bipartite uterus." The term "bipartite" was once used to describe bicornuate uteri with short (mare) to moderate length (cow) uterine horns. In an attempt to simplify the classification of mammalian uteri, the suggestion has been made that the term "bipartite" be dropped from the uterine classification nomenclature. This suggestion has been followed here.

The **simplex uterus** is characterized as having a single uterine body. Only small rudiments of a structure resembling a uterine horn may be apparent. Fusion of the paramesonephric ducts is almost complete, resulting in a single-chambered uterus without horns. The simplex uterus is found in primates, including humans.

> **The unique names of the components of the uterus are:**
> - *serosa = perimetrium*
> - *muscularis = myometrium*
> - *mucosa + submucosa = endometrium*

The uterus consists of a serosal layer called the **perimetrium** that is part of the peritoneum. It is continuous with the serosal layer covering the mesosalpinx. The perimetrium is quite thin and almost transparent. Beneath the serosal layer is a longitudinal layer of smooth muscle. The longitudinal layer of smooth muscle is easy to recognize because of the creases, or small ridges that run in a cranial-caudal direction. Beneath the longitudinal smooth muscle layer is a circular layer. The smooth muscle cells wrap around the uterine horn in a circular fashion. Collectively, the outer longitudinal layer and the inner circular muscle layer are referred to as the **myometrium**. The myometrium has several physiologic responsibilities. One of the most important is to provide motility (a form of contraction) for the uterus. In species other than the mare, the myometrium has a high degree of tone (a partial state of contraction) when estrogen is the predominant steroidal hormone. A high degree of tone can be palpated (felt) as turgidity or hardness and is distinguished easily from a soft or flaccid uterus, found when estrogen is low and progesterone is high. Uterine tone is presumably related to transport mechanisms for sperm and mucus-like material produced by the uterus. The transport mechanisms for spermatozoa will be addressed in more detail in Chapter 12. Under the influence of progesterone, the myometrium has a low degree of tone, except in the early stages of pregnancy in the mare. This lack of tone is appropriate,

since it is during this time that the embryo will enter the uterus for eventual attachment. A high degree of motility would undoubtedly minimize the possibility of successful attachment of the conceptus. A third important function of the myometrium includes its role during **parturition**. During parturition, the myometrium becomes a major driving force for expulsion of the fetus and fetal membranes.

> **The primary functions of the uterus are:**
> - *sperm transport*
> - *luteolysis and control of cyclicity*
> - *environment for preattachment embryo*
> - *maternal contribution to the placenta*
> - *expulsion of the fetus and fetal placenta*

The inner portion of the uterus is composed of the **mucosa** and **submucosa** (See Figure 2-16). The mucosa and the submucosa of the uterus comprise the **endometrium**. The mucosal epithelium is responsible for secreting materials into the lumen of the uterus that enhance embryo development and sperm viability. In the bitch, uterine glands may serve as a temporary storage site for spermatozoa following insemination. While spermatozoa have been observed within the uterine glands it is not known whether these sperm are stored there and later released to accomplish fertilization. The uterine glands develop from the mucosal layer of the uterus. They penetrate into the submucosa and begin to coil under the influence of estrogen (See Figure 2-16). However, they reach full secretory capacity under the influence of progesterone. Uterine glands produce materials that are believed to be important to the survival and function of the preimplantation embryo. The submucosa is predominantly connective and supporting tissue and houses the uterine glands. A distinct difference between lower mammals and primates, particularly humans, is that the endometrium of the uterus in the human is sloughed to the exterior. The endometrial glands in domestic mammals are not sloughed. The functionality of the uterine glands changes during the estrous cycle in a type of secretory "waxing and waning." In other words, secretory activity of the uterine glands changes as a function of the stage of the estrous

Figure 2-16. Schematic Illustration of Uterine Tissue

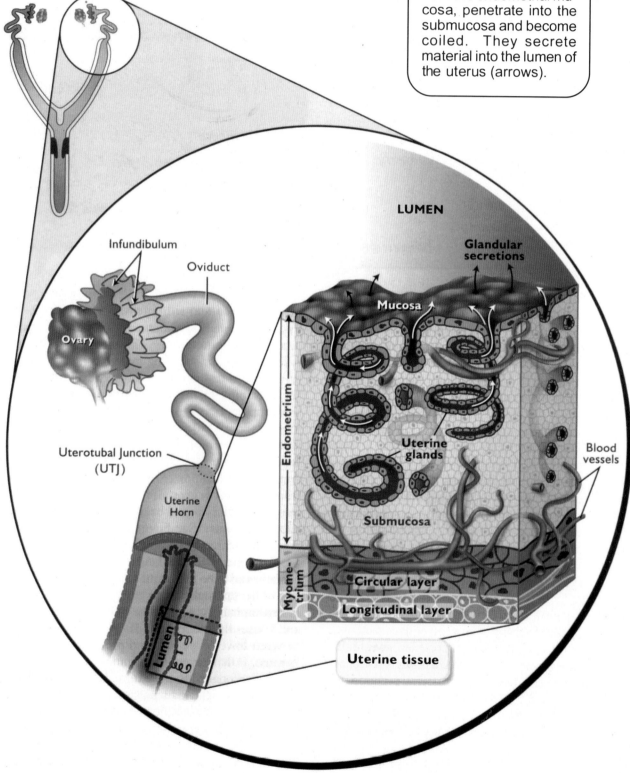

Uterine glands develop from the endometrial mucosa, penetrate into the submucosa and become coiled. They secrete material into the lumen of the uterus (arrows).

Uterine tissue

Figure 2-17. Excised Uterine Tissue

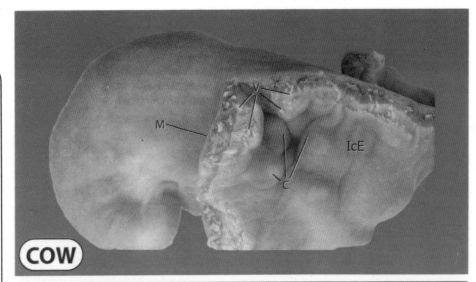

COW

The uterus has been incised so that the endometrial surface can be visualized. In the cow and the ewe, caruncles (C) can be observed as protrusions from the endometrial surface. Blood vessels (V) are white, cord-like structures located beneath the surface of each caruncle. The endometrium of the sow and mare is characterized as having many endometrial folds (EF). Both the caruncles and the endometrial folds contribute to the maternal placenta if pregnancy occurs.

C = Caruncles

EF = Endometrial
        Folds

IcE = Intercaruncular
         Endometrium

M = Myometrium

O = Ovary

UOL = Utero-Ovarian
          Ligament

V = Blood Vessels

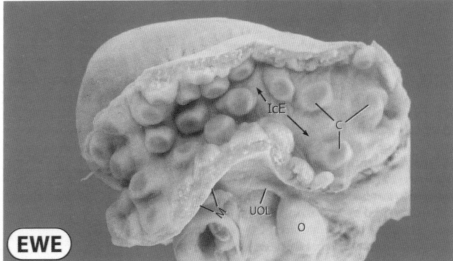

EWE

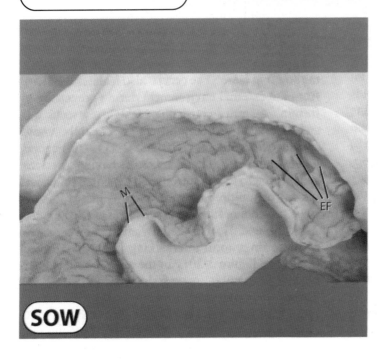

SOW

MARE

2

Figure 2-18. Excised Uterine Tissue

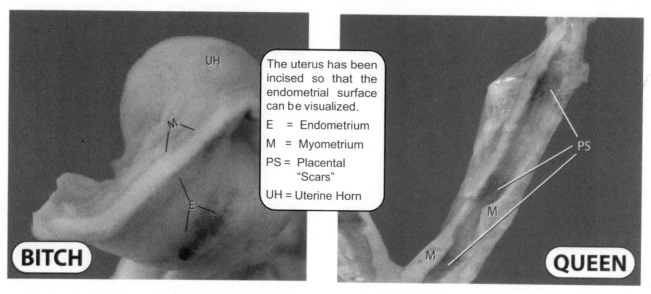

The uterus has been incised so that the endometrial surface can be visualized.

E = Endometrium

M = Myometrium

PS = Placental "Scars"

UH = Uterine Horn

BITCH

QUEEN

cycle. The mechanisms whereby uterine glands may be lost (or replenished) in domestic animals remains undefined.

At a critical time during the estrous cycle the cells of the uterine endometrium produce **prostaglandin $F_{2\alpha}$**. Prostaglandin $F_{2\alpha}$ causes luteolysis or regression of the corpus luteum if the animal is not pregnant. Details of these important mechanisms are presented in Chapter 9.

In ruminants, the surface of the endometrium is characterized as having small, nonglandular areas that protrude from the surface of the endometrium. These small protuberances are referred to as **caruncles** and can be observed with a high degree of detail in Figure 2-17. These caruncular regions are highly vascularized and will give rise to the maternal portion of the placenta if attachment of the embryo occurs. In contrast to the cow and ewe, the endometrium of the sow and mare have no caruncles. Their endometrium is characterized by having many endometrial folds (See Figure 2-17). The folds will provide the uterine surface for the development of the placenta. Placental "scars" in the uterus of the queen (See Figure 2-18) are pigmented regions of the endometrium that represent sites of previous placental attachment. They appear as bands around the luminal surface of the uterus indicative of zonary placentation (See Chapter 14). These sites are not true scars that are permanent fibrous replacements of normal tissue. The sites are zones of uterine repair that will become less conspicuous several months postpartum. The presence of these discrete endometrial repair zones is useful to wildlife biologists who use them in postmortem evaluation of wild animals to approximate the number of young produced by a female within a certain period of time. Evaluation of these regions is most useful in monoestrus females (canids, felids and ursids) that have no immediate postpartum estrus. Exposure to estrogen during repeated estrous cycles hastens the uterine repair process and causes these repair zones to disappear at a faster rate.

> *The cervix provides lubrication, a flushing system and a barrier during pregnancy.*

The cervix is a relatively thick-walled, noncompliant organ that serves as a barrier to sperm transport in the ewe, cow, bitch and queen but not in the sow and mare. The cervix also isolates the uterus from the external environment during pregnancy by forming a barrier consisting of highly viscous mucus. Cervical anatomy differs significantly among species (See Figures 2-20 and 2-21). In general, however, it can be characterized as having a cervical canal (lumen) that is surrounded by single (bitch and queen) or multiple (cow, ewe, sow, mare) folds or rings protruding into the cervical canal (See Figures 2-19, 20, and 21). In the cow and the ewe, several of these rings form interlocking finger-like projections (See Figure 2-20). In the sow, the rings interdigitate in a very intimate fashion (See Figure 2-20). These interdigitations require a special penile adaptation in the boar. The boar has a corkscrew or spiral twist in the glans penis so that during copulation the

Figure 2-19. A Schematic of the Cervix

In the cow, ewe and sow the cervix has distinct rings that protrude into the lumen. The surface of the cervix has many crypts and folds that are covered with columnar epithelium. Some cells are ciliated. In the cow, a distinct fornix is present. To observe actual specimens see Figures 2-20 and 21.

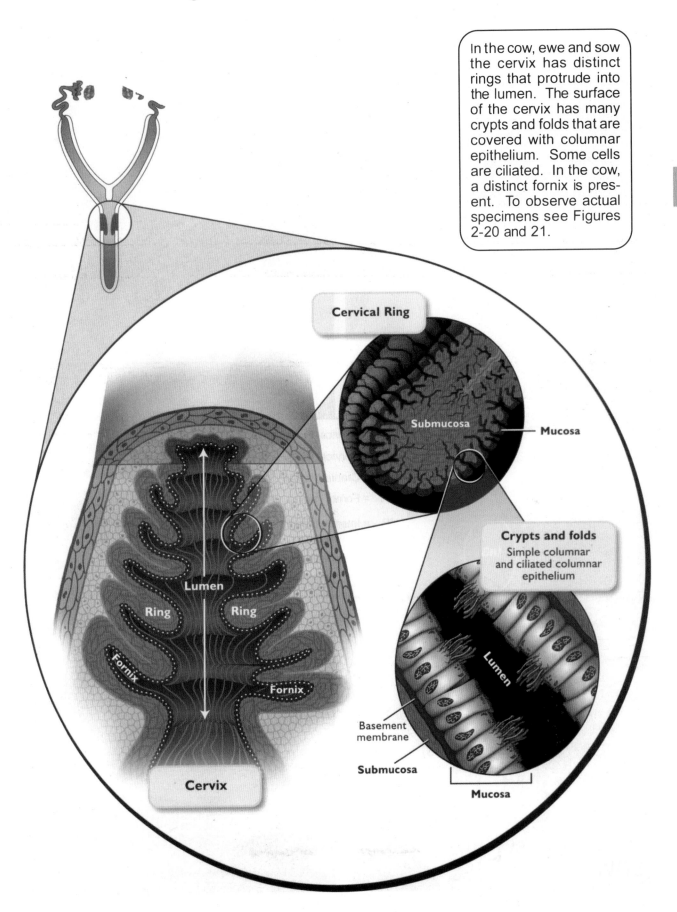

Cervical Ring

Submucosa

Mucosa

Lumen

Ring   Ring

Fornix

Fornix

Cervix

Crypts and folds
Simple columnar and ciliated columnar epithelium

Lumen

Basement membrane

Submucosa

Mucosa

Figure 2-20. Excised Cervical Tissue

The cervix of the cow and ewe have distinct, well developed protrusions called cervical rings (CR). The sow has interdigitating prominences (IP). The mare has no cervical rings but has many longitudinal cervical folds (CF) that are continuous with the endometrial folds of the uterus. Arrows indicate the pathway of the cervical canal from the cranial vagina (CV) toward the uterus.

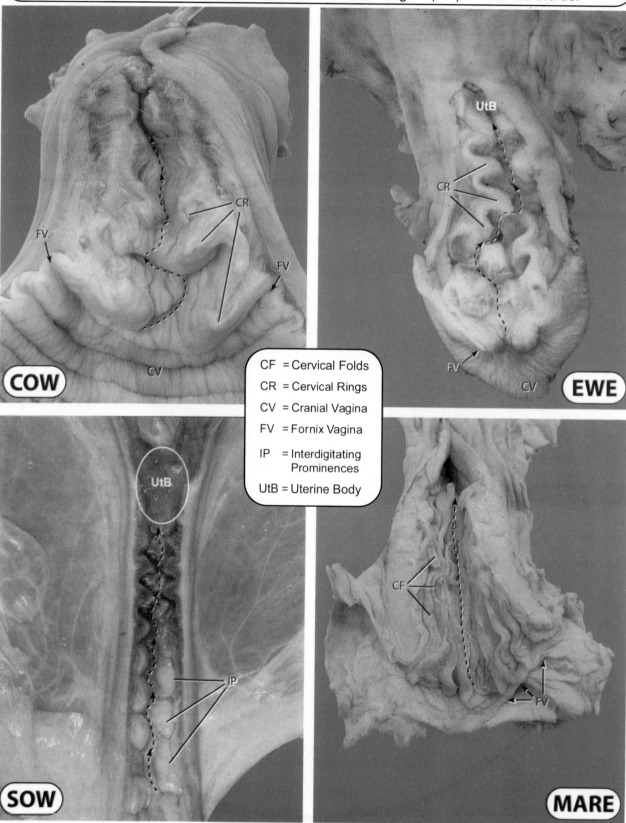

CF = Cervical Folds

CR = Cervical Rings

CV = Cranial Vagina

FV = Fornix Vagina

IP = Interdigitating Prominences

UtB = Uterine Body

Figure 2-21. Excised Cervical Tissue

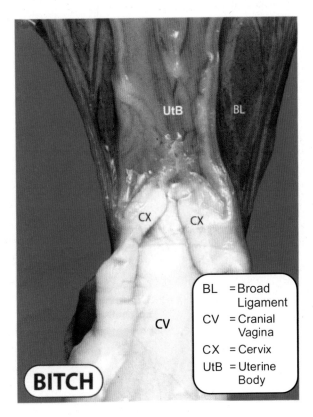

BL	= Broad Ligament
CV	= Cranial Vagina
CX	= Cervix
UtB	= Uterine Body

BITCH

boar's penis becomes "locked" into the cervix. Thus, in the pig, initial deposition of the semen occurs in the cervix. Because of the large volume (200-500ml), most of the ejaculate quickly enters the uterus. The distinguishing feature of the mare's cervix is the presence of conspicuous, loose folds of mucosa that protrude into the vagina. The cervix of the mare is soft during estrus. During copulation the penis of the stallion presses against the soft cervix. Semen is ejaculated under high pressure and enters the uterus during ejaculation.

In the canine, a portion of the cervix protrudes caudally into the cranial vagina (See Figure 2-21). The cervix of the bitch does not contain elaborate rings or folds and is relatively smooth. In the queen, the cervix is quite small but thick walled when compared to the uterus or the vagina. Like in the bitch, the cervix is smooth and does not have elaborate surface folds.

A primary function of the cervix in the cow and ewe is to produce mucus during estrus. In the sow and mare, a much smaller quantity of mucus is produced. This mucus flows from the cervix toward the exterior and lubricates the vagina during copulation. Foreign material introduced during copulation (including sperm) is flushed out of the tract by cervical mucus. This flushing action brought about by

outflow of mucus probably minimizes introduction of microorganisms into the uterus. The biochemical and physical properties of the mucus change as the stage of the estrous cycle changes. Details regarding the role of the cervix in the transport of spermatozoa will be presented in Chapter 12.

During pregnancy the cervix is responsible for isolation of the conceptus within the uterus from the external environment. Under the influence of progesterone, the mucus becomes quite viscous. In fact, the viscous mucus temporarily "glues" the folds of the cervix together so that foreign material cannot enter the uterus during gestation. This barrier is referred to as the **cervical seal of pregnancy**. Disruption of the cervical seal of pregnancy will generally cause abortion, because microorganisms can gain access to the interior of the uterus, causing infection and subsequent embryonic death.

The Vagina is the Copulatory Organ

The primary function of the vagina is to serve as a copulatory organ, as well as the site for expulsion of urine during micturition. It is also a passive birth canal during parturition. The vagina has a poorly organized and ill-defined muscular layer and a well developed, highly adapted mucosal epithelium.

Figure 2-22. Differences in the Mucosal Surfaces Between the Cranial and Caudal Vagina

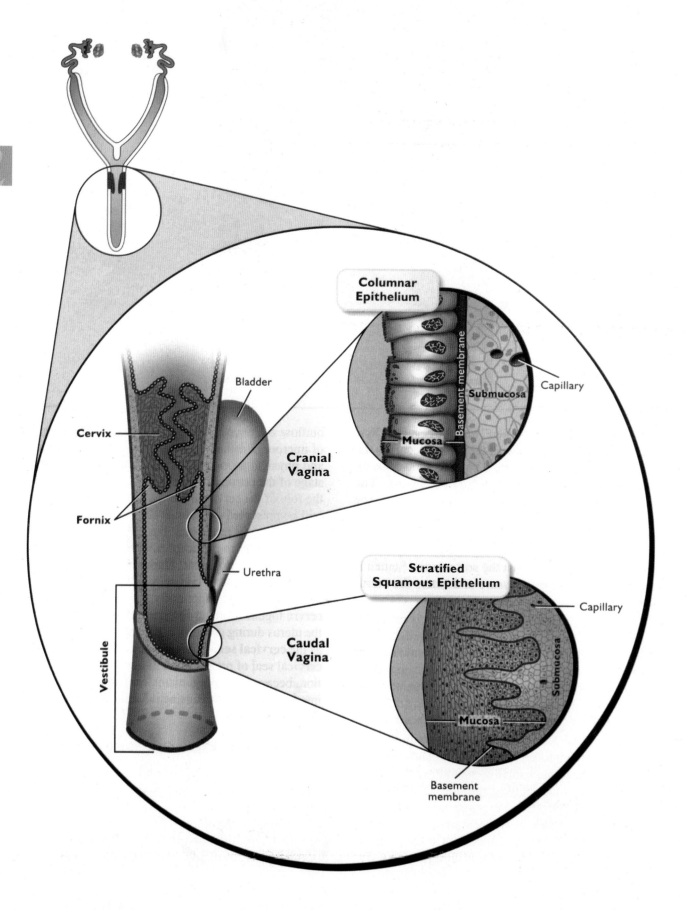

Figure 2-23. External Genitalia

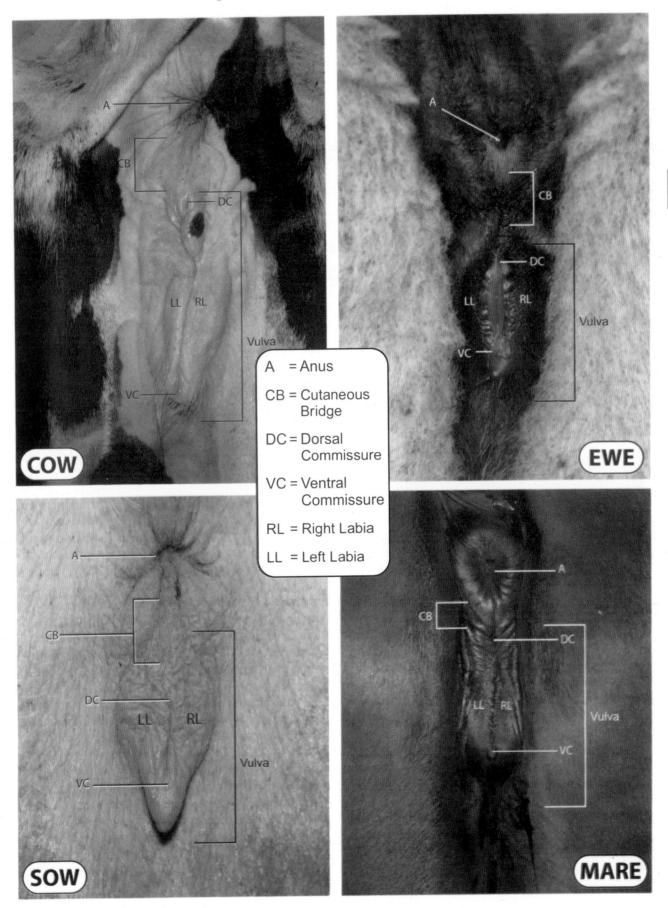

A = Anus

CB = Cutaneous Bridge

DC = Dorsal Commissure

VC = Ventral Commissure

RL = Right Labia

LL = Left Labia

2

Figure 2-24. External Genitalia

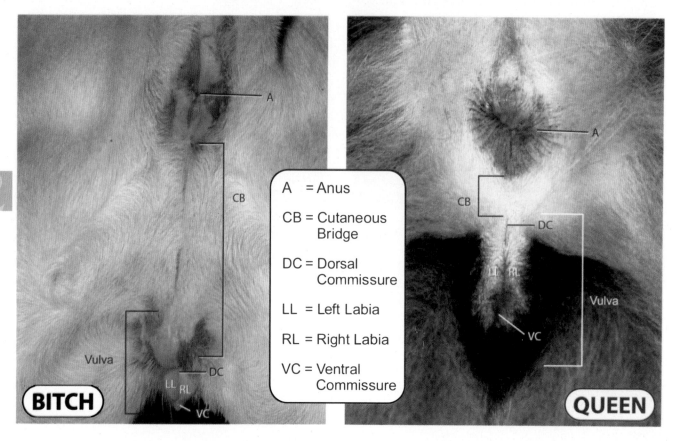

A = Anus

CB = Cutaneous Bridge

DC = Dorsal Commissure

LL = Left Labia

RL = Right Labia

VC = Ventral Commissure

BITCH

QUEEN

The mucosal epithelium varies depending on the specific region of the vagina. The luminal epithelium near the cervix (cranial vagina) is generally columnar and highly secretory in nature. In the cow, mare, and bitch the cervix protrudes into the anterior vagina, forming a crypt, or pocket. This crypt is referred to as the **fornix vagina** (See Figures 2-19 and 2-20). Spermatozoa are deposited in the fornix vagina by the bull during natural service. The fornix vagina is composed of columnar epithelial cells that, as in the cervix, secrete copious quantities of mucus during estrus. The sow does not have a fornix vagina.

Towards its caudal regions, the vagina begins to change its cellular composition. As you will see in Chapter 4, this organ is formed embryologically from two distinct anatomical regions. The cranial vagina originates from the paramesonephric ducts and fuses with the caudal vagina that originates from an invagination of the urogenital sinus. Thus, it is not surprising to see two distinct types of cells lining the cranial and caudal vagina. If you can inspect Figures 2-5, 2-7 and 2-9 you can readily observe the color difference between the vestibule and the vagina. This color difference is because of different epithelial types

that make-up the two regions. The cranial vagina is characterized as having a high degree of secretory activity as evidenced by **columnar epithelium**, and some ciliated columnar epithelium. The caudal vagina is characterized as having **stratified squamous epithelium** (the same type of epithelium that comprises the skin) (See Figure 2-22). The degree of secretory activity and the thickness of the stratified squamous epithelium in the caudal vagina change with the endocrine status of the female. During the time of estrogen dominance (estrus), the stratified squamous epithelium thickens dramatically. Such thickening likely serves two protective functions. First, it mechanically protects the vagina during copulation. Secondly, the thickened mucosa prevents microorganisms from gaining entrance to the vasculature in the submucosa.

The vaginal epithelium responds to endocrine changes by changing its thickness. It is possible to exfoliate cells by lavage or swabbing the vagina in some species to determine the stage of the cycle by observing microscopically the type of cells present in the fluid. For example, vaginal swabs from a bitch in estrus are characterized by containing sheets of squamous cells with distinct epithelial borders with or without nuclei. In the queen and rodents, squamous cells present in vaginal flushings indicate the influence of high estrogen upon the vaginal mucosa.

Since the caudal vagina, or the **vestibule,** develops from the ventral part of the cloaca, it belongs to both the urinary and the genital systems (See Chapter 4). The vestibule is the portion of the vagina that is common to the urinary system and the reproductive system (See Figure 2-22). It extends from the level of the external urethral orifice to the labia of the vulva. In most species, if the floor of the vestibule is carefully dissected, one can encounter **Gartner's ducts**. These often open directly into the vestibule and are blind sacs that represent the remnants of the **Wolffian duct**. These have no apparent function and simply represent an embryonic remnant of the male reproductive system of the embryo.

In the floor of the vestibule of the sow and the cow is a small, blind pouch that lies immediately ventral to the urethral opening. This blind pouch is referred to as the **suburethral diverticulum**. A **diverticulum** is a pouch or sac that diverts a main tube. The function of the suburethral diverticulum is unknown, but sometimes inexperienced inseminators can position the insemination rod or pipette into this blind pouch. Also, this blind pouch can be used as a landmark for the insertion of a urinary catheter to collect urine directly from a cow's bladder.

The vagina of the bitch contains a bulb-like structure that protrudes caudally into the vestibule. It lies directly above the urethral opening (See Figure 2-9). This structure is the **urethral tubercle** and it varies in size among bitches. The functional significance of the urethral tubercle is not known.

The **vulva** is the external part of the female reproductive tract. It consists of two **labia** (major and minor) that meet in the medial portion of the tract to form two **commissures** (sites of union). Under most conditions, the labia form a closure that minimizes the entrance of foreign material into the vagina.

The skin of the labia is part of the integument and has numerous sebaceous and sweat glands and hair follicles. The labia consist mainly of adipose tissue into which are imbedded small bundles of smooth muscle that are known as **constrictor vulvae** muscles. The purpose of these muscles is to insure that the labia stay in close apposition.

In the female, the region that surrounds the anus and the vulva and covers the pelvic outlet is referred to as the **perineum**. Between the dorsal commissure and the anus is a bridge of skin that is sometimes torn during parturition, generally resulting from an oversized or malpositioned fetus.

The ventral commissure of the vestibule houses the **clitoral fossa** (See Figure 2-9) that contains the **clitoris**, the female homologue of the penis. The clitoris is composed of erectile tissue and is covered with stratified squamous epithelium. It is well supplied with sensory nerve endings. The onset of estrus, accompanied by high estrogen levels, generally results in a continuous state of erection of the clitoris. The functional significance of this highly sensitized area has not been well established in domestic animals. However, clitoral stimulation at the time of insemination has been shown to increase conception rates in artificial insemination by up to 6% in beef cows, but not in heifers. The submucosa of the vestibule also houses the **vestibular glands** (also called Bartholin's glands). These glands are located in the caudal portion of the vestibule and actively secrete a mucous-like material during estrus.

2

Further PHENOMENA for Fertility

Early myths and folklore referred to "vagina dentata" that described a vagina with teeth. Vagina dentata is said to symbolize fear of castration, the dangers of sexual intercourse, of birth, etc.

The female bedbug has a vagina but it is apparently not the copulatory organ. When a male mounts the female bedbug, his penis cannot reach the vagina and therefore he thrusts it through her back and deposits sperm into her body cavity. The sperm lie dormant until the female bedbug sucks blood from her next human host. Once she has engorged her belly with blood the sperm are activated and swim to the ovaries. If a female mates multiple times she is likely to die from multiple stab wounds.

The Italian anatomist Gabriello Fallopius (1532-1562) is perhaps most widely recognized for his description of the oviducts that bear his name (Fallopian tubes). Fallopius, a recognized early authority on syphilis, has been credited with the invention of the condom. His Fallico Liber Absoltismus (published posthumously in 1564) contains a description of a "linen sheath" that is credited with decreasing the spread of syphilis that was very prevalent in Europe during his lifetime.

The word "hysterectomy" means surgical removal of the uterus. The word is derived from a notion espoused by Plato (347-266 BC). He thought that the uterus was a multichambered organ that could wander about the body causing hysteria in the host woman. He thought that if a woman went too long without becoming pregnant her uterus would become indignant and would wander around the body causing extreme anxiety, hysteria, respiratory insufficiency and all sorts of diseases. The cure was removal of the uterus that removed the possibility of hysteria and disease. In spite of its ancient and erroneous origin the term hysterectomy is still used today in the highest level of medical and scientific practice. A more descriptive term for removal of uterus would be "uterectomy". Author's Theory: This myth probably was originated by Greek males who recognized that pregnancy required copulation. The anxiety / disease causing fable "legitimized" their desire for frequent copulation.

Most birds have only a left ovary and oviduct that are functional. Some birds have two functional ovaries, but only the left oviduct is functional. Thus, when the right ovary ovulates there is nowhere for the oocyte to go except into the body cavity, where it is reabsorbed (the truest form of recycling). The oocyte cannot enter the left oviduct because a mesentery separates the right ovary from the left oviduct.

In the female hyena, the clitoris is very well developed. In fact, it is so well developed that it is almost impossible to distinguish the male hyena from the female hyena. The female also has a false scrotum. Of further note is the fact that the female is the dominant sex and produces as much or more testosterone than the typical male.

After mating, the female bumblebee eel worm undergoes a remarkable transformation. Her vagina actually inflates until it is almost 20,000 times larger than she is. At this point, the female's body is no longer needed, and it shrivels-up and disintegrates. However, as soon as the eggs within the vagina hatch and a new generation of worms emerge, the vagina also disintegrates.

In the small fish known as the Four-Eyed Anablep, the female's vagina is either on the left or the right. In the male, the penis is either on the right or the left. A male with a right penis must mate with a female with a right vagina and vice versa.

Key References

Dyce, K.M., W.O. Sack and C.J.G. Wensing. 1996. *Textbook of Veterinary Anatomy*. 2nd Edition, W.B. Saunders Co., Philadelphia. ISBN 0-7216-4961-0.

Evans, H.E. 1993. *Miller's Anatomy of the Dog*. 3rd Edition. W.B. Saunders Co., Philadelphia. ISBN 0-7216-3200-9.

Ginther, O.J. 1992. *Reproductive Biology of the Mare*. 2nd Edition, Equiservices Publishing, Cross Plains, WI. Library of Congress Cat. No. 91-075595.

Johnston, S.D., M.V. Root Kustritz and P.N.S. Olson. 2001. *Canine and Feline Theriogenology*. W.B. Saunders Co., Philadelphia. ISBN 0-7216-5607-2.

Kirkpatrick, R.L. 1980. "Physiological indices in wildlife management" in *Wildlife Management Techniques Manual*. 4th Edition-Revised. S.D. Schemnitz, ed. The Wildlife Society, Washington D.C. ISBN 0-9335-6408-2.

Knobil, E. and J.D. Neill (eds). 1998. *The Encyclopedia of Reproduction*. Vol. 1-4. Academic Press, San Diego. ISBN 0-12-227020-7.

Roberts, S.J. 1986. *Veterinary Obstetrics and Genital Diseases - Theriogenology*. 3rd Edition. David and Charles, Inc. North Pomfret, VT.

Schummer, A., R. Nickel and W.O. Sack. 1979. *The Viscera of the Domestic Mammals*. 2nd Revised Edition, Springer-Verlag, New York. ISBN 0-387-91139-1.

Tibary, A. and A. Anouassi. 1997. *Theriogenology in Camelidae*. United Arab Emirates. Ministry of Culture and Information. Publication authorization No. 3849/1/16. ISBN 9981-801-32-1.

2

CHAPTER 3

The Organization & Function of the
MALE REPRODUCTIVE TRACT

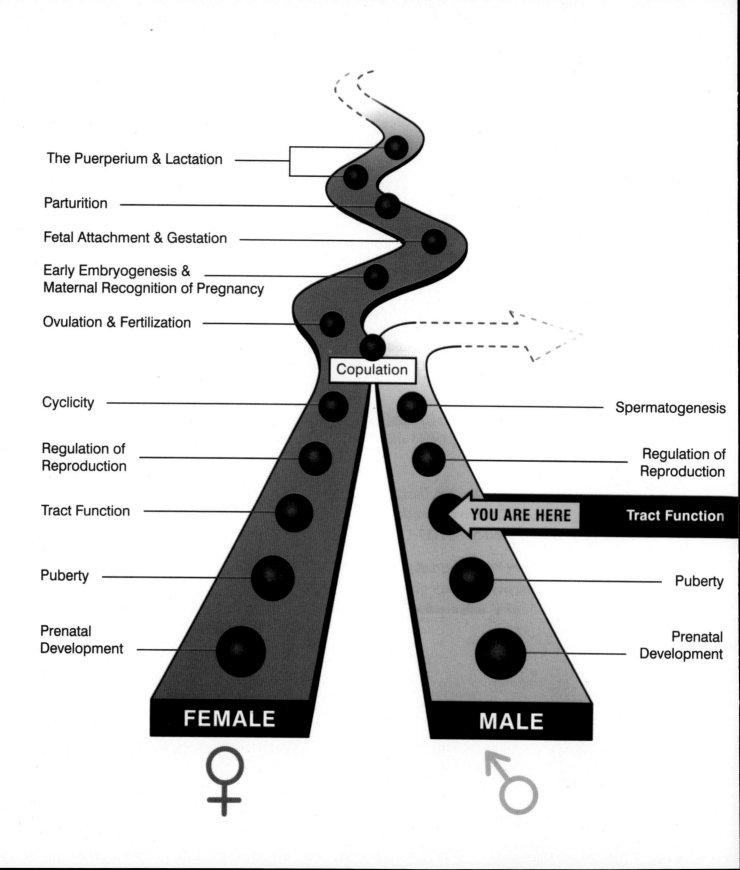

The Puerperium & Lactation

Parturition

Fetal Attachment & Gestation

Early Embryogenesis & Maternal Recognition of Pregnancy

Ovulation & Fertilization

Copulation

Cyclicity — Spermatogenesis

Regulation of Reproduction — Regulation of Reproduction

Tract Function — YOU ARE HERE — Tract Function

Puberty — Puberty

Prenatal Development — Prenatal Development

FEMALE   MALE

Take Home Message

The male reproductive system consists of the spermatic cord, testis, epididymis, accessory sex glands and the penis. The testis produces spermatozoa and testosterone, as well as other substances such as inhibin, estrogen and a variety of proteins. The epididymis provides the environment for final maturation of spermatozoa and serves as a storage organ for these cells. The accessory sex glands produce seminal plasma and the penis is the copulatory organ.

The male reproductive system is analogous to a manufacturing complex (See Figure 3-1). The primary products of the "manufacturing" process are fertile spermatozoa. Hormones (such as testosterone) and other secretory products (epididymal fluid and seminal plasma) of the male system contribute to the efficiency of the overall manufacturing and delivery process.

The **testes** serve as the manufacturing and assembly plant for spermatozoa and have an immense potential output of spermatozoa. In fact, spermatozoal production in mammals ranges from < 1 to 25 billion spermatozoa per day for both testes in normal males. This computes to an amazing production rate of around 35,000 to 200,000 spermatozoa per second. In most mammals the testes descend outside of the body into the scrotum. A specialized cooling mechanism is required for successful **spermatogenesis** (production of sperm). Once produced, spermatozoa pass through the rete tubules and the efferent ducts, and enter the **head** (caput) and **body** (corpus) of the **epididymis** (the "finishing shops"). In the head and body of the epididymis, spermatozoa undergo changes that allow them to become fertile. After gradual transport through the body and head over several days, spermatozoa enter the **tail** (cauda) of the epididymis. The tail of the epididymis is equivalent to a warehouse and shipping center. Spermatozoa in the tail of the epididymis are capable of fertilization and are motile if diluted into an appropriate buffer solution. The tail of the epididymis serves as a storage organ for spermatozoa prior to ejaculation and, in the sexually inactive male, may contain 4 to 8 days production of sperm. In males who are ejaculating with regular frequency, fewer sperm may be found. Upon sexual excitation, the spermatozoa in the tail of the epididymis are "shipped" via contractions of the epididymal duct and the **ductus deferens** to a new location in the reproductive tract, the **pelvic urethra**. Final alterations and packaging take place during emission when spermatozoa are mixed with fluids produced by the **accessory sex glands**. Collectively this mixture of fluids (from the epididymal tail and the accessory sex glands) is known as **seminal plasma**. Mixing of seminal plasma with spermatozoa causes dilution and undoubtedly some biochemical and surface changes that facilitate spermatozoal function. Once sperm are mixed with seminal plasma, they are available for delivery by ejaculation. The delivery system is the **penis** and specific muscles are responsible for **erection, protrusion of the penis** and **ejaculation** of semen.

The remainder of the chapter will assist you in developing knowledge about the anatomy and function of the specific components of the male reproductive system.

The basic components of the male reproductive system are the:

- *spermatic cord*
- *scrotum*
- *testis*
- *excurrent duct system*
- *accessory sex glands*
- *penis and muscles for protrusion, erection and ejaculation*

The Spermatic Cord Connects the Testis to the Body

The **spermatic cord** extends from the inguinal ring (the passageway from the body cavity into the scrotum) to its attachment on the dorsal pole of the testis. It suspends the testis in the scrotum (See Figures 3-2 through 3-8). It is most highly developed in males like the ram and bull that have a pendulous scrotum. The spermatic cord provides the pathway to and from the body for the testicular vasculature, lymphatics and nerves. The spermatic cord also houses the ductus deferens, the **cremaster muscle** and a specialized vascular network called the **pampiniform plexus**.

Figure 3-1. Male Reproductive System as a Manufacturing Complex

(Concept modified from Amann, *Proceedings of the 14th NAAB Technical Conference*, 1986)

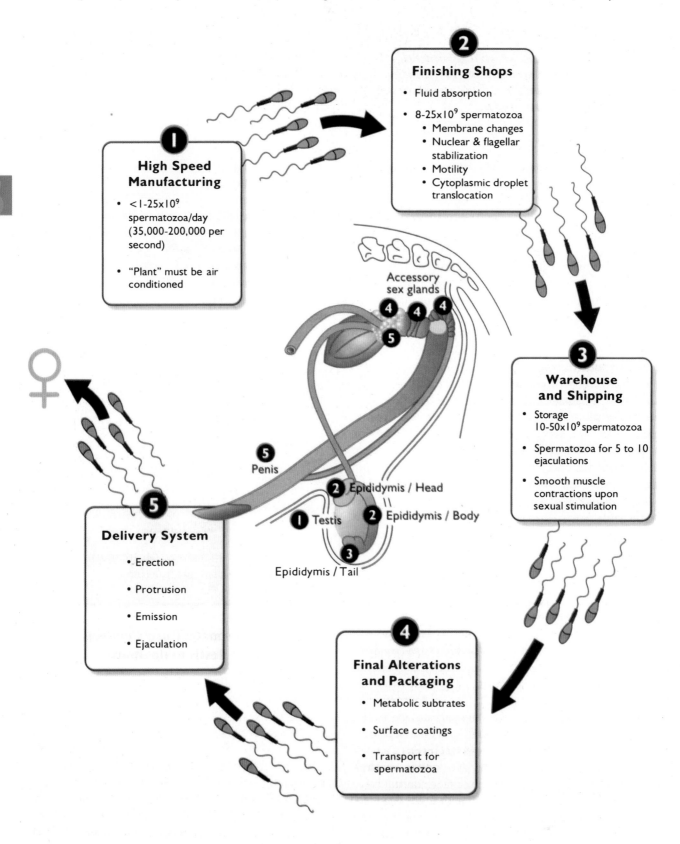

Figure 3-2. The Spermatic Cord and Its Components

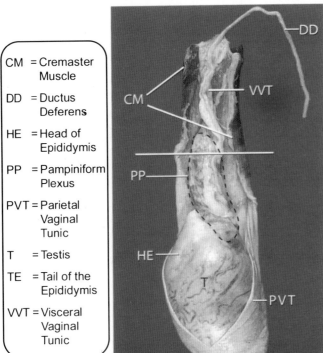

CM = Cremaster Muscle

DD = Ductus Deferens

HE = Head of Epididymis

PP = Pampiniform Plexus

PVT = Parietal Vaginal Tunic

T = Testis

TE = Tail of the Epididymis

VVT = Visceral Vaginal Tunic

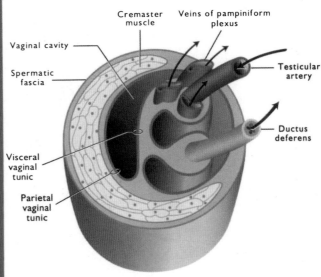

The line across the excised spermatic cord (photo at left) indicates the approximate plane of the cross-sectional schematic. Arrows indicate direction of fluid flow.

Figure 3-3. Alpaca Reproductive Tract

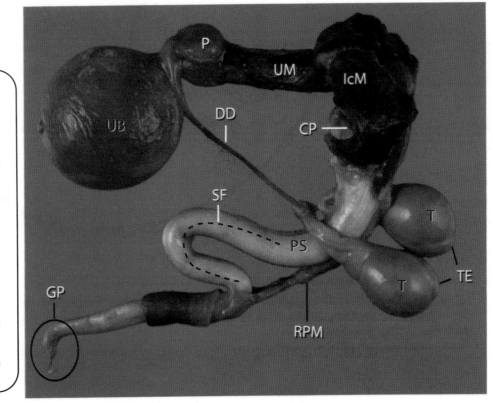

CP = Crus Penis

DD = Ductus Deferens

GP = Glans Penis

IcM = Ischiocavernosus Muscle

P = Prostate

PS = Penile Shaft

RPM = Retractor Penis Muscle

SF = Sigmoid Flexure

T = Testis

TE = Tail of Epididymis

UB = Urinary Bladder

UM = Urethralis Muscle

Figure 3-4. Bull Reproductive Tract

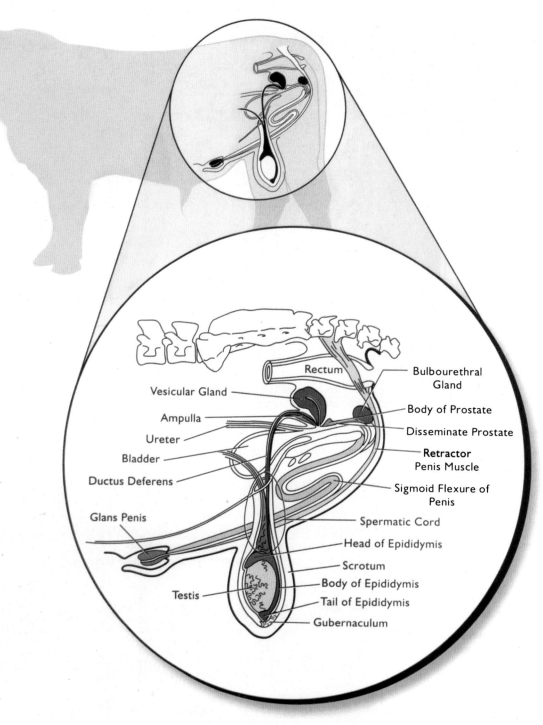

Schematic illustration of a sagittal view of the bull reproductive tract (Modified from Ellenberger and Baum, 1943, *Handbuch der Vergleichenden Anatomie der Haustiere,* 18th Edition. Zietzschmann, Ackerknecht and Grau, eds. Permission from Springer-Verlag, New York)

Figure 3-4. Extirpated Bull Reproductive Tract

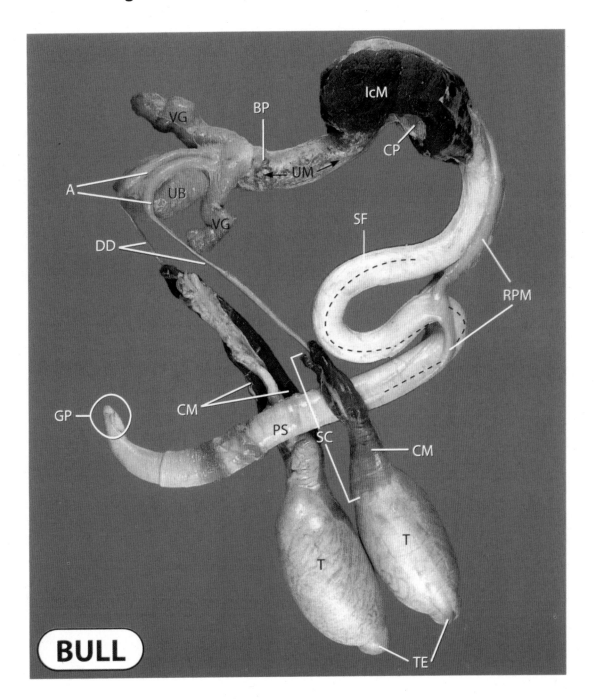

BULL

A = Ampulla	IcM = Ischiocavernosus Muscle	TE = Tail of Epididymis
BP = Body of Prostate	PS = Penile Shaft	UB = Urinary Bladder
CM = Cremaster Muscle	RPM = Retractor Penis Muscle	UM = Urethralis Muscle
CP = Crus Penis	SC = Spermatic Cord	VG = Vesicular Gland
DD = Ductus Deferens	SF = Sigmoid Flexure	
GP = Glans Penis	T = Testis	

Figure 3-5. Stallion Reproductive Tract

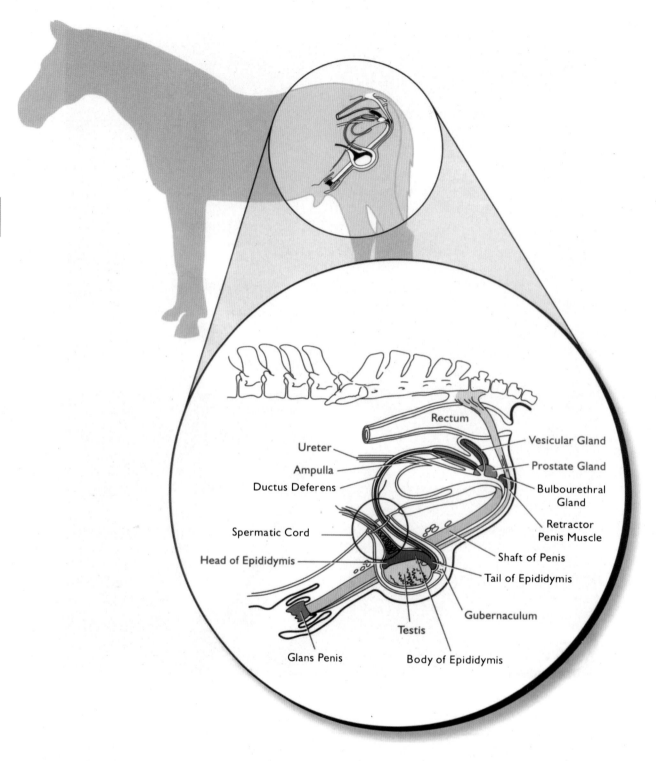

Schematic illustration of a sagittal view of the stallion reproductive tract (Modified from Ellenberger and Baum, 1943, *Handbuch der Vergleichenden Anatomie der Haustiere*, 18th Edition. Zietzschmann, Ackerknecht and Grau, eds. Permission from Springer-Verlag, New York)

Figure 3-5. Extirpated Stallion Reproductive Tract

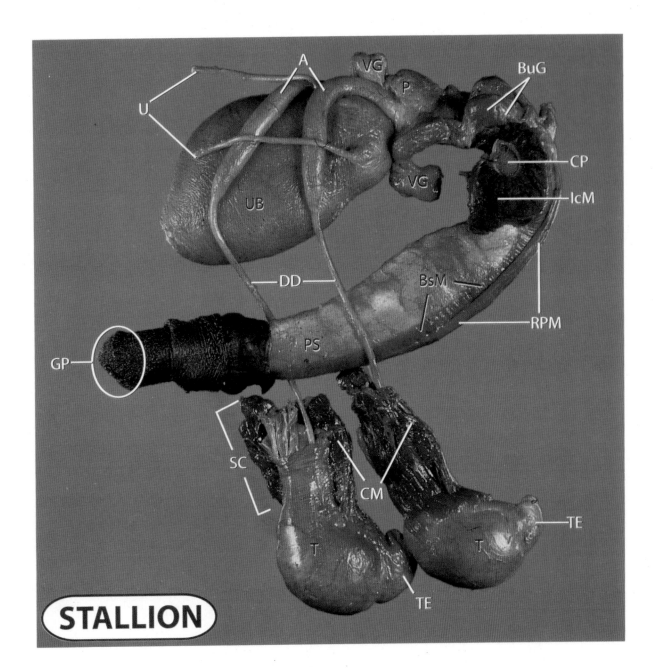

A = Ampulla	GP = Glans Penis	T = Testis
BsM = Bulbospongiosus Muscle	IcM = Ischiocavernosus Muscle	TE = Tail of Epididymis
BuG = Bulbourethral Gland	P = Prostate	U = Ureters
CM = Cremaster Muscle	PS = Penile Shaft	UB = Urinary Bladder
CP = Crus Penis	RPM = Retractor Penis Muscle	VG = Vesicular Gland
DD = Ductus Deferens	SC = Spermatic Cord	

Figure 3-6. Boar Reproductive Tract

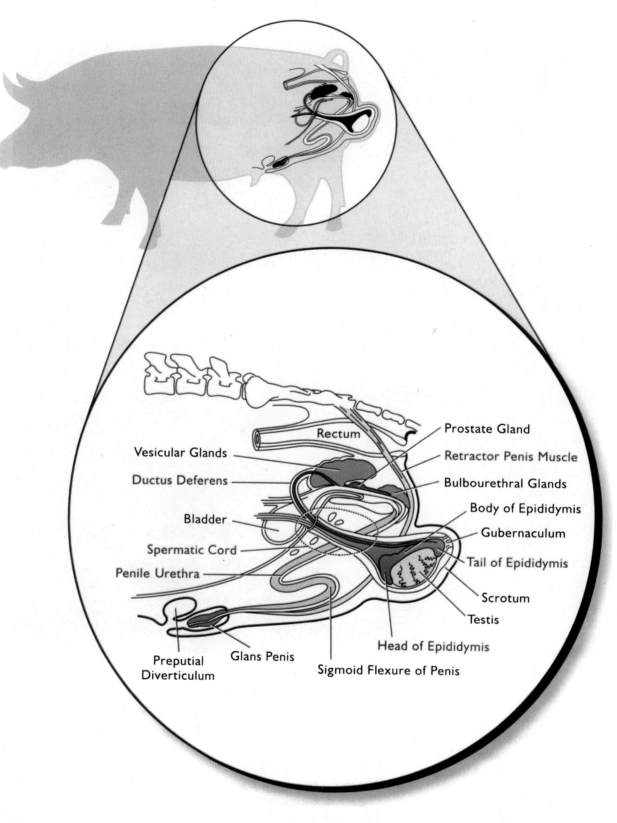

Schematic illustration of a sagittal view of the boar reproductive tract (Modified from Ellenberger and Baum, 1943, *Handbuch der Vergleichenden Anatomie der Haustiere*, 18th Edition. Zietzschmann, Ackerknecht and Grau, eds. Permission from Springer-Verlag, New York)

Figure 3-6. Extirpated Boar Reproductive Tract

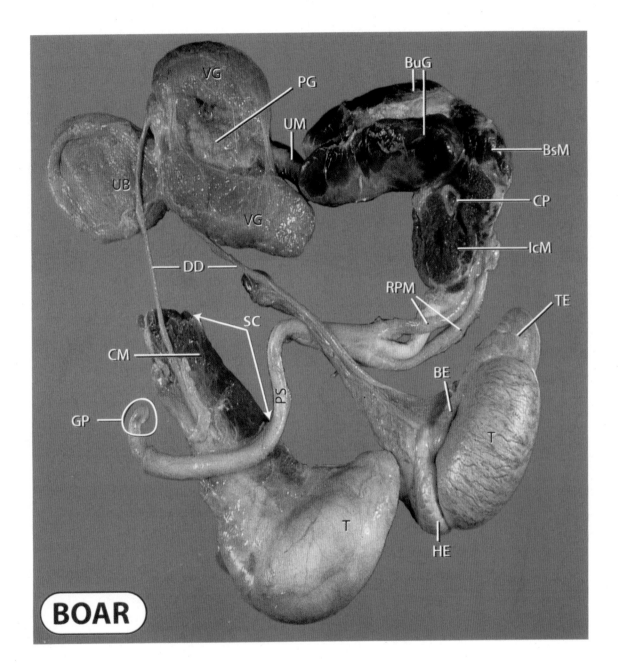

3

BOAR

BE = Body of Epididymis	HE = Head of Epididymis	TE = Tail of Epididymis
BsM = Bulbospongiosus Muscle	IcM = Ischiocavernosus Muscle	UB = Urinary Bladder
BuG = Bulbourethral Gland	PG = Prostate Gland	UM = Urethralis Muscle
CM = Cremaster Muscle	PS = Penile Shaft	VG = Vesicular Gland
CP = Crus Penis	RPM = Retractor Penis Muscle	
DD = Ductus Deferens	SC = Spermatic Cord	
GP = Glans Penis	T = Testis (left T-parietal vaginal tunic intact; right T-parietal vaginal tunic removed)	

Figure 3-7. Dog Reproductive Tract

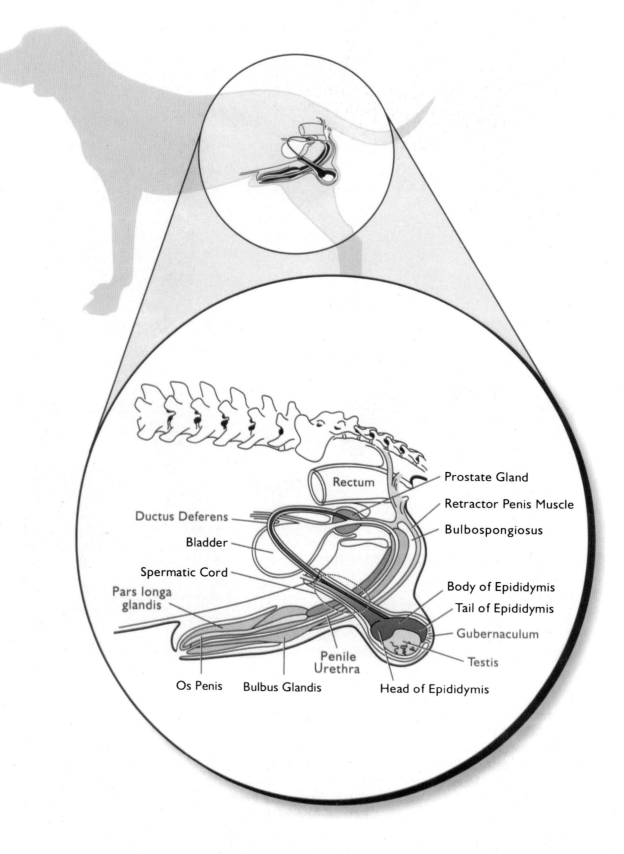

Figure 3-7. Extirpated Dog Reproductive Tract

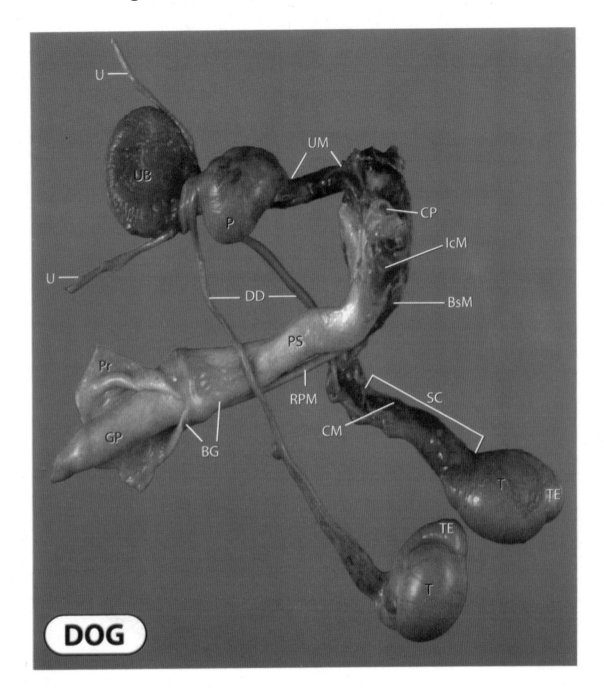

3

DOG

BG	= Bulbus Glandis	IcM = Ischiocavernosus Muscle	T = Testis
BsM	= Bulbospongiosus Muscle	P = Prostate Gland	TE = Tail of Epididymis
CM	= Cremaster Muscle	PS = Penile Shaft	U = Ureter
CP	= Crus Penis	PR = Prepuce	UB = Urinary Bladder
DD	= Ductus Deferens	RPM = Retractor Penis Muscle	UM = Urethralis Muscle
GP	= Glans Penis	SC = Spermatic Cord	

Figure 3-8. Tom Reproductive Tract

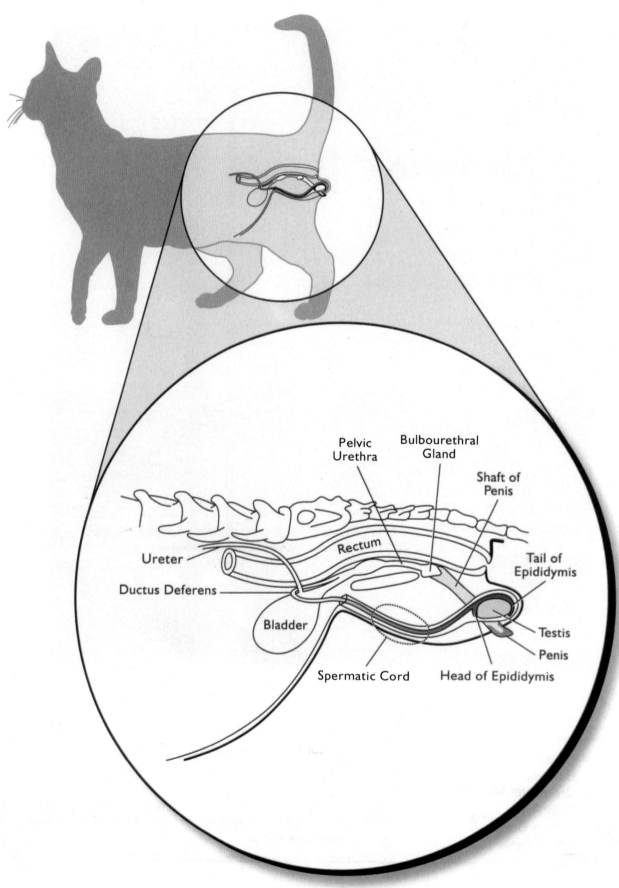

Figure 3-8. Extirpated Tom Reproductive Tract

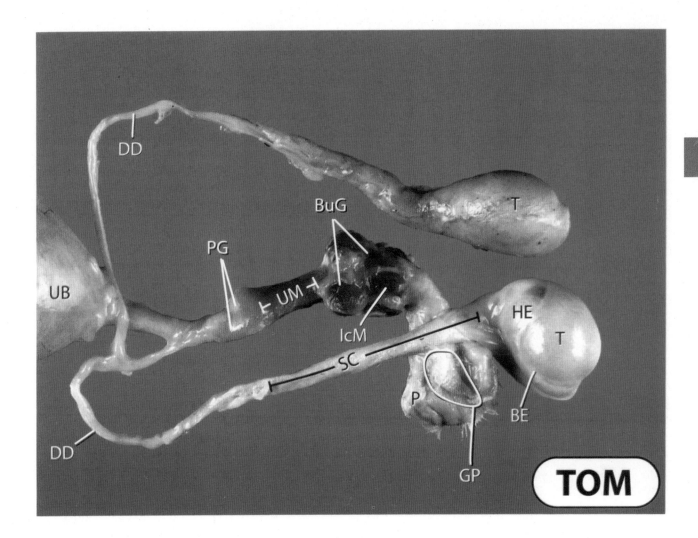

BE	= Body of Epididymis	HE	= Head of Epididymis	SC	= Spermatic Cord
BuG	= Bulbourethral Glands	IcM	= Ischiocavernosus Muscle	T	= Testis
DD	= Ductus Deferens	P	= Prepuce	UB	= Urinary Bladder
GP	= Glans Penis	PG	= Prostate Gland	UM	= Urethralis Muscle

Figure 3-9. Vascular Heat Exchanger

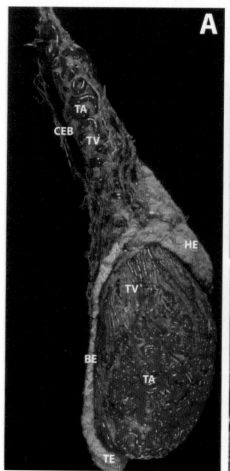

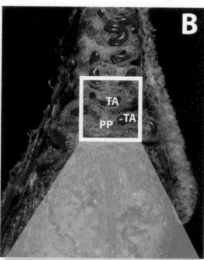

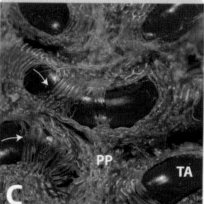

(Photos from Cody, et al. 1999. *Biol. Repod.* 60(suppl.1):90)

A

This photo enables visualization of the arterial and venous blood supply to the bull testis and epididymis. The testicular artery (TA) is highly convoluted and passes through the spermatic cord and surrounds the testis in the ventromedial area. In the spermatic cord, the testicular veins (TV) are in close proximity to the torturous testicular artery. The testicular veins (TV) seen on the surface of the testicle return venous blood to the spermatic cord. A branch of the testicular artery, the caudal epididymal branch (CEB) can be observed. The head of the epididymis (HE), body of the epididymis (BE) and tail of the epididymis (TE) can be seen.

B

An enlarged view of a portion of the vascular cone. The highly convoluted testicular artery (TA) has an intimate relationship with the veins of the pampiniform plexus (PP).

C

A highly enlarged photograph showing the intimate relationship of the pampiniform plexus with the testicular artery (TA). Notice the finger-like "wrappings" (arrows) of the pampiniform plexus surrounding the testicular artery (TA). This intimate relationship provides the anatomical basis for the countercurrent heat exchanger.

A large (6°C) temperature gradient exists between the body and the testes. Warm (39°C) arterial blood coming from the body is cooled on its way to the testis because the artery lies in close apposition to the veins that are returning cooler blood (33°C) from the testes.

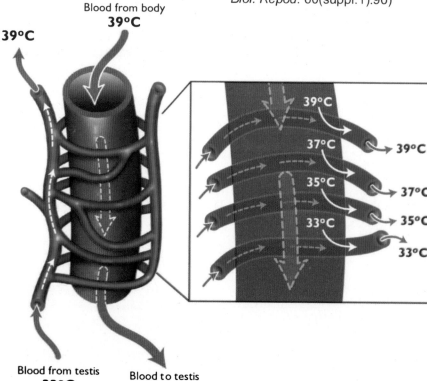

The **functions of the spermatic cords are to:**
- provide vascular, lymphatic and neural connection to the body
- provide a heat exchanger
- house the cremaster muscle

The majority of the spermatic cord mass consists of the testicular artery and veins. The **testicular artery** branches from the abdominal aorta and is rather straight until it passes through the inguinal canal. Thereafter it becomes highly convoluted (See Figure 3-9). The testicular veins in the spermatic cord branch into an elaborate network that forms many intimate finger-like "wrappings" surrounding the highly convoluted testicular artery. This venous network is called the **pampiniform plexus**. The pampiniform plexus eventually forms a single vein that runs into the caudal vena cava. These relationships are illustrated in Figure 3-9. These highly specialized structures are important for proper temperature control of the testis. In most mammals, the testes must be 4 to 6°C cooler than the body

3

Figure 3-10. Pulse Pressure Elimination in the Spermatic Cord

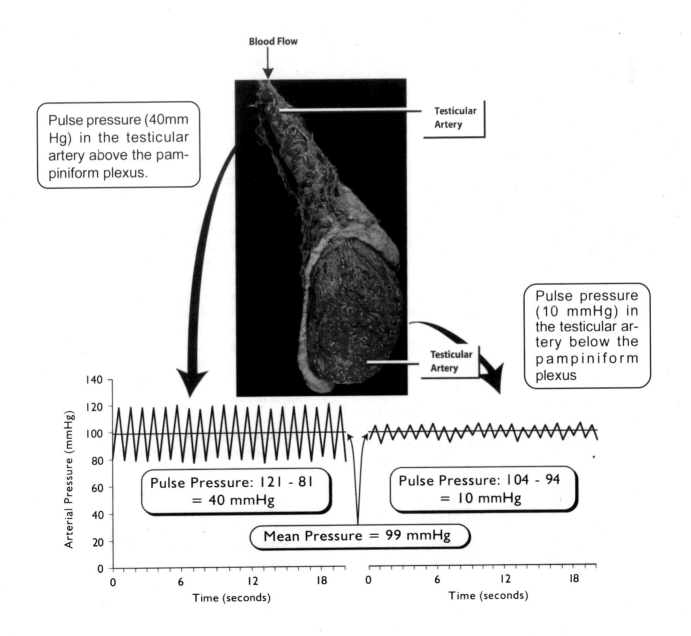

in order for spermatogenesis to occur. The complex, intimate network of the spermatic artery and the spermatic veins forms a **countercurrent heat exchanger** (See Figure 3-9). Heat from the warm (39°C) arterial blood from the body is transferred to the cooler (33°C) venous blood leaving the surface of the testes (See Figure 3-9). This venous blood has been cooled by direct heat loss from the testicular veins through the skin of the scrotum. Maintenance of low testicular temperature is obligatory for spermatogenesis in domestic animals and man. Disruption or modification of this cooling mechanism will severely compromise, if not completely suppress, spermatogenesis.

The long convoluted testicular artery serves as a **pulse pressure eliminator**. Pulse pressure exists in all arteries throughout the body. Pulse pressure is what you feel when you palpate the radial artery in your wrist or the carotid artery in your neck. It is the difference between **systolic pressure** (heart contraction) and **diastolic pressure** (heart relaxation). For example, if systolic pressure is 120 mm Hg and diastolic pressure is 80 mm Hg, the pulse pressure is 40 mm Hg. In the case of the **testicular artery**, this pulse pressure is almost eliminated between the inguinal ring and the surface of the testis (See Figure 3-10). Thus, blood entering the testis is almost "pulseless." However, the mean arterial pressure (the average of systolic and diastolic pressure) is only slightly reduced. The mechanism for the elimination of arterial pulse pressure is not known. It has been proposed that the testicular artery has a higher compliance (elasticity) than other arteries of comparable size. The functional significance of this pulse elimination is not understood clearly.

The close relationship between the venous and the arterial blood supply in the spermatic cord results in some opportunity for exchange of testosterone between the two vessels. Because testosterone is at high concentrations in the venous drainage from the testicle and levels are low in the arterial blood from the body supplying the testicle, testosterone moves from the vein to the artery. This concentration gradient allows some testosterone to be recirculated back into the testicle. In this context, the vessels in the spermatic cord are fundamentally quite similar to the vascular countercurrent exchange system between the uterine vein and ovarian artery in the female, where PGF$_{2\alpha}$ is transferred to the ovary (See Chapter 9).

The Testes are Supported by the Cremaster Muscle

The primary muscle supporting the testis and coursing the length of the spermatic cord is the cremaster muscle (See Figures 3-2 through 3-8). The cremaster is a striated muscle that is continuous with the internal abdominal oblique muscle. It helps support the testis and aids in control of testicular temperature. Its temperature control function is probably related to the fact that when the cremaster muscle contracts and relaxes, it creates a "pumping action" on the pampiniform plexus, thus facilitating blood flow and enhancing cooling efficiency. Blood flow returning to the body from the testes is quite sluggish because the pressure is quite low in this high surface area plexus and there are no frequent muscle contractions to enhance venous return (like in the legs). Contractions of the cremaster muscle promote venous return of testicular blood and thus facilitates heat exchange. In some species (the ram and, to some degree, the bull) sexual excitation promotes a high degree of intermittent contractile activity of the cremaster muscle. During sexual excitation the testes move up and down in a rapid manner. Unlike the smooth muscle in the scrotum (**tunica dartos**), the cremaster muscle is not capable of sustained contractions. Therefore, it is reasonable to assume that the function of the cremaster muscle is more related to facilitating blood movement in the pampiniform plexus than providing sustained contractions for elevating the testes close to the body wall during exposure to cold temperatures. The cremaster muscle may be important in short-term elevation of the testicles during fear or high planes of excitement. Such a function would tend to protect the pendular testes during periods of physical confrontation or flight from danger.

Not all animals have pendular testes that are located outside of the body. Obviously such animals do not have a scrotum. Birds, elephants, sloths, armadillos and some marine mammals (whales and dolphins) have testes located inside the body in a **retroperitoneal** position. Thus, mechanisms associated with temperature regulation are not important in these species, except where loss of control of deep body temperature occurs. The testes of some mammals (rat and rabbit) move into and out of the body cavity throughout their lives through a patent inguinal canal. The evolutionary basis for the descent of the testes and the need for testicular cooling is not clear.

The Scrotal Skin Serves as a Temperature Sensor and a Cooling System

The **scrotum** is a two lobed sac. It protects and supports the testes and is required for proper temperature regulation. The scrotum consists of four major layers. They are: 1) the **skin**; 2) the **tunica dartos**; 3) the **scrotal fascia** and 4) the **parietal vaginal tunic** (See Figure 3-15).

The scrotum is a:
- *thermosensor*
- *swamp cooler*
- *protective sac*

The scrotal skin is heavily populated with sweat glands. These sweat glands are required for maintenance of proper testicular temperature. The scrotal sweat glands are innervated by sympathetic nerves (See Figure 3-11). When the male experiences either elevated body temperature or elevated scrotal temperature, the hypothalamus detects this change and sends nerve impulses to the sweat glands. Sweating allows the scrotum (and thus the testes) to be cooled by evaporative heat transfer, like a swamp cooler.

The scrotal skin is endowed with large numbers of thermosensitive nerves. These sensory nerves govern both the degree of scrotal sweating and respiratory rate of the animal. In fact, in the ram changes in scrotal temperature can bring about dramatic changes in respiratory rate. For example, the rate of respiration of fully fleeced Merino rams begins to increase gradually when the skin temperature of the scrotum rises above 36°C. If the temperature of the scrotal skin continues to increase (40-42°C), the respiratory rate will increase suddenly and the ram will begin to pant (polypnea). Respiratory frequencies as high as 200 breaths per minute can occur under these conditions (See Figure 3-13). Warming an equivalent area of the flank or other parts of the body results in only small increases in respiratory rate. This response clearly shows that there is a highly developed neural pathway originating in the scrotum and terminating in the respiratory center of the brain (See Figure 3-11).

While cooling of the testes is obligatory for normal spermatogenesis, constant cooling does not appear to be necessary. For example, Australian researchers found that exposure of the scrotum to hot temperatures for periods of 16 hours per day did not influence sperm production rates. But after 8 hours or more of heat exposure motility was reduced significantly. An additional important finding was that when 16 hours per day of heat was applied to the scrotum,

Figure 3-11. Proposed Scrotal Sweating and Thermal Polypnea Pathways in Rams

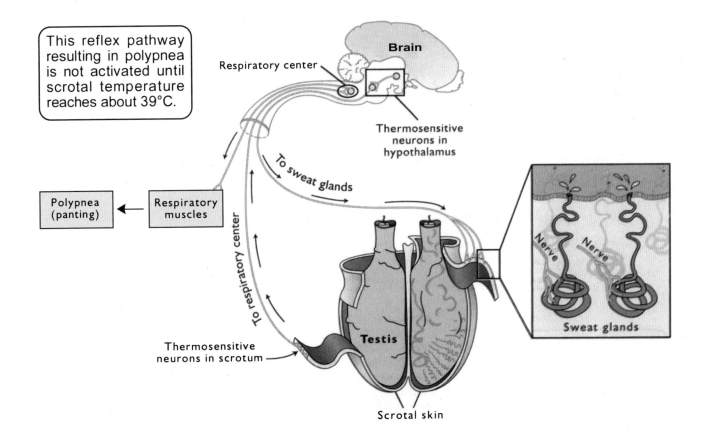

This reflex pathway resulting in polypnea is not activated until scrotal temperature reaches about 39°C.

Figure 3-12. Infrared Thermogram of Bull Scrotum
(Photo courtesy of G.H. Coulter, Agriculture and Agri-Food Canada, Lethbridge, Alberta *www.agr.gc.ca/science/*)

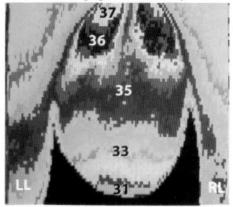

This is a caudal view of the scrotum of a mature bull. The symmetrical surface temperature pattern is typical of a bull with normal scrotal cooling. Each horizontal color band represents a different surface temperature. The warmest temperature (37°C) is in the region overlying the spermatic cords while the coolest region (31°C) is in the ventral scrotum. (LL = Left Leg, RL = Right Leg)

reduced survival of embryos produced by normal females was observed even though sperm numbers were adequate. Such a finding implies that DNA in sperm is damaged by heat and that eggs fertilized by these sperm have a low probability of surviving. There appears to be significant variability with regard to the effect of scrotal heating upon spermatozoal production and viability. Further research is needed in this important area since the ambient temperature can often be managed/manipulated in the environment of the sexually active male, especially males used for artificial insemination.

Measuring the cooling capacity of the testes is difficult. Historically, the cooling capacity and thermal regulatory function of the testes was measured by small temperature sensors that were implanted surgically in the vasculature and/or in the testicular tissue. A noninvasive technology called **infrared thermography** has been used by Canadian researchers to assess the cooling capacity of the testes. Infrared thermography measures the infrared emissions from a heat producing body. Thus, this technique quantitates the heat released from the surface of the scrotum. Males with faulty testicular cooling can be identified and eliminated as breeding males. While this technique

Figure 3-13. Scrotal Heating Induces Panting in Ram

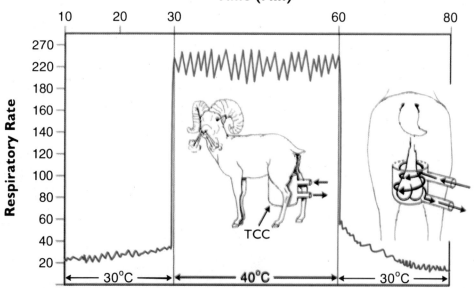

Warming of the scrotum using a temperature controlled chamber (TCC) causes little change in respiratory rate until the scrotal temperature reaches 40°C. Arrows indicate the direction of the fluid flow in temperature warming device.

When a scrotal temperature of 40°C is reached, marked polypnea (panting or rapid breathing) occurs with respiratory rates often exceeding 200 cycles per minute.

When scrotal temperature returns to about 30°C, respiratory rates suddenly returns to normal. (Adapted from Waites, *The Testis* Vol I, Johnson, Gomes and Vandemark)

Figure 3-14. Excised Testicles

The parietal vaginal tunic has been incised and reflected away from the testis. The lower right panel illustrates the intimate relationship between the tunica albuginea and the visceral vaginal tunic.

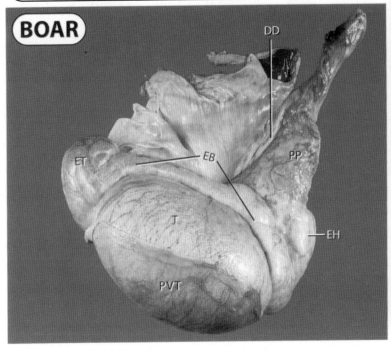

BOAR

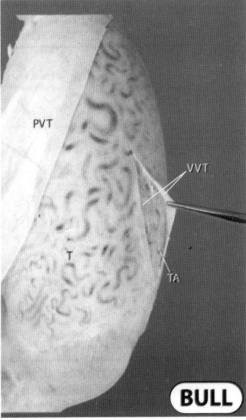

BULL

CM = Cremaster Muscle	PP = Pampiniform Plexus
DD = Ductus Deferens	PVT = Parietal Vaginal Tunic
EB = Epididymal Body	T = Testis
EH = Epididymal Head	TA = Tunica Albuginea
ET = Epididymal Tail	VVT = Visceral Vaginal Tunic

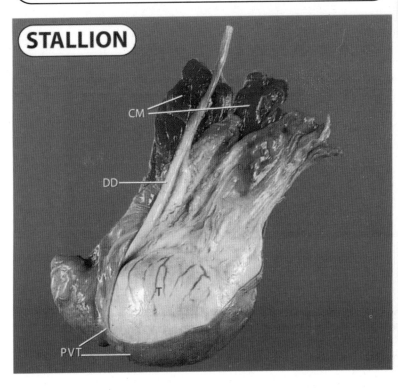

STALLION

BULL

Figure 3-15. Longitudinally Incised Testes

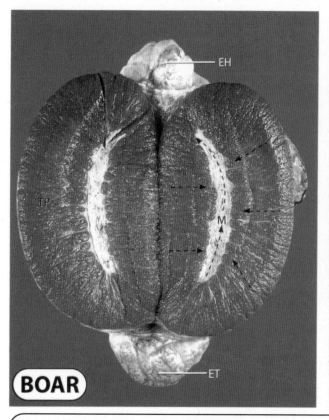

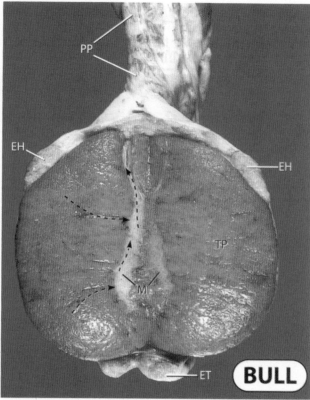

These testes have been incised longitudinally to expose the testicular parenchyma (TP) and the mediastinum (M). Arrows denote direction of flow of spermatozoa and fluids toward the efferent ducts and the head of the epididymis.

EH	=	Epididymal Head	PP =	Pampiniform Plexus
ET	=	Epididymal Tail	TP =	Testicular Parenchyma
M	=	Mediastinum		

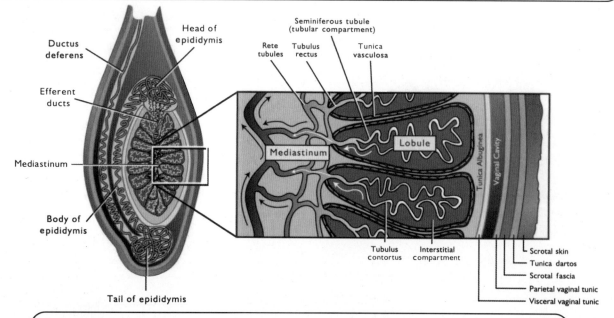

Schematic illustration of the scrotum, the connective tissue supporting structures and the tubular pathway of the typical mammalian testis. (Modified from Davis, Langford and Kirby; *The Testis* Vol. 1, Johnson, Gomes and Vandemark)

has not reached the stage where it can be applied to everyday livestock management activities, it has promise for evaluating testicular cooling capacity in bulls and other species. Testicular cooling is a function of both the vascular countercurrent heat exchanger (See Figure 3-9) and scrotal cooling (See Figure 3-11). Efficient testicular cooling requires that scrotal cooling occur so that the venous blood in the testicle can be cooled. Only after the venous blood has been cooled can the vascular countercurrent heat exchanger function properly.

In general, the scrotal skin (and spermatic cord) in mammals contains little fat. However, under certain management conditions, accumulation of scrotal fat may be a problem. For example, beef bulls being fed for maximum rate of gain in bull test stations are evaluated for their efficiency of growth. Under conditions of maximum nutrient intake, fat may accumulate in the scrotum as well as the spermatic cord. Such accumulation of fat would decrease the cooling effectiveness of the scrotum and pampiniform plexus and thus may reduce spermatogenic efficiency, spermatozoal viability and fertility.

The Tunica Dartos has the Ability to Elevate the Testes for a Sustained Period of Time

The **tunica dartos** (also called the **dartos muscle**) is a mesh-like smooth muscle layer that lies just beneath the scrotal skin (See Figure 3-15). The degree of contraction of this smooth muscle is constantly adjusted in response to changes in scrotal skin temperature. The sensory nerves initiating the changes in the tone (degree of contraction) of the tunica dartos are located in the scrotal skin. Unlike striated muscle (cremaster muscle), the smooth muscle of the tunica dartos can maintain sustained contractions. This characteristic allows the testes to be held close to the body for sustained periods during cold temperatures. On the contrary, during the hot summer months, the tunica dartos relaxes and thus the surface area of the scrotum increases substantially to facilitate cooling. This increase in surface area of the scrotum is closely linked to scrotal perspiration. As the scrotum perspires, the increased surface area allows for a greater rate of evaporative heat loss and more rapid and efficient cooling.

Development and maintenance of the contractile ability of the tunica dartos are under androgen control. For example, the ability of the tunica dartos to contract in response to cold temperatures is lost in castrated males because testosterone is absent.

Artificial manipulation of the scrotum has been used to sterilize beef bulls. The scrotum may be artificially shortened to hold the testes next to the body, resulting in elevated testicular temperature and causing significantly reduced spermatogenesis. A bull subjected to this procedure is referred to as a "**short scrotumed**" bull. This type of bull is physiologically an artificial cryptorchid (See Chapter 4). The testes are forced into the dorsal region of the scrotum by placing a large rubber band around the lower portion of the scrotum. In 3 to 4 weeks the lower scrotum sloughs at the juncture of the rubber band because of restricted circulation. As you might expect, the weight of the testes in these bulls is less than in unaltered bulls. In fact, they are about one-half the weight of an unaltered bull. "Short scrotumed" males, while sterile, maintain normal testosterone levels, and thus maintain a high rate of growth. Research has shown that these bulls have increased efficiency of growth and have leaner carcasses compared to steers. Although this technique is not in widespread use, it illustrates the importance of an intact scrotum for testicular cooling. Furthermore, it illustrates the importance of androgens as promoters of growth and leanness.

> *The testes are the primary reproductive organs in the male. Their functions are to produce:*
> - *spermatozoa*
> - *hormones and proteins*
> - *fluids*

The testes are paired organs that vary considerably in size and shape among species. They are considered the primary reproductive organs in the male because they produce both **spermatozoa** and the androgen **testosterone**. In addition, they produce inhibin, estrogens and a variety of proteins believed to be important to spermatozoal function. They also produce fluid that originates primarily from the seminiferous tubules. This fluid serves as a vehicle in which spermatozoa are suspended and facilitates their removal from the testes. The fluid produced by the testes (sometimes called rete fluid) also contains products synthesized by the Sertoli cells.

Figure 3-16. Relationship of the Germ Cells to the Adjacent Sertoli Cells

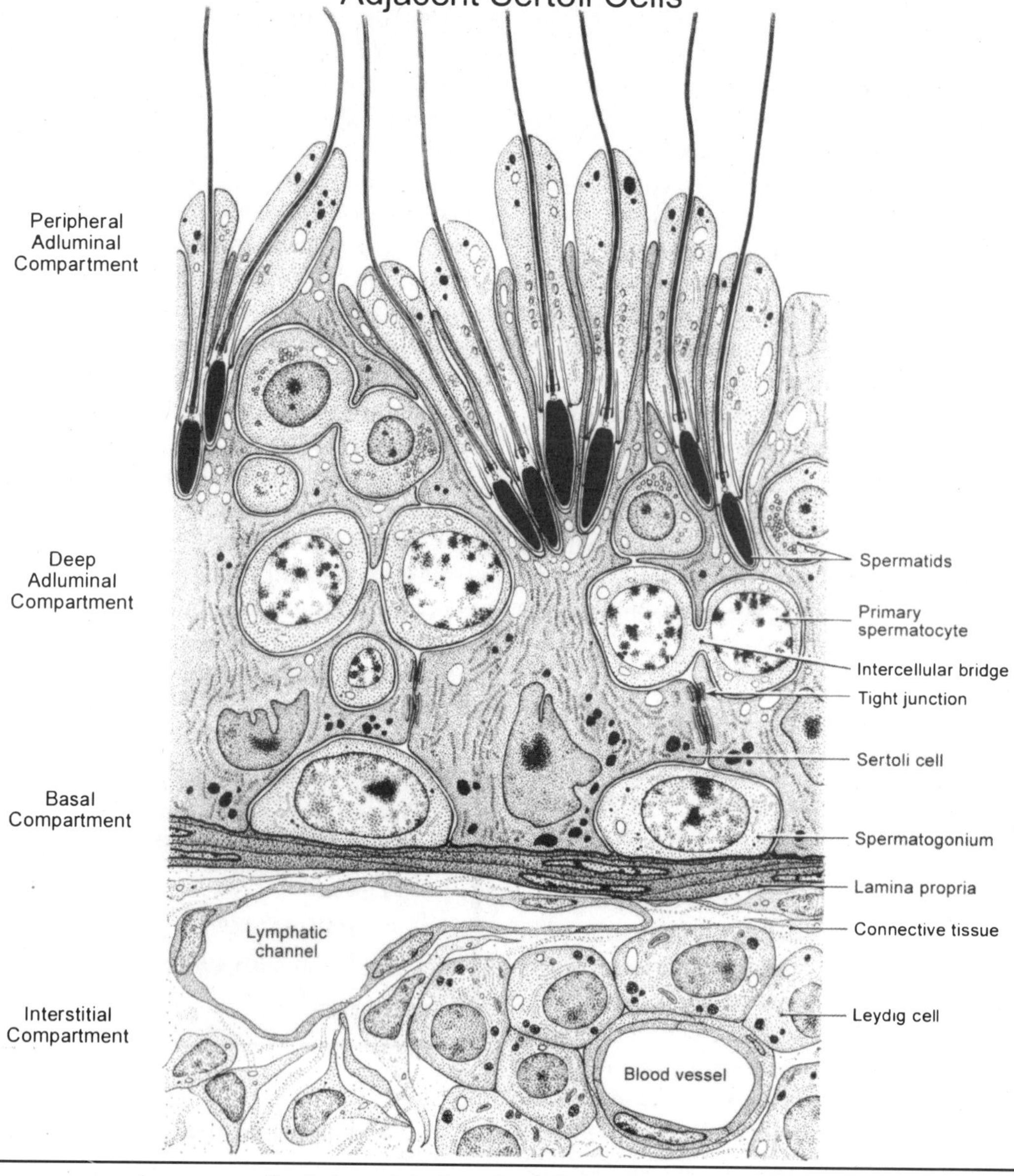

Peripheral Adluminal Compartment

Deep Adluminal Compartment

Basal Compartment

Interstitial Compartment

Spermatids

Primary spermatocyte

Intercellular bridge

Tight junction

Sertoli cell

Spermatogonium

Lamina propria

Connective tissue

Lymphatic channel

Leydig cell

Blood vessel

Peripheral Adluminal Compartment

During elongation of the spermatid nucleus, the spermatids are repositioned by the Sertoli cells to become imbedded within long pockets in the cytoplasm of an individual Sertoli cell. When released as a spermatozoon, a major portion of the cytoplasm of each spermatid remains as a residual body (cytoplasmic droplet) within a pocket of the Sertoli cell cytoplasm.

Deep Adluminal Compartment

The primary spermatocytes are moved from the basal compartment through the tight junctions between adjacent Sertoli cells into the adluminal compartment where they eventually divide to form secondary spermatocytes (not shown) and spherical spermatids. The spermatogonia, primary spermatocytes, secondary spermatocytes and spherical spermatids all develop in the space between two or more Sertoli cells and are in contact with them. Note the intracellular bridges between adjacent germ cells in the same cohort or generation.

Basal Compartment

Formation of spermatozoa in the seminiferous epithelium starts near the basement membrane. Here a spermatogonium divides to form other spermatogonia and, ultimately, primary spermatocytes. (From Amann, *J.Dairy Sci.* Vol. 66, No. 12, 1983)

> **The testis consists of the:**
> - *testicular capsule*
> - *parenchyma*
> - *mediastinum*
> - *rete tubules*

The Testicular Capsule is a Dynamic "Suborgan" Covering the Testes

The covering of the testis, or **testicular capsule** is composed of two layers. They are the **visceral vaginal tunic** and the connective tissue capsule known as the **tunica albuginea**. The visceral vaginal tunic is closely associated with the tunica albuginea and these two layers can be separated using careful dissection (See Figure 3-14). The tunica albuginea sends many finger-like projections into the parenchyma of the testicle. These septal projections join with the **mediastinum** (See Figure 3-15). The interior surfaces of the tunica albuginea and the surfaces of the septal divisions forming the lobules are quite vascular. These surfaces are thus called the **tunica vasculosa** (See Figure 3-15).

The testicular capsule was once considered to be an inert covering whose sole function was to form the outer boundary of the testes. It is now apparent that the testicular capsule is a dynamic "suborgan" capable of undergoing changes in direct response to hormones and neurotransmitters. The tunica albuginea is not only composed of connective tissue, but contains smooth muscle fibers. Contractions of capsular smooth muscle can be induced by both acetylcholine and norepinephrine, two of the most widespread neurotransmitters in the body. These two important compounds cause contraction and relaxation of smooth muscle in the blood vessels and visceral organs throughout the body. Rhythmic cycles of contractions and relaxation of the testicular capsule serve to provide a pumping action thought to facilitate movement of spermatozoa into the rete tubules and efferent ducts.

> **The testicular parenchyma consists of:**
> - *seminiferous tubules*
> - *interstitial cells of Leydig*
> - *capillaries*
> - *lymphatic vessels*
> - *connective tissue*

The word **parenchyma** refers to the specific cellular mass of a gland or organ that is supported by a connective tissue network. The major cellular mass of the testis is therefore referred to as the parenchyma. It is a soft, tan (sometimes brown or gray) mass made up of seminiferous tubules and interstitial tissue (blood vessels, nerves, lymphatics, connective tissue and Leydig cells) (See Figure 3-15). The parenchyma can be divided into the **tubular compartment** and the **interstitial compartment** (See Figure 3-15). The tubular compartment consists of **seminiferous tubules** and all of the cells and material inside them. The interstitial compartment consists of all cells and materials outside the seminiferous tubules, such as blood vessels, connective tissue, lymphatics, nerves and the **interstitial cells of Leydig**, that produce testosterone.

The mediastinum is the central connective tissue core of the testis (See Figure 3-15) that houses ducts called rete tubules. The rete tubules (or rete testis) are tiny channels through which spermatozoa are transported out of the testis (See Figure 3-15). The dense connective tissue of the mediastinum helps prevent compression or collapse of the rete tubules so spermatozoa and fluid originating in the seminiferous tubules can move freely out of the testis.

> **The tubular compartment consists of:**
> - *seminiferous epithelium*
> - *Sertoli cells*
> - *developing germ cells*
> - *peritubular cells*

The seminiferous tubules (comprising the tubular compartment of the parenchyma) are microscopic. They form highly convoluted loops (See Figure 3-15), the ends of which join with the **rete tubules**. Each loop of a seminiferous tubule is composed of a convoluted portion (**tubulus contortus**) and a straight portion (**rectus**) that join the rete tubule (See Figure 3-15). Spermatogenesis takes place predominantly in the tubulus contortus.

The seminiferous tubule is composed of a basement membrane and a layer of **seminiferous epithelium** (also called the **germinal epithelium**) (See Figure 3-16). The tubule is surrounded by contractile peritubular cells. Their contraction and the flow of fluid secreted by **Sertoli cells** allows newly formed spermatozoa to move into the rete tubules.

3

The seminiferous epithelium consists of two major regions known as the **basal compartment** and the **adluminal compartment**. Sertoli cells are anchored to the basement membrane and surround the developing population of germ cells. The relationship between the Sertoli cells and the germinal elements is shown in Figure 3-16.

Sertoli cells are the only somatic cells in the seminiferous epithelium. Once believed to be simply a supportive component for the germinal elements, they are now considered to be the cellular "governors" of spermatogenesis. Each Sertoli cell "hosts" a maximum number of developing germ cells, characteristic for a given species. Hence, testes with high numbers of Sertoli cells are capable of producing large numbers of spermatozoa. Conversely, testes with small numbers of Sertoli cells can only produce small numbers of spermatozoa. Sertoli cells are analogous to the granulosal cells of the ovarian follicle. However, unlike granulosal cells, the Sertoli cell contains receptors for both FSH and testosterone. Because Sertoli cells possess receptors to different hormones (protein and steroid), they have the capability of producing a variety of substances. A few examples are: 1) **androgen binding protein (ABP)**, a testosterone transport protein; 2) **sulfated glycoproteins (SGP) 1** and **2**, that are believed to be related to fertility acquisition (SGP-1) and providing a detergent effect that allows cells and fluids to move through the tubular network of the testis (SGP-2); 3) **transferrin**, an iron transport protein believed to be required for successful spermatogenesis and 4) **inhibin**, as in the female, a suppressor of FSH.

Adjacent Sertoli cells are tightly attached to each other on their lower lateral surfaces by a band of specialized junctions called **tight junctions**. The Sertoli cell junctional complexes separate the germinal epithelium into a basal compartment (See Figure 3-16) that houses spermatogonia and early primary spermatocytes and an adluminal compartment that houses all other germ cells. The name basal compartment reflects its position just above the basement membrane of the seminiferous tubule. The adluminal compartment implies a region adjacent to the lumen of the seminiferous tubule. The cell types found in the adluminal compartment are **primary** and **secondary spermatocytes** and **spermatids**. The junctional complexes between Sertoli cells form a specialized permeability barrier that prevents large molecular weight materials and immune cells from gaining access to the adluminal compartment.

> *The blood-testis barrier prevents immunologic destruction of developing germ cells.*

The peritubular cells surrounding the seminiferous tubule and the Sertoli cell junctional complexes form the **blood-testis barrier**. The primary purpose of the blood-testis barrier is to prevent autoimmune reactions from destroying the developing germ cells. Materials in the interstitial compartment are first "screened" by the peritubular layer surrounding the seminiferous epithelium. The peritubular layer thus acts as the first barrier against large molecular weight materials (mainly immunoglobulins).

The junctional complexes (tight junctions) between Sertoli cells serve as the second barrier against immune cells and immunoglobulins. The most important feature of the blood-testis barrier is the exclusion of immune cells (macrophages and lymphocytes) and immunoglobulins (antibodies) from the adluminal compartment. This exclusion is important since these molecules would recognize the developing germinal elements as foreign because they are undergoing meiosis. Therefore, they are immunologically different from other cells within the body and thus generate an immune response. In addition to forming the blood-testis barrier, the Sertoli cell junctional complexes provide a type of control for materials entering and, at least in part, leaving the adluminal compartment.

> *The excurrent duct system consists of:*
> - *efferent ducts*
> - *the epididymal duct*
> - *the ductus deferens*

Table 3-1. Time Required (Days) for Passage of Spermatozoa Through the Various Parts of the Epididymal Duct

Species	Head	Body	Tail	Total
Boar	3	2	4-9	9-14
Bull	2	2	10	14
Camel	0.2	0.3	1.5	4.2
Man	1-2	0.5	5	6.5-7.5
Ram	1	3	8	12
Stallion	1	2	6	9

The Excurrent Duct System Allows for Final Maturation, Storage and Delivery of Spermatozoa to the Pelvic Urethra

The efferent ducts converge to a single duct, the **epididymal duct**. The function of the efferent ducts is to convey newly formed spermatozoa and tubular fluid (rete fluid) into the epididymal duct. The head of the epididymis contains the point of connection between the efferent ducts and the initial segment of the epididymal duct (See Chapter 4 for embryologic origin). The function of the epididymis is to provide the environment for final maturation of spermatozoa, resulting in acquisition of motility and potential fertility. The epididymis also serves as a storage reservoir for spermatozoa. Epididymal function is androgen dependent.

The epididymis is organized into three distinct regions known as the head (caput), the body (corpus) and the tail (cauda) (See Figures 3-2 through 3-7, 3-14, 3-15 and 3-18).

The epididymal duct is a single, highly convoluted duct ranging in length from 30 to 60 meters depending on species. It is surrounded by smooth muscle. This muscular layer is responsible for rhythmic contractions of the duct, forcing spermatozoa to travel along its course to the tail. The time required to transport spermatozoa from the proximal head of the epididymis to the distal tail is referred to as **epididymal transit time**.

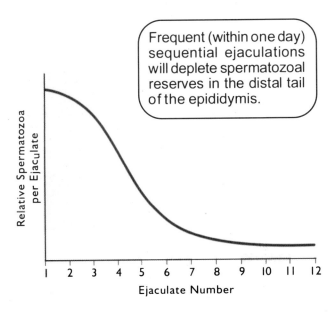

Figure 3-17. Depletion of Spermatozoal Reserves in the Distal Tail of the Epididymis

Frequent (within one day) sequential ejaculations will deplete spermatozoal reserves in the distal tail of the epididymis.

(y-axis) Relative Spermatozoa per Ejaculate

(x-axis) Ejaculate Number

Epididymal transit times through the head and body of the epididymis are remarkably constant within species (See Table 3-1). Smooth muscle in the tail of the epididymis is relatively quiescent except during periods of sexual excitation. When sexual stimulation occurs, the smooth muscle of the distal tail begins to contract vigorously, moving spermatozoa into the ductus deferens. Epididymal transit time through the head and body is not altered by sexual excitation. However, the number of sperm in the distal tail can be altered dramatically by the frequency of ejaculation. In sexually rested males, the sperm content of the tail is maximal, while males experiencing a high ejaculation frequency have 25% to 45% fewer sperm in the epididymal tail. Spermatozoa spending an unusually long time in the tail (such as after long periods of sexual rest) may be of poor quality when compared to sperm from animals ejaculated routinely (once or twice weekly). Some males tend to accumulate sperm in the epididymis rather than void them periodically, probably resulting in a loss of viability.

It is important to recognize that the epididymis is a dynamic organ that controls not only the maturation and fertility acquisition of spermatozoa but also their exit from the male reproductive system. With sperm production rates of several billion per day, it is easy to imagine that if the epididymis did not provide continual movement of sperm out of the male reproductive tract, there would be a buildup of immense pressure. Spermatozoal removal from the epididymis is caused by periodic contractions of the epididymis and ductus deferens, resulting in a gradual trickle of spermatozoa out of the tail, through the ductus deferens, into the pelvic urethra where they are flushed out of the tract during urination. This trickle allows removal of sperm from the epididymis on a continual basis. Sperm are not reabsorbed from the epididymal duct.

Factors that control epididymal transit are poorly understood but it is almost certain to be under the control of the nervous and the endocrine systems. Materials such as oxytocin, acetylcholine, prostaglandins and angiotensin II (a powerful vasoconstrictor produced by the kidney) have been shown to alter epididymal motility *in vitro*.

The changes in spermatozoal characteristics as they pass through the epididymis are summarized in Figure 3-18. As spermatozoa enter the efferent ducts and epididymal duct, their concentration is low because they are diluted in **rete fluid**. Most of this fluid is absorbed by the epithelium of the efferent ducts and the proximal head of the epididymis. Spermatozoa are concentrated immensely in the epididymis. For example, spermatozoal concentrations in the head of the epididymis may be 25 to 50 million, while in the tail concentration may exceed 2 billion. Changes in

Figure 3-18. Epididymis of a Typical Mammal

(The epididymis and sperm shown are from the bull. Micrographs of sperm are courtesy of Jere R. Mitchell, National Association of Animal Breeders, Columbia, MO, *www.naab-css.org*)

3

Head (Caput)

25-50 x 10⁶ sperm

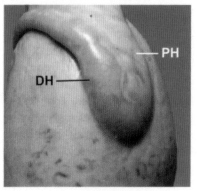

The head of the epididymis is subdivided into the proximal head (PH) and the distal head (DH). The proximal head reabsorbs a significant amount of rete fluid while the distal head secretes fluid into the lumen of the epididymal duct. Thus, concentration of sperm within the head of the epididymis increases and then decreases significantly.

Spermatozoal Characteristic

- **Not motile**
- **Not fertile**
- **Proximal cytoplasmic droplet**
- **Low disulfide crosslinking**

Body (Corpus)

8-25 x 10⁹ sperm

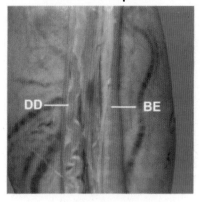

The body of the epididymis (BE) lies parallel to the ductus deferens (DD). Concentrations of sperm throughout the body of the epididymis remain relatively constant.

- **Some expression of motility after dilution**
- **Some expression of fertility**
- **Translocating cytoplasmic droplet**
- **Moderate to high degree of disulfide crosslinking**
- **Can bind to oocytes**

Tail (Cauda)

10-50 x 10⁹ sperm

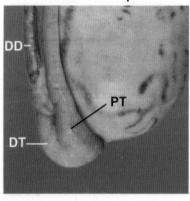

The tail of the epididymis consists of the proximal tail (PT) and the distal tail (DT). Sperm within the distal tail are eligible for ejaculation. Sperm in the proximal tail cannot be moved into an ejaculatory position following sexual stimulation. However, the sperm in the distal tail move through the ductus deferens (DD) and into the pelvic urethra during sexual stimulation.

- **Expression of normal motility after dilution**
- **Fertile potential**
- **Distal droplet**
- **High degree of disulfide crosslinking**
- **Can bind to oocytes**

spermatozoal concentration are the result of fluid reabsorption and secretion along the course of the epididymis. Not only is fluid absorbed, but the spectrum of proteins and other molecules in the fluid bathing the sperm is changed along the course of the epididymal duct.

The total spermatozoal content of the epididymal duct, the ductus deferens and the ampulla is referred to as the **extragonadal reserves (EGR)**. Only the distal tail reserves are eligible for ejaculation. On a per ejaculate basis, the number of sperm removed from the tail reserves can be increased dramatically when the male is subjected to a series of sexual preparation maneuvers such as false mounting or restraint from mounting. Sexual preparation likely stimulates release of oxytocin from the posterior pituitary. This causes contractions of the smooth muscle surrounding the tail of the epididymis that move spermatozoa into the ductus deferens. Oxytocin also causes contractions of the smooth muscle in the ductus deferens that transports spermatozoa to the pelvic urethra where they are positioned for ejaculation. These mechanisms will be detailed in Chapter 11.

It is important to recognize that even though a male might have adequate spermatozoal production by the testes, depletion of the reserves in the tail of the epididymis can occur rapidly if repeated ejaculations take place (See Figure 3-17). For example, in mature bulls sperm in the ejaculate can be reduced to near zero after eight to ten successive ejaculations during a relatively short time period (several hours). Therefore, the number of fertile breedings a male can achieve will be limited by the size of his sperm reserves in the epididymal tail. From a practical viewpoint, the number of females a male can service in a 1-2 day period is dependent on his epididymal tail reserves, not the spermatozoal producing capability of the testes. It should be emphasized that when males are exposed to several females in estrus at the same time there is a strong likelihood that the male will select one of the females and inseminate her repeatedly. Such repeated insemination of a single female can deplete the reserves in the tail of the epididymis and thus compromise the chances of successful pregnancies in other females that are in estrus the same day.

Spermatozoa entering the head of the epididymis possess a cytoplasmic droplet located near the base of the head of the spermatozoa. This droplet is referred to as the **proximal cytoplasmic droplet**. As spermatozoa move through the epididymis, the droplet moves down their tails and is called a **translocating cytoplasmic droplet**. Spermatozoa in the tail of the epididymis possess a **distal cytoplasmic droplet** (See Figure 3-18). Normally, the distal droplet is lost in the distal tail or during ejaculation. A high proportion of ejaculated spermatozoa retaining a cytoplasmic droplet indicates faulty epididymal maturation.

Seminal Plasma is a Non-Cellular Fluid Vehicle for Spermatozoal Delivery to the Female

The epididymis and accessory sex glands are responsible for production of secretions that contribute to the liquid, noncellular portion of semen known as seminal plasma. **Seminal plasma** is not required for fertility, but is important in natural insemination where a fluid vehicle for delivery of the sperm is needed. Spermatozoa that are removed from the tail of the epididymis are equally as fertile as those that are ejaculated. In fact, when dairy bulls of genetic superiority die, spermatozoa can be flushed from the epididymal tail, processed and frozen. Artificial removal of these reserves can result in the generation of 600 to 1000 additional units of frozen semen.

In some species (the boar and stallion), the seminal plasma possesses special coagulation properties that plug the female reproductive tract and minimize loss of spermatozoa following copulation and ejaculation. The accessory sex glands secrete their products into the lumen of the pelvic urethra.

The **ampullae** are enlargements of the ductus deferens that open directly into the pelvic urethra. The enlargement is the result of a dramatic increase in the mucosa within the ampulla. The mucosa of the ampulla forms numerous pockets. The boar does not have conspicuous ampullae.

Seminal plasma is produced by the:
- *epididymis*
- *ampulla*
- *vesicular glands (seminal vesicles)*
- *prostate gland*
- *bulbourethral glands (Cowper's glands)*

The **vesicular glands** are paired glands that are dorsocranial to the pelvic urethra. Vesicular gland secretions empty directly into the pelvic urethra. These glands were originally named the seminal vesicles. Early anatomists erroneously imagined that these glands were reservoirs for spermatozoa because there was a

Figure 3-19. Dorsal View of the Accessory Sex Glands

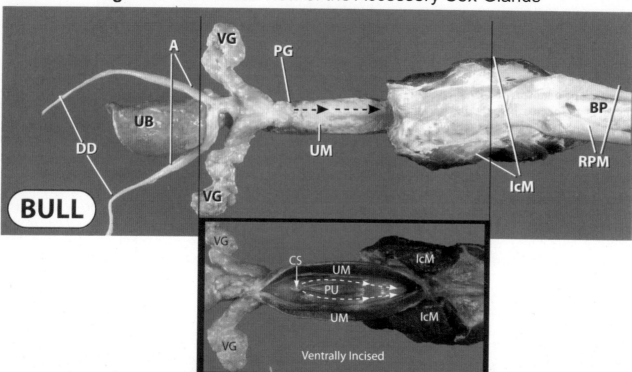

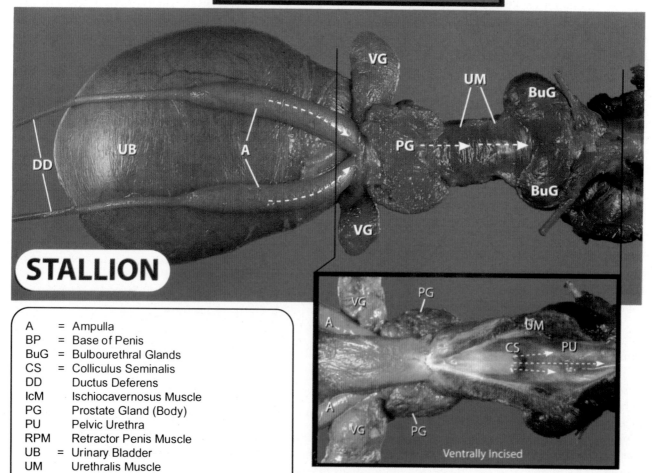

A   = Ampulla
BP = Base of Penis
BuG = Bulbourethral Glands
CS = Colliculus Seminalis
DD   Ductus Deferens
IcM   Ischiocavernosus Muscle
PG   Prostate Gland (Body)
PU   Pelvic Urethra
RPM   Retractor Penis Muscle
UB = Urinary Bladder
UM   Urethralis Muscle
VG   Vesicular Glands

Arrows indicate the direction of fluid flow
during emission and ejaculation

Figure 3-20. Dorsal View of the Accessory Sex Glands

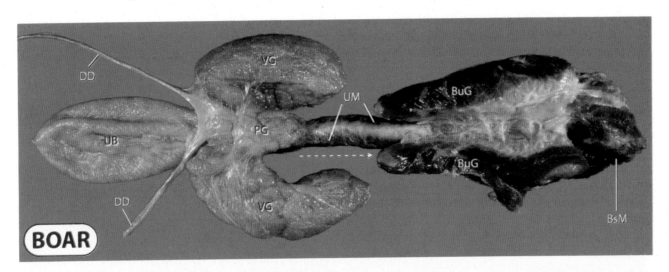

BOAR

3

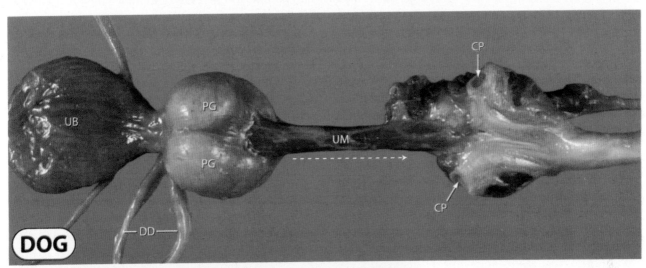

DOG

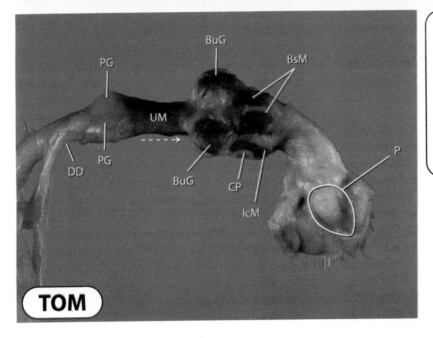

TOM

BsM	=	Bulbospongiosus Muscle
BuG	=	Bulbourethral Glands
CP	=	Crus Penis
DD	=	Ductus Deferens
IcM	=	Ischiocavernosus Muscle
P	=	Penis
PG	=	Prostate Gland (Body)
UB	=	Urinary Bladder
UM	=	Urethralis Muscle
VG	=	Vesicular Glands

visual similarity between the secretion of these glands and ejaculated semen. While the vesicular glands do serve as a reservoir for their own secretions, they do not serve as a reservoir for spermatozoa. The vesicular glands have openings within the pelvic urethra that are separate from those of the ampullae. In bulls and boars the vesicular gland contributes to a large proportion of the ejaculate volume. The gross anatomical configuration of the vesicular glands varies significantly among species. These are illustrated in Figures 3-19 and 3-20. In the bull and ram the vesicular glands are lobulated. In the boar they are well developed and contribute to a viscous, milky component of the seminal plasma. In the stallion the vesicular glands are elongated, hollow pouches.

The **prostate gland** lies in close proximity to the junction between the bladder and pelvic urethra. There is great species variation with regard to shape and location. The prostate may have two structural forms. The first is a **corpus prostate** in which the prostate is outside of the urethralis muscle and is visible as a heart-shaped (boar), or an H-shaped (stallion) structure. The second type is a **disseminate prostate** in which glandular tissue is distributed along the dorsal and lateral walls of the pelvic urethra. The disseminate prostate is sometimes referred to as the **urethral gland**. To observe the disseminate prostate one must make an incision in the pelvic urethra and expose the prostatic tissue. In the bull the prostate has two distinct forms and the corpus prostate is located near the neck of the bladder. In the boar the disseminate prostate is the major portion of the gland and the body of the prostate is often partially concealed by the vesicular glands. The ram does not have a prostatic body and its prostate is entirely disseminate. In contrast, the stallion has no disseminate prostate and the glands are characterized by two lateral lobes. The prostate is the only accessory sex gland in the dog and situated around the pelvic urethra at the neck of the bladder (See Figure 3-20). In the tom, the prostate consists of four lobes that are dorsal to the pelvic urethra (See Figure 3-20).

The **bulbourethral glands** are paired glands located on either side of the pelvic urethra near the ischial arch. These glands are usually small and ovoid and are characterized by being quite dense due to the high degree of fibrous connective tissue within them. In the ram, bull and stallion these glands are small and buried under the bulbospongiosus muscle. The boar is the notable exception with regard to the size of the bulbourethral glands. They are very large and dense and lie on the surface of the caudal two thirds of the pelvic urethra. These glands produce a viscous secretion that is important because it provides the gel fraction of the ejaculate and causes the seminal plasma to coagulate following ejaculation.

Secretions of the accessory sex glands contain an immense variety of components and ions, most of which have not been assigned a function. In general, most substances found in blood, including hormones and enzymes, can be found in seminal plasma. It is beyond the scope of this book to detail all of the secretory products of the accessory sex glands. However, among the most unique are fructose that serves as an energy source for spermatozoa.

The presence of these materials with regard to specific accessory sex glands varies among species. It should be emphasized that with the exception of fructose as an energy source, the precise role of the other materials is not known.

The accessory sex glands are dependent on testosterone for full development and maintenance of their structure and function. In fact, the weights of accessory sex glands can be used as a bioassay for androgens. In the absence of androgens, the weights of the accessory sex glands will be quite low. In contrast, when androgens are present the weights of the accessory sex glands are normal and their secretory activities are normal.

The Penis is the Copulatory Organ

The **penis** is composed of three parts. These are the **base** (root) **of the penis** where it is attached to the ischial arch, the **shaft** (the main portion of the penis) and the **glans penis** that is the specialized distal end.

The glans penis is heavily populated with sensory nerves and is the homologue of the female clitoris. Stimulation of the glans penis is the primary factor initiating the mechanisms of ejaculation. The morphology of the glans penis varies significantly among species. For example, the glans penis of the tom is covered with spines (See Figure 3-22). These penile spines are androgen dependent and disappear when orchidectomy (removal of the testicles) is performed. The purpose of the spines is not known but it has been proposed that these structures maximize vaginal stimulation during copulation and promote induction of ovulation. The glans penis of the alpaca contains a single stiff spiny appendage called the cartilaginous process. The function is not known but this modification can cause damage to the cervix and uterus if excessive copulation is allowed. The glans penis of the boar consists of a "corkscrew" configuration to enable penetration of the interdigitating prominences of the cervix.

Figure 3-21. Penis and Penile Shaft

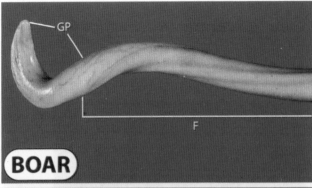

BOAR

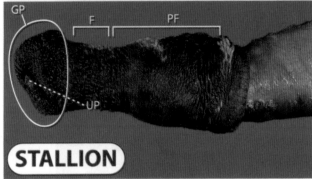

STALLION

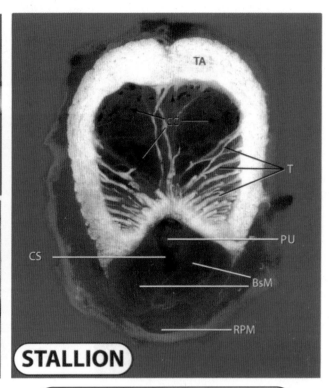

STALLION

F = Free end of penis
GP = Glans Penis
PF = Preputial Fold
UP = Urethral Process

BsM = Bulbospongiosus Muscle
CC = Corpus Cavernosum
CS = Corpus Spongiosum
DEC = Dorsal Erection Canals
RPM = Retractor Penis Muscle
TA = Tunica Albuginea
T = Trabeculae (from tunica albuginea)
PU = Penile Urethra

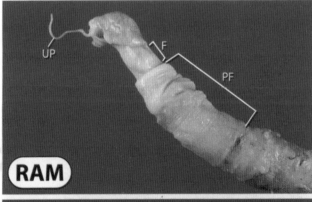

RAM

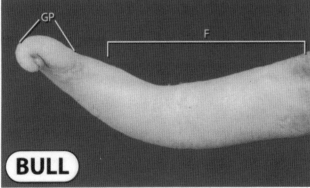

BULL

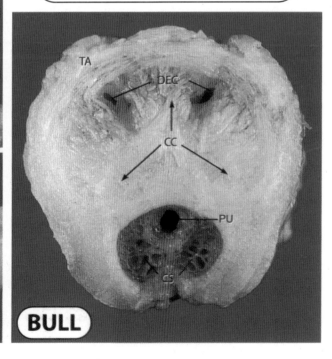

BULL

3

Figure 3-22. Glans Penis (Dog, Tom and Alpaca) and Penile Shaft (Dog)

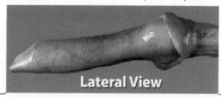

Lateral View

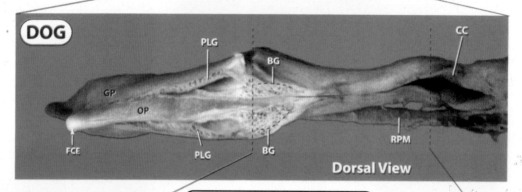

DOG

PLG
BG
CC
GP
OP
FCE
RPM
PLG
BG
Dorsal View

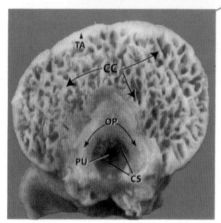

TA
CC
OP
PU
CS

BG	=	Bulbus Glandis
CC	=	Corpus Cavernosum
CP	=	Cartilaginous Process
CS	=	Corpus Spongiosum
FCE	=	Fibrocartilaginous end of Os Penis
GP	=	Glans Penis
OP	=	Os Penis
PLG	=	Pars longa glandis
PS	=	Penile Spines
PU	=	Penile Urethra
RPM	=	Retractor Penis Muscle
TA	=	Tunica Albuginea

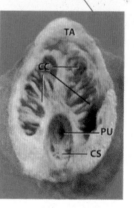

TA
CC
PU
CS

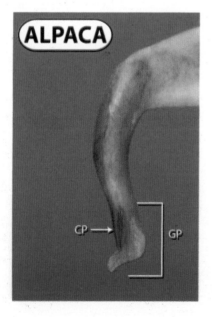

ALPACA

CP
GP

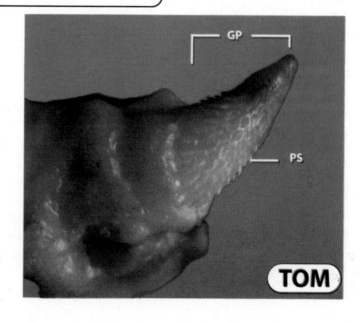

GP
PS
TOM

> *The penis consists of:*
> - *a base*
> - *a shaft*
> - *the glans penis*

Bulls, boars and rams have a fibroelastic penis with limited erectile tissue encased in a non-expandable, dense connective tissue structure (tunica albuginea). In species with a fibroelastic penis, there is a **sigmoid flexure** (See Figures 3-2, 3-4 and 3-7). This is an S-shaped configuration along the shaft of the penis. The sigmoid flexure allows the penis to be retracted inside the body (within the sheath) until erection occurs. Erection is stiffening without a significant change in diameter. The sigmoid flexure is maintained by a pair of smooth muscles known as the **retractor penis muscles** (See Figures 3-2 through 3-7). These are attached dorsally to the coccygeal vertebrae and attached ventrally to the ventrolateral sides of the penis. When contracted, the retractor penis muscle holds the penis inside the sheath. When relaxed, the penis protrudes.

The shaft of the penis has an area of spongy, erectile tissue known as the **corpus cavernosum** that makes up the majority of the penile interior. In the ventral portion of the penis immediately surrounding the **penile urethra** is another area of spongy erectile tissue called the **corpus spongiosum**. Erection in the bull, boar, ram, stallion and camelids is brought about by a combination of relaxation of the retractor penis muscles and the rushing of blood into the corpus cavernosum and the corpus spongiosum (See Figures 3-21 and 3-22). The mechanism of erection and ejaculation will be presented in Chapter 11. The penile shaft of stallions, dogs and men have large corporal sinusoids that fill with blood following sexual stimulation (See Figures 3-21 and 3-22 and Chapter 11). The cavernous tissue in the dog consists of two morphologically distinct regions. These are the bulbus glandis and the pars longa glandis. The bulbus glandis forms a turgid bulb during erection that allows the "copulatory lock" during the final stages of copulation (See Chapter 11). The dog penis also has an os penis (baculum) that runs through the bulbus glandis and the pars longa glandis (See Figure 3-22). The penile urethra and corpus spongiosum are housed by a groove in the os penis (See Figure 3-22).

Erection, Protrusion of the Penis and Ejaculation are Under Muscular Control

The paired **ischiocavernosus muscles**, the muscles associated with the pelvic urethra and the penis, vary in size and form depending on the species. The ischiocavernosus muscles are relatively short paired muscles in the area of the root of the penis. These are strong muscles enclosing the crura that insert broadly on the lateral surface of the penis above the sigmoid flexure. They also connect the penis to the ischial arch.

> *Muscles associated with the pelvic urethra and the penis are:*
> - **urethralis**
> - **bulbospongiosus**
> - **ischiocavernosus**
> - **retractor penis**

The **urethralis** is a striated muscle that surrounds the pelvic urethra in a circular manner. The urethralis muscle is a thick, powerful muscle responsible for movement of seminal plasma and spermatozoa into the penile urethra. The urethralis muscle is shown in Figure 3-19 and 3-20. The **bulbospongiosus muscle** overlaps the root of the penis and extends down the caudal and ventral surfaces. In the boar, ram and bull it extends only part way down the penis. This muscle also covers the bulbourethral glands. The function of the bulbospongiosus muscles is to empty the extrapelvic part of the urethra.

Further PHENOMENA for Fertility

In many mammalian species (bats, rodents, carnivores, shrews, moles and many primates--but not humans) there is a penile bone called the os penis or baculum. The baculum of the raccoon has a gentle sigmoid shape and makes an attractive, unique cocktail stirring device when cleaned, sterilized and polished.

The fully engorged penis of the bull elephant weighs over 25 kilograms (about 55 lbs).

The penis of lizards and snakes is paired and is called a hemipenis. It is an extension of the cloaca and is everted into the cloaca of the female during copulation. It contains spines and/or ridges that help sustain intromission.

In Brazil there is a species of monkey that has huge testicles relative to his body size. Unlike most mammals, this species of monkey has no competition amongst males for the right to breed the female. Instead, the female will copulate with many males in sequence. Therefore, the male with the largest testicles (that produce the most sperm) has the greatest probability of fathering the new baby monkey.

The word "testis" is derived from Latin and means "witness" or "spectator." The English words "testify" and "testament" were derived from testis. The reason for this derivation is not known. However, it has been proposed that the testes were witnesses to virility. Romans required that a witness be an adult intact male. Prepubertal boys, women or eunuchs could not serve as witnesses. Placing the hand on the testicles (or someone else's testicles) was a requirement while testifying in some cultures.

The prepuce of the male dromedary (one-humped camel) is pendulous and contains three groups of muscles that change the direction of the preputial orifice from caudal during urination to cranial during erection.

In parts of the world where the understanding of reproductive physiology is quite shallow, men wishing to father children try to improve their odds by eating sheep or bull testicles. Testicles are also believed to be an aphrodisiac (aphrodisiacs are named after the Greek goddess of love Aphrodite) and are believed to stimulate the reproductive appetite. Consumption of testicles is believed to increase the sex drive allowing the future father to copulate repeatedly. Little consideration was given to extragonadal reserves. One of the most potent forms of animal testes is believed to be the testicles of prisoners captured from neighboring tribes.

Every human male learns at a young age how painful it is to receive a blow to the testicles. The pain is excruciating and instantly radiates from the testis deep into the abdominal cavity. The testes are rich in nerve endings. The slightest blow to the testicle is painful. During embryogenesis, the testes are formed in the abdomen near the stomach and kidney. Nerves that originate in this region travel with the testes as they descends to hang freely in the scrotum. That is probably why the blow to the testicles feels like a punch in the stomach. Nerves in the scrotum are related to ones that are associated with the subcutaneous sensory nerves of the thigh and spinal cord. Thus, light stroking to the scrotum and the inner thigh is deemed pleasurable.

The armadillo has a penis that is about one-third its body length. A female armadillo gives birth to identical quadruplets. The four identical offspring are derived from a single fertilized egg that splits into four developing embryos (totipotency).

Key References

Cody, R.L., B.R. Voortman, R.E. Hill and P.L. Senger. 1999. "Intravascular polymerization as a method for observing countercurrent exchange systems in bovine reproductive tracts" in *Biol. of Reprod.* 60 (Suppl.1): 89.

Dyce, K.M., W.O. Sack and C.J.G. Wensing. 2002. *Textbook of Veterinary Anatomy*. 3rd Edition. W.B. Saunders Co., Philadelphia. ISBN 0-7216-8966-3.

Evans, H.E. 1993. *Miller's Anatomy of the Dog*, 3rd. Edition. W.B. Saunders Co. Philadelphia. ISBN 0-7216-3200-9.

Johnson, A.D., W.R. Gomes and N.L. Vandemark, eds. 1970. *The Testis*. Vol. I. Academic Press, New York.

Johnston, S.D., M.V. Root Kustritz and P.N.S. Olson. 2001. *Canine and Feline Theriogenology*. W.B. Saunders Co., Philadelphia. ISBN 0-7216-5607-2.

Knobil, E. and J.D. Neill (eds). 1998. *The Encyclopedia of Reproduction*. Vol 1-4. Academic Press, San Diego. ISBN 0-12-227020-7.

Nickel, R., A. Schummer and E. Seiferle. 1979. *The Viscera of the Domestic Mammals*. 2nd Revised Edition. Springer-Verlag, New York. ISBN 0-387-91139-1.

Tibary, A. and A. Anouassi. 1997. *Theriogenology in Camelidae*. United Arab Emirates. Ministry of Culture and Information. Publication authorization No. 3849/1/16. ISBN 9981-801-32-1.

3

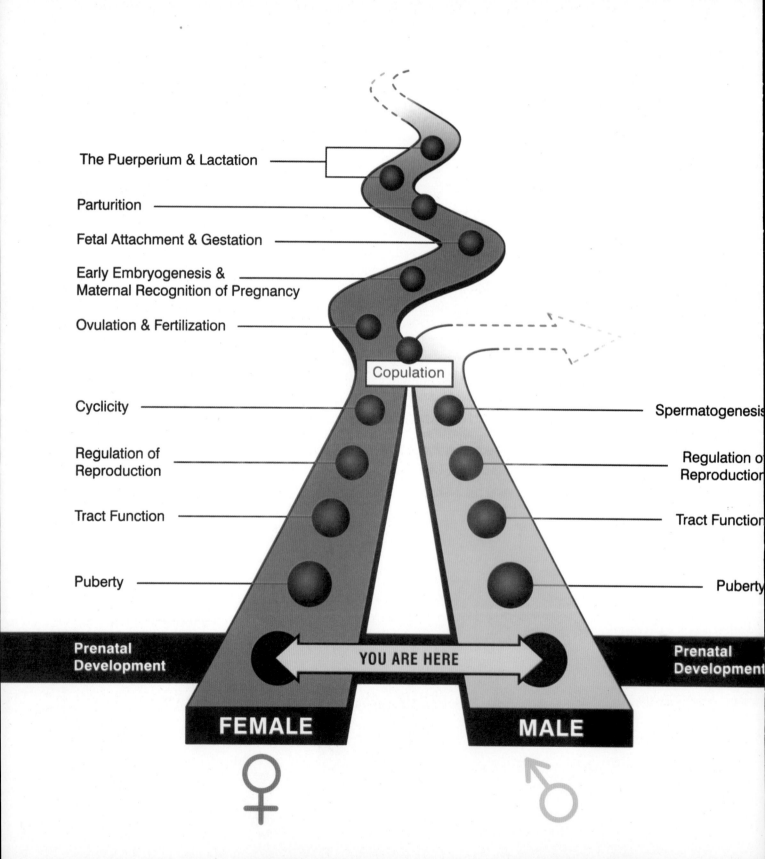

Take Home Message

The anterior and posterior lobes of the pituitary originate from two different tissue types (neural and epithelial) and anatomical regions in the developing embryo. The anterior lobe originates from the roof of the mouth and the posterior lobe originates from the brain. The embryonic gonad develops into testes or ovaries, depending upon the chromosomal makeup of the cells of the genital ridge. The development of the male reproductive tract requires the presence of a sex determining region (gene) on the Y chromosome (SRY). This gene controls the synthesis of SRY protein that initiates male sex determination. Development of the female tract takes place in the absence of SRY protein. Both the male and the female reproductive tracts originate from a series of tubes. In the male, the mesonephric tubules and ducts are used to form the excurrent duct system. In the female, the paramesonephric ducts form the oviducts, uterus, the cervix and the cranial vagina.

The **embryogenesis** of the pituitary and the male and female reproductive tracts is a remarkably coordinated series of events involving the merging of several types of tissue that will ultimately form complete reproductive glands and organs. The normal development of the urogenital system in mammals is among the most complex of all organ systems and requires critical timing for successful development. Faulty embryogenesis often results in reproductive failure of either the male or the female. The information presented in this chapter will not contain strict timelines because these vary significantly among species. However, the sequence of critical events is similar among most mammalian species.

During embryogenesis organs **differentiate** from discrete **germ layers** that make up the embryo. **Differentiation** is the process whereby a group of unspecialized cells develop into recognizable groups of cells that have a common function. The germ layers that appear prior to embryo attachment to the uterus, are called the **endoderm, mesoderm** and **ectoderm** (See Figure 4-1). The endoderm

Figure 4-1. Derivation of the Primary Embryonic Germ Layers

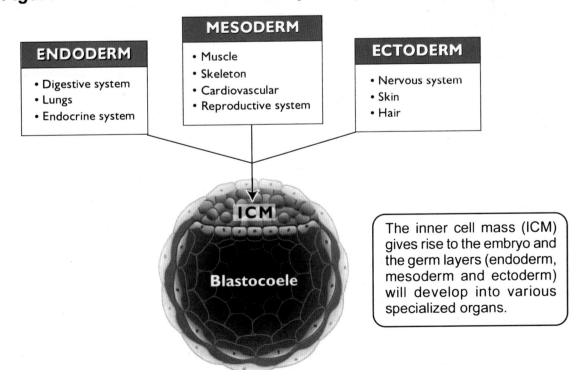

ENDODERM
- Digestive system
- Lungs
- Endocrine system

MESODERM
- Muscle
- Skeleton
- Cardiovascular
- Reproductive system

ECTODERM
- Nervous system
- Skin
- Hair

ICM

Blastocoele

The inner cell mass (ICM) gives rise to the embryo and the germ layers (endoderm, mesoderm and ectoderm) will develop into various specialized organs.

Table 4-1. Embryonic Origin of Various Organs and Systems from the Embryonic Germ Layers (**Bold** words indicate organs of reproductive importance)

Ectoderm	Mesoderm	Endoderm
• skin, hair, nails, sweat glands (including **mammary glands**)		
<u>Nervous system</u>	<u>Muscle</u>	<u>Digestive system</u>
• **hypothalamus**	<u>Blood vessels</u>	(including liver and pancreas)
• **both lobes of pituitary**	<u>Reproductive system</u>	<u>Respiratory system</u>
	• **gonads (male and female)**	<u>Most glands</u>
	• **uterus, cervix, part of vagina**	
	• **epididymis, ductus deferens**	
<u>Oral cavity</u>	• **accessory sex glands**	
<u>Nasal cavity</u>	<u>Urinary system</u>	
	<u>Skeletal system</u>	
<u>Reproductive tract</u>		
• portions of the **vagina and vestibule**		
• **penis, clitoris**		

4

(**endo**=inside, **derm**=skin or layer) is the innermost cellular layer of the embryo and will give rise to the digestive tract, liver, pancreas, lungs and endocrine organs. The ectoderm (**ecto**=outer, **derm**=skin or layer) develops from the outer cells of the inner cell mass. As you will see in Chapter 13, the inner cell mass is a clump of cells that will become the embryo. The ectoderm will give rise to the central nervous system, sensory organs, mammary glands, sweat glands, skin, hair, claws and hooves. The middle layer of the embryo is referred to as the mesoderm (**meso**=middle, **derm**=skin or layer). The mesoderm develops between the ectoderm and the endoderm. This germ layer gives rise to the circulatory, skeletal, muscular and urinary systems. Most of the reproductive system is derived from the mesoderm. A more complete listing of tissue derivations is presented in Table 4-1.

The Pituitary Gland Originates From the Brain and From Tissue in the Roof of the Mouth

As can be seen in Figure 4-2, the anterior and posterior lobes of the pituitary originate from two entirely different types of tissue. The **anterior lobe** of the pituitary originates from tissue in the roof of the embryo's mouth called **stomodeal ectoderm**. The stomodeal ectoderm gives rise to a diverticulum from the roof of the mouth and grows dorsally. This diverticulum is called **Rathke's pouch**, or sometimes **Rathke's pocket** (See Figure 4-2). As Rathke's pouch continues to develop, it loses its continuity with the stomodeum and forms a discrete body of cells. The cells of Rathke's pouch differentiate to form the **ad-**

enohypophysis (the anterior lobe). The prefix **adeno** refers to tissues that are glandular in nature.

Also early in embryo development, a **diverticulum** (a sac or pouch <u>diverting</u> from a main tube, channel or cavity) develops from the floor of the brain and grows ventrally toward Rathke's pouch (See Figure 4-2). This diverticulum is called the **infundibulum**. While the cells of the adenohypophysis are differentiating into various specialized cells capable of producing a variety of hormones, the infundibulum differentiates to form the **neurohypophysis** (posterior lobe). The posterior lobe contains the axons and nerve terminals (telodendria) of neurons whose cell bodies are located in the hypothalamus (See Chapter 5).

> *Hypophysis = pituitary*
> <u>*Adeno*</u>*hypophysis = anterior lobe*
> <u>*Neuro*</u>*hypophysis = posterior lobe*

As development of the pituitary nears its completion, a cranial bone known as the **sphenoid bone** (See Figure 4-2) begins to form around both the anterior and posterior lobes. This protective cavity is known as the **sella turcica**. This bony cavity is so named because it resembles the side view of the seat of a Turkish saddle.

It is important to understand that the dual embryonic origin allows the anterior and posterior lobe to perform entirely different functions. For example, the nerves of the posterior lobe cause a direct and rapid release of oxytocin that causes milk ejection by the mammary gland. In contrast, the adjacent anterior pituitary lobe consists of specialized glandular epithelial cells that secrete glycoprotein hormones like

Figure 4-2. Embryonic Development of the
Anterior and Posterior Lobes of the Pituitary
(Modified from Larsen, W.J., *Human Embryology*, with permission from Elsevier)

The posterior lobe of the pituitary is formed from a diverticulum (a sac diverting from the main cavity) from the floor of the brain. The third ventricle is a cavity within the brain that will be described more completely in Chapter 5. Once this outpocketing begins to form, it is referred to as the **infundibulum**.

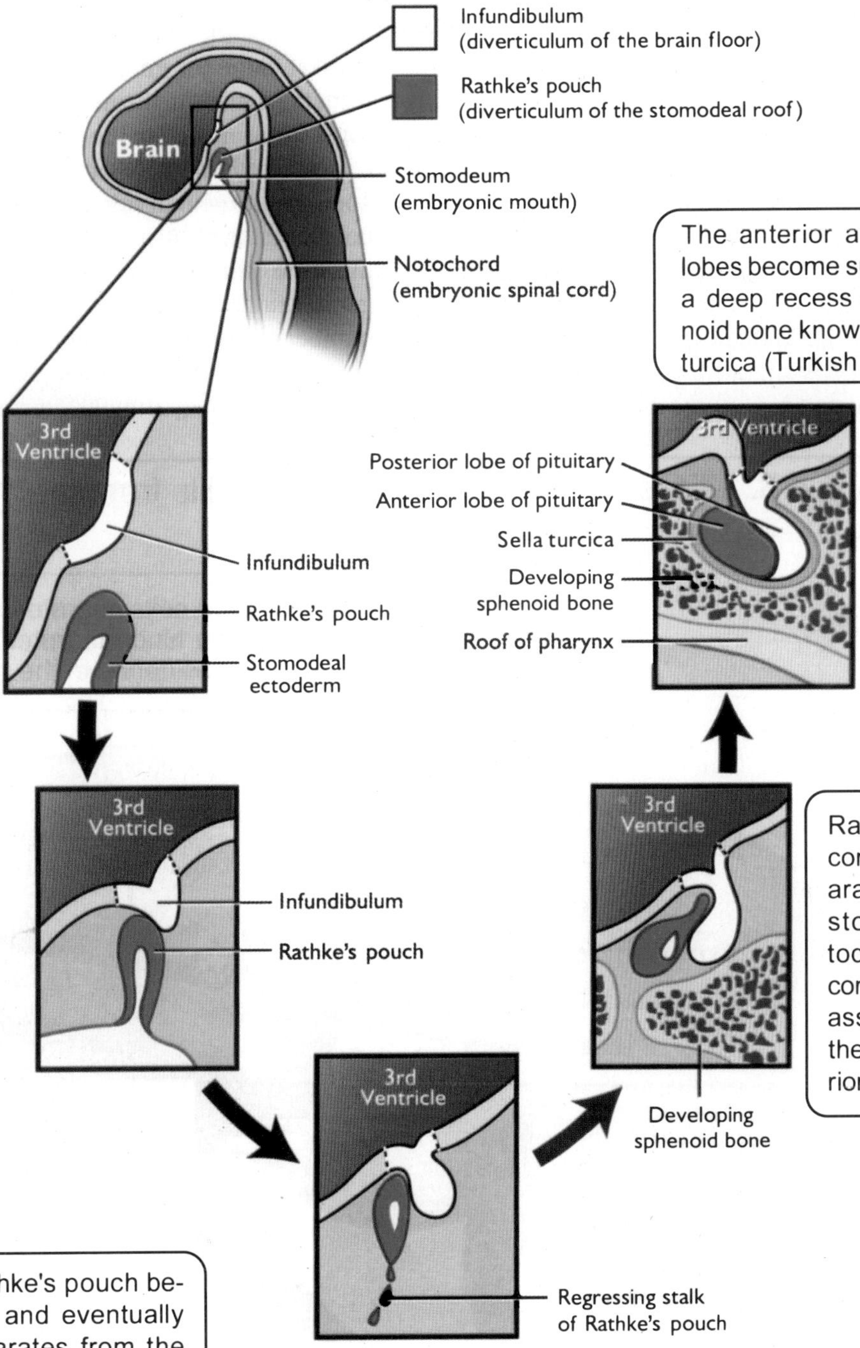

The anterior lobe of the pituitary forms as an evagination from the oral cavity or stomodeal ectoderm. The evagination is referred to as **Rathke's pouch**.

The stalk of Rathke's pouch begins to regress and eventually completely separates from the stomodeal ectoderm. At the same time, the infundibulum continues to evaginate to form the posterior lobe of the pituitary.

The anterior and posterior lobes become surrounded by a deep recess of the sphenoid bone known as the sella turcica (Turkish saddle).

Rathke's pouch completely separates from the stomodeal ectoderm and becomes intimately associated with the new posterior lobe.

4

follicle stimulating hormone and luteinizing hormone that are not secreted by nerve cells.

Sexual Differentiation of the Reproductive Tract Involves Specific Substances

The initial step in sex determination is at fertilization when a sperm delivers either an X (female) or Y (male) chromosome to the oocyte. Thus, the sex of the individual is determined by the sperm and the eventual genetic control of sex differentiation has been established. In the early embryo (first 15% of gestation), when the yolk sac is still present, primordial (primitive) germ cells develop. These cells originate from the base of the hindgut (See Figure 4-3). The primordial germ cells migrate by ameboid movement from the hindgut and base of the allantois and finally

reside in the **bipotential** gonad. Bipotential means capable of differentiating along two developmental pathways. In this case, developing into an ovary or testis. The sex of the embryo is not obvious. The bipotential gonad is located on the inner surface of the dorsal body wall and is known at this time as the **genital ridge** (or **gonadal ridge**). It will eventually form the gonads in the male or the female. The genital ridge forms medial to the embryonic kidneys that will be described below. Most of the primordial germ cells populate the genital ridge. Primordial germ cells that do not reside in this region will degenerate. During the time primordial germ cells are colonizing the genital ridges, they are undergoing mitosis and their numbers increase significantly.

When the primitive germ cells arrive in the genital ridge, they stimulate local connective tissue to

Figure 4-3. Migration of Primordial Germ Cells from the Yolk Sac Into the Gonadal Ridge

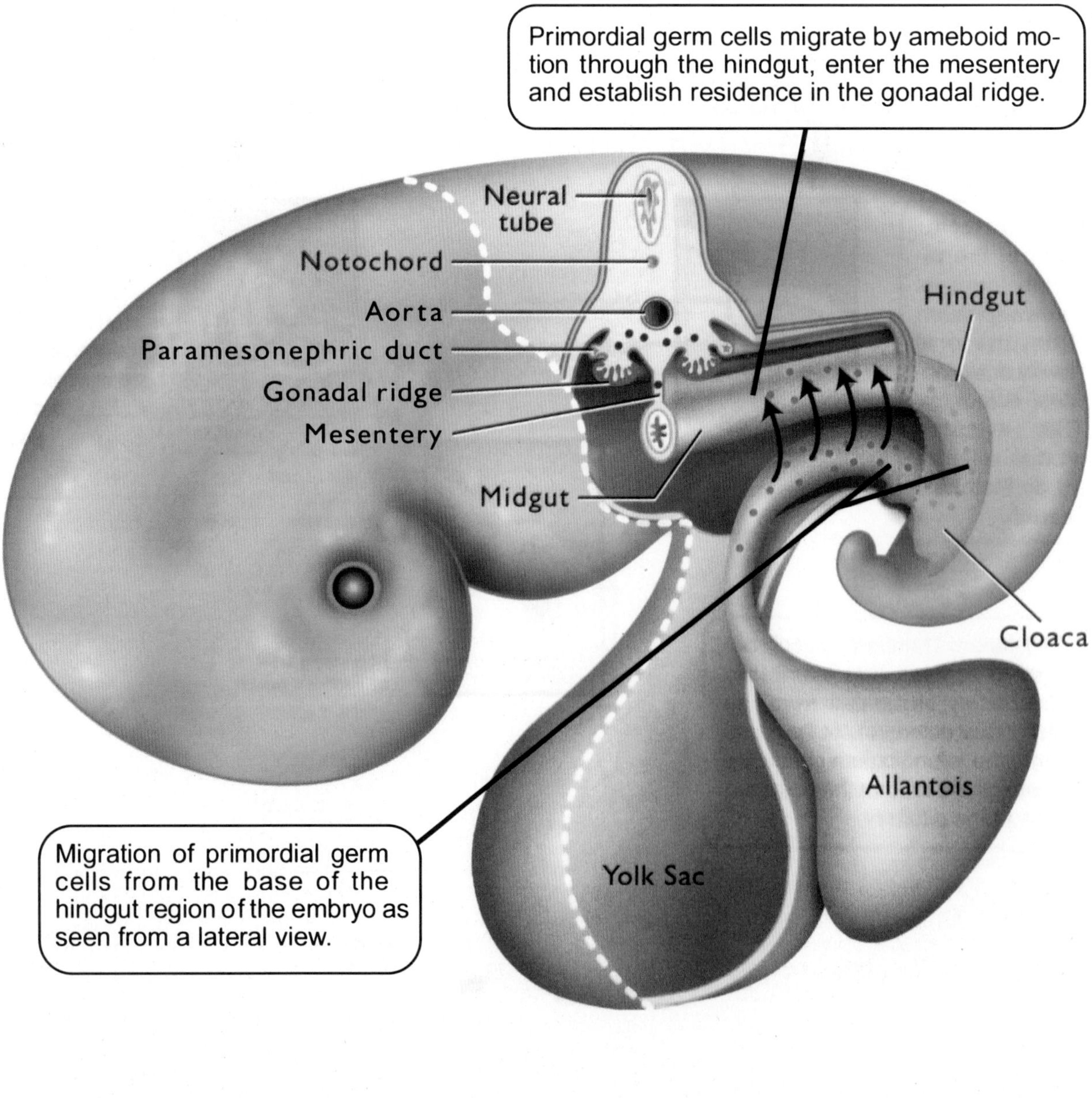

Primordial germ cells migrate by ameboid motion through the hindgut, enter the mesentery and establish residence in the gonadal ridge.

Migration of primordial germ cells from the base of the hindgut region of the embryo as seen from a lateral view.

proliferate. This results in the formation of compact strands of tissue called **primitive sex cords** (See Figure 4-4, Event 2). These proliferating sex cords cause the genital ridges to enlarge and push toward the developing kidney (mesonephros).

> **The reproductive system develops in close proximity to and at the same time as the renal system.**

During its development the embryo utilizes three morphologically distinct renal systems. The first, called the **pronephros (pronephric kidney)**, is a nonfunctional remnant of a primitive form of kidney found in lower animals. Early in embryogenesis, the pronephros regresses and is replaced by a functional, bilateral pair of intermediate kidneys known as the **mesonephros (mesonephric kidney)** (See Figure 4-5,1). The mesonephros forms urine that is drained by a bilateral pair of ducts called the **mesonephric ducts** (formerly called **Wolffian ducts**). The mesonephric ducts extend caudally and empty into the **urogenital sinus** (See Figure 4-5,3).

By the first 10% to 15% of gestation the final form of kidney begins to appear. This final renal form is known as the **metanephros (metanephric kidney)**. It will develop functional nephrons and will serve as the functional form of kidney in adult mammals. The metanephros becomes functional by the first 30% to 35% of gestation.

At the same time the mesonephros is developing, a new pair of ducts beside the mesonephric ducts begin to develop. These ducts are called the **paramesonephric ducts** or **Müllerian ducts.** They form on either side of the mesonephric duct, thus **para**mesonephric. The relationship of the paramesonephric ducts with other developing structures is presented in almost all the graphics in this chapter (See Figures 4-4, 4-5, 4-7, 4-11, 4-12 and 4-13).

Even though the mesonephric and the paramesonephric ducts are both present, the embryo is still "uncommitted" with regard to its sex at this time. Sexual differentiation of the organs *per se* still has not occurred. This stage is referred to as the **sexually indifferent stage** because morphologic discrimination between the male and female embryo cannot be made by simple observation.

Figure 4-4. The Main Embryological Events in the Development of the Reproductive System

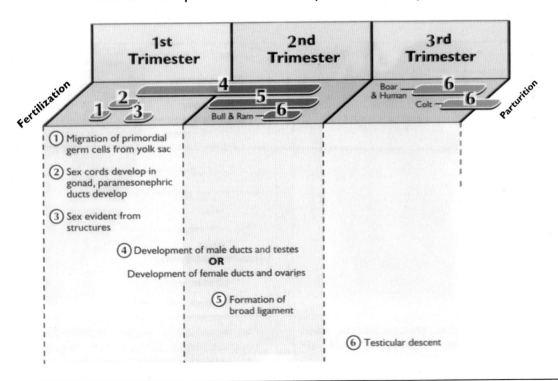

The above figure summarizes the six main embryological events in the reproductive system. Certain events (development of the male and female duct system and gonads) require substantially more time than others (migration of primordial germ cells) and timing is dependant on species.

Figure 4-5. Development and Regression of the Mesonephros with Concurrent Development of the Gonad (Dorsal View)

4

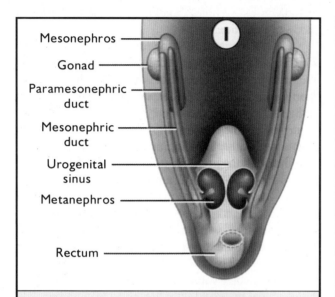

The mesonephros is closely associated with the undifferentiated gonad. At this stage, the mesonephros is functional and is a simple version of the adult kidney. The mesonephros is drained by a series of mesonephric tubules that merge into a larger mesonephric duct that transports urine to the urogenital sinus.

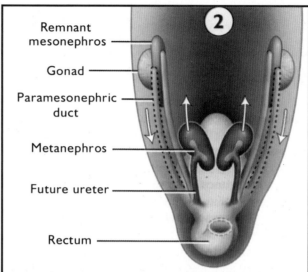

The metanephros initially forms as a small bud from the caudal mesonephric duct. The mesonephros begins to lose its function and decreases in size as the metanephros increases in size. The paramesonephric duct (dashed line) develops beside the mesonephric duct. Note that the gonad is also increasing in size relative to the mesonephros.

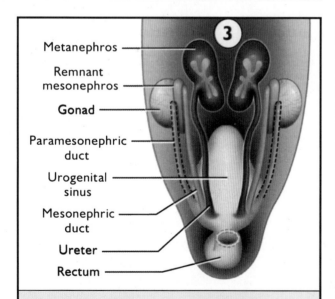

The gonad continues its enlargement as does the metanephros. The metanephric duct will become the ureter.

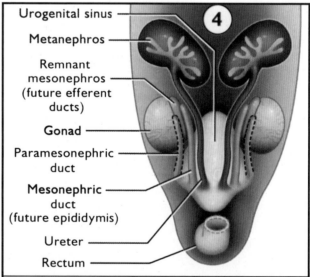

The metanephros becomes fully functional and the gonad becomes larger, while the mesonephros has almost completely regressed. In the male, some of the mesonephric tubules will form the efferent ducts and the mesonephric duct will form the epididymis and the ductus deferens. The paramesonephric ducts degenerate in the male.

Sexual Differentiation is Regulated by a Single Substance Directed by a Gene on the Y Chromosome (SRY)

Females possess two X chromosomes, whereas males have one X and one Y sex chromosome. The sex chromosomes within the spermatozoa determine whether the embryo will become a male and develop testes or whether it will become a female and develop ovaries. The Y chromosome contains a gene called Sex Determining Region on the Y chromosome (SRY). The substance that controls the pathway toward either male or female development is SRY protein and it is controlled by the SRY gene on the Y chromosome. The X chromosome does not have such a gene. When SRY protein is synthesized by the sex cords within the primitive gonad, the development of the male reproductive system is stimulated. On the other hand, cells without the SRY gene express female genes and at the same time inhibit the male genes. It should be emphasized that development of female and male gonads is an active process in both sexes. In other words, the development of the ovary requires an active pathway but under female gene control. Therefore, ovarian development is **NOT** by default in the absence of SRY. The pathway of events controlled by SRY protein is presented in Figure 4-6.

> *Part of the male tract is derived from the mesonephros*
> - *mesonephric tubules → efferent ducts*
> - *mesonephric ducts → epididymis and ductus deferens*

In the male embryo, portions of the mesonephric kidney are appropriated for use in the reproductive tract at about the same time that the paramesonephric ducts begin to degenerate. Between 5 and 15 **mesonephric tubules** penetrate into the primitive gonad and make connections with the primitive sex cords via the **rete testis**. The rete testis is a network of tiny ducts that connect the seminiferous tubules to the **efferent ducts**. The efferent ducts are derived from the mesonephric tubules (See Figure 4-7). The mesonephric duct will give rise to the epididymis and

Figure 4-6. Pathway of Events Leading to Formation of the Male and Female Reproductive System

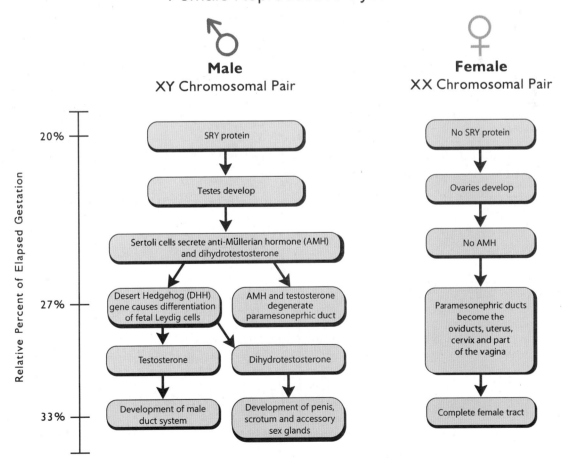

Figure 4-7. Developmental Sequence of the Testis

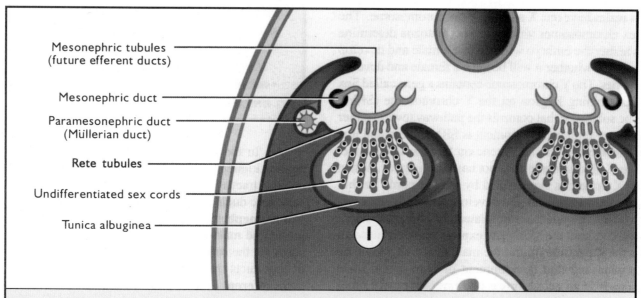

Mesonephric tubules
(future efferent ducts)

Mesonephric duct

Paramesonephric duct
(Müllerian duct)

Rete tubules

Undifferentiated sex cords

Tunica albuginea

A transverse section through the developing gonadal region of the embryo. The undifferentiated sex cords begin to align themselves with the small rete tubules. The mesonephric tubules have not interconnected with the rete tubules. The surface of the undifferentiated gonad is covered with a layer of connective tissue called the tunic albuginea. The paramesonephric duct (Müllerian duct) is present, but serves no function.

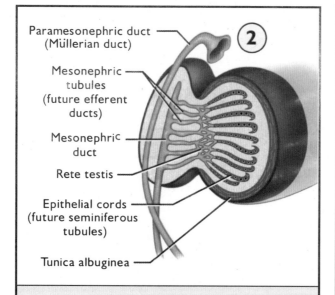

Paramesonephric duct
(Müllerian duct)

Mesonephric
tubules
(future efferent
ducts)

Mesonephric
duct

Rete testis

Epithelial cords
(future seminiferous
tubules)

Tunica albuginea

The rete tubules and the mesonephric tubules are now interconnected to provide continuity between the undifferentiated sex cords that are now developing into epithelial cords. These will become seminiferous tubules. The paramesonephric duct is beginning to degenerate. Degeneration of the paramesonephric duct is brought about by the production of antimüllerian hormone produced by the developing testis.

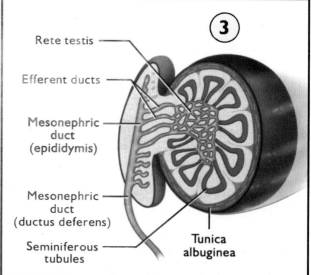

Rete testis

Efferent ducts

Mesonephric
duct
(epididymis)

Mesonephric
duct
(ductus deferens)

Seminiferous
tubules

**Tunica
albuginea**

The epithelial cords become seminiferous tubules. There is continuity between the rete testis and the efferent ducts. The mesonephric duct is gradually transformed into the epididymis and the ductus deferens. The paramesonephric duct has disappeared.

ductus deferens. Together, the **efferent ducts**, the **epididymis** and the **ductus deferens** are appropriated to become the **excurrent extragonadal duct system** of the male reproductive tract.

The Testes are Formed at the Level of the Ribs. They Descend into the Scrotum Late in Gestation

In most mammals, the testes descend into the **scrotum**. Understanding testicular descent is challenging because it involves two relatively unrelated phenomena. First, the testis must travel a substantial distance from a retroperitoneal position in the body cavity to the scrotum (See Figure 4-8). This movement involves the rapid growth followed by rapid regression of a ligamentous structure called the **gubernaculum**. The second challenge in understanding the process of testicular descent involves understanding how two layers of peritoneum cover the testis and descend with it. These two layers, the **visceral vaginal tunic** and the **parietal vaginal tunic** are separated by a **vaginal cavity** that is continuous with the peritoneal cavity. In order to more easily understand testicular descent and the anatomy of the testicular tunics we shall consider these two processes separately.

The descent of testicles has three phases. They are:

- *growth and elongation of the fetal body away from the testes (transabdominal)*

- *rapid growth of the extra abdominal gubernaculum (transabdominal)*

- *shrinkage of the gubernaculum within the scrotum (inguinal-scrotal)*

The testes lie in a retroperitoneal position and are attached caudally to the ligamentous gubernaculum (See Figure 4-8). The gubernaculum extends caudally and resides in the area of the future scrotum. As the fetal body grows the testes are pushed against the peritoneum. This "pushing-out" causes the peritoneum to wrap around the gubernaculum and the testes (See Figure 4-8).

The first phase involves growth and elongation of the body away from the stationary testis. The second phase involves the rapid growth of the distal gubernaculum. The distal portion of the gubernaculum is that portion that has passed through the inguinal ring (See Figure 4-8) and forms an outgrowth into the future scrotum.

Two Layers of Peritoneum Surround the Descended Testicle

After complete descent of the testes, you can see that the **vaginal process** is continuous with the peritoneal cavity and the testis is surrounded by a double layer of peritoneum (See Figure 4-8). The layer of peritoneum immediately adjacent to the testis is the **visceral vaginal tunic** and the layer away from the testis is referred to as the **parietal vaginal tunic** (See Chapter 3 for actual example). The space between the tunics is the vaginal cavity. The space between the visceral and parietal vaginal tunic is continuous with the body cavity that houses the viscera. These tunicae are slippery and allow the testis to move freely within the scrotum during physical activity and during contraction of the external cremaster and the tunica dartos muscles.

Now that you are able to visualize the mechanics of testicular descent, it is important to understand the factors that control this event. The most important component of testicular descent is the growth and regression of the gubernaculum. An important question is, "What controls this growth and regression?" The presence of the testes is required for the gubernacular growth to occur. Castration experiments indicate that the testis is essential for normal gubernacular growth. However, supplementation with gonadotropins and testosterone in castrated fetal pigs does not promote gubernacular growth. Therefore, it appears that there is a specific testicular component(s) other than testosterone that causes the dramatic gubernacular growth associated with the first phase of testicular descent. Descent of the testicles requires both testosterone and **Insulin like-3 (Insl-3)**. **Insl-3** is a member of the insulin super family and is synthesized and secreted by islet cells in the pancreas and Leydig cells in the testis. Insl-3 causes growth of the gubernaculum and testicular descent in male mice. Interestingly, overexpression of Insl-3 in the female results in abdominal descent of the ovaries.

Regression (shrinkage) of the gubernaculum results in the final passage through the inguinal canal and orientation of the peritoneum around the testis in the scrotum.

Two common testicular descent abnormalities are:
- *cryptorchidism*
- *inguinal herniation*

4

Figure 4-8. Major Steps in the Descent of the Testes

(Growth and subsequent retraction of the gubernaculum causes the testes to descend from the level of the tenth thoracic vertebra into the scrotum)

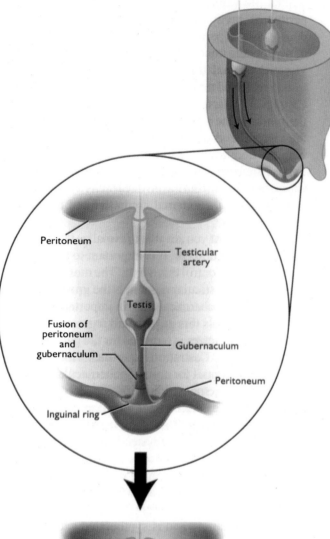

Transabdominal Phase

Before descent occurs, the testes lie in a retro-peritoneal position and are attached caudally to the ligamentous gubernaculum. Cells of the peritoneum infiltrate the gubernaculum in the inguinal region and form a junction with it. This fusion is important because it binds the peritoneum to the gubernaculum and will allow the vaginal process to form as the distal gubernaculum grows toward and into the scrotal region. This transabdominal phase is controlled by Insulin like growth factor 3 (Insl 3) and its receptor (Lgr8).

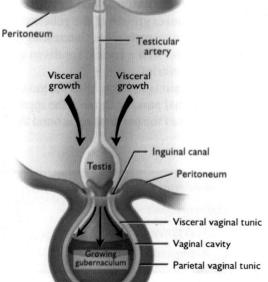

Inguinal-Scrotal Phase

After the gubernaculum penetrates the inguinal ring, there is rapid growth of the distal gubernaculum. This rapid growth of the gubernaculum in the scrotal region is the "force" responsible for mechanically moving the testes into the inguinal canal. This rapid gubernacular growth is androgen dependent.

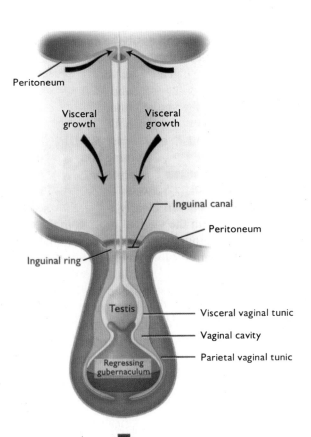

Peritoneum

Visceral growth   Visceral growth

Inguinal canal

Peritoneum

Inguinal ring

Testis

Visceral vaginal tunic

Vaginal cavity

Parietal vaginal tunic

Regressing gubernaculum

Inguinal-Scrotal Phase

Once the testes are in the inguinal region, they move through the inguinal opening because the gubernaculum shrinks. Also, it is possible that the pressure associated with visceral growth helps "push" the testis or at least hold it near the inguinal ring.

4

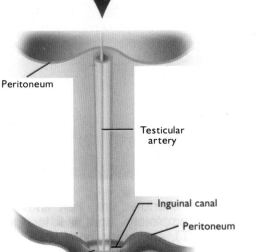

Peritoneum

Testicular artery

Inguinal canal

Peritoneum

Inguinal ring

Visceral vaginal tunic

Vaginal cavity

Parietal vaginal tunic

Testis

Fully regressed gubernaculum

Inguinal-Scrotal Phase

The gubernaculum continues to shrink. As this regression occurs, it continues to pull the testes deeper into the scrotum and cause a complete encapsulation of each testis by the inner layer of the peritoneum known as the visceral vaginal tunic. The outer layer of the peritoneum is the parietal layer of the vaginal tunic. When the testis has fully descended, the gubernaculum has regressed to a small knot that attaches the testis to the bottom of the scrotum. The vaginal process contributes to the two tunicae of the testis. The inner (visceral) layer covers the testis, epididymis and spermatic cord and the outer (parietal) layer forms a continuous fold that lies directly adjacent to (but is not attached to) the visceral vaginal tunic. Together these two layers form the vaginal cavity (vaginal process).

4

Descent of the testes from the body cavity into the scrotum occurs by mid-gestation in the bull and the ram and during the last quarter of gestation in the boar and the human (See Figure 4-4). In the stallion, the testes enter the scrotum either just before or just after birth. Failure of the testes to descend into the scrotum is called **cryptorchidism**. The prefix "crypt" means hidden, concealed or not visible to the naked eye. "Orchid" is a Latinized-Greek word referring to the testis. Thus, the word cryptorchid literally means "a testis that is hidden from view." In humans, the most common disorder of sexual differentiation is cryptorchidism. Between 3% and 5% of male neonates are affected. Bilateral cryptorchidism results in sterility. However, cryptorchid testes are capable of producing testosterone. Thus, the cryptorchid male possesses secondary sex characteristics that are normal and has normal reproductive behavior.

Because of the anatomical continuity between the vaginal process and the body cavity (See Figure 4-8), it is possible for portions of intestine to pass into the vaginal cavity and enter the scrotum. When a portion of the intestine passes through the inguinal canal into the vaginal cavity, **inguinal herniation** has occurred. In humans, diagnosis of the presence of an inguinal hernia can easily be made by applying pressure to the lateral inguinal regions and asking the patient to cough. Such a maneuver allows the physician to feel the intestine rebound (or bounce) during the cough, inside the vaginal tunics.

Inguinal herniation is not uncommon in swine and occurs in about 1 in 200 males. Figure 4-9 illustrates this condition in a young boar. Figure 4-10 schematically illustrates the position of the intestine in the vaginal cavity (between the visceral and parietal tunics). You can clearly see the presence of the intestine within the vaginal process in the young boar (middle photograph). In most cases, the herniation can be repaired quite easily during castration. By twisting the testicle (within the parietal vaginal tunic), the intestines are pushed back through the vaginal cavity (within the inguinal canal) into the body cavity. Since the inguinal canal in the boar is located more dorsally than in other species (See Chapter 3) the intestines tend to remain in the body cavity because it is difficult for them to reenter the

---

Figure 4-9. Caudal View of a Young Boar with an Inguinal Hernia

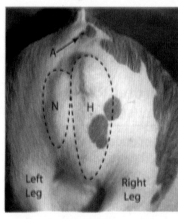 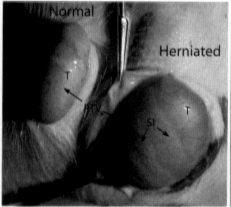 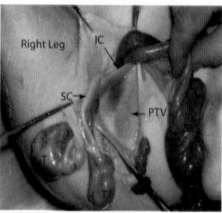

Caudal view of the scrotum showing the anus (A), the normal (N) and the herniated (H) side. Notice that the herniated side is significantly larger than the normal side.

Incised scrotum showing the normal and the herniated side containing the small intestine (SI) and testicle (T). The arrows indicate the parietal vaginal tunic (PVT), covering all of the structures inside the vaginal cavity.

Posterio-ventral view showing completely exteriorized testicles (T), spermatic cord (SC) and small intestine (SI). The SI shown was previously within the confines of the vaginal cavity. The parietal vaginal tunic (PVT) has been incised thus allowing structures to be viewed. The point of entrance for the small intestine and spermatic cord into the inguinal canal (IC) can be observed.

Figure 4-10. The Position of the Intestine After Inguinal Herniation Using the Boar as an Example

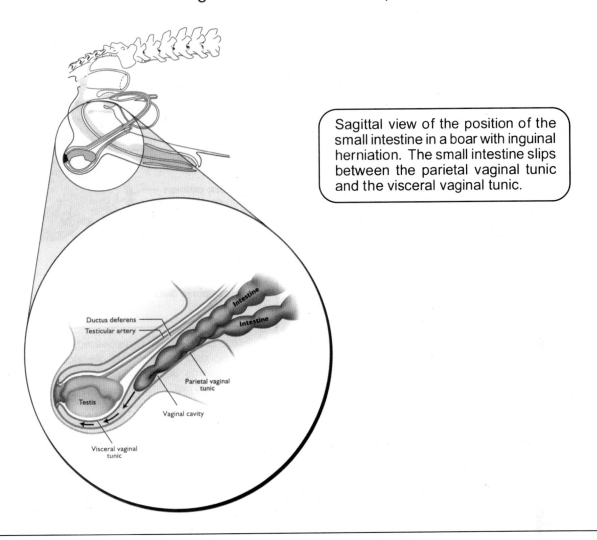

Sagittal view of the position of the small intestine in a boar with inguinal herniation. The small intestine slips between the parietal vaginal tunic and the visceral vaginal tunic.

4

vaginal cavity. Nevertheless, ligation of the parietal and visceral vaginal tunics is usually performed to prevent further herniation. Typically, this procedure is performed by members of the management team within the swine production unit.

Development of the Female Reproductive Tract Takes Place in the Absence of SRY Protein By Antagonizing the Male Pathway

In the absence of SRY protein, certain cells of the sex cords differentiate into primitive follicular cells and the bulk of the genital ridge becomes the ovary (See Figure 4-11).

Females have the X chromosome. It lacks the SRY gene that governs the production of SRY protein (See Figure 4-6). As a result, cells in the primitive gonad of the female do not differentiate into Sertoli cells. Since there are no Sertoli cells, anti-Müllerian hormone cannot be secreted. Therefore, the Leydig cells cannot secrete testosterone and the male reproductive tract cannot develop.

In the absence of SRY protein, the epithelial cords (sex cords), fragment into cellular clusters, each enclosing a primitive germ cell. These clusters germ cells penetrate less deeply into the interior of future ovary than in the male. Thus, primordial licles are formed along the outer surface of the that will eventually become the cortex of the Rete tubule formation in the ovary is not prono (See Figure 4-11) and a direct connection bet the rete tubules and the mesonephric tubules not exist. Therefore, there is no tubular outlet gametes. The development of the follicles (See 4-11) occurs throughout prenatal life and eve the number of gametes (follicles) will be max Thus, the female embryo will be born with a

Figure 4-11. Development of the Ovary, the Paramesonephric Ducts and Regression of the Mesonephros

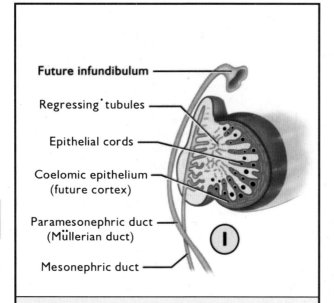

Future infundibulum

Regressing tubules

Epithelial cords

Coelomic epithelium (future cortex)

Paramesonephric duct (Müllerian duct)

Mesonephric duct

①

The paramesonephric duct and the mesonephric duct are still intact. The coelomic epithelium will develop into the ovarian cortex. The remnants of the mesonephric tubules do not make contact with the rete tubules.

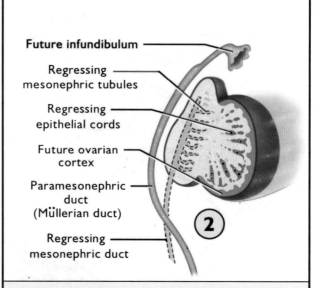

Future infundibulum

Regressing mesonephric tubules

Regressing epithelial cords

Future ovarian cortex

Paramesonephric duct (Müllerian duct)

Regressing mesonephric duct

②

The rete tubules have disappeared and the paramesonephric duct continues to develop and enlarge. The sex cords begin to regress, but the primitive germ cells do not.

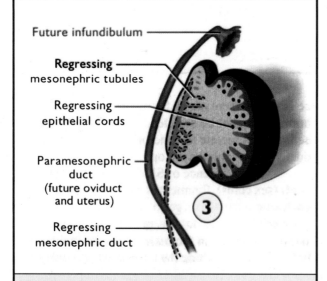

Future infundibulum

Regressing mesonephric tubules

Regressing epithelial cords

Paramesonephric duct (future oviduct and uterus)

Regressing mesonephric duct

③

Primitive follicles (black dots) begin to develop at the periphery of the ovary. The mesonephric tubules and ducts continue to regress while the paramesonephric duct continues to develop.

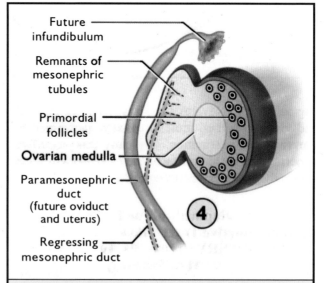

Future infundibulum

Remnants of mesonephric tubules

Primordial follicles

Ovarian medulla

Paramesonephric duct (future oviduct and uterus)

Regressing mesonephric duct

④

Distinct clusters of follicles surrounded by a single layer of cells develop at the periphery of the ovary. The sex cords have disappeared completely and the gonad resembles an ovary consising of a cortical region (region that contains the primordial oocytes) and a nongerminal region, the medulla. The mesonephric tubules and ducts have completely regressed.

oocytes from which folliculogenesis will occur for her reproductive lifetime. Figure 4-11 summarizes the major steps culminating in the formation of the ovary.

The ducts of the female reproductive tract are provided by the paramesonephric ducts. The cranial part of each paramesonephric duct runs parallel to the mesonephric duct (See Figures 4-5 and 4-12). The cranial part of the paramesonephric duct remains open to the peritoneal cavity, but the caudal end butts against the dorsal wall of the urogenital sinus (See Figure 4-12) and will fuse with it.

> ### The uterus and vagina result from a fusion of the paramesonephric ducts.

The oviducts, uterus, cervix and cranial vagina develop from the paramesonephric ducts. The paramesonephric ducts fuse together near their attachment to the caudal wall of the primitive urogenital sinus. The degree to which these ducts fuse determines the type of uterus the animal will have in adult life (See Figure 2-15).

You can see in Figure 4-12 that the caudal tip of the fused paramesonephric ducts fuses with a small bud protruding from the urogenital sinus. This fusion results in a duct system that is continuous from the exterior to the interior. Note that the cranial vagina, cervix and uterus originate from the paramesonephric ducts (and thus mesoderm). The caudal vagina and vestibule originate from the ectoderm that is a portion of the urogenital sinus.

It is important to note that both the male and female gonad and duct system originate behind the peritoneum (**retroperitoneal**). Even though it appears that the reproductive tract, particularly that of the female, is inside the body cavity, it is indeed located outside the peritoneum. The supportive tissue for the female tract is known as the broad ligament and surrounds the uterus, supporting it from a dorsal and lateral aspect. Figures 4-13 and 2-2 shows that the entire reproductive tract originates behind the peritoneum. In fact, the female tract is "sandwiched" between the genital fold. The genital fold will become the broad ligament consisting of the mesometrium, the mesosalpinx and the mesovarium. Recall from Chapter 2 that the female tract is suspended by the broad ligament that is continuous with the dorsal peritoneum.

In cattle, a condition exists that results in abnormal embryogenesis of the female reproductive tract. This condition is referred to as "**freemartinism.**" A freemartin (free=sterile, martin=bovine) results from a unique condition during the formation of the placenta in the cow. In the bovine, the extraembryonic membranes of each conceptus fuse to form a common chorion. These membranes (chorion) share the same cotyledons. Thus, there is a common blood supply between the male fetus and the female fetus. Because of this shared blood supply, each conceptus will be exposed to the same hormonal milieu (i.e., the female will be exposed to testosterone and anti-Müllerian hormone from the male fetus).

> ### A freemartin is a heifer born twin to a bull. The heifer calf is sterile, but the bull calf is fertile.

This common blood supply is established by about day 39 of gestation. In the bovine, the development of the testes occurs before the development of the ovaries. In fact, the testes are recognizable by day 40, whereas the ovaries require several weeks longer to develop. As you now know, the testes secrete a substance called anti-Müllerian hormone. This hormone inhibits the growth of the paramesonephric ducts (Müllerian ducts). Since the female twin is exposed to anti-Müllerian hormone as her reproductive tract is developing, the paramesonephric ducts do not develop completely. This incomplete development results in reproductive tracts that are "blind" and **canalization** of the tract (formation of a canal or lumen) is not complete. In addition, the potential ovaries cease to grow and do not develop the appropriate complement of germ cells. Therefore, the ovaries are incapable of secreting estradiol and often secrete substantial amounts of testosterone as well as androstenedione.

This atypical form of steroidogenesis not only causes abnormal female reproductive tract development, but also "programs" the central nervous system so that the genetic female behaves similarly to a male. The response of the freemartin to this elevated level of testosterone and androstenedione may range from asymptomatic to significant "bullish" behavior. From a practical perspective, the freemartin can be used effectively to detect estrus. Since these animals' central nervous system has been programmed to be male-like, they are generally more aggressive than the typical female in seeking out other females in estrus. By supplementing freemartin heifers with exogenous androgens, maleness can be further enhanced.

4

Figure 4-12. Fusion of Paramesonephric Ducts with the Urogenital Sinus to Form the Vagina (Dorsal View)

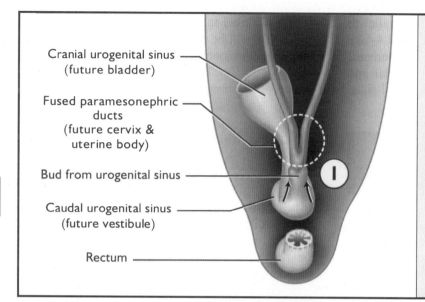

Cranial urogenital sinus (future bladder)

Fused paramesonephric ducts (future cervix & uterine body)

Bud from urogenital sinus

Caudal urogenital sinus (future vestibule)

Rectum

The paramesonephric ducts are beginning to fuse (circled area) and will form the cervix and uterine body. A small bud evaginates from the caudal urogenital sinus and attaches to the fused paramesonephric ducts.

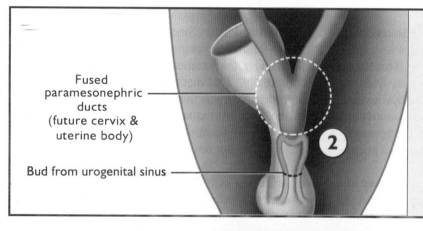

Fused paramesonephric ducts (future cervix & uterine body)

Bud from urogenital sinus

The paramesonephric ducts continue to fuse, forming a more defined cervix and a more developed vagina. The bud of the urogenital sinus elongates.

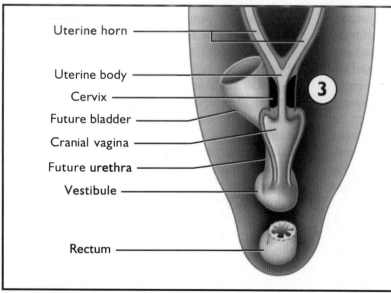

Uterine horn

Uterine body

Cervix

Future bladder

Cranial vagina

Future urethra

Vestibule

Rectum

Points of fusion have now formed a definitive cervix and the cranial and caudal vagina. The vestibule has stratified squamous epithelium because it originates from the urogenital sinus that invaginates from the exterior skin.

Figure 4-13. Formation of the Supportive Structures of the Female Tract

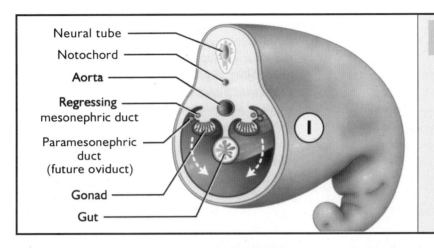

Cranial

In the more cranial region of the embryo the gonad and paramesonephric duct are quite separated. They may move ventrally (arrows) but never entirely fuse. Thus, the ovaries and the more cranial portions of the future uterus and oviducts (paramesonephric ducts) never fuse in most species.

Neural tube
Notochord
Aorta
Regressing mesonephric duct
Paramesonephric duct (future oviduct)
Gonad
Gut

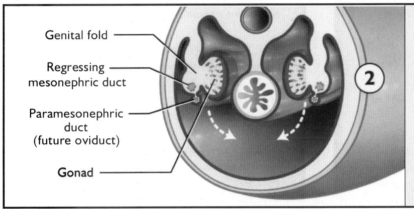

As the section becomes more caudal, the gonadal ridges as well as the paramesonephric ducts become more closely associated during their ventral movement. However, they still do not completely fuse.

Genital fold
Regressing mesonephric duct
Paramesonephric duct (future oviduct)
Gonad

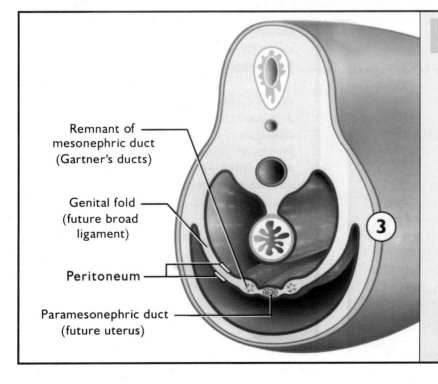

Caudal

In the more caudal regions, the paramesonephric ducts have comepletely fused, thus creating either the body of the uterus, the cervix or the cranial vagina. The remnants of the mesonephric ducts sometimes embed themselves in the wall of the vagina; these remnants can be seen in the adult animal and are called Gartner's ducts. It should be noted that the reproductive tract is sandwiched between two layers of peritoneum referred to as the genital fold. This connective tissue layer from the peritoneum forms the broad ligament that supports the femal reproductive tract in the abdominal cavity.

Remnant of mesonephric duct (Gartner's ducts)
Genital fold (future broad ligament)
Peritoneum
Paramesonephric duct (future uterus)

Further PHENOMENA for Fertility

All species do not develop a distinct sex (separate testes and ovaries) like this chapter explains. Some individuals possess both an ovary and a testis and are called hermaphrodites. Sea basses are synchronous hermaphrodites, meaning that fertile spermatozoa and oocytes in an ovotestes are present at the same time within a single fish. Self-fertilization is possible, but these fish have group-spawning events to insure genetic heterogeneity. Self-fertilization is advantageous if a sea bass is not present at the spawning event.

Testicles sometimes stray from the normal path of descent. In humans, they have been found under the skin of the root of the penis and in front of the anus.

In some species the guardian of embryogenesis is the male. The female bell toad lays her eggs in strings 3 to 4 feet long. The male wraps the egg string around his body. For about one month he serves as the "uterus," making sure that he and the eggs are exposed to the appropriate environment. He hides during the day (because he doesn't want his buddies to see him) and seeks water at night to moisten the eggs. Apparently, at "parturition" (hatching), the male sits in the water and the tadpoles swim away. We do not know the endocrine basis for this phenomenon.

In 1975, there were approximately 125 million babies born in the world. Of these, 6 million had chromosomal disorders, biochemical disorders or major congenital birth defects that required extensive medical resources. The most frequent type of disorder was a major congenital defect (4 million) due to faulty embryogenesis.

In chickens (and some ducks and doves) "sex" can be reversed after birth. Removal of the functional left ovary results in the development of the nonfunctional right gonad into a testis or ovotestis (a gonad containing follicles of ovulatory size and tubules with spermatozoa). The younger the bird at ovariectomy, the greater the probability that the right gonad will develop into a testis. The older the bird, the greater the probability that an ovotestis will develop.

The Mount Hagen people of New Guinea in the South Pacific believe that a child is formed from stored menstrual blood and semen. During gestation, the father helps form the child's body by frequent acts of intercourse. The more sex the couple has, the more robust the infant will become.

The Turnip Eel worm has unusual mating behavior. The female grows what appear to be buds on the surface of the body. When ready to mate, she brings herself close to the surface of the turnip, the inside of which she inhabits. She then breaks through the turnip's skin and pushes her vagina through the opening. Males periodically leave their "houses" in the turnip and move around the outside of the turnip looking for a suitable bud (the vagina) into which they can insert their hooked, fork-shaped penis. Such behavior probably minimizes exposure of the female Turnip Eel worm to predators.

Mateo Colombo, 16th Century anatomist, first understood that the clitoris was an analogue of the penis and that it had a role in orgasm. He only escaped being burned at the stake by having some influential patients who probably also understood the role of the clitoris.

Women in ancient Egypt (1850-1550 BC) plugged their cervixes with crocodile dung to prevent pregnancy.

Key References

Adham, I.M et.al. 2002. The overexpression of the Insl-3 in female mice causes descent of the ovaries. Mol. Endocrinol. 16:244-252.

Dubois, P. 1993. "The hypothalamic-pituitary axis: embryological, morphological and functional aspects" in *Reproduction in Mammals and Man*. Thibault, C., M.C. Levasseur and R.H.F. Hunter, eds., Ellipses, Paris. ISBN 2-7298-9354-7.

Dyce, K.M., W.O. Sack and C.J.G. Wensing. 2002. *Textbook of Veterinary Anatomy*, 3rd Edition. Elsevier Science, Philadelphia. ISBN 0-7216-8966-3.

George, F.W. and J.D. Wilson. 1994. "Sex determination and differentiation" in *Physiology of Reproduction*. 2nd Edition Vol. 2. p3-28. E. Knobil and J.D., Neill, eds., Raven Press, New York. ISBN 0-12-227023-1.

Hughes, I.A. and C.L. Acerini. 2008. Factors controlling testis descent. Eur J. Endocrinol. 159:575-582.

Knobil, E. and J.D. Neill (eds). 1998. *The Encyclopedia of Reproduction*. Vol 1-4. Academic Press, San Diego. ISBN 0-12-227020-7.

Larsen, W.J. 1993. *Human Embryology*. Churchill Livingstone, New York. ISBN 0-443-08724-5.

Sekido, R. and R. Lovell-Badge. 2008. Sex determination and SRY: Down to a wink and a nudge (feature review). Cell 25:19-29.

Toppari, J. and M. Kaleva. 1999. Maldescendus testis. Horm. Res. 51:261-269.

4

REGULATION OF REPRODUCTION
Nerves, Hormones & Target Tissues

CHAPTER 5

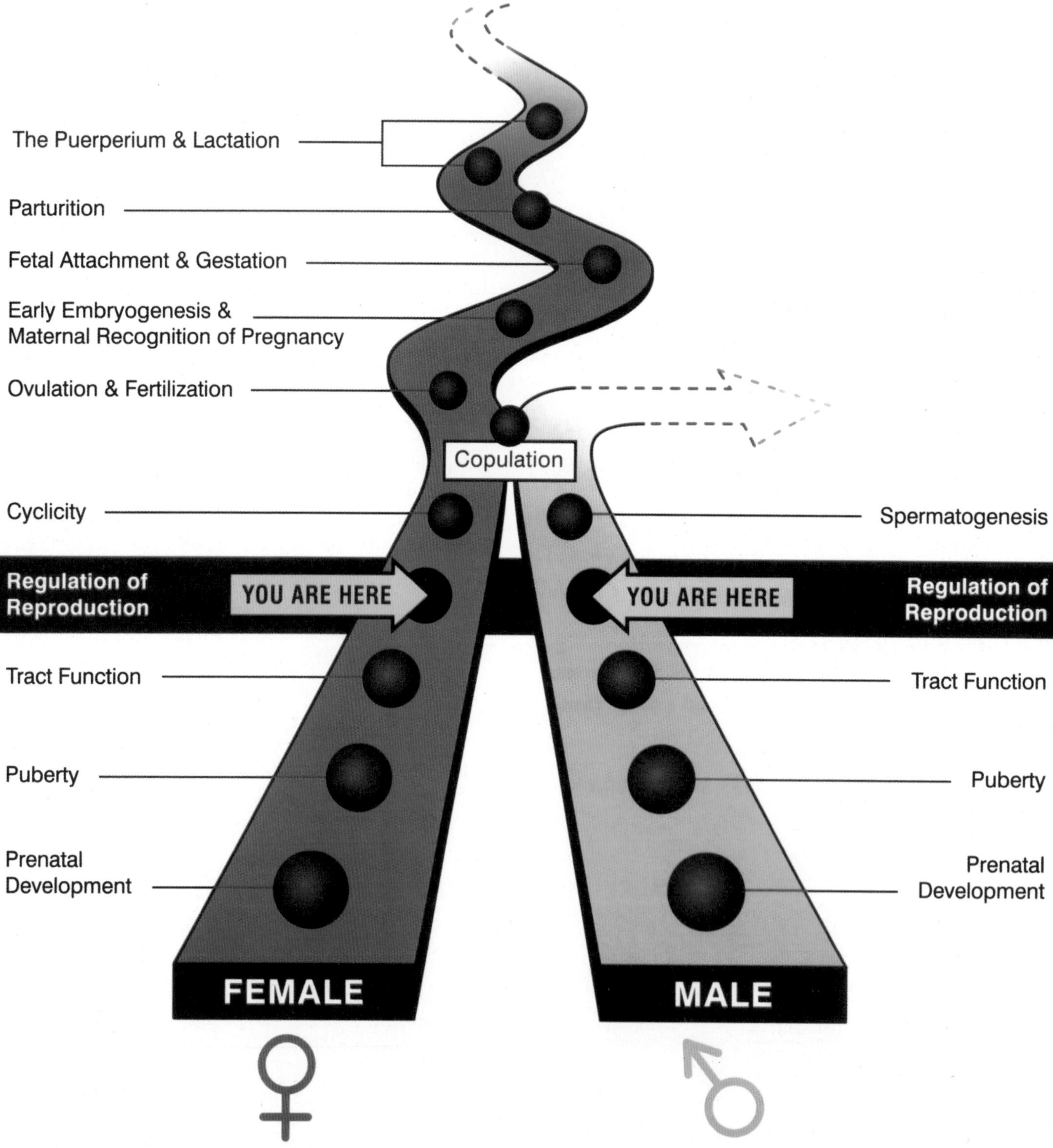

The Puerperium & Lactation
Parturition
Fetal Attachment & Gestation
Early Embryogenesis & Maternal Recognition of Pregnancy
Ovulation & Fertilization
Copulation
Cyclicity
Spermatogenesis
Regulation of Reproduction
YOU ARE HERE
YOU ARE HERE
Regulation of Reproduction
Tract Function
Tract Function
Puberty
Puberty
Prenatal Development
Prenatal Development
FEMALE
MALE

Take Home Message

Hormones are secreted by endocrine glands or nerves. They enter the blood and cause cells in target tissues containing specific receptors to secrete new products or new hormones. Hormones and their products are necessary for successful reproduction. Protein hormones act via plasma membrane receptors and exert effects in the cytoplasm of the target cell. Steroid hormones act through nuclear receptors that regulate transcription factors that cause gene expression ("slow responses", days to weeks) in target cells. Steroid hormones also act through plasma membrane receptors that cause "rapid responses" (minutes to hours) in target tissues. Both types of hormones cause changes in the function of the target cells.

Reproduction is regulated by a remarkable interplay between the **nervous system** and the **endocrine system**. These two systems interact in a consistent display of teamwork to initiate, coordinate and regulate all reproductive functions. In order to understand and appreciate the role of these two systems, we must first focus on the control that each system exerts independently.

> *Neural control requires:*
> • *simple neural reflexes or*
> • *neuroendocrine reflexes*

The fundamental responsibility of the nervous system is to translate or **transduce** external stimuli into neural signals that bring about a change in the reproductive organs and tissues. The primary pathways of nervous involvement are a **simple neural reflex** and a **neuroendocrine reflex**. The functional components of these two pathways are sensory neurons (afferent neurons taking neural signals toward the spinal cord), the spinal cord, efferent neurons (nerves leaving the spinal cord and traveling to the target tissue) and **target tissues** (See Figure 5-1). Target tissues are those organs that respond to a specific set of stimuli or hormone.

The basic difference between the simple neural reflex and the neuroendocrine reflex is the type of delivery system each uses. For example, a simple neural reflex employs nerves that release their neurotransmitters (messengers) directly onto the target tissue. In other words, the target tissue is directly innervated by a neuron and responds to a neurotransmitter. In contrast, a neuroendocrine reflex requires that a **neurohormone** (a substance released by a neuron) enter the blood and act on a remote target tissue. Neurons releasing neurohormones are also called **neurosecretory cells**. Direct innervation of the target tissue does not exist in the neuroendocrine reflex. Instead, the neurohormone in the blood is the messenger between the neurosecretory cell and the target tissue. Both of these neural pathways are illustrated in Figure 5-1.

Neural Reflexes and Neuroendocrine Reflexes Cause Rapid Changes in Target Tissues

In a simple neural reflex, afferent sensory neurons synapse directly with **interneurons** in the spinal cord (See Figure 5-1). These interneurons synapse with efferent neurons that travel directly to the target tissue. The target tissue responds to the neurotransmitter released by the efferent neuron. A **neurotransmitter** is a substance of small molecular weight that is released from the terminals of nerves that causes other nerves to fire or causes contraction of smooth muscle that surrounds portions of the reproductive tract (See Figure 5-1). An example of a simple neural reflex in reproduction is ejaculation. A stimulus originating in the glans penis is recognized by sensory neurons. Signals are then transmitted to the spinal cord where they synapse with efferent neurons that cause a series of muscular contractions resulting in expulsion of semen. A detailed pathway of this neural event will be presented in Chapter 11. Another example of a simple neural reflex that impacts the reproductive system involves temperature sensitive neurons located in the scrotum (described in Chapter 3). When scrotal temperature decreases, sensory neurons in the scrotum recognize this decrease and send sensory signals to the spinal cord. Efferent nerves travel to the tunica dartos in the scrotum and release neurotransmitters that initiate contraction that elevates the testicles to bring them closer to the body, thus warming them.

The **neuroendocrine reflex** (See Figure 5-1) is quite similar to a simple neural reflex. This type of reflex also starts with sensory neurons. They synapse with interneurons in the spinal cord. Efferent

Figure 5-1. Neural and Neuroendocrine Reflexes

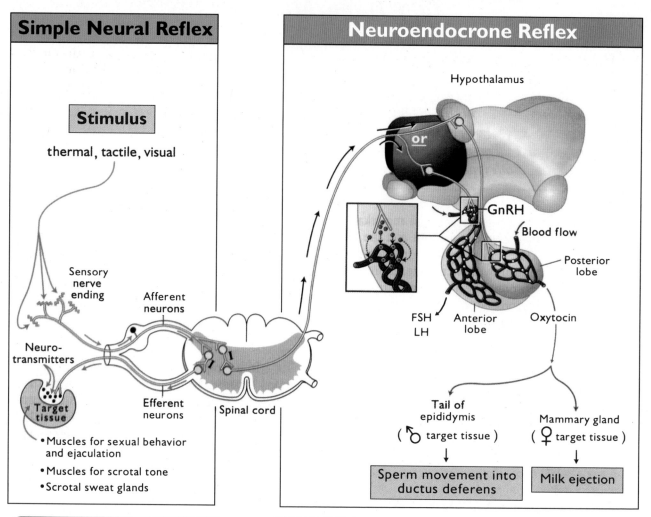

Simple Neural Reflex

Stimulus

thermal, tactile, visual

Sensory
nerve
ending

Afferent
neurons

Neuro-
transmitters

Target
tissue

Efferent
neurons

Spinal cord

• Muscles for sexual behavior
and ejaculation
• Muscles for scrotal tone
• Scrotal sweat glands

Neuroendocrone Reflex

Hypothalamus

or

GnRH

Blood flow

Posterior
lobe

FSH
LH

Anterior
lobe

Oxytocin

Tail of
epididymis
(♂ target tissue)

Mammary gland
(♀ target tissue)

Sperm movement into
ductus deferens

Milk ejection

Sensory nerves, responding to a
stimulus, synapse with interneurons
(I) in the spinal cord. Efferent
neurons travel directly to the target
tissue to cause a response.

Sensory nerves synapse with interneurons (I) in the spinal cord.
Efferent neurons travel to the hypothalamus where hypothalamic
neurons release neurohormones. These neurohormones enter
the blood and activate target tissues, such as the anterior lobe
of the pituitary, mammary gland or the epididymis.

neurons traveling from the spinal cord **synapse** with
other neurons in the hypothalamus. The hypothalamic
neurons release small molecular weight materials
from their terminals. These materials are referred to
as **neurohormones** because they are released into the
blood rather than directly onto the target tissue. Neurohormones released into capillaries travel to a target
tissue elsewhere in the body. The classic example of
a neuroendocrine reflex is the suckling reflex. When
suckling occurs, sensory nerves in the teat or nipple
of the lactating female detect the tactile stimulus.
These sensory signals travel to the spinal cord and
then to the hypothalamus where they synapse with
other nerves. The hypothalamic neurons then depo-

larize ("fire"), causing release of **oxytocin** directly
from nerve terminals located in the posterior lobe of
the pituitary. Oxytocin is stored as a neurosecretory
material in the nerve terminals of the posterior lobe
of the pituitary. When these neurosecretory cells
"fire," oxytocin is released, enters the blood, travels
to the target tissue (in this case, myoepithelial cells
of the mammary gland) (See Chapter 15) and causes
these cells to contract, resulting in milk ejection from
the mammary alveoli. In addition, other forms of
stimuli, such as visual or auditory, can cause milk
ejection if the animal is preconditioned to respond
to these stimuli. For example, the sight or sound of
the newborn may elicit a similar response without

direct mammary stimulation. Also, many dairy cows entering the milking parlor receive visual or auditory stimuli prior to actual mammary stimulation by either the sight or sounds of the equipment and begin to experience milk ejection prior to entering the parlor.

> *The hypothalamus is the neural control center for reproductive hormones.*

Figure 5-2. Anatomy of the Typical Mammalian Hypothalamus and Pituitary

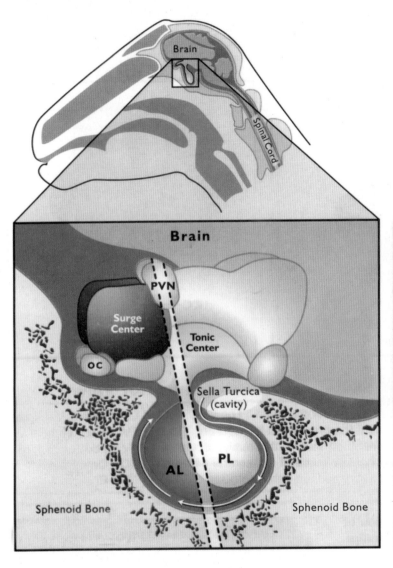

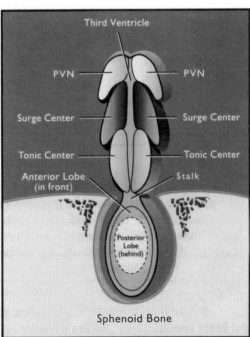

5

Saggital view

The hypothalamus is a specialized ventral portion of the brain consisting of groups of nerve cell bodies called hypothalamic nuclei that appear as lobules in the figure. The surge center, the tonic center and the paraventricular nucleus (PVN) have direct influence on reproduction. The anterior and posterior lobes of the pituitary are positioned in a depression of the sphenoid bone called the sella turcica.

Frontal view

This view illustrates the relationship of the paraventricular nucleus (PVN), the surge center and the tonic center to the third ventricle and pituitary. The vertical line in the left panel represents the plane of section shown in the right panel. Notice that the third ventricle (a brain cavity) separates the lateral portions of the hypothalamus. AL = Anterior Lobe of the Pituitary, PL = Posterior Lobe of the Pituitary, OC = Optic Chiasm.

Figure 5-3. Ventricular System of the Brain

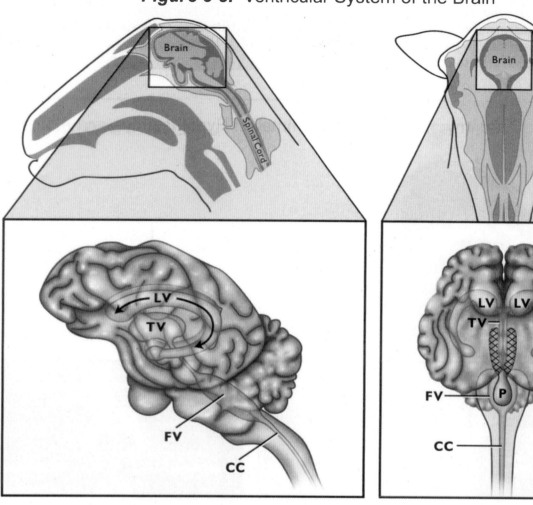

Lateral view   Anterior view

Lateral and anterior views of the ventricular system of the brain. The ventricles are blue-shaded "bags" and appear here as if the brain were transparent. The ventricular system is filled with cerebrospinal fluid that continuously circulates through the ventricles and into the subarachnoid spaces of the central nervous system. The hypothalamus (hatched area) surrounds the third ventricle.

LV = Lateral Ventricles
TV = Third Ventricle
FV = Fourth Ventricle
CC = Central Canal
P = Pituitary

The hypothalamus is a complex portion of the brain consisting of clusters of nerve cell bodies. The clusters, or groups of nerve cell bodies are called **hypothalamic nuclei**, each of which has a specific name. For example, groups of hypothalamic nuclei that influence reproduction are named the surge center and the tonic center (See Figure 5-2).

Neurons in these regions secrete **gonadotropin releasing hormone** (GnRH). Neurons in the paraventricular nucleus (PVN) secrete oxytocin. The hypothalamic nuclei surround a small cavity known as the third ventricle, found in the center of the brain (See Figure 5-3). It is important to understand that each hypothalamic nucleus has a different function and is stimulated by different sets of conditions.

> *The hypothalamo-hypopyseal portal system allows minute quantities of releasing hormones to act on the anterior pituitary before they are diluted by the general circulation.*

Axons from the cell bodies of the surge and tonic centers extend into the pituitary stalk region where the nerve endings (terminal boutons) terminate on a sophisticated and highly specialized capillary network. This capillary network is referred to as the **hypothalamo-hypophyseal portal system** (See Figure 5-4). The terminal boutons of the hypotha-

Figure 5-4. The Hypothalamo-Hypophyseal Portal System

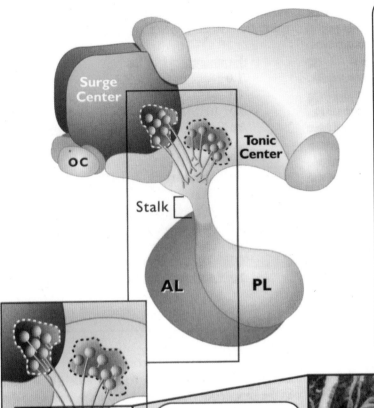

Axons from neurons in the surge center and the tonic center extend to the stalk region where their endings terminate upon blood vessels of the hypothalamo-hypophyseal portal system. This portal system consists of: the superior hypophyseal artery; the primary portal plexus, (where the surge center and tonic center neurons terminate); the medial hypophyseal artery that supplies part of the anterior lobe of the pituitary (AL); the portal vessels that transport blood containing releasing hormones; and the secondary portal plexus that delivers blood (and releasing hormones) to the cells of the anterior lobe.

5

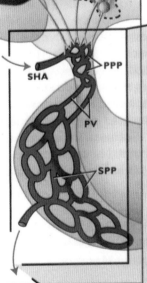

MHA = Medial Hypophyseal Artery

PPP = Primary Portal Plexus

PV = Portal Vessels

SHA = Superior Hypophyseal Artery

SPP = Secondary Portal Plexus

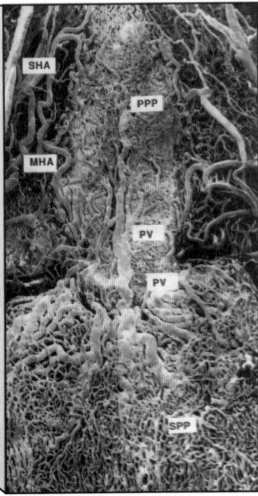

The photograph at the right is a scanning electron micrograph of the hypothalamo-hypophyseal portal system after vascular injection with latex (Mercox). It was provided with permission by Dr. H. Duvernoy, Faculte de Medecine et de Pharmacie de Besancon, Laboratoire d'Anatomie, Place St. Jacques, 25030 Besancon, France.

lamic neurons release neuropeptides that enter the specialized capillary system at the stalk of the pituitary. Blood enters the capillary system from the **superior hypophyseal artery** that divides into small arterial capillaries at the level of the pituitary stalk. This portal system enables extremely small quantities (picograms) of releasing hormones to be secreted into the capillary plexus (**primary portal plexus**) of the pituitary stalk. Releasing hormones are then transferred immediately to a second capillary plexus in the anterior lobe of the pituitary where they cause pituitary cells to release other hormones. The hypothalamo-hypophyseal portal system is important because it allows minute quantities of releasing hormones to act directly on the cells of the anterior lobe of the pituitary before the GnRH becomes diluted by the systemic circulation.

> *The posterior lobe of the pituitary does not have a portal system. Neurohormones are deposited directly into capillaries in the posterior lobe of the pituitary.*

The posterior lobe of the pituitary is organized quite differently from the anterior lobe (See Figure 5-5). Neurons from certain hypothalamic nuclei extend directly into the posterior lobe of the pituitary where the neurohormone is released into a simple arterio-venous capillary plexus. For example, cell bodies in the paraventricular nucleus synthesize oxytocin that is transported down the axon to the terminals in the posterior lobe. If the neuron is stimulated, oxytocin is released into the blood.

Endocrine Control is Generally Slower, but Longer Lasting than Neural Control

In contrast to neural regulation, the endocrine system relies on **hormones** to cause responses. A hormone is a substance produced by a gland that acts on a remote tissue (**target tissue**) to bring about a change in the target tissue. These changes involve alterations in metabolism, synthetic activity and secretory activity.

Extremely small quantities of a hormone can cause dramatic physiologic responses. Hormones act at blood levels ranging from nanograms (10^{-9}) to picograms (10^{-12}) per ml of blood (See Table 5-1). The ability to measure extremely small quantities of hormones has brought about an explosion of knowledge regarding the quantities, patterns of secretions and roles of hormones as they relate to reproductive processes.

Table 5-1. Illustration of exponents, decimal places and common weight designations used in describing quantities of substances. The shaded area indicates the range of hormone weights per milliliter of blood that cause physiologic responses.

Exponent		Name
1.0		**gram**
10^{-1}	.1	
10^{-2}	.01	
10^{-3}	**.001**	**milligram**
10^{-4}	.000,1	
10^{-5}	.000,01	
10^{-6}	**.000,001**	**microgram**
10^{-7}	.000,000,1	
10^{-8}	.000,000,01	
10^{-9}	**.000,000,001**	**nanogram**
10^{-10}	.000,000,000,1	
10^{-11}	.000,000,000,01	
10^{-12}	**.000,000,000,001**	**picogram**

Hormones are characterized as having relatively short half-lives. Hormonal **half-life** is defined as the time required for one-half of a hormone to disappear from the blood or from the body. Short half-lives are important because once the hormone is secreted and released into the blood and causes a response, it is degraded so that further responses do not occur. It should be emphasized, however, when hormones are continually produced (such as progesterone during pregnancy), their action continues for as long as the hormone is present. Compared to neural control, hormonal control is slower and has durations of minutes, hours or even days.

Positive and Negative Feedback are the Major "Controllers" of Reproductive Hormones

Now that you understand the basic anatomy and neural regulation of the reproductive system, the fundamental mechanisms controlling secretion of reproductive hormones must be described. These mechanisms are referred to as **positive feedback and negative feedback**. The principles of positive and negative feedback control is one of the most important concepts to understand. Almost all reproductive functions are controlled by these two mechanisms.

> *Negative feedback= suppression of*
> *GnRH neurons*
> *Positive feedback= stimulation of*
> *GnRH neurons*

Positive and negative feedback control the secretion of GnRH that in turn, controls the secretion of the gonadotropins FSH and LH. For the purpose of the discussion here, we will use progesterone that causes strong negative. feedback at the hypothalamic level. Progesterone strongly inhibits GnRH neurons and therefore when progesterone is high, GnRH neurons secrete only basal levels of GnRH. Such basal secretion while allowing for some follicular development will not allow sufficient follicular development for the secretion of high levels of estradiol. Therefore, females under the influence of progesterone (midcycle or pregnant) do not cycle for the period of time that progesterone is high.

> $\uparrow P_4 \rightarrow \downarrow GnRH \rightarrow \downarrow FSH \ \& \ LH =$
> *Incomplete follicular development*

5

Figure 5-5. Relationship Between the Paraventricular Nucleus and the Posterior Lobe of the Pituitary

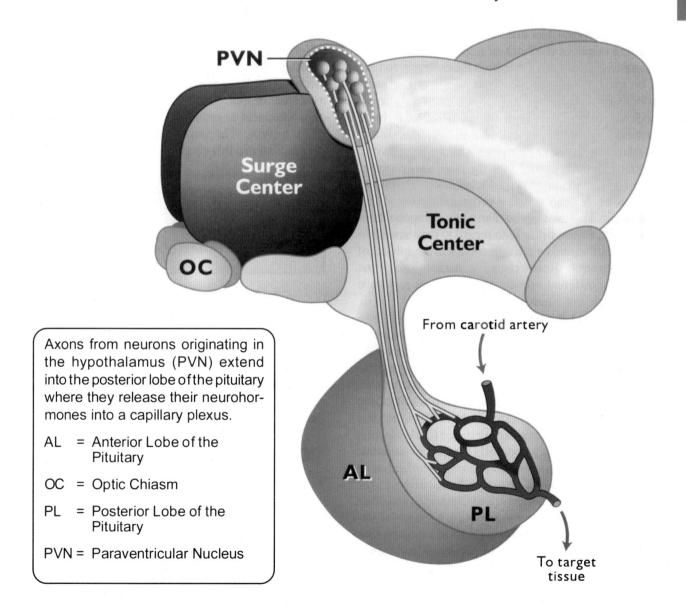

Axons from neurons originating in the hypothalamus (PVN) extend into the posterior lobe of the pituitary where they release their neurohormones into a capillary plexus.

AL = Anterior Lobe of the Pituitary

OC = Optic Chiasm

PL = Posterior Lobe of the Pituitary

PVN = Paraventricular Nucleus

In direct contrast to negative feedback, positive feedback activates the GnRH neurons in the hypothalamus. The female contains a surge center that is responsible for secreting large quantities of GnRH that induce ovulation. The surge center will not release large quantities of GnRH until there is positive feedback by estradiol. For example, when estradiol reaches a certain high level (a threshold level), the surge center will be positively stimulated and will release large quantities of GnRH that cause the release of large quantities of LH that stimulate ovulation.

$$\uparrow E_2 \rightarrow \uparrow GnRH \ (surge) \rightarrow LH \ surge = Ovulation$$

It is important to recognize that positive feedback and negative feedback are independent controls within the animal that exert two distinctly different outcomes. Reproductive endocrinologists think that the hypothalamus has different sensitivities to positive and negative feedback of gonadal steroids. For example, the tonic center in both the male and female is believed to respond mostly to negative feedback. While progesterone in the female exerts a strong negative feedback on both the surge and the tonic centers, it mostly exerts its effect on the tonic center. In other words, the tonic center is quite sensitive to negative feedback. In contrast, the surge center responds mostly to positive feedback of estradiol. Therefore, the surge center is very sensitive to positive feedback. The reasons that these two components of the hypothalamus differ with regard to their sensitivities to positive and negative feedback is the subject of current research. Researchers are attempting to define how these different subsets of neurons are regulated by two different controls.

During the past decade, a new class of neuropeptides has emerged as the possible "gatekeepers" for GnRH release. These neuropeptides are called **kisspeptins** and are secreted by hypothalamic neurons in the periventricular, preoptic and arcuate nuclei. Kisspeptin neurons send dendritic arborizations into hypothalamic nuclei where GnRH cell bodies are abundant. This is anatomical evidence that kisspeptin appears to act directly on GnRH neurons to stimulate GnRH secretion. Kisspeptin is now recognized as an important regulator of sexual differentiation of the brain, the timing of puberty (See Chapter 6) and adult regulation of gonadotropin secretion by gonadal steroids, especially as it relates to seasonal breeding (See Chapter 7). The emergence of new knowledge about the mechanism of action of kisspeptin indicates that positive and negative feedback by gonadal steriods

may act on kisspeptin neurons that in turn mediate GnRH secretion by GnRH neurons.

> *Reproductive hormones:*
> - *act in minute quantities*
> - *have short half-lives*
> - *bind to specific receptors*
> - *regulate intracellular biochemical reactions*

In order for a hormone to cause a response, it must first interact specifically with the target tissue. The cells of the target tissue must have receptors that bind the hormone. Binding of the hormone with its specific receptor initiates a series of intracellular biochemical reactions.

Hormonal regulation of a biochemical reaction is generally tied to secretory activity of the target cell. When exposed to a hormone, the target cell synthesizes substances that are not secreted unless the hormone is present. For example, estradiol (secreted by the ovary), causes the cells of the cervix to secrete mucus. This change is caused by a series of biochemical or synthetic pathways within the cells of the cervix. The steps in these processes will be detailed later in this chapter.

> *Hormones can be classified by:*
> - *source*
> - *mode of action*
> - *biochemical classification*

Reproductive hormones can be classified according to their source of origin, their primary mode of action and their biochemical classification. Table 5-2 summarizes hormonal classification by source, by target tissue and by their primary actions. Details about these hormones will be presented in subsequent chapters where their functions will be specifically described in the female and in the male.

Tissue Origin Constitutes One Method of Hormonal Classification

Hypothalamic hormones are produced by neurons in the hypothalamus. One of their roles is to cause the release of other hormones from the anterior lobe of the pituitary. The primary releasing hormone of reproduction is **gonadotropin releasing hormone (GnRH)**. **Neuropeptides** of hypothalamic origin are

Figure 5-6. Amino Acid Sequence of GnRH

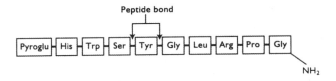

very small molecules generally consisting of less than twenty amino acids. These small peptides are synthesized and released from neurons in the hypothalamus. The most important neuropeptide governing reproduction is GnRH. The amino acid sequence for GnRH, a decapeptide, is shown in Figure 5-6. The molecular weight of GnRH is only 1,183.

Pituitary hormones are released into the blood from the anterior and posterior lobes of the pituitary. The primary reproductive hormones from the anterior lobe are **follicle stimulating hormone (FSH)**, **luteinizing hormone (LH)** and **prolactin. Oxytocin** is the primary reproductive hormone synthesized by nerves in the hypothalamus, stored and released from the posterior lobe.

Gonadal hormones originate from the gonads and affect function of the hypothalamus, anterior lobe of the pituitary and tissues of the reproductive tract. Gonadal hormones also initiate the development of secondary sex characteristics that cause "maleness" or "femaleness." In the female, the ovary secretes estrogens, progesterone, inhibin, some testosterone, oxytocin and relaxin. In the male, the testes secrete testosterone and other androgens, inhibin and estrogens.

Hormones are also secreted by the uterus and the placenta. These are responsible for governing cyclicity and maintenance of pregnancy. An example of a uterine hormone is **prostaglandin $F_{2\alpha}$ ($PGF_{2\alpha}$)**. Placental hormones include **progesterone, estrogens, equine chorionic gonadotropin (eCG)** and **human chorionic gonadotropin (hCG)**.

Research by reproductive physiologists at Auburn University and Rutgers University suggests that the mammary gland may also serve as a source of biologically active factors important for neonatal development. These researchers defined delivery of bioactive factors from mother to offspring as a specific consequence of nursing and the consumption of colostrum (first milk) as **"lactocrine signaling"**. Lactocrine signaling differs from endocrine signaling in that milk-borne bioactive factors, provided by virtue of lactation, are transported in colostrum/milk (not blood) and absorbed into the neonatal circulation where they act on target tissues. Lactocrine transmission of relaxin and its effects on development of the neonatal female reproductive tract is an example of this mechanism.

> *Reproductive hormones originate from the:*
> - *hypothalamus*
> - *pituitary*
> - *gonads*
> - *uterus*
> - *placenta*

Mode of Action is Another Method of Hormonal Classification

Neurohormones are synthesized by neurons and are released directly into the blood so that they can cause a response in target tissues elsewhere in the body. A neurohormone can act on any number of tissues provided that the tissue has cellular receptors for the neurohormone. An example is oxytocin that is synthesized by hypothalamic neurons, stored and released by the posterior lobe of the pituitary.

Releasing hormones are also synthesized by neurons in the hypothalamus and cause release of other hormones from the anterior lobe of the pituitary. They can also be classified as neurohormones because they are synthesized and released by neurons. An example is gonadotropin releasing hormone (GnRH) that controls the release of FSH and LH from the anterior lobe of the pituitary.

Gonadotropins are hormones synthesized and secreted by specialized cells in the anterior lobe of the pituitary gland called **gonadotropes**. The suffix **"tropin"** means having an affinity for or to nourish. Thus, these hormones have a stimulatory influence on the gonads (the ovary and the testis). Gonadotropins are **follicle stimulating hormone (FSH)** and **luteinizing hormone (LH)**. Luteinizing hormone is responsible for causing ovulation and stimulating the corpus luteum (CL) to secrete progesterone. Luteinizing hormone causes testosterone secretion in the male. Follicle stimulating hormone causes follicular growth in the ovary of the female. It stimulates Sertoli cells in the male and is probably a "key player" in governing spermatogenesis.

Sexual promoters (estrogens, progesterone, testosterone) are secreted by the gonads of both the male and the female to stimulate the reproductive tract, to regulate the function of the hypothalamus and the anterior lobe of the pituitary and to regulate

5

reproductive behavior. These hormones also cause the development of secondary sex characteristics. The sexual promoters are the driving force for all reproductive function.

Human chorionic gonadotropin (hCG) and **equine chorionic gonadotropin** (eCG) are secreted by the early embryo (conceptus). These placental hormones cause stimulation of the maternal ovary.

Pregnancy maintenance hormones are in high concentrations during times of pregnancy. They are responsible for maintenance of pregnancy (e.g., progesterone) and, in some cases, assisting the female in her lactation ability. **Placental lactogen** promotes development of the mammary gland of the dam and is therefore **lactogenic**.

General metabolic hormones promote metabolic well-being. Such hormones are **thyroxin** from the thyroid gland, the **adrenal corticoids** from the adrenal cortex and **growth hormone (somatotropin)** from the anterior lobe of the pituitary. Thyroxin regulates metabolic rate of the animal. The adrenal corticoids perform a host of functions ranging from mineral metabolism to regulation of inflammatory responses. Growth hormone helps regulate growth, lactation and protein metabolism. These general metabolic hormones are all necessary for optimum reproduction. However, they are considered to exert an indirect rather than a direct effect on reproductive function.

Luteolytic hormones cause destruction of the corpus luteum. The suffix **"lytic"** is a derivative of the word lysis. Lysis means decomposition, disintegration or dissolution. Luteolytic hormones, therefore, cause the corpus luteum to stop functioning. The major luteolytic hormone is **prostaglandin $F_{2\alpha}$ ($PGF_{2\alpha}$)**. As you shall see in Chapter 9, $PGF_{2\alpha}$ causes a decrease in secretion of progesterone by the corpus luteum.

Reproductive hormones can cause:

- *release of other hormones (releasing hormones)*

- *stimulation of the gonads (gonadotropins)*

- *sexual promotion (steroids)*

- *pregnancy maintenance*

- *luteolysis (destruction of the CL)*

Hormonal Biochemical Structure Constitutes Another Classification Method

Peptides are relatively small molecules with only a few amino acids joined by peptide bonds. The most important reproductive peptide is GnRH shown in Figure 5-6.

Prolactin is an example of a protein hormone that consists of a single polypeptide chain of 198 amino acids and is not glycosylated.

Relaxin is a two-chain nonglycosylated polypeptide. It consists of an alpha (α) chain and a beta (β) chain. These polypeptide chains are connected by two disulfide crosslinks. The primary source of relaxin is the corpus luteum of pregnancy. There is supporting evidence that relaxin is synthesized by the placenta as well.

Glycoproteins are polypeptide hormones that contain carbohydrate moieties and range in molecular weight from several hundred to 70,000. Some glycoprotein hormones are composed of two side-by-side polypeptide chains that have carbohydrates attached to each chain. These polypeptide chains have been designated as the α and β **subunits** (See Figure 5-7). The anterior lobe of the pituitary synthesizes and secretes glycoprotein hormones that all have the same α subunit but different β subunits. The α subunit for FSH, LH and thyroid stimulating hormone (TSH) are identical within species. However, the β subunit is unique to each individual hormone and gives each of these glycoprotein hormones a high degree of specificity and function. Individual α and β subunits of these molecules have no biological activity. If an α subunit of one hormone is combined with the β subunit of another hormone, the activity will be determined by the hormone that contributed the β subunit. The α and β subunits are held together with hydrogen bonds and van der Waals forces and thus <u>are not</u> covalently attached (See Figure 5-7).

Inhibin is another glycoprotein hormone that contains an α and one of two possible β subunits (designated β_A or β_B). This hormone appears to have the same physiologic activity regardless of which β subunit is present. Inhibin suppresses FSH secretion from the anterior lobe of the pituitary.

Researchers have identified a protein from follicular fluid that consists of two β subunits called **activin**. Activin causes release of FSH in pituitary cells in culture and therefore has the opposite effect of inhibin in-vitro.

Follistatin, a glycoprotein, was originally isolated from ovarian follicular fluid. It inhibited FSH secretion from pituitary cells in culture. However, compared to inhibin, it has low physiologic activity. Follistatin binds to activin and limits widespread actions of activin.

Figure 5-7. Generic Illustration of a Glycoprotein Hormone

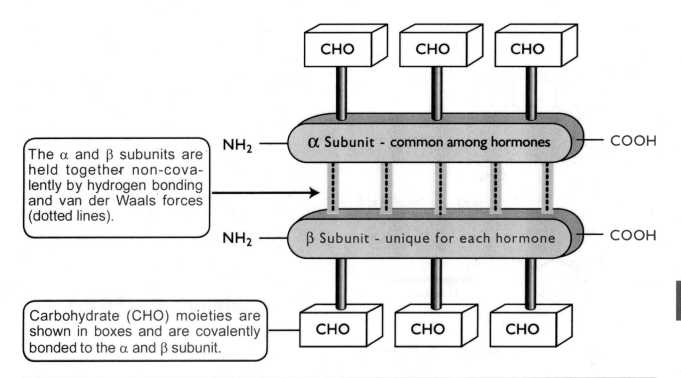

The α and β subunits are held together non-covalently by hydrogen bonding and van der Waals forces (dotted lines).

Carbohydrate (CHO) moieties are shown in boxes and are covalently bonded to the α and β subunit.

Dispersed along each subunit of the hormone are carbohydrate moieties that are thought to protect the molecule from short-term degradation that might occur during transport in the blood and interstitial compartments to target tissues. The quantity of carbohydrate moieties on the surface of the protein is thought to determine the duration of the hormone's half-life. In other words, the higher the degree of glycosylation (number of carbohydrate moieties), the longer the half-life of the hormone. Recent research findings indicate that a single glycoprotein hormone may have as many as 6 to 8 subtypes in which the degree of glycosylation varies significantly. Glycoprotein hormones can be degraded easily by proteolytic enzymes in the digestive tract. Therefore, they are not effective when given orally.

> ***Biochemical classifications include:***
> * *peptides*
> * *glycoproteins*
> * *steroids*
> * *prostaglandins*

Steroid hormones have a common molecular nucleus called the **cyclopentanoperhydrophenanthrene nucleus**. The molecule is composed of four rings designated A, B, C and D. Each carbon in the ring has a number, as shown in Figure 5-8.

Steroids are synthesized from cholesterol through a series of complex pathways involving many enzymatic conversions. Figure 5-9 illustrates the major biochemical transformations that occur in the gonadal steroid synthetic pathway. Steroid molecules are sexual promoters and cause profound changes in both the male and female reproductive tract and will be discussed in later chapters.

Figure 5-8. Standardized Labeling of the Steroid Molecule

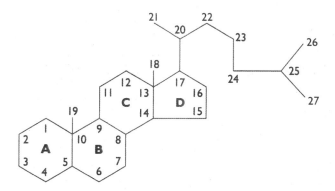

A, B, C and D designate specific rings. Numbers designate specific carbons.

Figure 5-9. Gonadal Steroid Synthetic Pathway

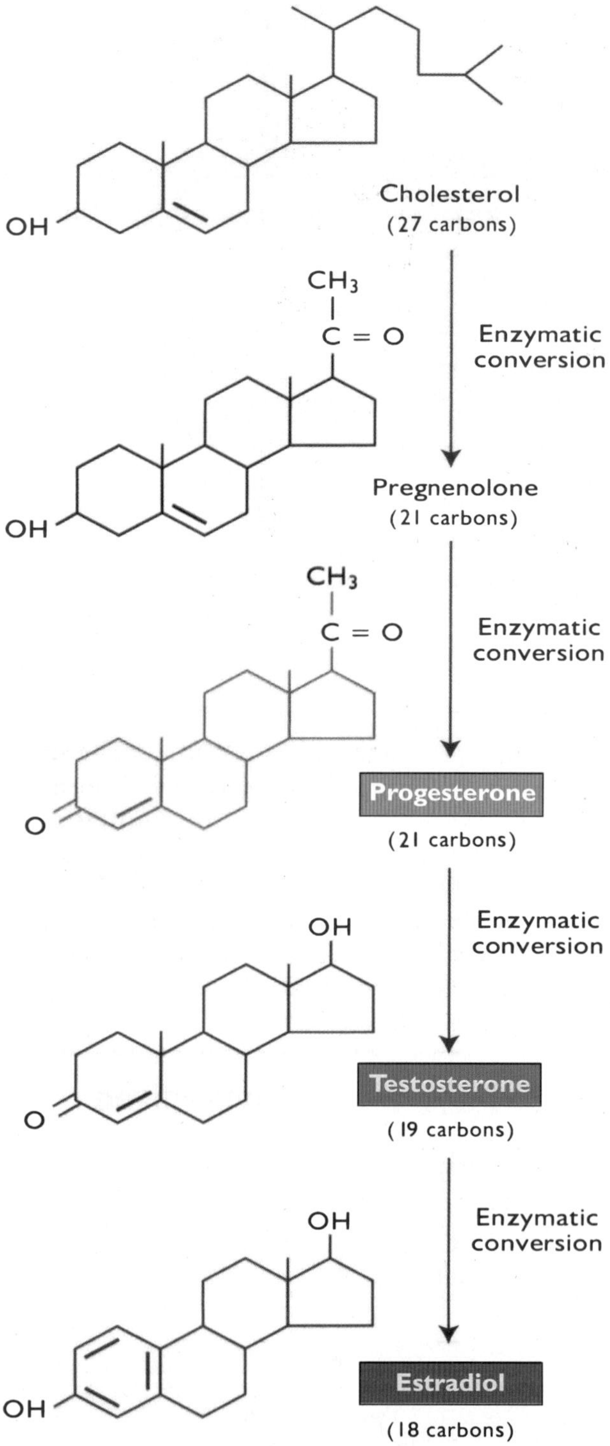
Cholesterol
(27 carbons)
OH
CH_3
C = O
Enzymatic conversion
Pregnenolone
(21 carbons)
OH
CH_3
C = O
Enzymatic conversion
Progesterone
(21 carbons)
O
OH
Enzymatic conversion
Testosterone
(19 carbons)
O
OH
Enzymatic conversion
Estradiol
(18 carbons)
OH

Figure 5-10. Structure of $PGF_{2\alpha}$ and PGE_2

(The dashed lines represent bonds that extend into the plane of the page)

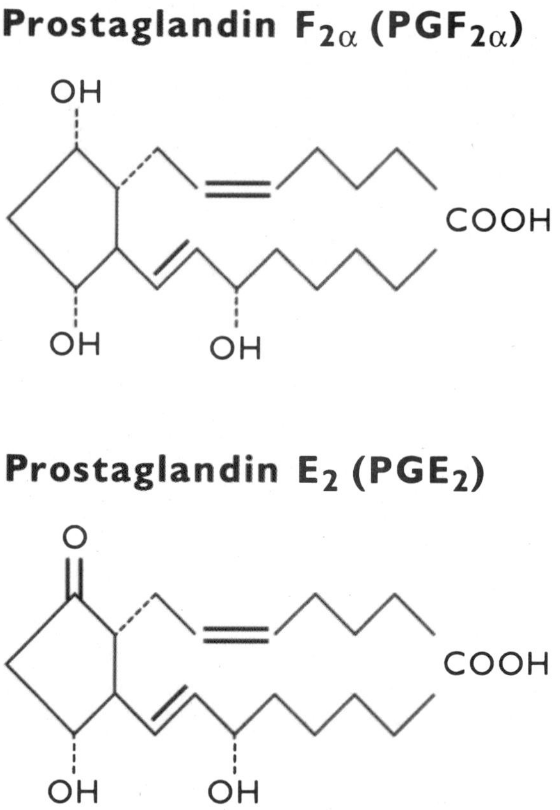
Prostaglandin $F_{2\alpha}$ ($PGF_{2\alpha}$)
OH
COOH
OH
OH
Prostaglandin E_2 (PGE_2)
O
COOH
OH
OH

Prostaglandins were first discovered in seminal plasma of mammalian semen and were thought to originate from the prostate gland. Thus, these compounds were named prostaglandins. The seminal vesicles are now known to secrete more prostaglandin than the prostate, at least in the ram. Prostaglandins are among the most ubiquitous and physiologically active substances in the body. They are lipids consisting of 20-carbon unsaturated hydroxy fatty acids that are derived from arachidonic acid. There are at least six biochemical prostaglandins and numerous metabolites that have an extremely wide range of physiologic activity. For example, prostaglandin E_2 (PGE_2) lowers blood pressure, while prostaglandin $F_{2\alpha}$ ($PGF_{2\alpha}$) increases blood pressure. Prostaglandins also stimulate uterine smooth muscle, influence lipid metabolism and mediate inflammation. As far as the reproductive system is concerned, the two most important prostaglandins are $PGF_{2\alpha}$ and PGE_2 (See Figure 5-10). Ovulation is controlled, at least in part, by $PGF_{2\alpha}$ and PGE_2.

The discovery that $PGF_{2\alpha}$ caused luteolysis (destruction of the corpus luteum) in the female opened a new world of application for the control of the estrous cycle. Use of prostaglandins as a tool for reproductive management is now routine and some of these strategies will be discussed in Chapter 9. Prostaglandins are rapidly degraded in the blood. In fact, almost

Figure 5-11. Target Tissues Bind Hormones, Other Tissues Do Not

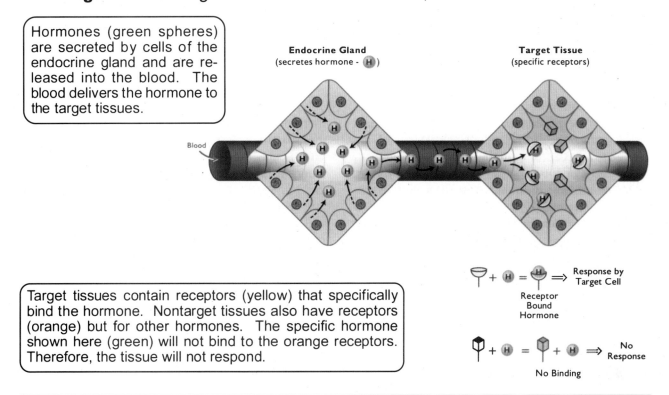

Hormones (green spheres) are secreted by cells of the endocrine gland and are released into the blood. The blood delivers the hormone to the target tissues.

Endocrine Gland
(secretes hormone - H)

Target Tissue
(specific receptors)

Blood

Target tissues contain receptors (yellow) that specifically bind the hormone. Nontarget tissues also have receptors (orange) but for other hormones. The specific hormone shown here (green) will not bind to the orange receptors. Therefore, the tissue will not respond.

Receptor Bound Hormone → Response by Target Cell

No Binding → No Response

5

all of $PGF_{2\alpha}$ is removed from blood during one pass through the pulmonary circulation (30 seconds). Thus, $PGF_{2\alpha}$ has an extremely short half-life (seconds).

Pheromones are Another Class of Substances that Cause Remote Effects

In addition to molecules that are transported by blood, another class of materials exists that directly influences reproductive processes. These materials are called **pheromones**. Pheromones are substances secreted to the outside of the body. They are generally volatile and are detected by the olfactory system (and perhaps the vomeronasal organ) by members of the same species. Pheromones cause specific behavioral or physiologic responses by the percipient. Pheromones are known to influence the onset of puberty, the identification of females in estrus by the males and other behavioral traits.

Endocrine glands are composed of many cells that synthesize and secrete specific hormones. These hormone molecules enter the blood and are transported to every cell in the body. In spite of the fact that every cell in the body is exposed to the hormone, only certain cells with specific receptors are capable of responding to the hormone. Tissues containing these cells are called **target tissues**. For example, if a hormone's responsibility is to cause the cervix to synthesize mucus, other organs such as the liver, the kidney or the pancreas will not secrete mucus in response to the hormone.

Hormone action requires the presence of specific receptors on target cells.

Target tissues are distinguished from other tissues because their cells contain specific molecules that bind a specific hormone. These specific molecules located in the cells of target tissues are known as **hormone receptors** (See Figure 5-11). Receptors have a specific affinity (degree of attraction) for a specific hormone and thus bind it. Once the receptor in the target tissue has bound the hormone, the target tissue begins to perform a new function. Often, the target

Figure 5-12. Hypothetical Model of the LH Receptor

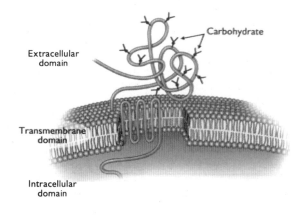

Carbohydrate

Extracellular domain

Transmembrane domain

Intracellular domain

tissue secretes another hormone that acts upon another tissue elsewhere in the body.

> ### Protein hormones bind to plasma membrane receptors.

Receptors for protein hormones are an integral part of the plasma membrane of the target cell. They contain three distinct regions. These regions are referred to as **receptor domains**. The configuration of the LH receptor consists of an **extracellular domain**, a **transmembrane domain** and an **intracellular domain** (See Figure 5-12).

The extracellular domain has a specific site that binds the specific hormone. When this site is occupied, the transmembrane domain changes its configuration and activates other membrane proteins known as G-proteins. The number of transmembrane "loops" may vary as a function of receptor type. The function of the intracellular domain of the receptor is not clear.

Steps of Action for Protein Hormones

Step 1 - <u>Hormone-Receptor Binding</u>. The hormone diffuses from the blood into the interstitial compartment and binds to a membrane receptor that is specific for the hormone. The binding occurs on the surface of the target cells (See Figure 5-13). In general, receptors to the gonadotropins are sparsely distributed on the surface of the target cells. In fact, only 2,000 to 20,000 LH or FSH receptors are present per follicle cell. Hormone-receptor binding is thought to be brought about by a specific geometric configuration of the receptor

5

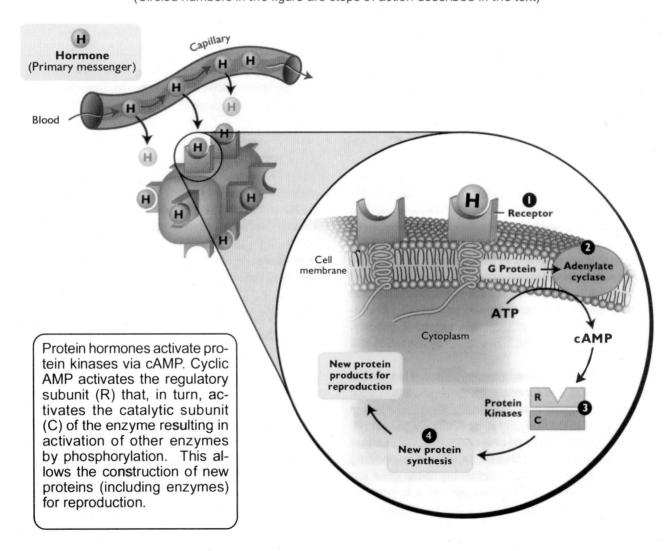

Figure 5-13. Protein Hormone Mechanisms of Action
(Circled numbers in the figure are steps of action described in the text)

Protein hormones activate protein kinases via cAMP. Cyclic AMP activates the regulatory subunit (R) that, in turn, activates the catalytic subunit (C) of the enzyme resulting in activation of other enzymes by phosphorylation. This allows the construction of new proteins (including enzymes) for reproduction.

that "fits" the geometric configuration of the hormone. The hormone receptor binding is much like fitting two adjacent pieces of a puzzle together. The affinity of the hormone-receptor binding varies among hormones.

Step 2 - Adenylate Cyclase Activation. The hormone-receptor complex activates a membrane bound enzyme known as **adenylate cyclase** and membrane bound **G-proteins**. When the hormone receptor complex is formed, the G-protein is transformed in a way that activates adenylate cyclase (See Figure 5-13). The active form of this enzyme converts **ATP** to **cyclic AMP** (cAMP) within the cytoplasm of the cell. Cyclic AMP has been termed the "**second messenger**" in the pathway because cAMP must be present before further "downstream" events can occur. The primary messenger is the hormone itself.

Step 3- Protein Kinase Activation. Cyclic AMP activates a family of control enzymes located in the cytoplasm called **protein kinases**. These proteins kinases are responsible for activating enzymes in the cytoplasm that convert substrates into products. Protein kinases consist of a regulatory and a catalytic subunit. The regulatory subunit binds cAMP and this binding causes activation of the catalytic subunit that initiates the conversion of existing substrates to new products.

Step 4 - Synthesis of New Products. The products made by the cell are generally secreted and these secretory products have specific functions that enhance reproductive processes. For example, the gonadotropins (FSH and LH) bind to follicle cells in the ovary that results in the synthesis of a new product, estradiol. When steroids are synthesized, they are not actively secreted, but simply diffuse through the plasma membrane into the interstitial spaces and into the blood.

> ### *Steroid hormones have two types of receptors.*

Until recently, it was thought that steroid hormones acted exclusively through nuclear receptors to produce a response in target cells. Research has shown that in addition to nuclear receptors, steroid hormones also bind to membrane receptors of target cells. There is a functional difference between membrane receptor binding and nuclear receptor binding. Nuclear receptor binding causes "slow" responses (hours to days) that require transcriptional involvement, followed by product synthesis and secretion by the target cell. For example, a target tissue for estradiol in the female is the cervix. When estradiol binds to nuclear receptors in the cervical cells, it promotes the synthesis and secretion of cervical mucus. This process requires several days.

Steroid hormone binding to membrane receptors typically results in "fast" responses (seconds to minutes). The myometrium has membrane estradiol receptors. When estrogens bind to these receptors they cause permeability changes in the calcium channels in myometrial smooth muscle, causing increased motility (contraction) of the myometrium. As illustrated in Figure 5-14, it is thought that the steroid hormone target cells contain both membrane-bound receptors and nuclear receptors.

Steps of Action for Steroid Hormones: Membrane Receptors ("Fast Response")

Although several variations in the biochemical pathways following binding to membrane receptors are known, for this purpose we will use the pathway as described for protein hormones (See Figure 5-14).

Step 1- Steroid Binding to Membrane Receptors
Step 2- Adenylate Cyclase Activation
Step 3- Protein Kinase Activation
Step 4- Changes in Ca^{++} channel permeability

Steps of Action for Steroid Hormones: Nuclear Receptors ("Slow Response")

Step 1 - Steroid Transport. Steroid hormones are transported in the blood by a complex system. Steroids are not water soluble and therefore cannot be transported as free molecules. Therefore, they must attach to molecules that are water soluble. Steroids bind to a variety of plasma proteins in a nonspecific manner althrough some steroids have specific carrier proteins. These transport proteins carry steroids in the blood and interstitial fluid to the cell membranes of all cells. The binding of steroids to plasma proteins tends to extend their half-life.

Step 2 - Movement Through the Cell Membrane and Cytoplasm. When the steroid-carrier protein complex travels into the interstitium and comes in contact with target cells, the steroid disassociates from the carrier protein and diffuses through the plasma membrane because they are lipid solubile (See Figure 5-14). After the steroid molecule enters the cell, it diffuses through the cytoplasm and into the nucleus.

Step 3 - Binding of Steroid to Nuclear Receptor. If the cell is a target cell, the steroid binds to a specific nuclear receptor. The steroid-receptor binding is similar to protein-receptor binding in that the steroid must "fit" the receptor. The steroid-receptor complex is referred to as a **transcription factor** and initiates DNA-directed messenger RNA synthesis (transcription).

Figure 5-14. Mechanisms of Steroid Hormone Action
(Circled numbers in the figure are steps of action described in the text)

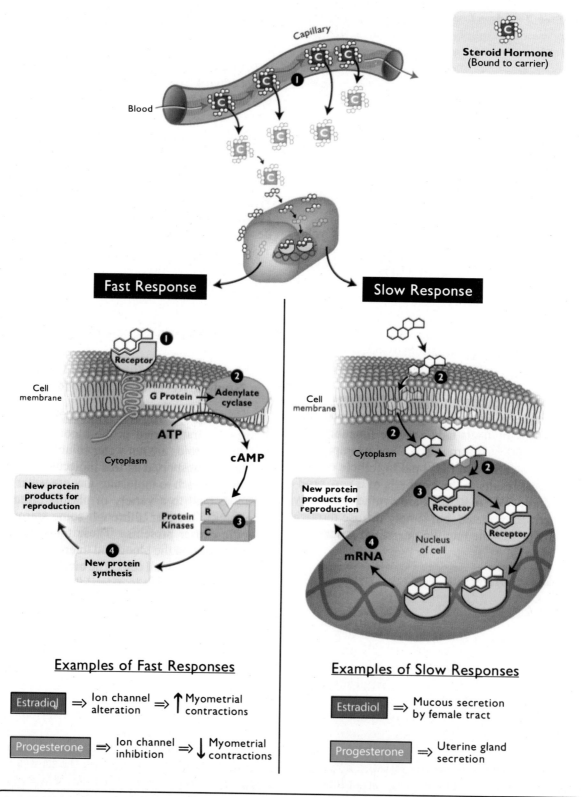

Steroid Hormone
(Bound to carrier)

Capillary

Blood

Fast Response

Slow Response

Cell membrane

Receptor

G Protein → Adenylate cyclase

ATP

Cytoplasm

cAMP

New protein products for reproduction

Protein Kinases

R
C

New protein synthesis

Cell membrane

Cytoplasm

New protein products for reproduction

Receptor

Receptor

mRNA

Nucleus of cell

Examples of Fast Responses

Estradiol ⇒ Ion channel alteration ⇒ ↑ Myometrial contractions

Progesterone ⇒ Ion channel inhibition ⇒ ↓ Myometrial contractions

Examples of Slow Responses

Estradiol ⇒ Mucous secretion by female tract

Progesterone ⇒ Uterine gland secretion

Steroid hormones can bind to membrane receptors and nuclear receptors causing different "downstream" effects. Numbers in each graphic represent the steps in each mechanism that are explained in the text.

Step 4 - <u>mRNA Synthesis and Protein Synthesis</u>. The newly synthesized mRNA leaves the nucleus and attaches to ribosomes where it directs the synthesis of specific proteins that will enhance the reproductive process. A few examples of steroid-directed synthesis are: 1) mucus from the cervix during estrus; 2) uterine secretions from the uterine glands; and 3) seminal plasma components from the accessory sex glands in the male.

> *"Strength" of hormone action depends on:*
> - *pattern and duration of secretion*
> - *half-life*
> - *receptor density*
> - *receptor-hormone affinity*

The physiologic activity of a hormone depends on several factors including pattern and duration of hormone secretion, half-life of the hormone, receptor density and receptor-hormone affinity. These factors determine the magnitude and duration of action of hormones. In general, hormones are secreted in three types of patterns (See Figure 5-15). One type is **episodic secretion** that generally is associated with

hormones under nervous control. When nerves in the hypothalamus "fire," neuropeptides are released in a sudden burst (episode) and thus hormones from the anterior lobe of the pituitary tend to be released in an episodic manner as well. A typical pattern of episodic release is shown in Figure 5-15. Organization of episodes into a predictable pattern is referred to as **pulsatile secretion**. Pulsatile secretion is required for an animal to have a normal estrous cycle. Prepubertal and noncyclic lactating animals are characterized by episodic secretion (unpredictable pattern) of hormones. A second type of secretion is a **basal** (tonic) pattern. Here, the hormone stays low, but fluctuates with low amplitude pulses. An example of a basal pattern would be GnRH secretion from the tonic center in the hypothalamus. **Sustained** is a third type of hormonal pattern or profile. In this type, the hormone remains elevated, but in a relatively steady, stable fashion for a long period of time (days to weeks). Steroids tend to be secreted in a more stable fashion because the glands secreting the steroids are generally producing them continuously rather than as a function of neural activity (that causes a pulsatile release). High progesterone during diestrus or pregnancy is an example of a sustained pattern of hormone secretion.

5

Figure 5-15. Typical Patterns of Hormonal Secretion by the Reproductive System

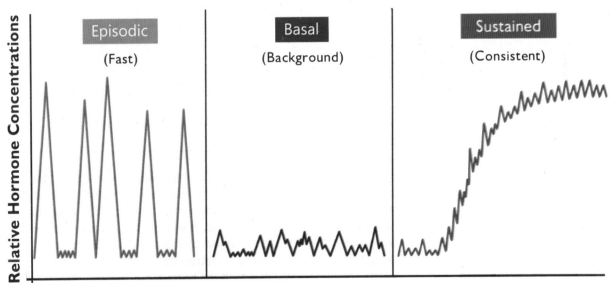

Episodic secretion is generally associated with hormones under nervous control. When nerves of the hypothalamus fire, neuropeptides are released in a sudden burst or pulse.

In a basal secretion pattern, the hormone stays low but fluctuates with low amplitude pulses.

In the sustained hormone release profile, the hormone remains elevated, but in a relatively steady fashion for a long period (days to weeks). Steroids tend to be secreted in this manner.

Half-Life of a Hormone Determines How Long It Will Act

Different hormones have different life expectancies within the systemic circulation. The rate at which the hormone is cleared from the circulation determines its half-life. The longer the half-life, the greater the potential biological activity. Some hormones have exceptionally short half-lives (seconds; e.g. $PGF_{2\alpha}$), while other hormones have quite long half-lives (days; e.g. eCG).

> *Hormonal potency is influenced by:*
> * *receptor density*
> * *hormone receptor affinity*

The density of target tissue receptors varies as a function of the cell type as well as the degree to which hormones promote (**up-regulate**), or inhibit (**down-regulate**) synthesis of hormone receptors. Factors such as animal condition and nutrition may play a role in influencing receptor numbers. As you will see later on, different hormones promote synthesis of receptors to either themselves or other hormones. For example, FSH promotes the synthesis of LH receptors by the follicular cells. The higher the degree to which a cell is populated with receptors, the higher potential for target cell responses.

Receptor affinity for hormones vary. In general, the greater the affinity of the hormone for the receptor, the greater the biologic response.

Hormone **agonists** are **analogs** (having a similar molecular structure) that bind to the specific receptor and initially cause the same biologic effect as the native hormone. Some agonists promote greater physiological activity because they have greater affinity for the hormone receptor. Other analogs, called **antagonists**, have greater affinity for the hormone receptor, but promote weaker biologic activity than the native hormone. Antagonists decrease the response of target cells by having a weaker biological activity than the native hormone or by occupying hormone receptors and thus preventing the native hormone from binding. In either case, the antagonist interferes with native hormone action.

> *Hormones disappear from the body because they are metabolized and then eliminated in the urine and feces.*

Figure 5-16. Metabolism of Progesterone and Testosterone

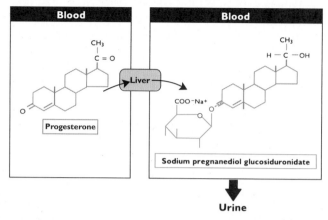

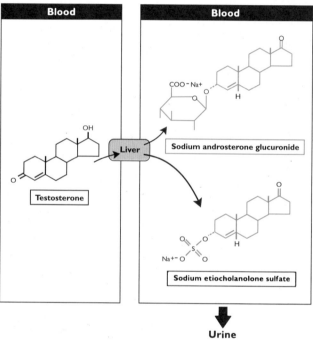

The half-life of a hormone is determined by the rate at which it is metabolized within the body. Relatively rapid turnover of a hormone is essential so that the biologic action will not last for an undesired period of time. Blood concentrations of hormones not only reflect the secretion rate by the various organs but the rate at which the hormone is metabolized.

Steroids are Metabolized (inactivated) by the Liver and Excreted in the Urine and Feces

The liver inactivates steroid molecules in two ways. First, any double bond within the steroid molecule becomes saturated. When double bonds are reduced, the molecule is rendered inactive. The second change to the steroid molecule is that a sulfate or **glucuronide** residue is attached (See Figure 5-16). The glucuronide form of the steroid molecule is water-soluble and thus it can be excreted into the urine. This is important because there are no specific binding proteins to carry steroids into the bladder. The fact that steroid metabolites appear in the urine is the basis for testing athletes for "illegal" performance enhancing steroids. The equation in Figure 5-16 illustrates the transformation that occurs in the progesterone molecule in the liver and its excretion metabolites. Notice that all three unsaturation sites (double bonds) in progesterone have been reduced. Each steroid is metabolized in slightly different ways and produces different metabolites. For example, testosterone forms both a glucuronide (like progesterone) and a **sulfate salt** that is excreted in the urine (See Figure 5-16).

Steroids are also eliminated in the feces. It is assumed that they enter the gut through the bile duct in a conjugated form (glucuronide or sulfate). They are not digested per se in the gut. But, bacterial action undoubtedly modifies the form of the steroid prior to defecation. The amount of time that steroids (or their conjugates) remain intact (stable) in feces has yet to be completely defined. It is known that fecal concentrations change after defecation as a function of bacterial metabolism, and exposure to ultraviolet radiation. The specific type of steroid molecule also impacts its longevity in the gut and the feces. Endocrinologists recommend that fecal samples be collected and analyzed within one day after defecation. The general pathway of excretion/elimination of steroids from the body after they are metabolized is presented in Figure 5-17.

The presence of steroids in the feces is fortuitous because it enables steroid concentrations in wild animals to be described without collecting blood samples. Much of our knowledge about the reproductive endocrinology of elephants and wild felids has been generated by evaluating fecal samples (See Key References).

The potential importance of progesterone metabolism involves the high producing dairy cow. High producing dairy cows (20,000 lbs or more of milk per year) have significantly larger livers than do low producing dairy cows. One theory suggests that high producing dairy cows may metabolize progesterone and even estradiol at a faster rate than their lower producing contemporaries. Such rapid metabolism may cause temporary sub-fertility because the uterus, during early pregnancy, may not be capable of providing an optimum environment for embryo survival (because progesterone is low). Further research is needed to validate this theory. Nevertheless, the rate of hormone metabolism may be an important ingredient that governs fertility of the female in many species.

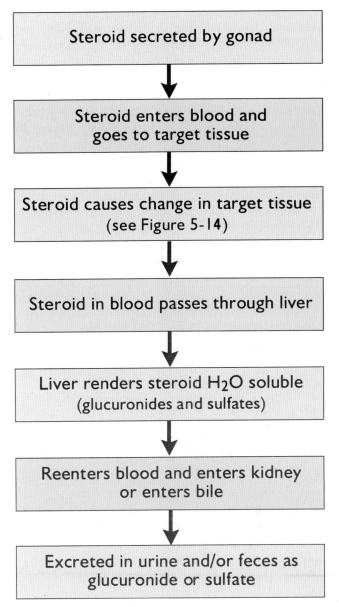

Figure 5-17. Fate of Steroids After Secretion

Steroid secreted by gonad

↓

Steroid enters blood and goes to target tissue

↓

Steroid causes change in target tissue (see Figure 5-14)

↓

Steroid in blood passes through liver

↓

Liver renders steroid H_2O soluble (glucuronides and sulfates)

↓

Reenters blood and enters kidney or enters bile

↓

Excreted in urine and/or feces as glucuronide or sulfate

Protein Hormones are Degraded in the Liver and Kidneys

The half-life of pituitary gonadotropins is very short and is between 20 and 120 minutes depending on the hormone and species. **Chorionic gonadotropins** (human chorionic gonadotropin-hCG and equine chorionic gonadotropin-eCG) have longer half-lives (hours to days). This longer half-life has practical application because hCG and eCG have been used as superovulation drugs in domestic animals because their physiologic activity generally lasts a longer period of

5

time in-vivo than GnRH. Removal of polysaccharide side chains (**glycosylation sites**) from gonadotropins significantly reduces their half-life. Gonadotropin molecules that have lost their glycosylation, bind to liver cells, are internalized and degraded within the cytoplasm of the liver cell. In addition to denaturation in the liver, the kidneys likely play an important role in elimination of glycoprotein hormones. For example, glycoprotein hormones are significantly smaller than typical serum glycoproteins. The glomerular filtration limit for molecules within the kidney is around 55,000 Daltons. Any glycoprotein hormone that has a molecular weight of less than 55,000 potentially can be eliminated in the urine. Such is the case for human chorionic gonadotropin.

Human chorionic gonadotropin at least in part is filtered through the kidney and eliminated in the urine thus providing an avenue for a rapid patient-side pregnancy test in women. It should be emphasized that oral administration of protein hormones is not effective because these proteins are denatured in the gastrointestinal tract and lose their biologic potency because here they are broken-down into amino acid fragments.

> *Hormones can be detected in blood, saliva, milk, urine, lymph, tears, and feces using radioimmunoassay (RIA) and enzyme-linked immunosorbent assay (ELISA) technology.*

The **radioimmunoassay (RIA)** has revolutionized our understanding of endocrine physiology in almost all species of animals during the past 50 years. The radioimmunoassay requires the use of radioactive hormones. In the test tube, radioactive hormone competes with the same hormone from an animal's blood that is not radioactively labeled. The amount of radioactive hormone that binds is inversely proportional to the concentration of unlabeled hormone in the animal's blood. A detailed description of the RIA is beyond the scope of this text (See Key References). Radioimmunoassay technology requires specialized radioisotope-approved laboratories, expensive isotope detection equipment and the need for expensive disposal methods.

The RIA is being replaced by a more user-friendly assay called the **enzyme-linked immunosorbent assay (ELISA)**. The **ELISA** has provided many convenient ways to detect and measure hormones. The principle of the ELISA involves a series of steps designed to determine the presence or absence of specific hormones under a variety of conditions. The ELISA can also determine the quantity of the hormone present in a sample under more sophisticated laboratory conditions. The major steps of the ELISA are described in Figure 5-18.

The advantage of the ELISA over the RIA is that no radioisotopes are required, the test can be conducted on-site with minimal training, it has no health/safety hazard issues and it is relatively inexpensive. One of the most successful and popular applications of the ELISA is a one-step, over-the-counter pregnancy test for women. ELISA tests are also being used for pregnancy detection in cows and bison. A more complete description of the hormones of pregnancy will be presented in Chapter 14. In addition to pregnancy detection, ELISA has very widespread on-site use, ranging from detection of pathologic microorganisms to environmental contaminants. It should be emphasized that there are many variations and biochemical strategies used to produce ELISA systems. However, the basic principle involved in all applications is the use of a color-generating enzyme linked to a specific antibody (See Figure 5-18).

For a summary of hormone classification, source and target tissues, refer to Table 5.2 at the end of the chapter.

Figure 5-18. Use of the ELISA as a Method to Measure Hormones

Step 1: Two types of antibodies are required. One antibody reacts specifically with a hormone ("hormone antibody"). A second antibody reacts with the hormone-antibody complex and this antibody has an enzyme attached to it ("enzyme antibody").

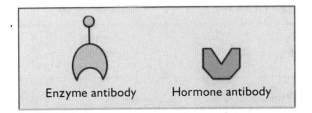

Step 2: The "hormone antibody" (a protein) is tightly attached to a solid support surface.

Step 3: When the specific hormone (usually a protein) is present in a solution, it binds ("immunosorbent") to the "hormone antibody" and forms a hormone-antibody complex.

Step 4: The "enzyme antibody" then reacts against the hormone-antibody complex, generating a larger antibody complex with the enzyme component exposed to the solution.

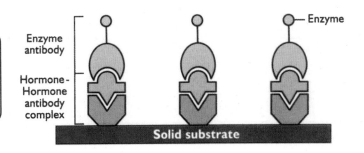

Step 5: After the "enzyme antibody" binds to the original complex, a substrate is added to the solution and the enzyme attached to the "enzyme antibody" causes a color to be generated. Generation of a color is the basis for the ELISA system.

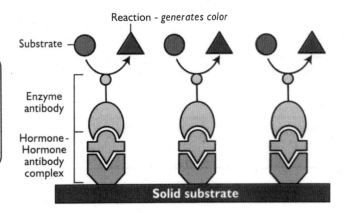

Table 5-2. Summary of Reproductive Hormones

(Colors shown below are used in graphics throughout the book)

Name of Hormone (Abbrev.)	Biochemical Classification	Source	Male Target Tissue
Gonadotropin Releasing Hormone (GnRH)	Neuropeptide (decapeptide)	Hypothalamic surge and tonic centers	Anterior lobe-pituitary (gonadotroph cells)
Luteinizing Hormone LH)	Glycoprotein	Anterior lobe (pituitary) (gonadotroph cells)	Test (interstital cells of Leydig
Follicle Stimulating Hormone (FSH)	Glycoprotein	Anterior lobe-pituitary (gonadotroph cells)	Testis (Sertoli cells)
Prolactin (PRL)	Protein	Anterior lobe-pituitary (lactotroph cells)	Testis and brain
Oxytocin (OT)	Neuropeptide (octapeptide)	Synthesized in the hypothalamus, stored in the posterior lobe-pituitary; synthesized by corpus luteum.	Smooth muscle of epididymal tail, ductus deferens and ampulla
Estradiol (E$_2$)	Steroid	Granulosal cells of follicle, placenta, Sertoli cells of testis	Brain Inhibits long bone growth
Progesterone (P$_4$)	Steroid	Corpus luteum and placenta	
Testosterone (T)	Steroid	Interstitial cells of Leydig, cells of theca interna in female	Accessory sex glands tunica dartos of scrotum, seminiferous epithelium, skeletal muscle
Inhibin	Glycoprotein	Granulosal cells (female) Sertoli cells (male)	Gonadotrophs of anterior lobe-pituitary
Prostaglandin F$_{2\alpha}$ (PGF$_{2\alpha}$)	Prostaglandin (C-20 fatty acid)	Uterine endometrium, vesicular glands	Epididymis
Relaxin (RLN or RLX)	Protein Polypeptide	Corpus lutem, placenta prostate	Sperm and male tract
Human chorionic gonadotropin (hCG)	Glycoprotein	Trophoblast of blastocyst (chorion)	
Equine chorionic gonadotropin (eCG)	Glycoprotein	Chorionic girdle cells	
Placental lactogen	Protein	Placenta	

Table 5-2. Summary of Reproductive Hormones

Female Target Tissue	Male Primary Action	Female Primary Action
Anterior lobe-pituitary (gonadotroph cells)	Release of FSH and LH from anterior lobe-pituitary	Release of FSH and LH from anterior lobe-pituitary
Ovary (cells of theca interna and luteal cells)	Stimulates testosterone production	Stimulates ovulation, formation of corpora lutea progesterone secretion
Ovary (granulosal cells)	Sertoli cell function	Follicular development and estradiol synthesis
Mammary cells, corpus luteum in some species (rat and mouse)	Can induce maternal behavior in females and males	Lactation, maternal behavior and corpora lutea function (some species)
Myometrium and endometrium of uterus, myoepithelial cells of mammary gland	$PGF_{2\alpha}$ synthesis and pre-ejaculatory movement of spermatozoa	Uterine motility, promotes uterine $PGF_{2\alpha}$ synthesis, milk ejection
Hypothalamus, entire reproductive tract and mammary gland	Sexual behavior	Sexual behavior, GnRH, elevated secretory activity of the entire tract, enhanced uterine motility
Uterine endometrium, mammary gland, myometrium, hypothalamus		Endometrial secretion, inhibits GnRH release, inhibits reproductive behavior, promotes maintenance of pregnancy
Brain, skeletal muscle, granulosal cells	Anabolic growth, promotes spermatogenesis, promotes secretion of accessory sex glands	Substrate for E_2 synthesis, abnormal masculinization (hair patterns, voice, behavior, etc.)
Gonadotrophs of anterior lobe-pituitary	Inhibits FSH secretion	Inhibits FSH secretion
Corpus luteum, uterine myometrium, ovulatory follicles	Affects metabolic activity of spermatozoa, causes epididymal contractions	Luteolysis, promotes uterine tone and contraction, ovulation
Pelvic ligaments, cervix, mammary gland, nipples		Softening of pelvic ligaments, cervix, connective tissue remodeling in tract
Ovary	Sperm motility, tract growth	Facilitate production of progesterone by ovary
Ovary		Causes formation of accessory corpora lutea
Mammary gland of dam		Mammary stimulation of dam

5

5

Further PHENOMENA for Fertility

In the 19th century, French doctors reported that the eating of frog legs by French soldiers in North Africa caused two outbreaks of priapism (painful and prolonged penile erection). The attending physicians noted that the symptoms amongst the soldiers resembled those seen in men who had overindulged in a drug called cantharidin (popularly known as "Spanish Fly"). This material is extracted from a beetle for its purported value as an aphrodisiac. One of the attending French physicians dissected a local frog and discovered that its gut was full of beetles that produced cantharidin. Recently, researchers have shown that frogs eating this beetle have levels of cantharidin in their thigh muscles that are high enough to cause human priapism.

The word pituitary is derived from the Latin word "pituita" that means mucus. The existence of the pituitary gland was recognized as early as 200 AD. It was thought to be a mucus-secreting organ for lubrication of the throat. Mucus from the pituitary was thought to be transported into the nose and then into the nasopharynx where it could lubricate the throat.

The dramatic effects of male castration have been recognized for over 2,000 years. The testis was known to control virility and sterility. Castration was always (and still is) regarded as a catastrophic event. However, it was deemed useful under certain sets of conditions such as generating guardians for harems and male singers with high pitched voices.

The scientific discipline of endocrinology originated from a belief in "organ magic." Consumption of human or animal organs was thought to increase powers or cure ailments. For example, warriors thought that eating the hearts of their enemy increased their courage. Eating the thyroids of sheep was thought to improve the intelligence of the mentally challenged; liver from wolves cured liver ailments; brain from rabbits cured nervousness and fox lungs cured respiratory disorders. Throughout recorded history sex gland consumption was believed to increase sexual prowess. As early as 1400 BC, Hindus prescribed testicular tissue for male impotence. The "birthday" of modern endocrinology was stimulated by the famous report of Brown-Séquard who injected himself with testicular extracts. The aging Brown-Séquard reported in 1889 that these extracts reversed the effects of age, made him feel significantly more vigorous and corrected his failing memory. His report, even though erroneous, prompted a rush of "gland treatments" by the medical profession of the day. Brown-Séquard's error stimulated careful scrutiny by scientists and physicians. This scientific scrutiny led to the development of modern endocrinology.

The leading cause of death in the early 1900's in young women was childbirth...they bled to death. The discovery that an extract from the brain caused uterine contractions and reduced uterine blood flow was a major breakthrough. It was soon discovered that the brain extract was oxytocin. It was and still is administered to women to prevent bleeding during childbirth as well as to enhance uterine contractions for expulsion of the fetus.

The first interest in reproductive physiology was strongly linked to human sex. The first account of "reproductive physiology" was recorded in about 3200 B.C. in Mesopotamia. People of that age had no idea how the reproductive system functioned or even what its parts were (except for the external genitalia). However, they were apparently quite anxious to apply "technology" to evaluate reproduction. For example, women in Mesopotamia devised "home pregnancy tests" that involved urinating on different materials such as grain and sprouts. Whether or not the sprouts germinated determined the pregnancy status of the female. Also, women wishing to know their pregnancy status would insert an onion into the vagina. If the onion smell was detected on her breath she was deemed pregnant.

Key References

Bartol, F.F. and C.A. Bagnell (2011). Lactocrine programming of female reproductive tract development: Environmental connections to the reproductive continuum. *Molecular and Celular Biology,* 10: 1016.

Bear, M.F., B.W. Connors and M.A. Paradiso. 1996. *Neuroscience: Exploring the Brain.* Williams & Wilkins, Baltimore. ISBN 0-683-00488-3.

Brown, J.L., L.H. Graham, N. Wielebnowski, W.F. Swanson, D.E. Wildt and J.G. Howard. 2001. "Understanding the basic reproductive biology of wild felids by monitoring faecal steroids" in *Advances in Reproduction in Dogs, Cats and Exotic Carnivores.* P.W. Concannon, G.C.W. England, W. Farstad, C. Linde-Forsberg, J.P. Verstegen and C. Doberska, eds. J. *Reprod. Fertil. Suppl.* 57, p71-82. Portland Press, Colchester, UK.

Combarnous, Y. 1993. "Gonadotropins: Structure-Synthesis-Functions" in *Reproduction in Mammals and Man.* p61-78. Thibault, C., M.C. Levasseur and R.H.F. Hunter, eds. Ellipses, Paris ISBN 2-7298-9354-7.

Cupps, P.T., ed. 1991. *Reproduction in Domestic Animals,* 4th Edition. Academic Press, San Diego. ISBN 0-12-196575-9.

Dubois, P. 1993. "The hypothalamic-pituitary axis: embryological, morphological and functional aspects" in *Reproduction in Mammals and Man.* p17-50. Thibault, C., M.C. Levasseur and R.H.F. Hunter, eds. Ellipses, Paris. ISBN 2-7298-9354-7.

Nalbandov, A. 1976. *Reproductive Physiology of Mammals and Birds.* W.H. Freeman Co., San Francisco. ISBN 0-7167-0843-4.

Nett, T.M. and J.M. Malvey. 1998. "Radioimmunoassay" in *Encyclopedia of Reproduction.* Vol. 4. p181-194. Knobil, E. and J.D. Neill (eds.) Academic Press, San Diego. ISBN 0-12-227024-X.

Roa, J., V.M. Nararro and M. Tena-Sempere. 2011. "Kisspeptins in reproductive biology: Concensus knowledge and recent developments." Biol. Reprod. 85:650-660.

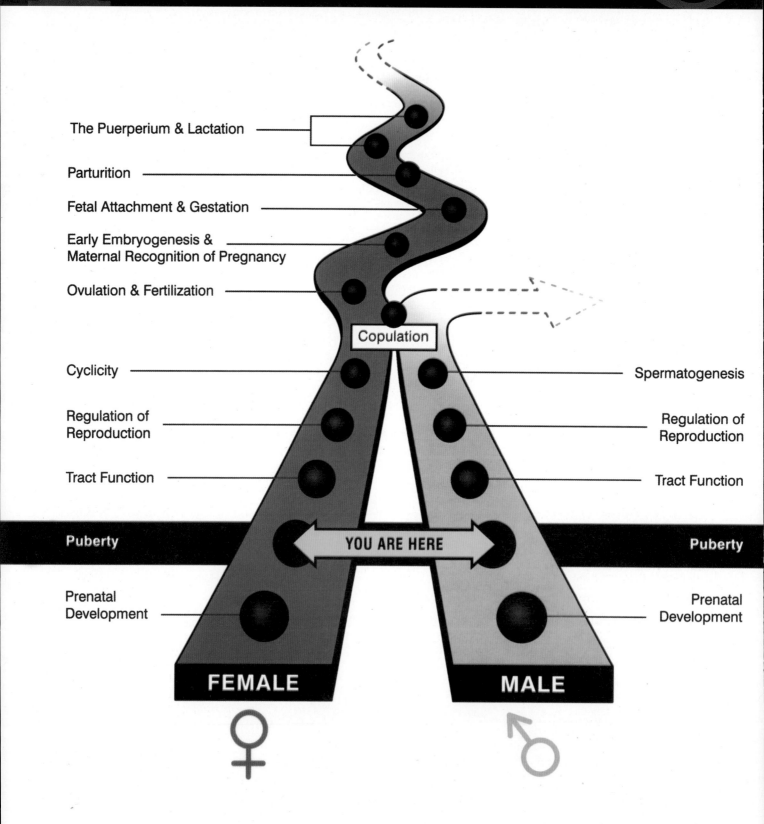

The Puerperium & Lactation

Parturition

Fetal Attachment & Gestation

Early Embryogenesis &
Maternal Recognition of Pregnancy

Ovulation & Fertilization

Copulation

Cyclicity

Spermatogenesis

Regulation of
Reproduction

Regulation of
Reproduction

Tract Function

Tract Function

Puberty

YOU ARE HERE

Puberty

Prenatal
Development

Prenatal
Development

FEMALE

MALE

Take Home Message

Puberty is the acquisition of reproductive competence. It is a process that occurs over time, not an event. The onset of puberty depends on the ability of specific hypothalamic neurons to produce GnRH in sufficient quantities to promote and support gametogenesis. In the female, hypothalamic GnRH neurons must develop the ability to respond to estradiol positive feedback before they can cause sufficient quantities of GnRH to induce ovulation. Development of hypothalamic GnRH neurons is influenced by genetic and environmental factors and their interactions.

Before engaging the subject of puberty it is necessary for you to understand that there are fundamental differences in the hypothalamus of the male and female. These differences are established prenatally and remain throughout the reproductive life of both sexes.

> *The hypothalamus is inherently female. Testosterone defeminizes the hypothalamus during embryogenesis and "eliminates" the GnRH surge center in the male.*

During prenatal development in the male, testosterone from the fetal testis "defeminizes" the brain. In contrast, the female fetus has no testis to secrete testosterone and she therefore develops a GnRH surge center in the hypothalamus. In order for testosterone to "defeminize" the hypothalamus, it must first be converted to estradiol. Since the fetal ovaries produce estradiol, a logical question is, "Why doesn't the female hypothalamus become defeminized?" The answer to this question lies in the inability of fetal estradiol in the female to cross the blood-brain barrier of the hypothalamus. A protein called **alpha-fetoprotein** binds estradiol and prevents it from crossing the blood-brain barrier (See Figure 6-1). Therefore, estradiol cannot affect the hypothalamus. Alpha-fetoprotein is a glycoprotein synthesized by the embryonic yolk sac and later the fetal liver. It serves as a fetal blood osmotic regulator and a carrier of fatty acids.

In the male, testosterone crosses the blood-brain barrier, is converted to estradiol in the brain and the estradiol "defeminizes" the hypothalamus, thus minimizing surge center function. There is good evidence that complete "defeminization" of the male hypothalamus requires postnatal exposure to androgens. For example, if bulls are castrated at or near birth, they have some ability to secrete a GnRH surge. Continued exposure to androgens is apparently required to render the surge center inoperative.

> *The female hypothalamus contains a surge center and a tonic center. The male hypothalamus does not appear to have a surge center.*

The fundamental difference in the endocrine profiles of the postpubertal male and female is that LH does not surge in the male, but maintains a relatively consistent day-in and day-out pulsatile pattern of secretion. These pulses occur every 2 to 6 hours in the postpubertal male. This steady GnRH pulsatile rhythm results in steady pulses of LH and, in turn, steady pulsatile secretion of testosterone. In contrast, you can readily see in Figure 6-2 that estradiol and LH surge about every 20 days in the female depending on the length of the cycle. During the time between the surges, low amplitude, repeated LH pulses are present.

Generally, **puberty** can be defined in both the male and female as the ability to accomplish reproduction successfully. Puberty should be considered as a process that occurs over time, not a single event. The fundamental requirement for puberty is the secretion of GnRH at the appropriate frequency and quantities to stimulate gonadotropin release by the pituitary. Gonadotropins promote gametogenesis, steroidogenesis and the development of reproductive tissues. The number of neurons that secrete GnRH, their morphology and their distribution within the hypothalamus are established well before puberty. However, the degree to which they function increases as puberty begins. Neuroendocrinologists believe that the most important "drivers" of pubertal onset are the ability of presynaptic neurons to provide information to the

Figure 6-1. Alpha Fetoprotein (α-FP) and the Blood Brain Barrier

In the female, α-FP prevents E_2 from entering the brain. The hypothalamus is thus "feminized" and the surge center develops.

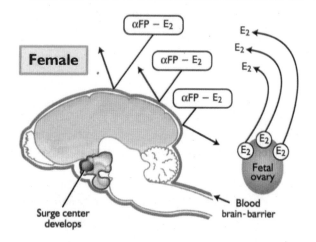

In the male, Testosterone freely enters the brain because α-FP does not bind it. Testosterone is aromatized into estradiol and the male brain is "defeminized". Therefore, a GnRH surge center **does not** develop.

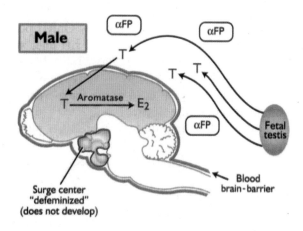

GnRH neurons. In other words, the limiting factor for pubertal onset appears to be the ability of presynaptic neurons to transmit information to GnRH neurons so that GnRH secretion will increase. Function of these presynaptic neurons may be influenced by: 1) plane of nutrition, 2) exposure to certain environmental or social cues and 3) the genetics of the individual.

The Onset of Puberty has Many Definitions in Females

Several criteria can be used to define puberty in the female. Some examples are presented below.

Age at first estrus (heat). This is the age that the female becomes sexually receptive and displays her first estrus. The age at first estrus is relatively easy to determine because females show outward behavioral signs of sexual receptivity, especially in the presence of the male. The first ovulation generally is not accompanied by behavioral estrus in heifers and ewes. This has been termed "silent ovulation." Thus, the age at first estrus may not reflect true acquisition of puberty.

Age at first ovulation. This is the age when the first ovulation occurs. To determine this critically, manual or visual validation is required. This can be accomplished using palpation or ultrasonography of the ovary per rectum in animals. Also, laparoscopy and endoscopy can be used to determine when ovulation has occured. All of the above techniques require frequent observations of the ovary to determine precisely when ovulation occurred. Thus, although age at ovulation is a good criterion for puberty, it is difficult to determine.

Age at which a female can support pregnancy without deleterious effects. This definition is most applicable from a practical standpoint in all domestic animals and humans.

The Onset of Puberty has Many Definitions in Males

As in the female, the onset of puberty in the male can be defined in several ways.

Age when behavioral traits are expressed. Generally, males of most species acquire reproductive behavioral traits (mounting and erection) well before they acquire the ability to ejaculate and produce spermatozoa. These behavioral traits are relatively easy to determine since mounting behavior and erection of the penis can be observed readily.

Age at first ejaculation. The process of ejaculation is quite complex and requires closely coordinated development of nerves, specific muscles and secretion of seminal fluids from the accessory sex glands. When development of all these components occurs, ejaculation can take place. Generally, the ability to ejaculate substantially precedes the ability to produce sufficient spermatozoa to achieve fertilization.

Age when spermatozoa first appear in the ejaculate. The male acquires the ability to produce seminal fluid and to ejaculate before spermatozoa are

Figure 6-2. Females and Males are Quite Different in Their LH Secretory Pattern

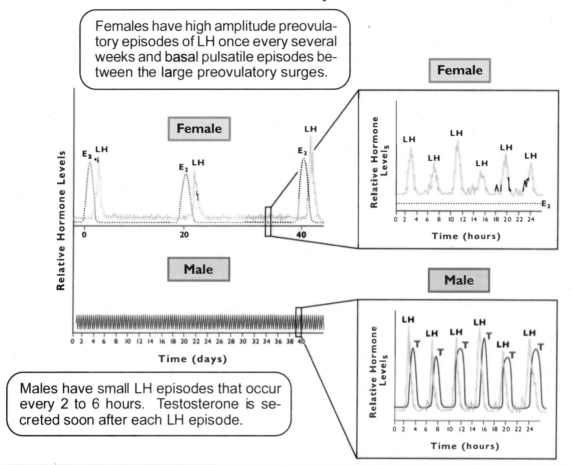

Females have high amplitude preovulatory episodes of LH once every several weeks and basal pulsatile episodes between the large preovulatory surges.

Males have small LH episodes that occur every 2 to 6 hours. Testosterone is secreted soon after each LH episode.

available to be ejaculated. To determine precisely when the first spermatozoa are available, one must collect ejaculates at least once per week. This is relatively easy to do, since ejaculates can be collected by an artificial vagina from the boar, bull, dog, ram or stallion. After behavioral characteristics have developed and the male is willing to mount a receptive female (or surrogate female), frequent seminal collections can be made. This enables determination of the age at which spermatozoa appear in the ejaculate.

Age when the ejaculate contains a threshold number of spermatozoa. Even though an ejaculate may contain spermatozoa, there may be insufficient numbers for fertilization. Therefore, the presence of a threshold (minimum number) of spermatozoa is required. These thresholds vary among species. In general, they reflect minimum seminal characteristics required to achieve pregnancy following copulation. From a practical viewpoint, this is the most valid criterion for puberty in the male since it defines the ability of the male to provide enough spermatozoa for successful fertilization.

> *The female must reach a threshold body size before puberty can be achieved.*

The age at puberty varies among and within species. This variation is summarized in Tables 6-1 and 6-2. The factors contributing to the variation in pubertal onset constitute the discussion in the remainder of this chapter.

At least two general factors impact the development of the hypothalamic GnRH neurons in the female. They are: 1) development of a threshold body size and/or composition and 2) exposure to certain environmental or social cues.

> *Certain external or social factors influence the onset of puberty in the female.*

Table 6-1. Mean Age (Range) of Puberty in Males and Females of Various Species

Species	Male	Female
Alpaca[2]	2-3 yrs	1 yr
Bovine	11 mo (7-18)	11 mo (9-24)
Camel[2]	3-5 yrs	3 yrs
Canine[1]	9 mo (5-12)	12 mo (6-24)
Equine	14 mo (10-24)	18 mo (12-19)
Feline	9 mo (8-10)	8 mo (4-12)
Llama[2]	2-3 yrs	6-12 mo
Ovine	7 mo (6-9)	7 mo (4-14)
Porcine	7 mo (5-8)	6 mo (5-7)

[1] Very breed dependent - See Johnston *et al*. in **Key References**.
[2] See Tibary and Anouassi in **Key References**.

Table 6-2. Influence of Breed on Age at Puberty in Domestic Animals

Species	Average Age at Puberty (Months)	
	Female	Male
Cattle		
Holstein	8	9
Brown Swiss	12	9
Angus	12	10
Hereford	13	11
Brahman	19	17
Dogs		
Border Collie	9	---
Bloodhound	12	---
Whippet	18	---
Sheep		
Rambouillet	9	---
Finnish Landrace	8	---
Swine		
Meishan	3	3
Large White	6	6
Yorkshire	7	7

As far as we know, all female mammals must acquire a certain body size before the onset of puberty can be initiated. A current hypothesis contends that the female must develop a certain degree of "fatness" before reproductive cycles can be initiated. The relationship between metabolic status and function of GnRH neurons has not been completely described, but there is good evidence that metabolic signals affect GnRH secretion.

Several external factors modulate the timing of puberty and these vary significantly among species. These factors include: 1) season during which the animal is born (sheep); 2) the photoperiod that the animal is experiencing during the onset of puberty (sheep); 3) the presence or absence of the opposite sex during the peripubertal period (swine and cattle) and 4) the density of the groups (within the same sex) in which the animals are housed (swine). Almost certainly, similar external factors impact puberty in humans but these have not been studied intensively. Whatever the species-specific factor(s) may be, they affect the secretion of GnRH.

> ***Genetics (breed) influence age at puberty.***

The breed of the animal has an important influence on the age at which puberty is attained in both the male and the female. For example, dairy heifers reach puberty at around 7 to 9 months of age while British beef breeds reach puberty between 12 and 13 months. *Bos indicus* breeds may not reach puberty until 24 months of age. Table 6-2 summarizes the influence of breed on age of puberty in cattle, swine, sheep and dogs.

How Do the Hypothalamic GnRH Neurons Acquire the Ability to Release GnRH in High Frequency Pulses?

It has been well established that the onset of puberty is not limited by the potential performance of the gonads or the anterior lobe of the pituitary. For example, the anterior lobe of the pituitary of the prepubertal animal will secrete FSH and LH if stimulated by exogenous GnRH. Also, the ovaries of prepubertal females will respond by producing follicles and estradiol when stimulated with FSH and LH. The major factor limiting onset of puberty is the failure of the hypothalamus to secrete sufficient quantities of GnRH to cause gonadotropin release.

The developing hypothalamus can be compared to a rheostatically controlled switch for a lighting system. As the rheostatically controlled switch is gradually turned up, the lights in the room gradually become brighter and brighter until they reach full intensity. Likewise, the development of the hypothalamus occurs in a gradual fashion during growth of the animal, rather than suddenly, like an on-off switch. The factors that cause the rheostatically controlled switch (hypothalamus) to turn on completely will be described in subsequent sections of this chapter.

As you have read previously in Chapter 5, the hypothalamus contains a **tonic GnRH center** and a **preovulatory GnRH center (surge center)**. Before ovulation can occur, full neural activity of the surge center must be achieved (See Figure 6-3). Such an activity results in sudden bursts of GnRH known as the **preovulatory GnRH surge**. In other words, the GnRH neurons must fire frequently and release large quantities of GnRH in order to cause the preovulatory LH surge (See Figure 6-3). As you will soon discover in Chapter 8 the preovulatory GnRH surge is a series of rapid, high amplitude pulses. Inability of the surge center to function results in ovulation failure. In addition to the need to have a functional surge center in the female, the tonic center must also reach a certain functional state. The tonic GnRH center regulates the pulse frequency of GnRH.

> *Even though the neurons in the surge center in prepubertal females are sensitive to estradiol, they cannot secrete much GnRH because estradiol is too low.*

The prepubertal female is characterized by having a lack of gonadal estradiol to stimulate the surge center. The surge center is capable of functioning at a very early age when experimentally stimulated. However, under normal conditions it remains relatively inactive until puberty. For example, in the prepubertal female, the tonic GnRH center stimulates LH pulses from the anterior lobe of the pituitary. The amplitude of these LH pulses can be as great as those of the postpubertal female. However, the frequency of the GnRH pulses in the prepubertal female is much lower than the frequency of GnRH pulses in the postpubertal female (See Figures 6-3 and 6-4). Prior to puberty, low-frequency GnRH pulses provide insufficient stimuli to cause the anterior lobe of the pituitary to release FSH and LH at high levels. Therefore, follicular development (even though it does occur before puberty), cannot result in high circulating estradiol concentrations. Estradiol therefore remains below the minimum threshold that is necessary to trigger firing of GnRH neurons in the surge center.

6

Figure 6-3. Changes in Hypothalamic Secretion of GnRH Before and After Puberty

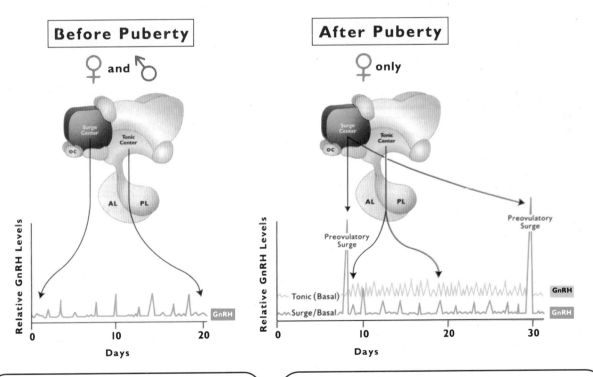

Before puberty in both the female and male, GnRH neurons in the tonic center and the surge center of the hypothalamus release low amplitude and low frequency pulses of GnRH.

After puberty in the female, the tonic center controls basal levels of GnRH, but they are higher than in the prepubertal female because the pulse frequency increases. The surge center controls the preovulatory surge of GnRH. The male does not develop a surge center.

Figure 6-4. LH Frequency
Before and After Puberty

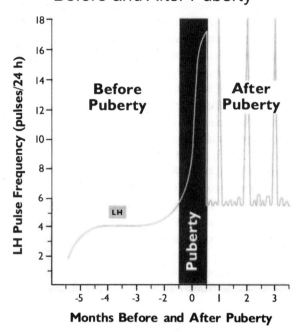

Frequency of LH pulses (as a reflection of GnRH pulses) in heifers prior to the onset of puberty. Note the substantial time required (approximately 2 months-shaded area) for the pulse frequency to become high enough for puberty to be achieved. The variation in LH pulse frequency after puberty reflects the changes occurring during the estrous cycle.
(Modified from Kinder *et al.* 1994)

6

> *In the male, the onset of puberty is brought about because of decreased hypothalamic sensitivity to negative feedback by testosterone/estradiol.*

As you recall from Chapter 5, the secretion of GnRH from neurons in the surge center and the tonic center is controlled by positive and negative feedback to gonadal steroids. Puberty will be initiated when GnRH neurons can respond completely to positive and negative feedback. Understanding the acquisition of this ability is the key to understanding how the onset of puberty occurs. We know that GnRH neurons are similar in number, function and distribution within the hypothalamus in both the male and the female. We also know that the endocrine profiles of males and females are quite different after puberty (See Figure 6-2).

As described earlier in this chapter, the male does not develop a surge center because the hypothalamus is completely defeminized shortly before or after birth. Thus, the male has a very simple feedback system after puberty. It involves a negative feedback loop only. You should recognize that the negative feedback in the male is due to some testosterone and mostly to estradiol because testosterone is converted to estradiol within the brain by aromatization (See Figure 6-1). In the male the GnRH neurons become less and less sensitive to the negative feedback of testosterone and estradiol as puberty approaches. This means larger and larger quantities of testosterone and estradiol are needed to inhibit the GnRH neurons. With this decreased sensitivity to the negative feedback of testosterone/estradiol, the hypothalamus can secrete more and more GnRH and thus more and more LH/FSH to stimulate the testis and stimulate puberty.

> *In the prepubertal female, the surge center is quite sensitive to the positive feedback of estradiol. But, the surge center cannot release "ovulatory quantities" of GnRH because the ovary cannot secrete high levels of estradiol.*

From a functional perspective, the surge center responds primarily to a positive feedback stimulus. For example, the prepubertal female does not ovulate although the sensitivity of the surge center to positive feedback by estradiol is quite high. Failure to ovulate occurs because the ovaries do not secrete enough estradiol to activate the highly sensitive surge center. In a sense, the surge center lies "dormant" in the prepubertal female even though it is capable of responding to estradiol. The reason that it lies "dormant" is that the prepubertal ovary does not secrete sufficient quantities of estradiol to stimulate the surge center to secrete high amplitude pulses of GnRH. At low concentrations of estradiol, the tonic center has a high sensitivity to negative feedback and therefore does not secrete high levels of GnRH and gonadotropins remain low. During the pubertal transition, however, the negative feedback sensitivity by the tonic center to estradiol decreases and consequently higher and higher amounts of GnRH are secreted causing an increase in pulse frequency of LH. This elevated pulse frequency stimulates the ovary to secrete more and more estradiol. When estradiol concentrations reach a certain threshold, it now causes a massive discharge of GnRH from the surge center (positive feedback). Ovulation can take place and puberty follows. It should be emphasized that the sensitivity of the surge center to positive feedback changes very little and remains high even before birth. It is the sensitivity to negative feedback that is decreased and triggers the onset of puberty in the female. The decreased sensitivity to negative feedback by the tonic center means that smaller and smaller quantities of estradiol can stimulate the release of GnRH and thus LH and FSH are secreted. These gonadotropins then stimulate more follicles and more and more estradiol is secreted until finally the surge center releases the preovulatory surge of GnRH.

A Certain Degree of "Fatness" is Required for the Onset of Puberty in the Female

The priority for the neonate is to use its energy towards maintenance of vital physiologic functions. Therefore, nonessential processes such as reproduction are of low priority. As the neonate begins to grow, energy consumption increases, its body mass becomes larger and the relative surface area of the body decreases. This allows a shift in the metabolic expenditure so that nonvital physiological functions begin to develop. As this shift occurs, the overall metabolic rate

decreases and more internal energy becomes available for nonvital functions. This excess internal energy can be converted into fat stores and the young animal begins to place priority on reproduction and the onset of puberty begins. However, the threshold level of fat accumulation required for the onset of puberty has not been determined.

> *Hypothalamic neurons that regulate GnRH secretion detect "moment-to-moment" changes in blood glucose and fatty acids.*

The central question regarding how metabolic status triggers puberty is, "What metabolic factors affect GnRH neurons and how are these factors recognized?" There is evidence to indicate that initiation of high frequency GnRH pulses is under the influence of glucose and free fatty acid concentrations in the blood. For example, when female hamsters were treated concurrently with inhibitors of fatty acid (methylpalmoxorate) and glucose oxidation (2-deoxyglucose, 2DG) their estrous cycles were disrupted due to their effect on GnRH secretion (See Figure 6-5). These results suggest

6

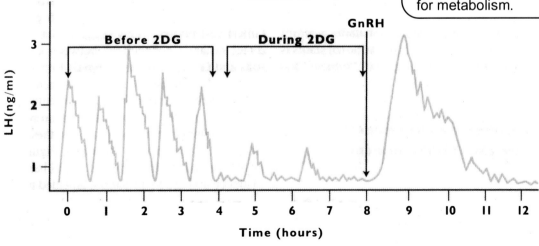

Figure 6-5. Glucose Can Affect Hypothalamic
Control of GnRH Secretion
(Modified from Foster, 1994)

In ovariectomized ewe lambs, low amplitude LH pulses occurred hourly before 2-deoxyglucose (Before 2DG) was injected into to each animal.

When the ewe lambs were injected with 2DG, the frequency and amplitude of the LH pulses were reduced significantly (During 2DG).

When the same animals receiving 2DG were injected with exogenous GnRH, a surge of LH resulted. These data suggest that moment-to-moment regulation of GnRH occurs only when significant glucose is available for metabolism.

that the hypothalamic GnRH secretion is sensitive to concentrations of a variety of energy-related materials such as glucose in the circulating blood.

A practical illustration of the impact of nutrition on the age of pubertal onset in dairy heifers is shown in Figure 6-6. A major goal in the management of the dairy heifer is to achieve a successful, uncomplicated birth by 24 months of age. In order for this to occur, appropriate nutrition and adequate body size must be achieved. Figure 6-6 describes the relationship between age and weight of heifers as it relates to the onset of puberty and nutritional level. Curve A illustrates the growth rate and age at onset of puberty (first estrus) when heifers were fed to gain 2.0 pounds per day for the first 12 months. Heifers fed this diet reached puberty between 6 and 8 months. If continued into the second year, this feeding regimen can result in over-conditioned heifers. The second nutritional level (curve B) allows the heifer to reach the same target weight (1200 pounds at 24 months), but heifers grow at a uniform weight of 1.5 pounds per day for the entire 24 month period. All heifers in this group will be in estrus for the first time between 9 and 11 months of age. Growth illustrated in curve C is slower (1.2 pounds per day), resulting from restricted feeding or lower quality feeds. Most of these heifers will reach puberty by 12 months, but they will be too small for successful pregnancy and parturition even though they are capable of becoming pregnant.

Any discussion of the metabolic signals that may influence the onset of puberty would not be complete without mentioning **leptin**. Leptin is a hormonal peptide, discovered in 1994, that is secreted by **adipocytes** (fat cells). The amount of leptin in the blood is directly related to the amount of fat in the body. Receptors to leptin are found in the liver, kidney, heart, skeletal muscles and pancreas.

The discovery that leptin receptors are also present in the anterior lobe of the pituitary and hypothalamus has sparked significant interest in the possibility that leptin might play an important role in mediating the onset of puberty in mammals. Leptin may be an important signal that "notifies" key hypothalamic neurons that influence GnRH secretion that nutritional status is adequate because a threshold degree of "fatness" has been achieved (See Figure 6-7).

> *Kisspeptin neurons may act directly on GnRH neurons.*

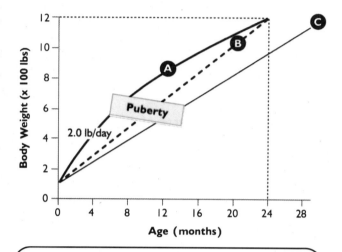

Figure 6-6. The Relationship Between Plane of Nutrition, Growth and Average Daily Gains with Onset of Puberty in Dairy Heifers

A = High plane of nutrition (2.0 lb/day average daily gain)

B = Moderate plane of nutrition (1.5 lb/day average daily gain)

C = Low plane of nutrition (1.2 lb/day average daily gain)

Age at first parturition should be 24 months and the primiparous heifer should weigh 1,200 lb.

(Modified from Head in *Large Herd Dairy Management*, Van Horn and Wilcox, eds. American Dairy Science Association. 1992)

The exact mechanisms whereby metabolic signals are detected and converted to hypothalamic neural activity have not been described. Kisspeptin neurons in the hypothalamus send dendritic arborizations into hypothalamic areas containing high populations of GnRH cell bodies. This suggests that there may be direct synaptic connections between kisspeptin neurons and GnRH neurons. Signals from hypothalamic neurons that respond to leptin, fatty acids and glucose may promote neural activity in kisspeptin neurons and thus stimulate the firing of GnRH neurons (See Figure 6-7). It is important to recognize that these possibilities have yet to be proven. Therefore, Figure 6-7 should be interpreted as a hypothetical model based on current evidence and not as a final documented mechanism.

Figure 6-7. Possible Influence of Metabolic Signals Upon GnRH Neurons

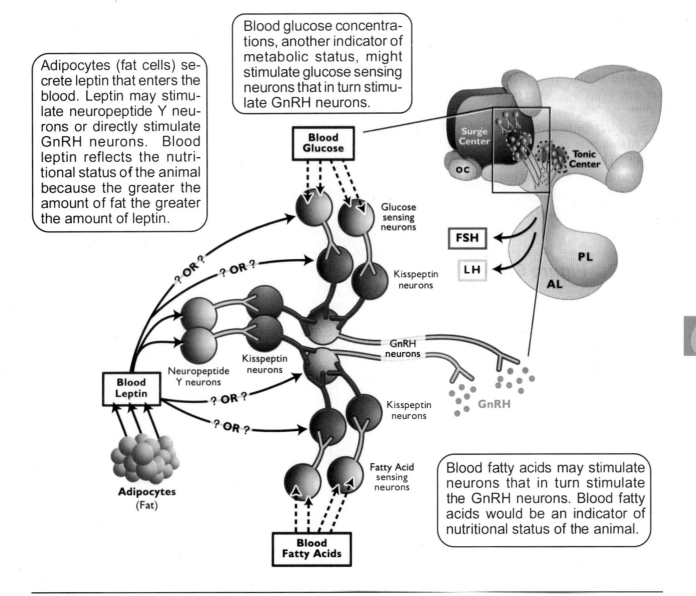

Adipocytes (fat cells) secrete leptin that enters the blood. Leptin may stimulate neuropeptide Y neurons or directly stimulate GnRH neurons. Blood leptin reflects the nutritional status of the animal because the greater the amount of fat the greater the amount of leptin.

Blood glucose concentrations, another indicator of metabolic status, might stimulate glucose sensing neurons that in turn stimulate GnRH neurons.

Blood fatty acids may stimulate neurons that in turn stimulate the GnRH neurons. Blood fatty acids would be an indicator of nutritional status of the animal.

6

Environmental and Social Conditions Impact the Onset of Puberty in the Female

External factors have a significant influence upon the onset of puberty. These factors include season of birth and social cues such as the presence of the male or size of the social group in which females are housed. In general, environmental information that influences pubertal onset is perceived by sensory neurons of the optic and olfactory systems. Stimuli are processed by the central nervous system and delivered as neural inputs to the GnRH neurons of the hypothalamus. The net effect is that the hypothalamus gains the ability to produce high frequency and low amplitude pulses of GnRH at an earlier age (provided that optimum size and energy balance requirements are met).

Season of Birth and Photoperiod are Important Modulators of Pubertal Onset

The month of birth will influence the age of puberty, particularly in seasonal breeders, provided no artificial illumination alters natural photoperiod cues. Sheep are a good example because they are seasonal breeders that begin their estrous cycles in response to short day lengths. In natural photoperiods, spring-born (February-March) lambs receiving adequate nutrition attain puberty during the subsequent fall (September-October). The age at puberty is about 5 to 6 months after birth. In contrast, fall-born lambs do not reach puberty until about 10 to 12 months.

In heifers there is good evidence that age at puberty is influenced by the season of birth. For example, heifers born in autumn tend to reach puberty earlier than those born in spring. Exposure during the second six months of their life to long photoperiods and spring/summer-like temperatures hastens the onset of puberty.

In the bitch there is little seasonality associated with the onset of puberty. However, in the queen increased photoperiod prompts the onset of puberty. For example, the onset of puberty occurs in January and February in the Northern Hemisphere where length of daylight begins to increase. Queens born in February and March may not reach puberty until the following spring. Those queens born in the summer or fall are likely to display their first estrus the following January. These pubertal time lines in the dog and cat assume adequate nutrition and growth.

Social Cues Alter the Onset of Puberty

Social cues significantly impact the onset of puberty in many mammalian species. Such mediation is caused by olfactory recognition of **pheromonal** substances present in the urine. While the original work demonstrating this phenomenon was conducted in rodents, enhancement of the onset of puberty by the presence of the male has been demonstrated in the ewe, sow and cow. The evolutionary advantage of such a stimulus is obvious. Females reaching puberty in the presence of the male have a greater opportunity to become pregnant. One should be reminded that pubertal onset cannot be accelerated in animals that have not achieved the appropriate metabolic body size to trigger hypothalamic responsiveness to estradiol.

Figure 6-8. The Effects of Small Groups vs. Male Exposure on the Onset of Puberty

Large Groups (>10) = Normal Puberty

Small Groups (2-3 gilts) = Delayed Puberty

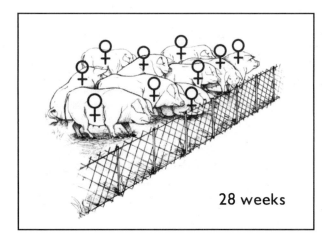

28 weeks

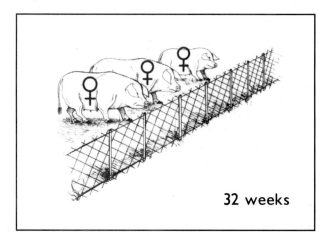

32 weeks

Exposure to a Boar = Accelerated Puberty

24 weeks
(no physical contact)

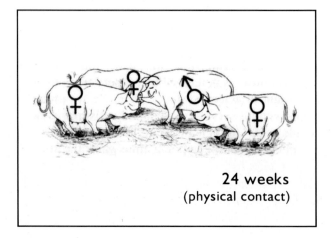

24 weeks
(physical contact)

Certain social cues inhibit the onset of puberty. Gilts housed in small groups have delayed puberty when compared to gilts housed in larger groups. If prepubertal gilts are housed in groups of 10 or more, these females will enter puberty at the expected time (28 weeks). However, if the group size is decreased to only two or three gilts, they will enter puberty at a later time than their counterparts housed in larger groups (See Figure 6-8).

Presence of the male hastens the onset of puberty.

Gilts housed in small groups and exposed to a boar will enter puberty at an earlier age than their large or small grouped counterparts that are not exposed to a boar. An important point to recognize is that the presence of the male, either in visual contact with the females or in direct physical contact with them, will hasten the onset of puberty in gilts (See Figure 6-8). Such observations are valuable for swine management because the age of puberty can be reduced by properly managing the social environment.

Nebraska researchers have shown conclusively that bulls accelerate the onset of puberty in beef heifers. However, there was an interaction between growth rate and exposure to the bull (See Figure 6-9). For example, heifers with a high growth rate (1.75 lb/day) and exposure to a bull for about 6 months reached puberty at about 375 days. Those with a moderate growth rate (1.4 lb/day) coupled with bull exposure (6 months) reached puberty at about 422 days. Figure 6-9 summarizes the influence of growth rate and exposure to a bull upon the age at puberty in beef heifers.

Metabolic status for puberty in the male is not well understood.

Little research has been conducted on the influence of metabolic status on the onset of puberty in the male. The energy expenditure associated with spermatogenesis and copulation is "microscopic" in comparison to the energy expenditure associated with gestation, parturition and lactation. In addition, little research has been conducted describing the effect of female-on-male or male-on-male social influences and their impact on the onset of puberty. Virtually all of the research has been conducted describing the influence of the male on the onset of puberty in the female rather than the opposite.

Figure 6-9. Influence of Growth Rate and Bull Exposure Upon the Age of Puberty in Beef Heifers

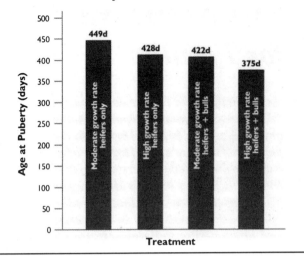

The Story of Puberty is Not Complete

As you now know, the onset of puberty involves the capability of the hypothalamic neurons to produce high frequency and low amplitude GnRH pulses. This capability is influenced by achieving the appropriate energy metabolism/body size and appropriate exposure to external modulators such as photoperiod, size of social groups and the presence of the male. Genetics of the animal likely plays a role in how these cues are generated within the animal (metabolic signals) and/or perceived (external cues, metabolic signals).

The exact mechanisms that enable estradiol to control GnRH secretion by the hypothalamus during the peripubertal period are unknown. A major challenge is to understand the impact of metabolism on the development of the hypothalamus. Currently, there is shallow understanding of how the brain recognizes growth so that the proper signals are sent to the hypothalamus and reproduction can commence.

With regard to social cues, the presence of certain pheromones secreted by the same or opposite sex alters puberty. The pathway whereby these pheromones send their message to the hypothalamus is, as yet, not well defined. The pathway is mediated through the olfactory and the vomeronasal organs (See Chapter 11), but neither specific agents nor a clear pathway have been described. Further, the visual pathway may be quite important in mediating pubertal onset, but this sensory avenue has received little research attention.

6

Further PHENOMENA for Fertility

An anomaly of the captive environment for the endangered clouded leopard is that males and females must be paired before they reach puberty. If they are housed together after puberty the male becomes very aggressive and frequently injures or even kills the female. This happens even after long introduction efforts with animals kept in adjacent pens and making sure that animals are placed together only when the female is in estrus. This behavior does not happen in the wild.

It is said that puberty begins during the night in children. Concentrations of gonadotropins are low during the day and night in prepubertal children but as the transition into adulthood occurs, the nighttime concentrations also increase as puberty progresses. The notion that night is a special time for maturation is really not true because when the sleep cycle is reversed, the pubertal rises in gonadotropin secretion are also reversed. It seems as if these increases in GnRH secretion are associated with REM (rapid eye movement) stages of sleep, although the physiological and adaptive reasons for this phenomenon are not known.

The famous boys' choirs in Europe consisted entirely of prepubertal boys. It was recognized that their high pitched clear voices were "ruined" during and after puberty. Many of these boys were orchidectomized so that their boyhood voices could be retained. Castrato choirs were composed of adult male singers castrated in boyhood so as to retain soprano or alto voices.

The age of puberty in girls is decreasing. From records kept (in Norway) about the time of menarche (first menses) we know that puberty occurred at about 17 years of age in the mid-1800s. Today, this same reproductive endpoint occurs at 12 years of age in Europe and the US. Interestingly, the body weight at menarche is the same now as it was 150 years ago. Young women today are growing faster than they did 150 years ago. The likely explanation for this is that nutrition today is much better and that more energy is available in wealthy countries. In poorer countries where nutrition is not adequate, puberty continues to occur at older ages.

In naked mole rats, the dominant female (called the queen) suppresses puberty in the subordinates (i.e. there is no vaginal opening that occurs at puberty). Once thought to be due to the suppressive effects of pheromones, a more recent theory is that the queen actually uses tactile stimulation to suppress puberty by regularly having physical contact with each female.

Some young women do not find out until puberty that they are genetically males but their sex cannot be reassigned. The condition is most commonly diagnosed when girls are brought to the clinic because of delayed pubertal progression (no breast development, no menarche). Upon genetic evaluation, such rare individuals are diagnosed as males having a deficiency in receptors for androgens. Clearly, they will never be able to bear children, but they also cannot be treated to become normal males physiologically as exogenous testosterone will have no effect because of the receptor deficiency. The only course of action is to administer estrogens and to produce the secondary sex characteristics typical of a woman. The testes should be removed surgically to prevent the development of carcinomas that are often associated with intra-abdominal testicular tissue.

Victorian women (1837-1901 AD) inserted wooden blocks inside their vaginas to obstruct the passage of sperm.

Key References

Clarke, I.J. and B.A. Henry, 1999. "Leptin and Reproduction." *Reviews of Reproduction*. 4:48-55.

Foster, D.L. 1994. "Puberty in the Sheep" in *The Physiology of Reproduction* 2nd Edition, Vol. 2 p 411-452. E. Knobil and J.D. Neill, eds. Raven Press, Ltd., New York. ISBN 0-7817-0086-8.

Foster, D.L. and S. Nagatani. 1999. "Physiological perspectives of leptin as a regulator of reproduction: role in timing puberty." *Biol. Reprod*. 60:205-215.

Head, H.H. 1992. "Heifer performance standards: rearing systems, growth rates and lactation" in *Large Herd Dairy Management*. Van Horn and Wilcox, eds. American Dairy Science Association. Champaign, Illinois. ISBN 0-9634491-0-9.

Johnston, S.D., M.V. Root Kustritz and P.N.S. Olson. 2001. *Canine and Feline Theriogenology*. W.B. Saunders Company, Philadelphia. ISBN 0-7216-5607-2.

Kinder, J.E., M.S. Roberson, M.W. Wolfe and T.T. Stampf. 1994. "Management factors affecting puberty in the heifer" in *Factors Affecting Calf Crop* M.J. Fields and R. Sands, eds. CRC Press, Inc. ISBN 0-8493-8754-X.

Plant, T.M. 1994. "Puberty in primates" in *The Physiology of Reproduction*, 2nd Edition, Vol 2 p 453-486. E. Knobil and J.D. Neill, eds. Raven Press, Ltd., New York. ISBN 0-7817-0086-8.

Roa, J., V.M. Nararro and M. Tena-Sempere. 2011. "Kisspeptins in reproductive biology: Concensus knowledge and recent developments." Biol. Reprod. 85:650-660.

Tibary, A. and A. Anouassi. 1997. *Theriogenology in Camelidae*. United Arab Emirates, Ministry of Culture and Information. Publication authorization No. 3849/1/16. ISBN 9981-801-32-1.

Williams, G.L. 1999. "Nutritional Factors and Reproduction" in *Encyclopedia of Reproduction*, Vol 3 p 412-421. Knobil E. and J.D. Neil, eds. Academic Press, San Diego. ISBN 0-12-227023-1.

6

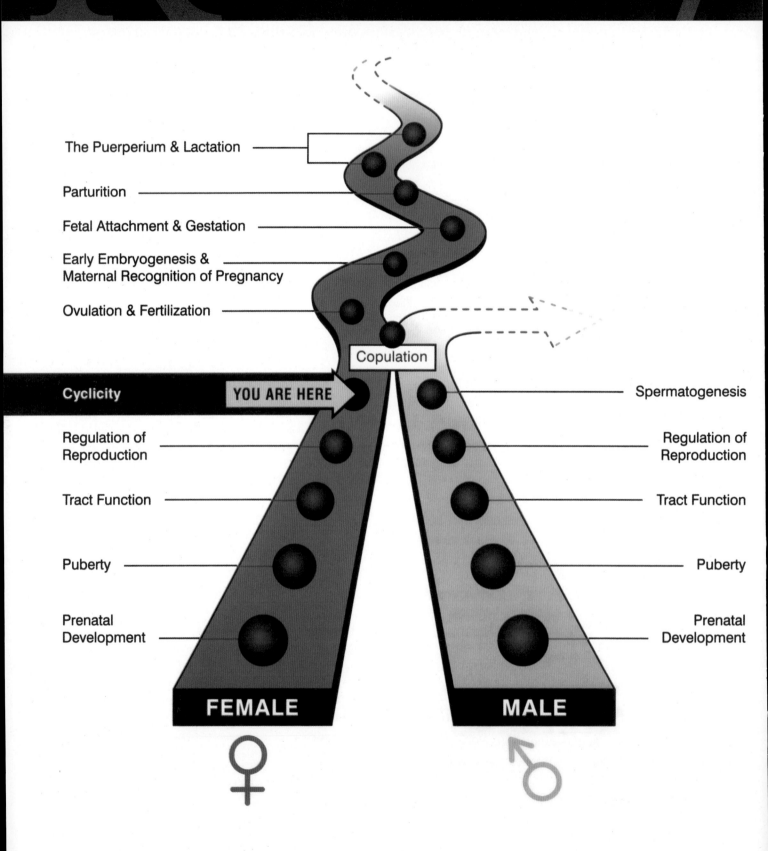

The Puerperium & Lactation

Parturition

Fetal Attachment & Gestation

Early Embryogenesis &
Maternal Recognition of Pregnancy

Ovulation & Fertilization

Copulation

Cyclicity

YOU ARE HERE

Spermatogenesis

Regulation of
Reproduction

Regulation of
Reproduction

Tract Function

Tract Function

Puberty

Puberty

Prenatal
Development

Prenatal
Development

FEMALE

MALE

Take Home Message

The two types of reproductive cycles are the estrous cycle and the menstrual cycle. Reproductive cyclicity provides females with repeated chances for pregnancy.

An estrous cycle consists of the physiologic events that occur between successive periods of sexual receptivity (estrus or heat) and/or ovulations. The length of cycle varies from about four days in rodents to as long as 14-16 weeks in elephants. Each cycle consists of a follicular phase and a luteal phase. The follicular phase is dominated by estradiol secreted by ovarian follicles. Estradiol causes marked changes in the female tract and initiates sexual receptivity. The luteal phase is dominated by progesterone from the corpus luteum that prepares the reproductive tract for pregnancy. Periods of time when estrous cycles cease are called anestrus. Anestrus is caused by pregnancy, season of the year, lactation, certain forms of stress and pathology.

A menstrual cycle consists of the physiological events that occur between successive menstrual periods (about 28 days). At the conclusion of the luteal phase in the menstrual cycle, the endometrium is sloughed to the exterior (menstruation). No endometrial sloughing occurs in animals with estrous cycles. Each menstrual cycle consists of 3 distinct phases that reflect the condition of the uterine endometrium. The cycle starts with menses (about a 4-6 day period) where the endometrium is sloughed to the exterior. The second phase (about 9 days) is the proliferative phase in which follicles develop and secrete estradiol. The endometrium begins to grow and increase in thickness. The final phase, the secretory phase (14 days), is dominated by the corpus luteum that secretes progesterone and estradiol. The endometrium grows and continues to increase in thickness as a function of progesterone. At the end of this 28 day period the endometrium begins to slough again if the woman is not pregnant and a new cycle begins. Amenorrhea refers to the lack of menstrual periods and is caused by many of the same factors that cause anestrus.

This chapter will provide you with fundamental knowledge about female reproductive cyclicity. Among mammals, reproductive cyclicity consists of the estrous cycle and the menstrual cycle. Both types of cycles provide the female with repeated opportunities to become pregnant. The fundamental differences between these types of reproductive cycles will be presented in the two sections that follow entitled, **Estrous Cycles** and the **Menstrual Cycle**. There are species exceptions to some of the principles described. Most of these exceptions will be described in later chapters especially Chapters 8 and 9 that deal specifically with the follicular and luteal phases.

THE ESTROUS CYCLE

After puberty, the female enters a period of reproductive **cyclicity** that continues throughout most of her life. **Estrous cycles** consist of a series of predictable reproductive events beginning at **estrus** (heat) and ending at the subsequent estrus. They continue throughout the adult female's life and are interrupted by pregnancy, nursing and by season of the year in some species. Cyclicity may also cease if nutrition is inadequate or environmental conditions are unusually stressful. Pathologic conditions of the reproductive tract, such as uterine infection, persistent corpora lutea or a mummified fetus may also cause **anestrus** (a period when cyclicity stops). **Estrous cycles** provide females with repeated opportunities to copulate and become pregnant. Sexual receptivity and copulation are the primary behavioral events that occur during estrus. Copulation generally occurs prior to ovulation. If conception (pregnancy) does not occur, another estrous cycle begins, providing the female with another opportunity to mate and conceive. When pregnancy occurs, the female enters a period of **anestrus** that ends after **parturition** (giving birth), **uterine involution** (acquisition of normal uterine size and function) and **lactation**.

__Author's Note:__ After years of teaching about reproductive cyclicity and listening to repeated student feedback, I have concluded that developing a thorough understanding of the estrous cycle in animals makes understanding the menstrual cycle easy. The reverse is not necessarily true.

Terminology Describing Reproductive Cyclicity can be Confusing

The words used to describe the estrous cycle are spelled similarly, but have subtly different meanings. The proper use of the words **estrus** and **estrous** must be understood to prevent confusion. The word estrus is a noun, while estrous is an adjective. **Oestrus** and **oestrous** are the preferred spellings in British and European literature. **Estrual** is also an adjective and is used to identify a condition related to estrus. For example, an estrual female is a female in estrus. An estrous cycle is the period between one estrus and the next. Estrus is the period of sexual receptivity. Estrus is commonly referred to as **heat**. The term estrus (oestrus) originated from a Greek word meaning "gadfly, sting or frenzy". This word (oestrus) was used to describe a family of parasitic biting insects (*Oestridae*). These insects caused cattle to stampede with their tails flailing in the air as the insect buzzed around them. The behavior occurring in females in estrus was deemed similar to that observed during these insect attacks. Thus, the term oestrus or estrus was applied to the period of sexual receptivity in mammalian females. Another common term used to describe a reproductive pattern is **season**. This refers to several estrous cycles that may occur during a certain season of the year. For example, a mare "coming into season" begins to show cyclicity and visible signs of estrus. She will cycle several times during her "season" (See Figure 7-1).

> *ESTRUS is a noun.*
> *"The cow is displaying <u>estrus</u>."*
>
> *ESTROUS is an adjective.*
> *"The length of the estrous cycle in the pig is 21 days."*

Figure 7-1. Types of Estrous Cycles as Described by Annual Estradiol (E₂) Profiles

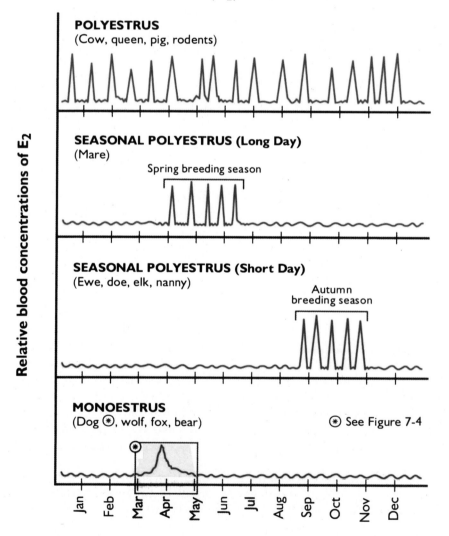

Examples of other words that can lead to confusion in spelling and usage are: **anestrous** vs. **anestrus** and **polyestrous** vs. **polyestrus**. If the word is used as an adjective, it is spelled **-ous**. For example, "polyestrous females have repeated estrous cycles." If the word is used as a noun, it is spelled **-us**. For example, "the female is experiencing anestrus."

The three types of estrous cyclicity are:
- *polyestrus*
- *seasonally polyestrus*
- *monoestrus*

Estrous cycles are categorized according to the frequency of occurrence throughout the year. These classifications are **polyestrus, seasonally polyestrus** and **monoestrus** (See Figure 7-1). Polyestrous females, such as cattle, swine and rodents, are characterized as having a uniform distribution of estrous cycles throughout the entire year. Polyestrous females can become pregnant throughout the year without regard to season. Seasonally polyestrous females (sheep, goats, mares, deer and elk) display "clusters" of estrous cycles that occur only during a certain season of the year. For example, sheep and goats are **short-day breeders** because they begin to cycle as day length decreases in autumn. In contrast, the mare is a **long-day breeder** because she initiates cyclicity as day length increases in the spring.

Monoestrous females are defined as having only one cycle per year. Dogs, wolves, foxes and bears are animals that are characterized as having a single estrous cycle per year. Domestic canids typically have three estrous cycles every two years but they are generally classified as monoestrus. In general, monoestrous females have periods of estrus that last for several days. Such a prolonged period of estrus increases the probability that mating and pregnancy can occur. Each type of cycle pattern is represented in Figure 7-1.

The Estrous Cycle Consists of Two Major Phases

The estrous cycle can be divided into two distinct phases that are named after the dominant structure present on the ovary during each phase of the cycle. These divisions of the estrous cycle are the **follicular phase** and the **luteal phase**. The follicular phase is the period from the regression of corpora lutea to ovulation. In general, the follicular phase is relatively short, encompassing about 20% of the estrous cycle (See Figure 7-2). During the follicular phase, the primary ovarian structures are large growing follicles that secrete the primary reproductive hormone, **estradiol**.

During the follicular phase:

- *large antral follicles = the primary ovarian structure*

- *estradiol (secreted by follicles) = the primary hormone*

The **luteal phase** is the period from ovulation until corpora lutea regression. The luteal phase is much longer than the follicular phase and, in most mammals, occupies about 80% of the estrous cycle (See Figure 7-2). During this phase, the dominant ovarian structures are the corpora lutea (CL) and the primary reproductive hormone is **progesterone**. Even though the luteal phase is dominated by progesterone from the CL, follicles continue to grow and regress during this phase but they do not produce high concentrations of estradiol. Details of follicular growth are presented in Chapter 8.

During the luteal phase:
- *corpora lutea = the primary ovarian structures*

- *progesterone (secreted by corpora lutea) = the primary hormone*

The Estrous Cycle can Also be Divided into Four Stages

The four stages of an estrous cycle are **proestrus, estrus, metestrus** and **diestrus**. Each of these stages is a subdivision of the follicular and luteal phases of the cycle. For example, the follicular phase includes proestrus and estrus. The luteal phase includes metestrus and diestrus.

Follicular phase = Proestrus + Estrus
Luteal phase = Metestrus + Diestrus

7

Figure 7-2. Phases of the Estrous Cycle

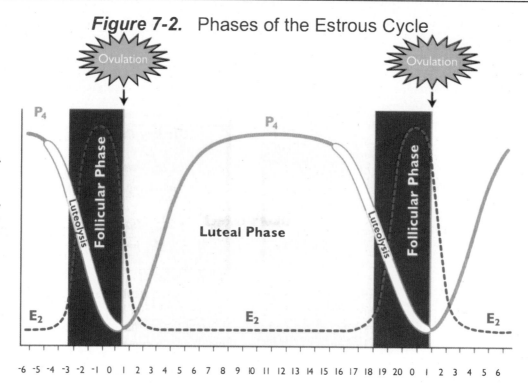

The follicular phase begins after luteolysis that causes the decline in progesterone. Gonadotropins (FSH and LH) are therefore secreted that cause follicles to secrete estradiol (E_2). The follicular phase is dominated by estradiol secreted by ovarian follicles. The follicular phase ends at ovulation. Estrus is designated as day 0.

The luteal phase begins after ovulation and includes the development of corpora lutea that secrete progesterone (P_4). The luteal phase also includes luteolysis that is accompanied by a rapid drop in progesterone. Luteolysis is brought about by prostaglandin $F_{2\alpha}$.

Proestrus is the Period Immediately Preceding Estrus

Proestrus begins when progesterone declines as a result of luteolysis (destruction of the corpus luteum) and terminates at the onset of estrus. Proestrus lasts from 2 to 5 days depending on species and is characterized by a major endocrine transition, from a period of progesterone dominance to a period of estradiol dominance (See Figure 7-3). The pituitary gonadotropins, FSH and LH, are the primary hormones responsible for this transition. It is during proestrus that antral follicles mature for ovulation and the female reproductive system prepares for the onset of estrus and mating.

Estrus is the Period During Which the Female Allows Copulation

Estrus is the most recognizable stage of the estrous cycle because it is characterized by visible behavioral symptoms such as sexual receptivity and mating. Estradiol is the dominant hormone during this stage of the estrous cycle. Estradiol not only induces profound behavioral alterations, but causes major physiologic changes in the reproductive tract.

When a female enters estrus, she does so gradually and is not sexually receptive at first. She may display behavioral characteristics that are indicative of her approaching sexual receptivity.

Proestrus = Formation of ovulatory follicles + E_2 secretion

Estrus = Sexual receptivity + peak E_2 secretion

Metestrus = CL formation + beginning of P_4 secretion

Diestrus = Sustained luteal secretion of P_4

Figure 7-3. Stages of the Estrous Cycle

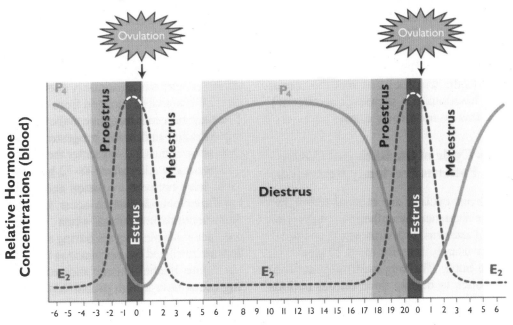

| Proestrus is characterized by a significant rise in estradiol (E₂) secreted by maturing follicles. | When estradiol reaches a certain level, the female shows behavioral estrus and then ovulates. | Following ovulation, cells of the follicle are transformed into luteal cells that form the corpus luteum (CL) during metestrus. | Diestrus is characterized by a fully functional CL and high progesterone (P₄). |

These include increased locomotion, phonation (vocal expression), nervousness and attempts to mount other animals. However, during this early period she will not accept the male for mating. As the period of estrus progresses, so does the female's willingness to accept the male for mating. This willingness is referred to as **standing estrus**. It is during the time of estrus that the female displays a characteristic mating posture known as **lordosis**, so named because of a characteristic arching of the back in preparation for mating. Standing behavior (lordosis) is easily observed and is used as a diagnostic tool to identify the appropriate time to inseminate the female artificially or to expose her to the breeding male. The average duration of estrus is characteristic for each species. However, the range in the duration of estrus can be quite large even within species (See Table 7-1). Understanding and appreciating the magnitude of these ranges is important because it allows one to predict cyclic events with a degree of accuracy.

Metestrus is the Transition from Estradiol Dominance to Progesterone Dominance

Metestrus is the period between ovulation and the formation of functional corpora lutea. During early metestrus both estradiol and progesterone are relatively low (See Figure 7-3). The newly ovulated follicle undergoes cellular and structural remodeling resulting in the formation of an intraovarian endocrine gland called the corpus luteum. This cellular transformation is called **luteinization** (See Chapter 9). Progesterone secretion begins in metestrus and is detectable soon after ovulation. However, two to five days are usually required after ovulation before the newly formed corpora lutea produce significant quantities of progesterone (See Figure 7-3).

Diestrus is the Period of Maximum Luteal Function

Diestrus is the longest stage of the estrous cycle and is the period of time when the corpus luteum is fully functional and progesterone secretion is high.

It ends when the corpus luteum is destroyed (luteolysis). High progesterone prompts the uterus to prepare a suitable environment for early embryo development and eventual attachment of the conceptus to the endometrium. Diestrus usually lasts about 10 to 14 days in most large mammals. The duration of diestrus is directly related to the length of time that the corpus luteum remains functional (i.e. secretes progesterone). Females in diestrus do not display estrous behavior.

The Estrous Cycle of the Bitch and Queen Varies from Patterns Previously Described

The estrous cycle of the domestic bitch has a different stage sequence than other mammals. The cycle consists of anestrus, proestrus, estrus and diestrus. Anestrus usually lasts for about 20 weeks in the nonpregnant bitch. The long anestrus (5 months) causes the the bitch to display three estrous periods in two years. However, wild canids (wolf, coyote, Australian dingo) display only one estrous period per year and these periods are usually seasonal. Figure 7-4 illustrates the stages, sequence, relative timeline and the endocrine profiles of the cycle in the bitch. The onset of proestrus is usually considered to be the beginning of the estrous cycle. The drop in blood FSH that occurs during proestrus is presumably due to negative feedback on FSH by inhibin secreted from developing follicles. The bitch becomes receptive to the male during decreasing estradiol and rising progesterone concentrations. Ovulation occurs 2-3 days after the LH surge. Fertilization generally takes place 48-72 hours after ovulation. This delay between ovulation and fertilization allows for **superfecundation** to occur frequently in canids. Superfecundation occurs when multiple ovulations produce multiple oocytes during a single estrus period that are fertilized by spermatozoa from different males. Therefore, bitches that are allowed to "roam free" during estrus have a high probability of delivering litters with multiple breeds of puppies.

7

Figure 7-4. The Annual Reproductive Cycle of the Bitch

(Modified from Johnston, Root Kustritz and Olson. 2001. *Canine and Feline Theriogenology*)

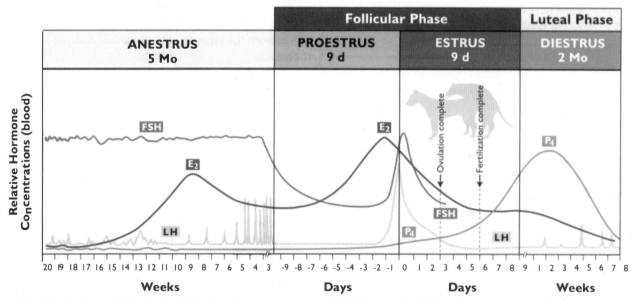

Anestrus	Proestrus	Estrus	Diestrus
A period of reproductive quiescence. This long anestrus period is responsible for a cyclic profile of three cycles in two years.	Proestrus is considered the beginning of the cycle and is characterized by the appearance of a blood-tinged vaginal discharge. It ends when the bitch copulates with the male. Estradiol gradually increases and peaks slightly before the onset of estrus.	Shortly after peak estradiol, behavioral estrus begins. Both LH and FSH peak in early estrus. Ovulation is completed at about the third day of estrus and fertilization is completed at about the sixth day. Progesterone increases during the latter part of estrus signifying luteinization.	Both pregnant and open bitches are considered to be in diestrus. Pregnancy status does not alter the length of diestrus. Progesterone peaks at about 15 days then decreases gradually. Bitches that do not become pregnant are often considered to be pseudopregnant.

As you can see from Figure 7-4, the bitch does not have a defined metestrus as in other species. The initial development of luteal tissue occurs during estrus shortly after ovulation as in other mammals.

In the queen, stages of the estrous cycle include proestrus, estrus, **postestrus**, diestrus and anestrus. There is little evidence for seasonality in queens and they tend to be polyestrus. However, as photoperiod increases, the length of estrus increases. Felids are induced ovulators and copulation is required for induction of the LH surge.

Postestrus is a term used to describe an inter-estrus period that follows estrus in a queen that has not been induced to ovulate by copulation (See Figure 7-5). In queens that have not copulated, no ovulation occurs and no corpora lutea form. Therefore, neither metestrus (CL formation) nor diestrus occurs. As in most induced ovulators, it would be appropriate to consider that the female would remain in a constant follicular phase until copulation occurs. After copulation the female ovulates and only then do corpora lutea form. In this context induced ovulators constitute a special form of estrous cycle that does not have a true luteal phase.

Anestrus Means "Without Estrus (Heat)"

Anestrus is a condition when the female does not exhibit estrous cycles. During anestrus the ovaries are relatively inactive and neither ovulatory follicles nor functional corpora lutea are present. Anestrus is the result of insufficient GnRH release from the hypothalamus to stimulate and maintain gonadotropin secretion by the pituitary.

It is important to distinguish between **true anestrus** caused by insufficient hormonal stimuli and **apparent anestrus** caused by failure to detect estrus

Figure 7-5. Reproductive Cyclicity Profile of Queens With and Without Copulation

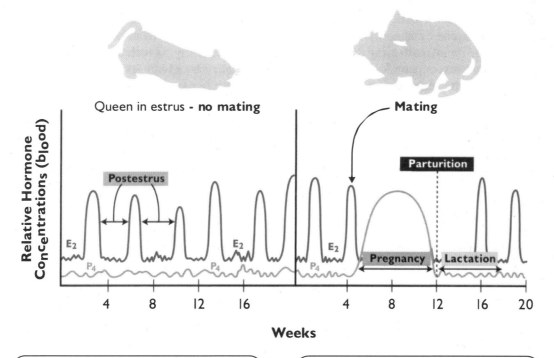

A queen enters estrus (about 9 days) every 17 days. If copulation does not occur, the queen enters a postestrus phase and comes into estrus a few days later. Since the queen is an induced ovulator, when mating does not occur, ovulation does not occur and a CL is not formed.

When mating occurs during estrus, ovulation is induced, fertilization occurs and pregnancy takes place. After ovulation corpora lutea are formed causing a marked elevation in progesterone. After a 60 day gestation period, parturition occurs and lactation ensues. Lactational anestrus does not occur in the cat because she will come into estrus while lactating.

Table 7-1. Characteristics of Estrous Cycles in Domestic Animals

Species	Classification	Length of Estrous Cycle		Duration of Estrus		Time From Onset of Estrus to Ovulation	Time From LH Surge to Ovulation
		Mean	Range	Mean	Range		
Alpaca	Polyestrus	15d	(11-18d)	5d	(4-5d)	Induced Ovulator	26-36h
Bitch	Monoestrus	6 mo	(3-9 mo)	9d	(4-21d)	4-24d	2-3d
Cow	Polyestrus	21d	(17 - 24d)	15h	(6 - 24h)	24 - 32h	28h
Ewe	Seasonally polyestrus (Short Day)	17d	(13 - 19d)	30h	(18 - 48h)	24 - 30h	26h
Llama	Polyestrus	10d	(8-12d)	5d	(4-5d)	Induced Ovulator	24-36h
Mare	Seasonally polyestrus (Long Day)	21d	(15 - 26d)	7d	(2 - 12d)	5d	2d
Queen	Polyestrus	17d	(4-30d)	9d	(2-19d)	Induced Ovulator	30-40h
Sow	Polyestrus	21d	(17 - 25d)	50h	(12 - 96h)	36 - 44h	40h

7

or failure to recognize that a female is pregnant. To eliminate true anestrus, one must normally improve the female's nutrition, remove offspring to terminate lactation, or eliminate stress or pathologic factors. To eliminate apparent anestrus, one must improve detection of estrus, detection of pregnancy, or both.

> *Anestrus can be caused by:*
> * *pregnancy*
> * *lactation*
> * *presence of offspring*
> * *season*
> * *stress*
> * *pathology*

Gestational Anestrus is a Normal Condition Brought About by Inhibition of GnRH by Progesterone

From a practical perspective, lack of cyclicity is a major clue that a female is pregnant. Estrous cycles do not occur during pregnancy because elevated progesterone from either the CL and/or the placenta exerts negative feedback to inhibit GnRH secretion. This prevents sufficient secretion of FSH and LH from the pituitary to allow follicular maturation and ovulation. Thus, expression of estrus and potential preovulatory surges of LH do not occur. Occasionally however, cows and ewes will display behavioral estrus during pregnancy, but the incidence is low (3% to 5%). The reason for display of estrus in pregnant cows and ewes is not understood. In certain breeds of pregnant sheep (Rambouillet) estrous behavior is seen frequently. Ovulation can be induced during pregnancy by giving exogenous gonadotropins, but pregnant females induced to ovulate generally do not show behavioral estrus.

Progesterone declines rapidly just before parturition. Even though progesterone drops rapidly and estradiol increases in the periparturient female (shortly before or after parturition), she will remain anestrus for a period of time after parturition. This relatively short period of postpartum anestrus provides time for uterine repair or involution before a subsequent estrus (See Chapter 15). It should be emphasized that resumption of postpartum ovarian activity depends on species. For example, mares, alpacas and llamas resume cyclicity within a week after parturition and acquire normal fertility within 2 to 3 weeks after parturition.

Seasonal Anestrus is a Normal Condition

Seasonal anestrus probably evolved as a way of preventing females from conceiving during periods of the year when survival of the developing embryo and the neonate would be low. For example, preattachment embryo survival is known to be reduced significantly when ambient temperatures and humidity are high during the summer months. High temperatures coupled with high humidity cause elevated body temperature of the pregnant female and can result in death of the preattachment embryo. Females that cycle

Figure 7-6. Influence of Estradiol (E_2) and Progesterone (P_4) On the Brain and Subsequent Behavioral Estrus in the Cow and Ewe

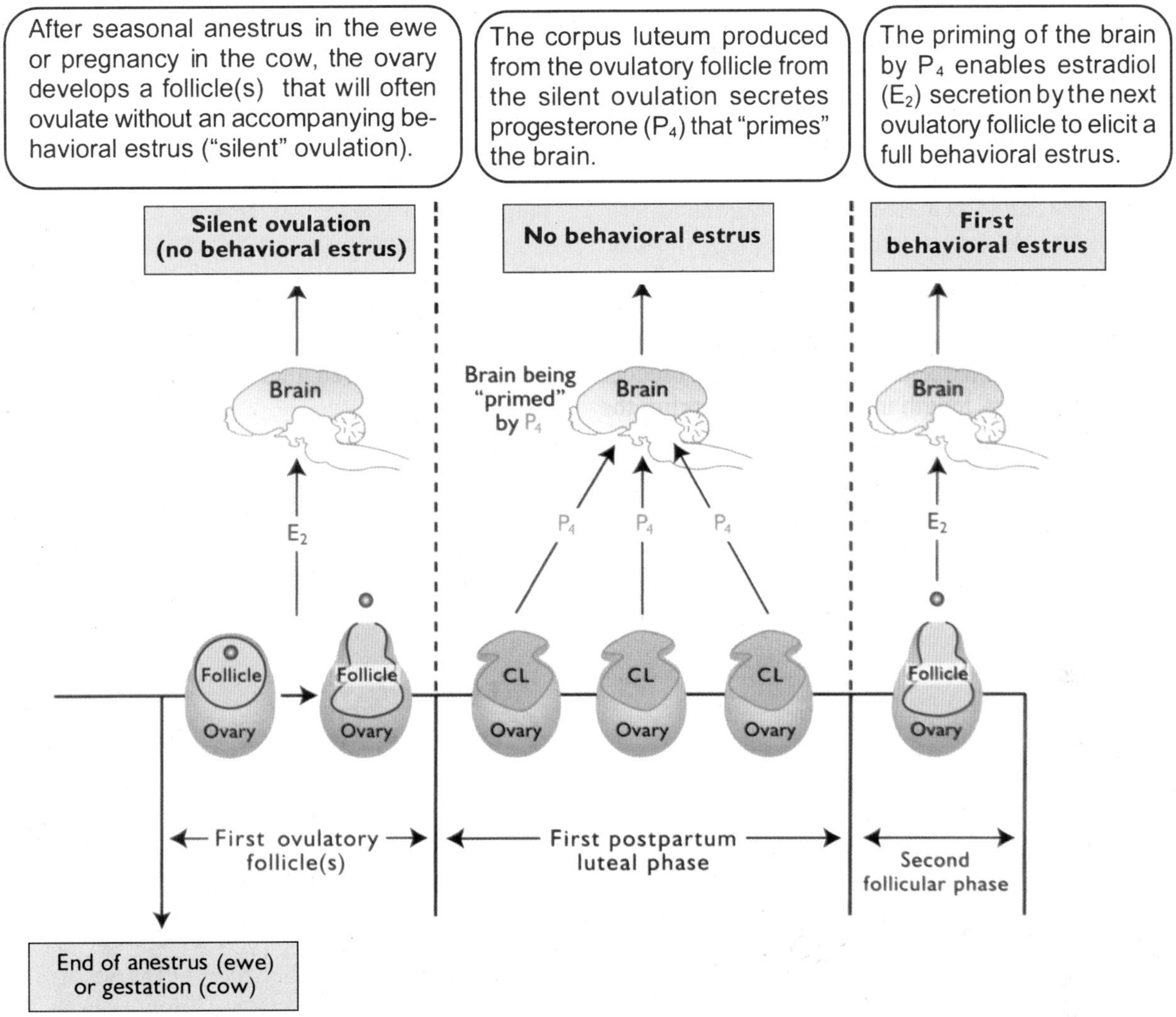

After seasonal anestrus in the ewe or pregnancy in the cow, the ovary develops a follicle(s) that will often ovulate without an accompanying behavioral estrus ("silent" ovulation).

The corpus luteum produced from the ovulatory follicle from the silent ovulation secretes progesterone (P_4) that "primes" the brain.

The priming of the brain by P_4 enables estradiol (E_2) secretion by the next ovulatory follicle to elicit a full behavioral estrus.

in the fall (sheep, deer and elk) conceive during times of moderate ambient temperature. Seasonal breeders give birth during the spring when nutritional conditions favor lactation and growth of the young following weaning. Seasonal breeders normally make the transition from the cyclic state to the anestrus state and back again on an annual basis. This transition is controlled by **photoperiod**.

The mare begins to cycle in the spring and generally conceives well before the hot summer months. The developing embryo is well established within the uterus before the onset of hot weather. Also, the relatively long length of pregnancy (11 months) enables the foal to be born the following spring, again providing optimum timing for conception and birth as it relates to environmental/nutritional conditions.

In the ewe, the first ovulation after seasonal anestrus is not accompanied by a behavioral estrus. This situation, whereby an ovulation is not preceded or accompanied by behavioral estrus, is referred to as a **silent ovulation**. For maximal expression of behavioral estrus, progesterone must be present for a certain period of time prior to exposure to estradiol. In other words, progesterone from the first postpartum CL formed after the first ovulation and after seasonal anestrus "primes" the brain so that its sensitivity to estradiol is optimized (See Figure 7-6). When estradiol from the second group of follicles after anestrus appears, the female displays behavioral estrus because her brain has been primed by progesterone thus allowing it to be "turned on" by estradiol. A similar priming effect probably is necessary in cattle, since the first ovulation after parturition (calving) is generally a silent one. The corpus luteum from the first postpartum ovulation provides the cow with a "priming" of progesterone prior to the initiation of postpartum cyclicity (See Figure 7-6).

Onset of Seasonal Cyclicity is Similar to the Onset of Puberty

Seasonal anestrus is characterized by a reduction in the frequency of hypothalamic GnRH secretion (as in the prepubertal female). Before the breeding season can begin, the hypothalamus must be able to secrete sufficient quantities of GnRH to elicit a response by the anterior lobe of the pituitary. The release of FSH and LH at levels capable of maintaining follicular development and causing ovulation is required.

Seasonal breeders can be categorized as either **long-day breeders** or **short-day breeders** (See Figure 7-1). The mare is characterized as a long-day breeder because as the day length increases in the spring the mare begins to cycle. During the short days of the winter months, the mare is anestrus. Short-day breeders are animals that begin to cycle during the shorter days of fall. Animals such as sheep, deer, elk and goats are categorized as short-day breeders. The duration of the breeding season varies among and within species. For example, in sheep, the Merino breed has a period of cyclicity that ranges from 200 to 260 days, while blackface breeds have shorter periods of cyclicity ranging from 100 to 140 days.

The two primary factors that influence the onset of the breeding season are photoperiod and temperature. Photoperiod is by far the most important. It is well known that artificial manipulation of the photoperiod can alter the cyclicity of the seasonal breeder.

Figure 7-7. Possible Role of Kisspeptin Neurons in the Regulation of Cyclicity in Long-Day and Short-Day Breeders

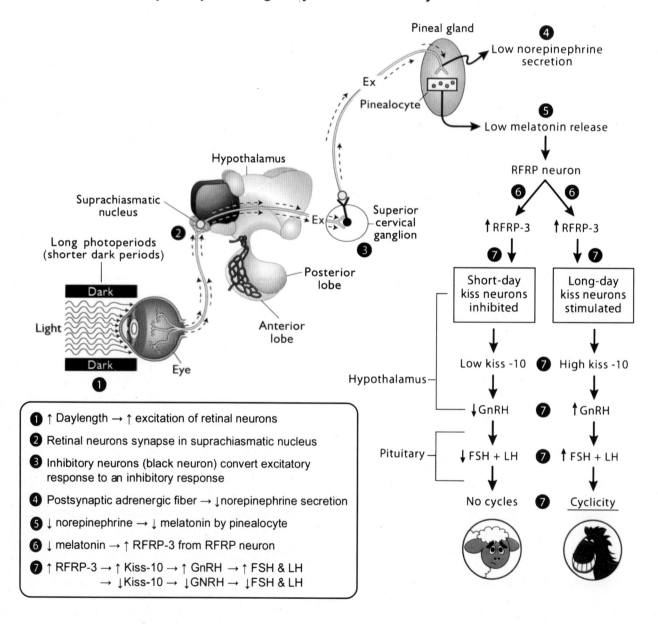

❶ ↑ Daylength → ↑ excitation of retinal neurons

❷ Retinal neurons synapse in suprachiasmatic nucleus

❸ Inhibitory neurons (black neuron) convert excitatory response to an inhibitory response

❹ Postsynaptic adrenergic fiber → ↓norepinephrine secretion

❺ ↓ norepinephrine → ↓ melatonin by pinealocyte

❻ ↓ melatonin → ↑ RFRP-3 from RFRP neuron

❼ ↑ RFRP-3 → ↑ Kiss-10 → ↑ GnRH → ↑ FSH & LH
    → ↓Kiss-10 → ↓GNRH → ↓FSH & LH

A major question that must be answered in order to understand the influence of day length on the onset of reproductive activity is, "How is photoperiod translated into a physiologic signal?"

A proposed pathway for both the long-day and short-day breeder is presented in Figure 7-7. During long photoperiods, the retina of the eye is stimulated by light. This results in elevated tonic excitation of retinal neurons. This excitation is transmitted by a nerve tract to a specific area of the hypothalamus known as the suprachiasmatic nucleus. From the suprachiasmatic nucleus a second nerve tract travels to the superior cervical ganglion. The presynaptic neurons synapse with inhibitory neurons that convert an excitatory signal into an inhibitory response. As a result, the postsynaptic adrenergic fibers are inhibited and they reduce their secretion of norepinephrine. Reduced norepinephrine results in low melatonin secretion from the pineal gland. Low melatonin results in excitation of RFRP neurons and they increase secretion of their neurotransmitter, RFRP-3. The RFRP neuron's name is derived from the following: a) the "RF" designation refers to "amide related proteins" that are small peptides secreted by the neurons; b) the second "R" refers to the amino acid arginine and c) the second "P" refers to the amino acid phenylalanine. The RF amide molecule has an arg-phe-NH_2 at the C terminus and is probably 10 amino acids in length. Elevated RFRP-3 has different effects in the short and long-day breeder. For example, in the long-day breeder, RFRP-3 stimulates groupings of kisspeptin neurons in the hypothalamus and they secrete high levels of kisspeptin-10. It is thought that kisspeptin-10 acts directly on GnRH neurons to stimulate the secretion of FSH and LH. As as consequence, the long-day female begins to cycle. In the short-day breeder, kisspeptin neurons are thought to be inhibited by RFRP-3 and thus kisspeptin-10 secretion is reduced and GnRH neurons do not stimulate the release of FSH and LH.

In summary, it is thought that the fundamental reason that differences between seasonal breeders exists (short-day versus long-day) is related to genetic differences in the responsiveness of certain groups of kisspeptin neurons to RFRP-3. When days are short, melatonin increases, which in turn decreases the RFRP-3 inhibition on kisspeptin neurons. In short-day breeding females, this signal elevates levels of GnRH and thus FSH and LH to initiate cyclicity. On the other hand, these conditions (high melatonin during short days) signal the long-day breeding female to reduce levels of GnRH and thus low FSH and LH terminates cyclicity.

7

Figure 7-8. Influence of Suckling Frequency Upon Blood LH (a Direct Indication of GnRH Release) in Postpartum Beef Cows

(Derived from the data of Dr. G.L. Williams, Texas A&M University, Beeville)

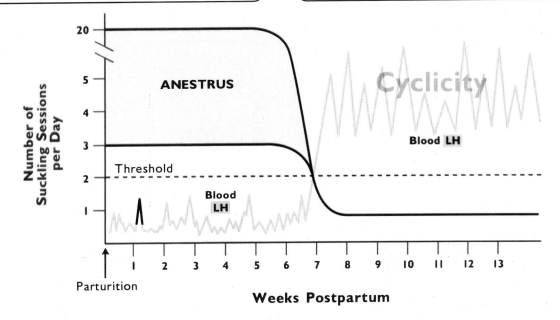

When the number of suckling sessions is between 3 and 20 per day, amplitude and pulse frequency of blood LH are quite low and the cow remains in anestrus.

When the number of suckling sessions is limited to two or less per day, the amplitude and pulse frequency of LH increases dramatically and the cow will begin to cycle.

Lactational Anestrus Prevents a New Pregnancy Before Young are Weaned

Almost all mammalian females nursing their young experience **lactational anestrus** that lasts for variable periods of time. The mare and the alpaca are exceptions and do not experience lactational anestrus. Both begin cycling soon after they give birth. Cyclicity is completely suppressed during lactation in the sow. When weaning takes place, the sow will display estrus and ovulate within 4 to 8 days. In the suckled cow, cyclicity is delayed by as much as 60 days after parturition. The duration of lactational anestrus is influenced by the degree of suckling in the cow. However, suckling by itself does not appear to

be important when the frequency is greater than two suckling sessions per day. Suckling sessions of two or less per day promote return to cyclicity, while greater than two sessions per day tend to cause postpartum anestrus (See Figure 7-8). There is a threshold of about two sessions per day. Greater than two suckling session causes anestrus. If fewer than two per day, the cow will return to cyclicity. It does not seem to matter whether there are 3 or 20 suckling sessions per day. In other words, the effect of suckling does not operate in a continuum but rather in a threshold manner.

> *Mammary stimulation is not totally responsible for lactational anestrus.*

Figure 7-9. *Ad Libitum* Suckling Results in Suppression of LH Amplitude and Pulse Frequency

Intact cow	Mammary denervated cow
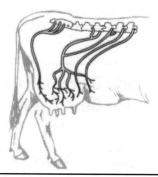	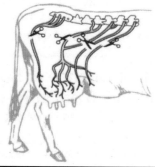

When calves are weaned suddenly from cows with intact mammary nerves, the LH pulse frequency and amplitude increases dramatically.

In cows with the afferent neural pathway severed, acute weaning causes the same effect as in cows with intact afferent pathways. **Conclusion**--suckling cannot be totally responsible for suppressing LH in the postpartum cow.

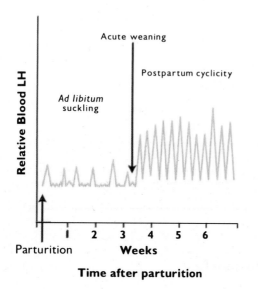

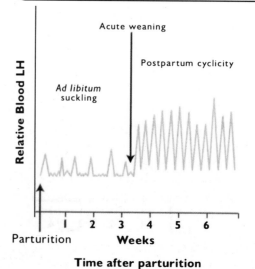

Time after parturition

It has been widely accepted that repeated sensory stimulation of the teat during suckling causes inhibition of gonadotropin release from the anterior lobe of the pituitary in the postpartum female. Research findings from Texas A&M University Research Center in Beeville, indicate that this long-standing concept is probably incorrect. In fact, data indicate that direct neural stimulation of the mammary gland does not inhibit gonadotropin release in the cow. Figure 7-9 illustrates the typical pattern of LH release during *ad libitum* suckling in the beef cow. During the time of intense suckling, LH in the blood is quite low. When suckling is suddenly terminated (acute weaning), increased episodes of LH occur within 2 to 3 days after calf removal and the postpartum female resumes cyclicity.

The response for the intact cow shown in Figure 7-9 implies that mammary stimulation is the cause of inhibition of GnRH, resulting in basal LH levels during the suckling period. However, when cows were subjected to complete mammary denervation (transection of the nerve tracts supplying the mammary gland), the response in blood LH was identical to that of the intact cow. Transection of all of the nerves to the mammary gland would be expected to remove immediately any inhibition on the hypothalamus brought about by mammary stimulation. However, as you can see by comparing the right and left panels of Figure 7-9, there was no difference between suckled females with intact neural pathways to the mammary gland when compared to suckled females with transected mammary neural pathways. Clearly, if suckling alone prevented the hypothalamus from secreting GnRH, then females in which nerves supplying the mammary gland were transected would have hastened elevations of LH following parturition. Since this did not occur, the interpretation is that factors other than teat stimulation are responsible for inhibition of GnRH during the postpartum period. These factors may be 1) visual encounter with the offspring, 2) olfactory encounter with the offspring, 3) auditory encounter with the offspring or all of the above.

It is also now known that the cow's own calf is important for maintenance of postpartum anestrus. If a cow's own calf is replaced with an alien (unrelated calf) the LH secretion increases dramatically and ovarian activity soon follows, even though the alien calf is permitted to suckle. The precise role of calf identity on central nervous system control of gonadotropin release has yet to be fully explained. Regardless, it appears that maintenance of postpartum anestrus is a combination of sensory inputs to the dam apparently involving sight, sound and smell.

In dairy cows, calves are removed from the dam very soon (hours to a few days) after parturition.

The fact that dairy cows do not experience lactational anestrus suggests that presence of the calf contributes to this suppression of reproduction in beef cows.

The bitch does not have lactational anestrus because the anestrus that occurs normally during the cycle lasts about 4-5 months in the presence **or** absence of lactation. You will recall from Figure 7-4 that the bitch has significantly elevated progesterone following estrus. This elevated progesterone is sufficiently long to support and maintain pregnancy. Following parturition and during lactation, the bitch enters a period of anestrus that is independent of lactation. In this context, lactational anestrus does not exist in the bitch.

Many queens display estrus and ovulate seven to ten days after parturition (See Figure 7-5). Some of these queens will be bred and conceive during the time that they are lactating. Other queens will not conceive at this first postpartum estrus. Most reproductive physiologists agree that the queen may have some lactational anestrus, but it is not uniform. In some queens, lactational anestrus appears to exist until about two to three weeks after weaning. Critical experiments describing the impact of lactation, suckling, and presence of the neonate have not been conducted in the bitch or the queen. Understanding the mechanisms of lactational anestrus may enable the development of techniques that suppress reproduction in these species. Such suppression is important since many pregnancies in these species of pets are not desired by pet owners.

Anestrus can result from negative energy balance.

Females consuming low quantities of energy or protein often have sustained periods of anestrus. Nutritional anestrus is characterized by an absence of GnRH pulses from the hypothalamus, inadequate secretion of gonadotropins and inactive ovaries. In lactating females, inadequate nutrition will prolong the duration of lactational anestrus. This is particularly true in **primiparous** females (those that have given birth for the first time) where restricted dietary intake is compounded with the energy requirements of lactation and growth. The primiparous female represents one of the most difficult to manage from a reproductive standpoint since growth and lactation impose two strong energy demands. Providing first-calf lactating heifers with optimum nutrition cannot be overemphasized. During early lactation in dairy cows, the metabolic demands for milk production are often so great that the female cannot consume enough dietary energy to meet her metabolic needs. This negative energy balance is often related to delayed postpartum cyclicity (nutritional anestrus). In non-lactating cycling females, prolonged periods of inadequate nutrition will also cause anestrus. However, undernutrition must be severe and must occur for a prolonged period for cyclicity to cease entirely. Nutritionally anestrous females respond to adequate nutrition by resuming estrous cycles.

THE MENSTRUAL CYCLE

The menstrual cycle is defined as the events that occur between the onset of two successive menstrual periods. The duration of the menstrual cycle in women averages 28 days with a range to 24-35 days. **Menses (menstruation)** is defined as the sloughing of the endometrium to the exterior. Menses is commonly referred to as the **menstrual period** (or period). The fundamentals of the menstrual cycle are quite similar to the estrous cycle.

7

> *The menstrual cycle differs from the estrous cycle in the following ways:*
>
> • *no defined period of sexual receptivity*
>
> • *a period of endometrial sloughing called menses (menstruation)*
>
> • *the timeline for description of the cycle begins with menses, not ovulation or estrus*

In the menstrual cycle, the follicular phase occupies one half of the cycle while in species with an estrous cycle it only occupies 20% or less of the cycle. During the follicular phase, follicles grow and develop producing high levels of estradiol causing an LH surge that causes a spontaneous ovulation in women. A major difference is that ovulation occurs in the middle of the cycle (around day 14) rather than at the beginning of the cycle. The menstrual cycle begins with the onset of menses because it was an observable component like behavioral estrus in the estrous cycle. Menses lasts between 2 and 5 days. Following sloughing of the endometrium there is a gradual increase in GnRH that triggers the release of FSH and LH. As you can see from Figure 7-10, estradiol increases with advancing follicular development during the follicular phase and progesterone is low as in other mammals.

> *In the menstrual cycle:*
>
> *The follicular phase = menses (5 days) + proliferative phase (9 days)*
>
> *The luteal phase = secretory phase (14 days)*

The **proliferative** and **secretory** phases of the cycle refer to the changes in endometrial thickness. At the beginning of the proliferative phase, the endometrium sloughs (menses) and then it begins to increase in thickness in response to estradiol (See Figure 7-10). During the secretory phase, progesterone increases dramatically (as does estradiol). Both are secreted by the corpus luteum. Under the influence of progesterone and estradiol the endometrium begins to proliferate and increase to its maximum thickness. This proliferation prepares the endometrium for secretory activity that provides an optimum environment for the embryo if conception occurs following ovulation. Figure 7-10 illustrates the endocrine profile during the menstrual cycle and relates this to the proliferative and secretory phase of the cycle. For comparison, the top panel of Figure 7-10 illustrates the typical hormone profiles of the estrous cycle.

A question that is invariably asked is "Why have most species evolved with definitive periods of sexual receptivity and the human female has not?" While experiments to discover the reasons for this discrepancy have never been conducted, a prominent theory explaining this lack of defined periods of sexual receptivity is presented below. It is thought that at one time during the evolution of primates there was a significant amount of competition for the right to mate with the female. It is believed during this evolutionary period there were periods of sexual receptivity amongst primates. But, because males spent undue time competing for the opportunity to copulate with sexually receptive females the role of the male and female in food gathering was compromised. Fighting for the right to copulate was a huge distraction. Groups of females who displayed more widespread sexual receptivity created a situation in which males did not spend as much time competing for the opportunity to copulate because copulation could occur over a wider time-frame, thus allowing more opportunities to seek food and shelter. This proved beneficial and gradually continuous sexual receptivity evolved.

Figure 7-10. Comparison Between the Estrous Cycle and Menstrual Cycle

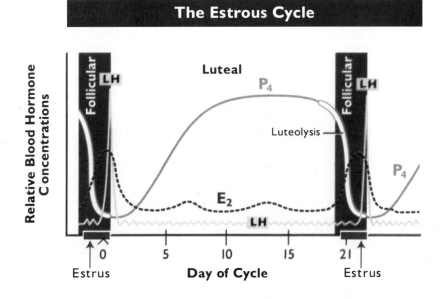

The estrous cycle begins, and ends, with estrus and/or ovulation. The follicular phase is short and the luteal phase long.

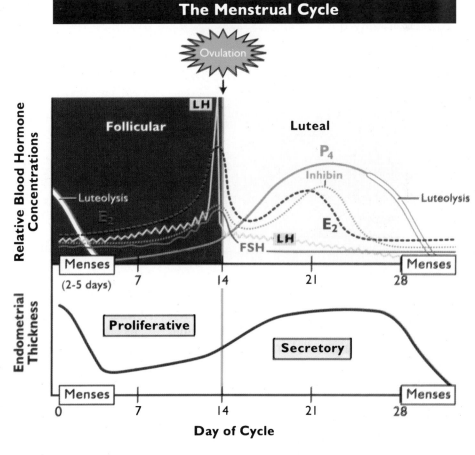

The menstrual cycle begins (day 0) and ends with the start of menses (day 28). Ovulation occurs in the middle of the cycle. The follicular and the luteal phase are about the same length (about 14 days each).

During the initial 3-5 days of the proliferative phase the endometrium decreases rapidly in thickness because it is sloughed to the exterior during menses. With rising E_2, the endometrium begins to proliferate and increase in thickness. After ovulation, the CL produces P_4 that causes further proliferation and initiates secretory activity of the endometrium. Luteolysis initiates another menstrual period.

Table 7-2. Cycle Event Comparison Between the Estrous Cycle and Menstrual Cycle

EVENT	ESTROUS CYCLE	MENSTRUAL CYCLE
Follicular Phase	Short (20% or less of cycle duration)	Long (50% of the cycle duration)
Ovulation	At the beginning and end of the cycle	Middle of cycle (day 14)
Luteal Phase	80% of the cycle	50% of the cycle
Fertile Period	24 hrs or less (5% of cycle)	Up to 6 days before ovulation (18% of cycle)
Endometrial Sloughing	None	After luteolysis
Luteolysis	Uterine $PGF_{2\alpha}$	Ovarian $PGF_{2\alpha}$
Sexual Receptivity	Well defined	Relatively uniform throughout cycle
Progesterone function and sexual receptivity	Inhibits GnRH release Inhibits sexual receptivity	Inhibits GnRH release Does not influence sexual receptivity
Menopause	None described	Well characterized (follicular depletion)

Amenorrhea is the human equivalent to anestrus. It can be caused by:

- *menopause*
- *low nutritional intake*
- *lactation*

Lack of Cyclicity is Called Amenorrhea in Women

Menopause is a period without cyclicity. Menopause is due to the depletion of follicles within the ovary that secrete estradiol and progesterone after ovulation. As you now should know, cyclicity is "driven" by ovarian steroids. Thus, menopause occurs in women when their ovarian supply of follicles is depleted. A more detailed discussion of menopause will be presented in Chapter 16.

It is well known that women who have isocaloric intake or negative energy balance enter a period of acyclicity called **amenorrhea**. Amenorrhea is the absence of menses for an extended time in women of reproductive age. Female athletes particularly marathon runners and those engaged in sustained high levels of intense training may experience amenorrhea because of reduced energy availability.

Lactational amenorrhea is a relatively prolonged period of ovarian inactivity in women. Lack of ovarian activity is reflected by lack of menstruation (See Figure 7-11). Please note from Figure 7-11 that lactating women from India and Sri Lanka displayed significant retardation of cyclicity when compared to women from the USA and the United Kingdom. While cultural differences exist between these subpopulations, nutritional aspects may be important. Lactation can be considered a form of contraception where nutrition is a limiting factor. The physiologic mechanism causing lactational amenorrhea is believed to be regulated by high prolactin during lactation. High prolactin causes a decrease in GnRH frequency and amplitude and thus a decrease in LH and FSH. This system is very effective during the first 6 months postpartum but more and more women start cycling after 6 months postpartum. The primary events of the menstrual cycle and the estrous cycle are fundamentally the same. However, there are marked differences in how these events are expressed between the two types of cycles. These differences are summarized in Table 7-2.

Figure 7-11.   Influence of Lactation Upon Return to Cyclicity in Women
(Modified from Mepham. 1987. *Physiology of Lactation*)

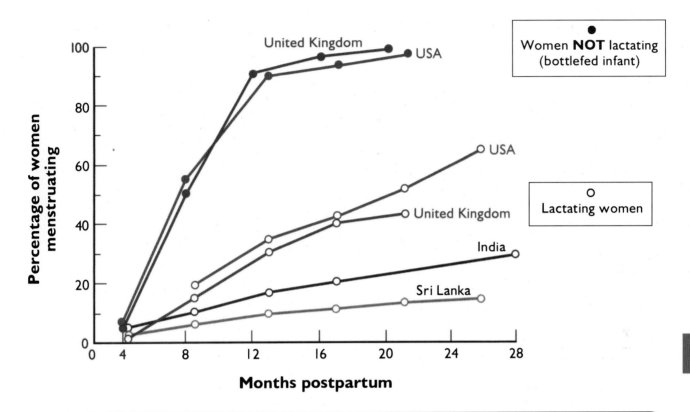

Women who are not lactating begin menstruating sooner than lactating women. About 90% of non-lactating women start menstruating by 12 months postpartum. However, cyclicity is delayed in postpartum women even without the suckling stimulus. Other sensory inputs (tactile, auditory, visual and perhaps olfactory) may inhibit GnRH. Only 5-30% of lactating women begin menstruating by 12 months. Also, only about 70% of postpartum lactating women begin cycling within 2 years in the U.S. and United Kingdom. Indian and Sri Lankan women have an even greater delay in their return to cyclicity.

7

Further PHENOMENA for Fertility

The word "menstrual" (as in menstrual cycle) is derived from the Latin word meaning month. In historical Latin folklore the moon was believed to regulate not only the tides of the sea, but also the monthly "emotional tides" of women.

Some female bats are very aggressive and prey on the males of their species, thus minimizing the opportunity for successful copulation and pregnancy. To offset this problem, males hibernate after the females. Thus, males can then safely breed the "sleeping" females. This is not a "silent estrus"!!! Ovulation does not occur until after hibernation. The sperm are stored in the female tract until ovulation when they fertilize the oocytes.

In primitive societies, menstruating women were isolated from the tribe and forced to occupy a small "menstrual hut" located away from the village. Menstruation was believed to be responsible for assorted ills such as crop failures, bad luck in hunting and fishing, death of livestock, failure of food to be preserved and failure of beer to ferment. Reproductive processes were blamed because of ignorance about them.

Dairy cows are afflicted by a condition called cystic ovarian disease, often called "cystic ovaries". One type of cystic ovarian disease results in nymphomania (excessive or uncontrollable sexual desire). Follicles fail to ovulate and continue to produce estradiol that causes the cow to be in constant estrus.

Women were not employed in the opium industry during the 19th century because it was believed that menstruating women would make the opium bitter.

Prostitutes encounter spermatozoa on a frequent basis. It is known that prostitutes have blood titers of antisperm antibodies. Some prostitutes even have severe allergic reactions.

The mouthbrooder fish is so called because fertilization actually takes place in the female's mouth. First, she releases her ova into the water, then she turns around and swallows them. When the male swims by she mistakes the distinctive spots on his anal fin for more of her eggs. She opens her mouth to swallow them and catches his sperm instead. It is not known whether fertilization rates are higher in these species where it occurs in a confined space to other species of fish where milt is deposited over the eggs in moving water.

Unlike humans, other animals apparently do not have menopause. For example, chimpanzees live to be forty years old but show no signs of menopause. The female African elephant remains reproductively competent until she is in her nineties.

Lactational amenorrhea can be considered as a form of contraception. !Kung hunter gatherers live in the Kalahari Desert in southern Africa. In the absence of any form of artificial birth control, the mean birth interval is 4.1 years and the mean completed family size 4.7 children. Nutritional status may be a contributory factor. However, !Kung neonates practice a very high suckling frequency. The mother always carries her infant in a sling so that it is able to suckle ad libitum. Suckling occurs about four times an hour, for periods of 1-2 minutes; frequent suckling also occurs at night. It is not known if there is a threshold number of suckling sessions required to inhibit GnRH in women (like in cows).

During the Middle Ages (500-1500 AD) women throughout Europe hollowed out lemon halves and used them to cover the cervix in the same way women use the diaphragm today.

Key References

Asdell, S.A. 1964. *Patterns of Mammalian Reproduction*. Comstock Publishing Co., Ithaca, N.Y. Library of Congress Catalog No. 64-25162.

Driancourt, M.A., D. Royere, B. Hedon and M.C. Levasseur. 1993. "Oestrus and menstrual cycles" in *Reproduction in Mammals and Man*. C. Thibault, M.C. Levasseur and R.H.F. Hunter, eds. Ellipses, Paris. ISBN 2-7298-9354-7.

Johnston, S.D., M.V. Root Kustritz and P.N.S. Olson. 2001. *Canine and Feline Theriogenology*. W.B. Saunders Co., Philadelphia. ISBN 0-7216-5607-2.

Mepham, T.B. 1987. *Physiology of Lactation*. Open University Press. Philadelphia ISBN 0-335-15152-3.

Roa, J., V.M. Nararro and M. Tena-Sempere. 2011. "Kisspeptins in reproductive biology: Concensus knowledge and recent developments." Biol. Reprod. 85:650-660.

Tibary, A. and A. Anouassi. 1997. *Theriogenology in Camelidae*. United Arab Emirates. Ministry of Culture and Information Publication authorization No. 3849/1/16 ISBN 9981-801-32-1.

Williams, G.L., O.S. Gazai, G.A. Guzman Vega and R.L. Stanko. 1996. "Mechanisms regulating suckling mediated anovulation in the cow." *Anim. Reprod. Sci.* 42: 289-297.

7

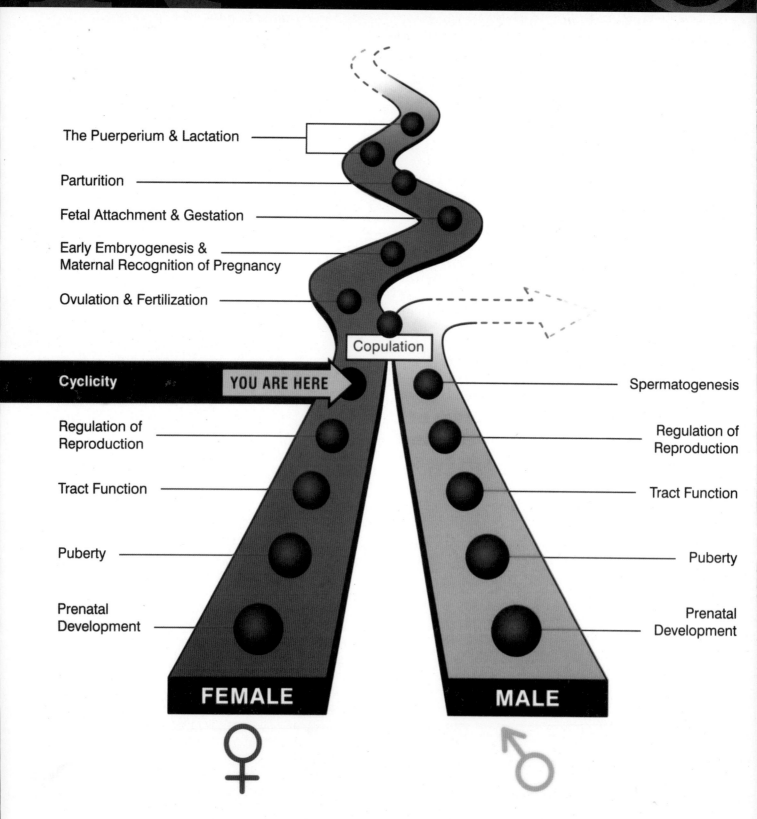

The Puerperium & Lactation

Parturition

Fetal Attachment & Gestation

Early Embryogenesis & Maternal Recognition of Pregnancy

Ovulation & Fertilization

Copulation

Cyclicity

YOU ARE HERE

Spermatogenesis

Regulation of Reproduction

Regulation of Reproduction

Tract Function

Tract Function

Puberty

Puberty

Prenatal Development

Prenatal Development

FEMALE

MALE

Take Home Message

The follicular phase consists of four major events. They are: 1) elevated gonadotropin secretion from the anterior lobe of the pituitary; 2) follicular growth and preparation for ovulation; 3) sexual receptivity and 4) ovulation. Estradiol is the dominant hormone secreted by developing follicles and causes profound changes that prepare the reproductive tract for copulation. Reproductive behavior is induced by estradiol in non-primate mammals. Estradiol also controls the onset of the preovulatory LH surge that causes ovulation. Ovulation is a cascade of physiological and biochemical changes that culminate in rupture of preovul tory follicles and release of the oocyte from the ovary.

The "driving force" for the initiation of the follicular phase is luteolysis. Luteolysis causes the corpus luteum to become nonfunctional. Thus, there is a marked reduction in progesterone secretion by the corpus luteum. The negative feedback by progesterone on the hypothalamus is removed and GnRH is released at higher amplitudes and frequencies than during the preceding luteal phase. At first, this causes FSH and LH to be released at higher concentrations, thus promoting final follicular development and the secretion of estradiol. Later in the follicular phase, FSH secretion declines (See Figure 8-4). The main steps in this process are presented in Figure 8-1.

Recall from Chapter 7 that the follicular phase consists of **proestrus** and **estrus**. During the follicular phase four significant events take place. They are: 1) gonadotropin release from the anterior lobe of the pituitary; 2) follicular preparation for ovulation; 3) sexual receptivity (estrus) and 4) ovulation. These events will be described in the remainder of this chapter and in Chapter 11 (Reproductive Behavior).

Figure 8-1. Primary Steps Leading to the Preovulatory LH Surge

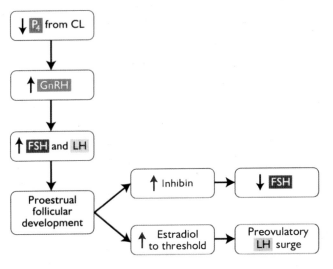

Gonadotropin Release is Controlled by Ovarian Estrogen and Hypothalamic GnRH

The follicular phase is governed by the hypothalamus, the anterior lobe of the pituitary and the ovary through the secretion of estradiol in the absence of progesterone. The relationship between these components is illustrated in Figure 8-2.

The hypothalamus plays an obligatory role in regulating estrous cycles because it produces **gonadotropin releasing hormone (GnRH)** that is responsible for stimulating the release of the gonadotropins FSH and LH.

> *The tonic and surge centers in the hypothalamus control GnRH release. The surge center responds dramatically to high blood concentrations of estradiol.*

As you should remember from Chapter 5, secretion of GnRH in the female is controlled by two separate areas in the hypothalamus. These areas are composed of clusters of nerve cell bodies that represent anatomically discrete regions known as **hypothalamic nuclei**. At least two hypothalamic nuclei (the **ventromedial nucleus** and the **arcuate nucleus**) make up the tonic GnRH center. The tonic center is responsible for basal secretion of GnRH. The neurons in this center release small pulses of GnRH over a substantial period of time (days to weeks). The profile of tonic GnRH release is characterized by having many small pulses or episodes (See Figure 8-3). These pulses have various frequencies and amplitudes depending on the degree of neural activity (rate of firing) in the tonic center. Thus, as with many neurally controlled hormonal profiles, this pattern is referred to as an **episodic profile** (See Chapter 5). In contrast, another hypothalamic center known as the **surge center** (also called the "preovulatory center") is responsible for the preovulatory

8

release of GnRH that stimulates a surge of LH, causing ovulation. Anatomically, the surge center consists of three nuclei called the **preoptic nucleus**, the **anterior hypothalamic area** and the **suprachiasmatic nucleus**. The surge center secretes basal levels of GnRH until it receives the appropriate positive stimulus. This stimulus is known to be a threshold concentration of estradiol in the absence of progesterone. When the estradiol concentration in the blood reaches a certain level, a large quantity of GnRH is released from the terminals of neurons, the cell bodies of which are located in the surge center. Secretion of GnRH is caused by depolarization (action potentials) originating in the cell bodies of neurosecretory cells. In natural conditions, the preovulatory surge of GnRH occurs only once during the estrous or menstrual cycle. However, tonic secretion of GnRH occurs from these same neurons during the entire estrous cycle.

The release of GnRH by the tonic and preovulatory centers in the hypothalamus may be compared to water faucets. Tonic (basal) secretion is analogous to a leaky faucet (See Figure 8-3) from which small quantities of water drip from the faucet over a relatively long period of time. In contrast, release of GnRH from the preovulatory center is analogous to opening a faucet fully for a short period of time and then suddenly turning it off. Water gushes forth and then stops. A threshold concentration of estradiol (without progesterone) is necessary to open the faucet fully.

Figure 8-2. The Relationship Between the Hypothalamus, the Pituitary and the Ovary During the Follicular Phase

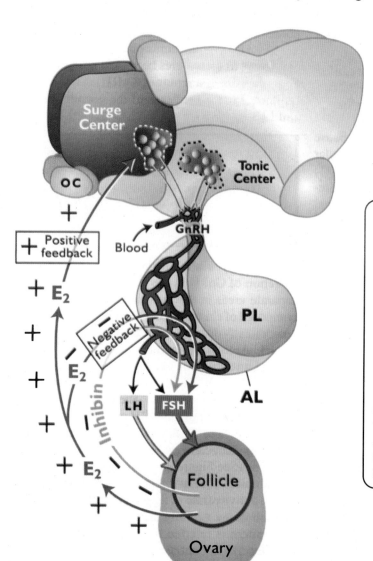

AL	=	Anterior Lobe
E$_2$	=	Estradiol
OC	=	Optic Chiasm
PL	=	Posterior Lobe

Early in the follicular phase, GnRH pulse frequency begins to increase (because of low P$_4$), thus causing FSH and LH to be secreted from the anterior lobe of the pituitary. These gonadotropins stimulate ovarian follicles to secrete estradiol, a positive feedback on the neurons of the hypothalamic surge center occurs and the GnRH neurons secrete a burst of GnRH (See Figure 8-3). Later in the follicular phase, follicles secrete inhibin that causes a negative feedback on FSH secretion from the anterior lobe of the pituitary. Estradiol is thought to suppress FSH secretion by the anterior lobe.

Figure 8-3. GnRH Secretion From the Hypothalamic Tonic and Surge Centers

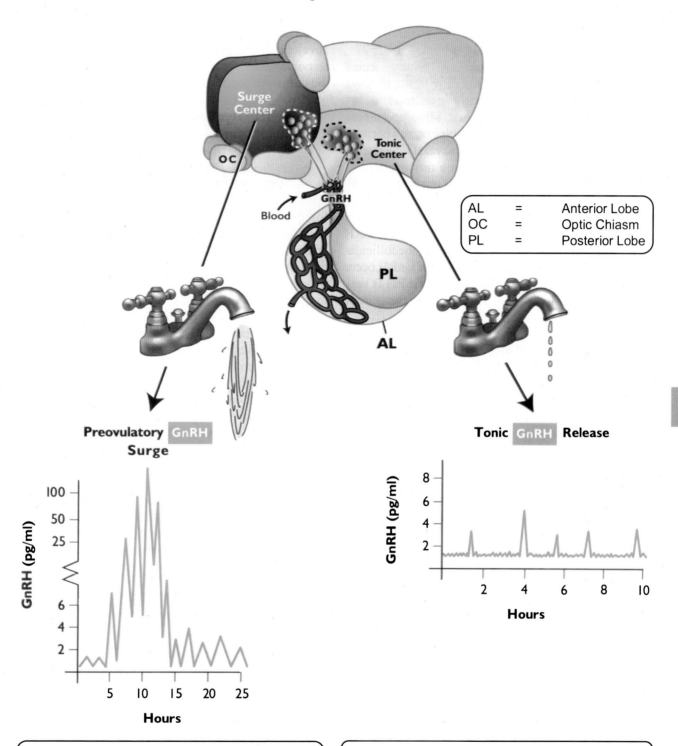

The surge center is sensitive to positive feedback and secretes high amplitude, high frequency pulses of GnRH (like a gushing, wide-opened faucet) in a relatively short period (hours) after estradiol reaches a threshold concentration.

The tonic center secretes small episodes of GnRH in a pulsatile fashion similar to a dripping faucet. The episodic secretion is continuous throughout reproductive life.

8

> **GnRH secretion from the tonic center appears to be spontaneous but is influenced by progesterone.**

As described previously, secretion of GnRH from nerve terminals in the tonic GnRH center occurs in periodic pulses. Controls for the pattern of tonic pulsatile GnRH secretion are poorly understood and not easy to study because such small, short-lived pulses are difficult to quantify. Each GnRH pulse occurs because of simultaneous depolarizations of several GnRH neurons. Each GnRH neuron secretes a tiny quantity of GnRH and summation of these small quantities causes a pulse or an episode to occur. The release of GnRH from tonic center neurons occurs spontaneously in a rhythmic fashion (See Figure 8-3). In fact, small GnRH episodes occur every 1.5-2.0 hours during the follicular phase. During the luteal phase episodes of GnRH occur every 4 to 8 hours. Neural secretion of GnRH is very low (5pg/ml of blood serum) and thus, low amplitude pulses of LH are released.

> **GnRH secretion from the surge center is controlled by high estradiol accompanied by low progesterone.**

The preovulatory surge of GnRH is controlled by the combination of high estradiol and low progesterone. In mammals (including humans), estradiol in the presence of low progesterone exerts a differential effect on GnRH. For example, estradiol in low concentrations causes a negative feedback (suppression) on the preovulatory center. That is, low estradiol reduces the degree of firing by GnRH neurons in the preovulatory center. However, when estradiol levels are high, as they would be during the mid-to late follicular phase (See Figure 8-4), the preovulatory center responds dramatically by secreting large quantities of GnRH. This stimulation in response to rising concentrations of estradiol is referred to as **positive feedback**. You should recognize that during the middle part of the cycle, when estradiol is low and progesterone is high, there is **negative feedback** by progesterone on the preovulatory center, thus reducing frequency of GnRH pulses. During the follicular phase (proestrus), the follicles begin to produce more and more estradiol (See Figure 8-4). Once estradiol reaches a threshold concentration, or peak (during estrus), the preovulatory center is "turned on" and secretes large quantities of GnRH that stimulate the anterior lobe of the pituitary to secrete a preovulatory surge of LH (See Figure 8-3). In fact, the LH surge is at least 10 times greater than a tonic LH pulse.

In summary, elevated GnRH is essential for initiating the follicular phase of the estrous cycle. The tonic center secretes small amplitude episodes (pulses) of GnRH that stimulate secretion of FSH and LH from the anterior lobe of the pituitary, causing growth and development of ovarian follicles. The surge center is responsible for secretion of large quantities of GnRH, thus causing a surge of LH that causes ovulation.

Follicular Dynamics is Controlled by FSH and LH and Involves Both Growth and Death of These Follicles

Even though the **follicular phase** comprises only about 20% of the estrous cycle, the process of follicular growth and degeneration (known as **follicular dynamics**) occurs continuously throughout the entire estrous cycle. Antral follicles of various sizes develop in response to basal levels of FSH and LH and these antral follicles are always present. If you were to examine the ovaries at any point during the estrous cycle, you would see a significant number of antral follicles of various sizes. These antral follicles have been classified by scientists studying follicular dynamics as small, medium or large depending on their diameter. For example, in the pig the small, medium and large classifications consist of follicles measuring less than 3mm, 4 to 6mm and greater than 6mm in diameter, respectively. However, in the mare, the sizes of these same classifications are: less than 10mm, 10 to 20mm and greater than 20 mm respectively. The number of small antral follicles may exceed 100 for a pair of ovaries in the pig. Large follicles almost always can be seen on the ovaries in species where only a single follicle ovulates, like the cow and the mare. These large follicles represent those that have reached the greatest size possible under the existing endocrine conditions.

> **Dynamics of antral follicles consist of:**
> - *recruitment (emergence)*
> - *selection*
> - *dominance*
> - *atresia*

The dynamics of antral follicles involve four processes. These processes are **recruitment (or emergence)**, **selection**, **dominance** and **atresia** (See Figure 8-5). Atresia means degeneration. Recruitment (or emergence) is the phase of follicular development in which a **cohort** (group) of small antral follicles begins to grow (emerge) and secrete estradiol. Most of the recruited follicles undergo atresia. Following recruitment, a group of growing follicles that have not undergone atresia are selected. Selected follicles may become dominant or they may undergo atresia. In pigs, dogs and cats, a cohort of follicles becomes dominant. However, in cattle, mares and women only a single follicle becomes dominant. As the selected follicles proceed toward dominance, they continue to secrete increasing amounts of estradiol as well as the hormone inhibin. Recall that inhibin is a protein hormone secreted by the antral follicle that selectively inhibits the release of FSH from the anterior lobe of the pituitary. As you can see from Figure 8-4, FSH does not surge to the same extent as LH.

In **monotocous** species (giving birth to a single offspring) such as the cow, mare and woman, most reproductive physiologists consider that a single follicle is selected and will develop dominance. However, in **polytocous** species (litter bearers) there are multiple dominant follicles. The condition of dominance is characterized by one or more large preovulatory follicles exerting a major inhibitory effect on other antral follicles from the recruited and selected cohort. This inhibitory influence is thought to be caused by a combination of the production of inhibin and estradiol by the dominant follicle and reduced blood supply to some follicles. Suppressed FSH concentrations in the blood, coupled with reduced blood supply to some follicles results in atresia. Only those follicles receiving a large blood supply (and thus higher levels of gonadotropin) continue to grow and ovulate.

> ***Atresia occurs continuously throughout folliculogenesis.***

Figure 8-4. Hormonal Changes During the Follicular Phase

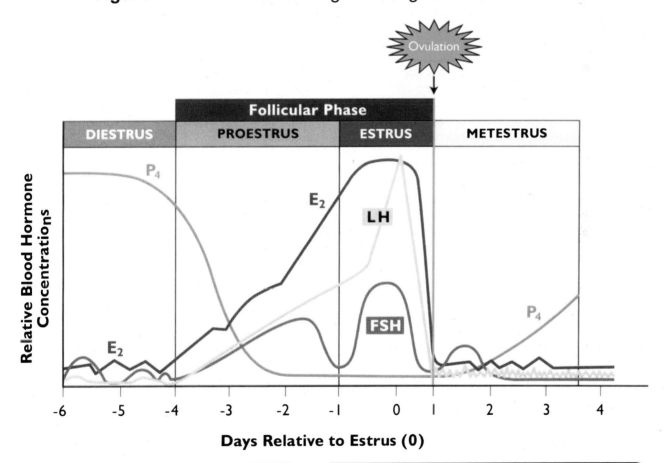

Proestrus
On day -6 (day 15) FSH surges to recruit the preovulatory wave, then FSH drops and remains low until it surges again with LH prior to ovulation.

Estrus
When recruited follicles develop dominance, they secrete estradiol and inhibin that suppresses FSH secretion from the anterior lobe of the pituitary. Thus, FSH does not surge with the same magnitude as LH. When estradiol reaches a threshold concentration (peak), the preovulatory surge of LH occurs, inducing ovulation.

Figure 8-5. Several Follicular Waves May Occur During One Cycle
in the Cow
(Modified from Lucy et al. 1992)

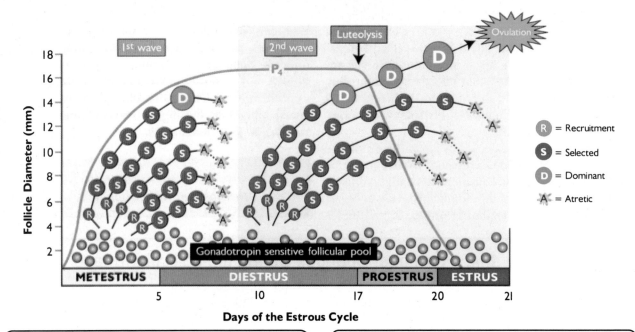

The first follicular wave occurs either as progesterone is rising or during peak progesterone secretion. Follicles recruited and selected during the first wave will become atretic. *Note: about 80% of estrous cycles in the cow have two waves, but some have three waves. This model illustrates a two-wave cycle.*

The second follicular wave is initiated before luteolysis and results in a dominant follicle that will ovulate. Only those follicles in a growing phase when luteolysis occurs will become eligible for ovulation.

The process of **atresia** involves far more follicles than does the process of dominance. In fact, over 90% of ovarian follicles undergo an irreversible degenerative process called atresia. The word atresia in the follicular context refers to the closure or disappearance of the antrum that accompanies the degenerative changes. At any one point in time during the postpubertal reproductive period, the proportion of atretic antral follicles is quite high. For example, if you were to examine the ovaries of a rat, about 70% of antral follicles would be in some stage of atresia. In the mouse 50% are atretic, in the rabbit 60% and in the human 50 to 75%.

As you can see in Figure 8-5, during metestrus (days 2 to 5 in cattle), a group of follicles is recruited. However, these follicles are not exposed to the appropriate endocrine conditions for continued development and undergo atresia within the ovary. Note that the first follicular wave begins and terminates during times in the cycle when progesterone is increasing or is at its highest level. Neither complete follicular development nor ovulation can occur under progesterone dominance. However, the dominant follicle of each wave will ovulate if luteolysis occurs. During progesterone dominance, GnRH is secreted in low quantities only and thus FSH and LH are low. However, FSH increases briefly before each follicular wave. It should be emphasized that even though follicles in the first follicular wave become atretic they still secrete some estradiol. In fact, midcycle estradiol increases and declines with each follicular wave but blood concentrations are low. After luteolysis (corpus luteum regression), follicles of either the second or third wave develop into a dominant preovoulatory follicle. One or more of these follicles will develop into the dominant and the preovulatory follicle. It must be emphasized that the endocrine condition for final follicular development will exist only after luteolysis and subsequent decline in progesterone that removes the negative feedback on the hypothalamus. Also it is important to recognize that the number of follicular waves within a given cycle varies among and within species.

The phenomenon of follicular dynamics was described in the cow using ultrasonography. Ultrasonography is among the most important imaging techniques used in reproductive research and diagnostics. It can be used in pregnancy diagnosis, fetal aging and growth, description of change in ovar-

Figure 8-6. Bovine Ovarian Follicles and Their Respective Ultrasonographic Images

This ovary contains many small antral follicles (SF). More follicles appear in the ultrasonographic image than appear in the photograph because ultrasound imaging allows observation of follicles beneath the surface of the ovary. Fluid-filled cavities generate a black image while dense tissue like the ovarian stroma (OS) generates a gray to white image.

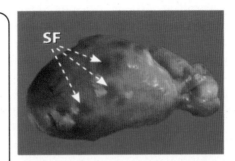

This ovary contains three medium antral follicles (MF) and a corpus luteum (CL) that appear in both images.

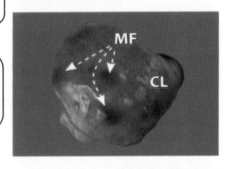
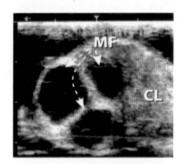

This ovary contains a dominant follicle (DF). The ultrasonogram shows that the follicle penetrates deep into the center of the ovary. This follicle could easily be palpated per rectum. However, the exact size of the follicle would be difficult to ascertain. Ultrasound technology allows changes in diameter to be measured precisely.

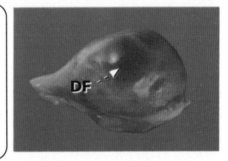
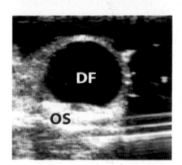

ian structures, detection of fetal abnormalities and diagnosis of the presence of twins in mares, cows and women. One of the primary advantages of ultrasonography is that it is minimally invasive and can be used without surgery. By examining the ovaries with ultrasonography in large animals on a daily basis, one can determine how populations of antral follicles change in size and numbers over time. In addition, follicular dynamics can be studied intensely in food producing animals because ovaries can be obtained postmortem and large numbers of females are slaughtered annually.

This provides an opportunity to directly relate the actual ovarian structures to their ultrasonographic images. Figure 8-6 is a series of ovaries showing dominant, small and intermediate sized follicles on the surface of ovaries and their respective ultrasonographic images.

Follicular waves of antral follicles occur before puberty, during pregnancy, during anestrus (or amenorrhea) and during the puerperium. However, follicular waves occurring during these times do not yield dominant follicles that secrete threshold levels of estradiol. The above discussion has focused almost entirely on growth and atresia of antral follicles.

Recruitment = *high FSH + low LH pulse frequency + low inhibin + low estradiol*

Selection = *low FSH + moderate LH + low inhibin*

Dominance = *low FSH + high LH pulse frequency + high inhibin*

Atresia = *degeneration of follicles*

You should recognize that the majority of a follicle's lifetime is spent in preantral stages. Recruitment, selection and dominance are relatively short-term processes when compared to the preantral follicle stages. Recent scientific literature proposes that follicular dynamics be subdivided into two components. The first has been designated as the **initial recruitment phase** involving a continuous recruitment of primordial follicles into a growing follicle pool that terminates with atresia. The second has been termed **cyclic recruitment**. Cyclic recruitment starts after puberty and is the result of elevated FSH levels that occur during each cycle.

FSH and LH Exert Different Effects on Follicles. Their Secretion Rates are Controlled Differently.

Figure 8-7A describes FSH concentrations during the course of one estrous cycle in the cow. In the face of rising progesterone concentrations (during metestrus), small quantities of FSH are secreted from the anterior pituitary. This small amount stimulates the emergence (recruitment) of small antral follicles. These small follicles begin to grow and secrete estrogen. FSH secretion soon drops because low concentrations of estrogen and inhibin (secreted by the growing follicles) cause negative feedback on the anterior pituitary that selectively inhibits FSH secretion. A second rise in FSH sometimes occurs in diestrus even though progesterone concentrations are high. Like in the first wave, FSH secretion drops and this is followed by a drop in estradiol and inhibin.

The primary role of LH is to promote final growth and maturation of dominant follicles and to stimulate ovulation. Figure 8-7B describes LH pulse frequency changes that occur during the cycle. During metestrus and diestrus, the LH pulse frequency is maintained at about 6 pulses per day or one pulse every four hours. This pulse frequency does not provide enough LH to stimulate selected and dominant follicles in the first two follicular waves and all of these follicles undergo atresia. After luteolysis, progesterone drops and increasing concentrations of LH are secreted. The pulse frequency increases to about 24 pulses per day or about one every hour. LH pulse frequency culminates in the preovulatory surge.

> *FSH and LH are controlled differently:*
>
> *Estradiol + Inhibin → ↓ FSH*
>
> *GnRH pulse frequency → ↑ LH*

FSH and LH are regulated differently. FSH secretion is controlled by estrogen and inhibin that is secreted by growing follicles. They exert negative feedback on the secretion of FSH by the anterior pituitary. LH secretion is regulated by GnRH pulses that control the pulse frequency of LH.

Almost all follicles undergo atresia during the cycle. This is because they lack sufficient numbers of LH receptors on the granulosal cells to fully respond to LH in the final stages of growth and maturation. Only those follicles with threshold numbers of LH receptors will enter the final stages of dominance and gain preovulatory status. The factors that control LH receptor numbers in growing follicles are poorly understood.

Figure 8-8 summarizes the relationship between FSH and LH with regard to recruited, selected, dominant and preovulatory follicles. In summary, recruited and selected follicles are FSH dependent while more mature selected follicles, dominant and preovulatory follicles are LH dependent

"The 2-Cell, 2-Gonadotropin Model" Describes Estrogen Synthesis

During follicular development, LH binds to LH-specific membrane receptors located on the cells of the theca interna of the developing follicle (See Figure 8-9). The binding of LH to its receptors activates a cascade of intracellular events, described in Chapter 5. The net effect is conversion of cholesterol to testosterone. Testosterone then diffuses out of the cells of the theca interna and enters the granulosal cells. The granulosal cells contain receptors for FSH. When FSH binds to its receptor, it causes the conversion of testosterone to estradiol. This 2-cell, 2-gonadotropin pathway continues to function until levels of estrogen increase to a threshold that induces the preovulatory LH surge. An important step in the preparation of the follicle for ovulation is the synthesis of LH receptors by granulosal cells. When the LH receptors are present, the preovulatory LH surge can exert its full effect on the follicle to cause ovulation.

The primary target for estradiol is the reproductive tract tissue. The mucosal epithelium of the female tract responds dramatically to estrogens depending on the specific organ within the tract. In the vagina (particularly the caudal vagina) the mucosa increases in thickness in response to estradiol. Stage of the estrous cycle in some species (dog, cat, rodents) can be diagnosed by performing vaginal lavage by flushing fluid back-and-forth within the vagina and then removing a portion of the fluid. If an isotonic buffered solution is used to lavage the vagina, squamous cells will exfoliate into the solution without significant damage. They can then be stained and observed with

Figure 8-7. Relative Progesterone, Estradiol, FSH (A) and LH (B)
Secretion During the Estrous Cycle in the Cow

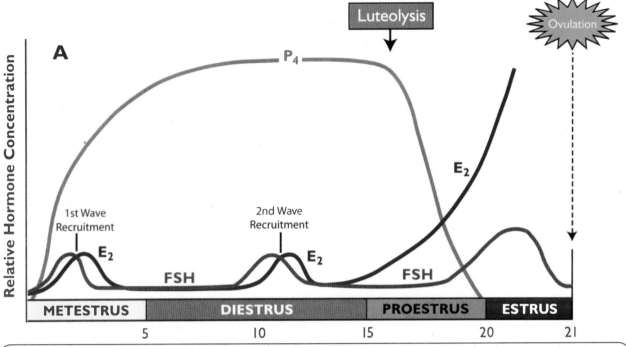

FSH secretion followed by estradiol secretion occurs during metestrus even though progesterone is high. Antral follicles secrete estradiol in response to FSH. They also secrete inhibin and this causes FSH secretion to drop. After luteolysis, progesterone decreases. As a consequence, FSH and estradiol increase dramatically. FSH secretion is controlled by inhibin and estradiol.

8

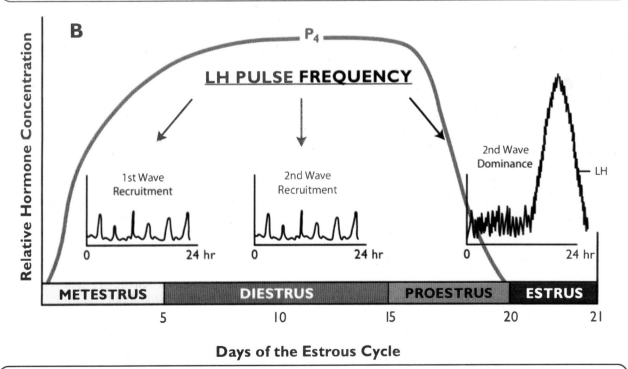

Days of the Estrous Cycle

LH pulse frequency is low during metestrus (6 pulses per day) and diestrus (6 pulses per day). After luteolysis, progesterone secretion decreases and the negative feedback on GnRH is lifted and the pulse frequency for LH increases dramatically to about one pulse every hour. This frequent pulses of LH drives final follicular development and ovulation.

Figure 8-8. Relative Roles of FSH and LH in Follicular Dynamics

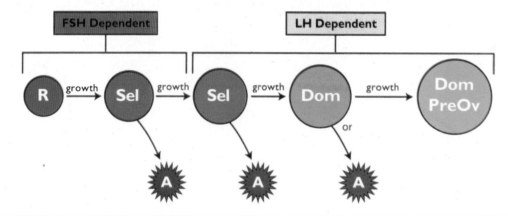

Emerging or recruited follicles and early selected follicles are predominantly FSH dependent. Larger selected follicles and dominant follicles are predominantly LH dependent. Follicles with high numbers of LH receptors become preovulatory follicles.

a microscope. Cells from rodents in estrus are cornified like that of skin. Cornified cells are irregular in shape and appear "crusty" using the microscope. The presence of these cornified cells reflects the growth of the vaginal mucosa during estrus under the influence of estradiol. In other species like the dog and cat sheets of squamous cells indicate estrus. Changes in vaginal cytology are species unique and their appearance has various clinical interpretations.

> ***The major effects of estradiol on the reproductive tract are:***
> - *increased blood flow*
> - *genital swelling*
> - *change in tissue electrical conductivity*
> - *leukocytosis*
> - *increased mucosal secretion*
> - *initiation of uterine gland growth*
> - *elevated myometrial tone*

The cervix and cranial vagina respond to estradiol by producing mucus. This mucus serves to: 1) lubricate the vagina and cervix in preparation for copulation; 2) flush foreign material such as bacteria out of the tract following copulation and 3) in the cow, low viscosity mucus provides "privileged pathways" for spermatozoa to traverse the cervix and enter the uterus.

The uterus responds to estradiol by proestrual development of the uterine glands. As you learned in Chapter 2, uterine glands originate from the luminal epithelium and penetrate into the submucosa of the endometrium. The secretion of estradiol by the dominant follicles brings about initiation of glandular growth.

As pointed out in Chapter 2, the oviductal mucosa consists of simple columnar and ciliated columnar epithelium. Like the rest of the reproductive tract, the epithelium of the oviduct increases its secretory rate under the influence of estradiol. In addition, the cilia within the oviduct increase their beat frequency to allow for gamete and fluid transport.

One of the major effects of estradiol on the female reproductive tract is increased blood flow (**hyperemia**) to all of the organs. This increased blood flow facilitates secretion throughout the entire reproductive tract including the uterus and the oviduct. In addition to facilitating secretory activity, hyperemia plays two other important roles. First, it allows for delivery of leukocytes into the submucosal region of the reproductive tract so that invading foreign materials (including sperm) may be phagocytized after copulation. This influx of leukocytes into the tissue and the lumen of the reproductive tract is referred to as **leukocytosis**. In the vagina of rodents, leukocytes that move into the lumen will remain throughout diestrus and are a diagnostic tool for that stage of the cycle. One of the diagnostic features of estrus in most species is swelling (edema) of the external genitalia. Swelling of the vulva is brought about also by elevated blood flow that increases the local capillary pressure and causes lymph to buildup in the external genitalia (edema). While not definitive, this vulvar edema may serve as a diagnostic indicator of estrus.

Figure 8-9. The "2-Cell, 2-Gonadotropin Model" For Estradiol Synthesis

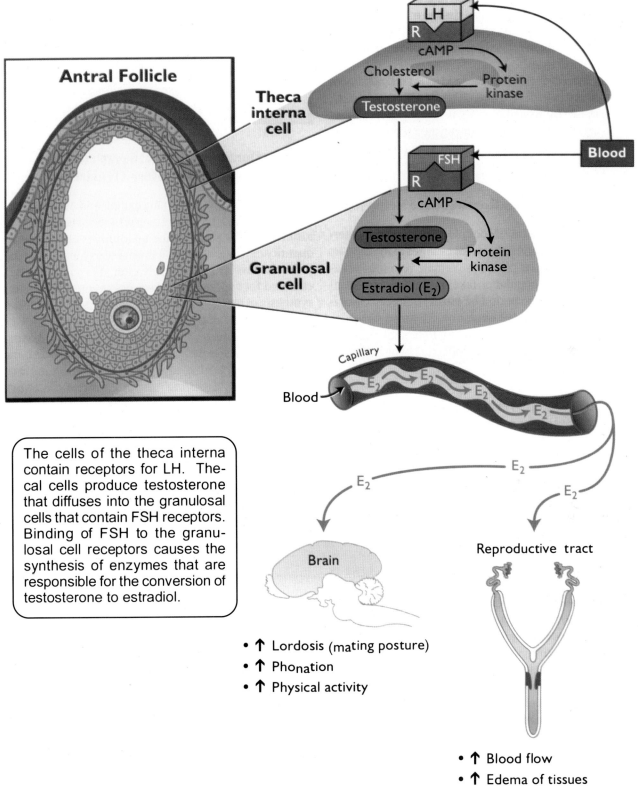

The cells of the theca interna contain receptors for LH. Thecal cells produce testosterone that diffuses into the granulosal cells that contain FSH receptors. Binding of FSH to the granulosal cell receptors causes the synthesis of enzymes that are responsible for the conversion of testosterone to estradiol.

- ↑ Lordosis (mating posture)
- ↑ Phonation
- ↑ Physical activity

- ↑ Blood flow
- ↑ Edema of tissues
- ↑ Secretion - mucus
- ↑ Leukocytes
- ↑ Smooth muscle motility
- ↑ Growth of uterine glands

Changes in the tissue fluid content of the reproductive tract alter its electrical conductivity (impedance). Implanting electrodes into the reproductive tract allows monitoring of this change in a manner that can predict the stage of cycle in cows. As estradiol increases, the electrical resistance (impedance) within the vulva decreases.

Estradiol causes increased tone and motility of the muscularis in all regions of the reproductive tract. This increase in tone and motility is responsible, at least in part, for sperm transport. The elevated tone (brought about by myometrial contractions) of the reproductive tract can be felt when palpated per rectum.

Estradiol Induces Reproductive Behavior

Elevated estradiol coupled with low progesterone induces profound behavioral changes in the female. During the follicular phase, the female becomes sexually receptive and copulation takes place. It is important to recognize that the period of estrus is closely associated with, but precedes ovulation. Estrous behavior culminates with the female standing to be mounted by the male. The physiology of reproductive behavior will be discussed in detail in Chapter 11.

Ovulation Results from a Cascade of Events Starting with the LH Surge

The preovulatory surge of LH is critically important because it sets in motion a series of biochemical events that lead to ovulation. Ovulation is a complicated process that involves purposeful destruction of follicular tissue. The main events of the ovulatory cascade resulting from the LH surge are shown in Figure 8-10.

Hyperemia (local elevated blood flow) is thought to be controlled at the tissue level by histamine and prostaglandin E_2 (PGE_2). Blood flow to the ovary has been shown to increase 7-fold after an injection of human chorionic gonadotropin (hCG), an LH-like hormone. In addition, there is elevated local blood flow to dominant follicles. Accompanying this local hyperemia, the theca interna becomes edematous because of increased vascular permeability brought about by histamine. This edematous condition causes elevated hydrostatic pressure around the follicle that may facilitate its eventual rupture. In addition to increased blood flow brought about by histamine and PGE_2, dominant follicles are thought to produce **angiogenic factors** (substances that promote the growth of new blood vessels). Angiogenic factors have been found in follicular fluid and this implies that the dominant follicle can potentially control its own blood flow.

The net effect of elevated blood flow is to ensure that the dominant preovulatory follicle is provided with the necessary hormonal and metabolic ingredients for final maturation.

> *Ovulation is brought about by:*
> - *elevated blood flow*
> - *breakdown of connective tissue*
> - *ovarian contractions*

The Dominant Follicle Begins to Secrete Progesterone Before Ovulation

Following the LH surge, the cells of the theca interna begin to produce progesterone instead of testosterone. At first, this transition involves only a small quantity of progesterone that is produced locally (at the follicular level). This local elevation of progesterone is essential for ovulation because progesterone stimulates synthesis of an enzyme called **collagenase** by the theca interna cells. Collagenase causes the breakdown of collagen, a major component of connective tissue. Connective tissue makes up the tunica albuginea, the outer covering of the ovary. At the same time that collagenase is "digesting" the collagen of the tunica albuginea, follicular fluid volume inside the follicle increases. Thus, follicular enlargement is closely coordinated with the enzymatic degradation of the tunica albuginea. As these two processes advance, the apex of the follicle, called the **stigma** begins to push outward and weaken. Examples of these structures can be observed in the camel ovary (See Figure 8-12).

Prostaglandins Cause Ovarian Contraction and Aid in Follicular Remodeling

After the LH surge, both prostaglandin E_2 and prostaglandin $F_{2\alpha}$ are synthesized and secreted locally by the ovary. Prostaglandin $F_{2\alpha}$ causes **lysosomes** within the granulosal cells to rupture, releasing their enzymes. These lysosomal enzymes cause further connective tissue deterioration at the apex of the follicle. Prostaglandin $F_{2\alpha}$ also causes contractions of the myoid (smooth muscle) components of the ovary. Thus, intermittent contractions may increase pressure locally and force the stigma to protrude even more dramatically from the surface of the ovary.

The role of prostaglandin E_2 is to help the follicle remodel itself into a corpus luteum after ovulation. The follicle receives its direction for this reorganization from prostaglandin E_2. Prostaglandin E_2 is thought to activate a substrate called plasminogen. Plasminogen is converted to plasmin by plasminogen activator (either tissue, tPA or urokinase, uPA). Plasmin is the

Figure 8-10. Ovarian Events Caused by the Preovulatory LH Surge

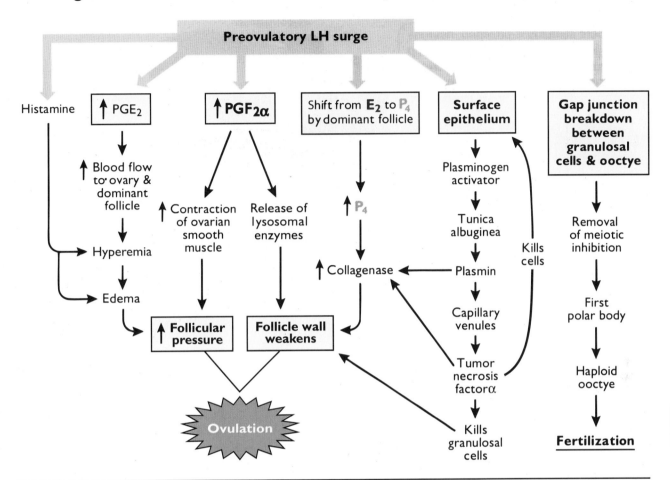

active enzyme that participates in tissue remodeling. It is not unique to the ovary and is found throughout the body. Plasminogen helps dissolve the coagulum of the corpus hemorrhagicum and aids in "remodeling" the follicle into a corpus luteum.

Some Species Require Copulation Before Ovulation Can Occur

Among mammals there are two types of ovulators. These are known as **spontaneous ovulators** and **reflex (induced) ovulators**. Spontaneous ovulators ovulate with a regular frequency and do not require copulation. In the spontaneous ovulator, ovulation is brought about totally in response to hormonal changes. Examples of spontaneous ovulators are the cow, sow, ewe, mare and the woman.

The **reflex (induced) ovulator** requires stimulation of the vagina and/or cervix for ovulation to occur. Examples of reflex ovulators are the rabbit, felids, the ferret and the mink. With the exception of the rabbit, induced ovulators have a relatively long copulation time (Camelids; 1hr) or copulate with intense frequency (over 100 times per estrus in lions). Such copulation

patterns ensure that adequate neural stimulation will take place and cause ovulation. The pathway for induced ovulation is illustrated in Figure 8-11.

Females that are reflex ovulators can be induced artificially using electrical or mechanical stimulation. The tactile stimulation associated with copulation is converted into action potentials that travel through a pathway from the vagina and/or cervix to the spinal cord. Afferent pathways innervate the hypothalamus. The elevated frequency of action potentials in the sensory nerves in the vagina and cervix causes increased firing of hypothalamic neurons that then results in a preovulatory surge of GnRH. This release of GnRH in turn causes LH to be released, prompting the cascade of events leading to ovulation. In cats, a single copulation will induce ovulation about 50% of the time. Multiple copulations cause a much higher LH surge amplitude than single copulations. Reflex ovulators, particularly the rabbit, make excellent experimental models, since the time of ovulation relative to the onset of reproductive tract stimulation can be controlled. In the rabbit, the timing of ovulation is quite precise relative to stimulation. Thus, if one has the desire to recover embryos or oocytes from the reproductive tract, a higher degree of

Figure 8-11. The Pathway for Induced Ovulation

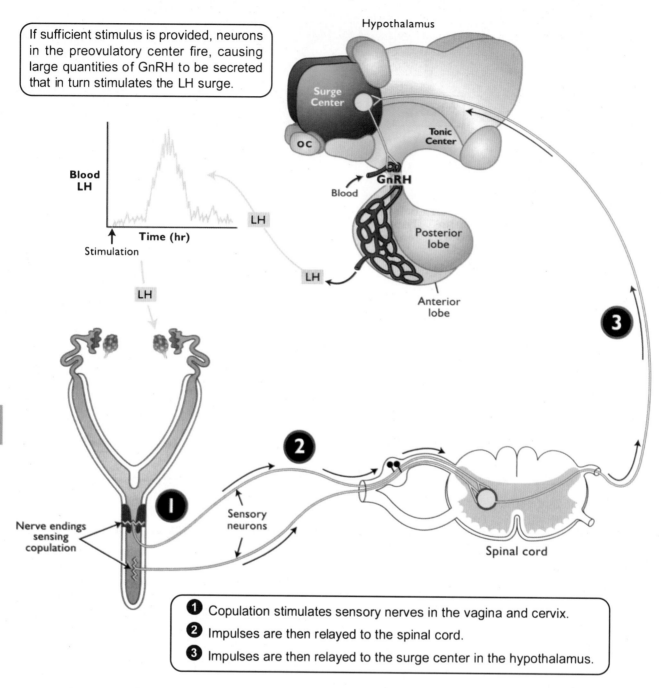

If sufficient stimulus is provided, neurons in the preovulatory center fire, causing large quantities of GnRH to be secreted that in turn stimulates the LH surge.

❶ Copulation stimulates sensory nerves in the vagina and cervix.

❷ Impulses are then relayed to the spinal cord.

❸ Impulses are then relayed to the surge center in the hypothalamus.

precision (relative to the stage of early embryo development) can be achieved in the reflex ovulator than with the spontaneous ovulator.

Some spontaneous ovulators (cow) apparently have some residual neural input from the reproductive tract that can alter the timing of the LH surge. For example, research has shown that when heifers (but not cows) are artificially inseminated and the insemination is accompanied by clitoral massage, the LH surge shifts toward the time of clitoral stimulation. This manipula-

tion of the LH surge by neural stimulation indicates that the time of ovulation can be altered to some degree in spontaneous ovulators.

Camelids Appear to Be Modified Induced Ovulators

In camelids (camels, alpacas and llamas) the presence of seminal plasma in the female reproductive tract appears to be more important for inducing ovulation than tactile stimulation (like in felids). There appears to be an "ovulation inducing factor" present in seminal plasma that acts through a hormonal pathway. This factor is GnRH-like because when seminal plasma from camels (Bactrian) was injected into rabbits an LH surge followed. A similar response (LH surge) in camels was observed when seminal plasma was deposited into the skeletal muscle, vagina, cervix or uterus. Seminal plasma appears to be important as an ovulation inducer in these species. However, biochemical characterization of the material within seminal plasma has not been reported.

Folliculogenesis and Ovulation Can Be Induced Artificially Using Various Hormones

Understanding the basic hormonal requirements for follicular dynamics and ovulation has enabled the manipulation of the timing of ovulation for management and convenience purposes. Two main approaches have been developed. These are hormonally induced ovulation (generally coupled with induced estrus) and **superovulation**. Hormonally induced ovulation requires premature luteolysis. Premature luteolysis can be accomplished using the administration of exogenous prostaglandin $F_{2\alpha}$. Prostaglandin $F_{2\alpha}$ causes luteolysis and therefore causes a decline in blood progesterone. This allows endogenous GnRH to be released, thus stimulating the release of FSH and LH from the anterior lobe of the pituitary. The applications of superovulation to embryo transfer will be presented in Chapter 13.

Superovulation is due to an abnormally high number of follicles that are selected followed by ovulation. It requires the administration of exogenous gonadotropins that cause abnormally high numbers of follicles to be selected (See Figure 8-12). Superovulated females ovulate abnormally high numbers of ova. Methods of superovulation usually include injections of equine chorionic gonadotropin (eCG) or FSH followed by administration of LH, GnRH or human chorionic gonadotropin (hCG) several days later to induce ovulation. The principle of superovulation involves providing the female with higher than normal levels of FSH so that greater numbers of follicles are recruited and selected. Dosages of exogenous gonadotropins required to induce superovulation vary both among and within species.

Oocyte maturation is not limited to the follicular phase, but occurs throughout the lifetime of the female conceptus. Maturation of oocytes occurs in four phases beginning during embryonic development of the female and continuing throughout her reproductive lifetime.

8

Figure 8-12. Superstimulated Ovaries

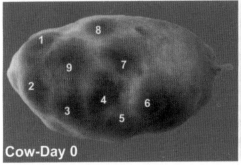 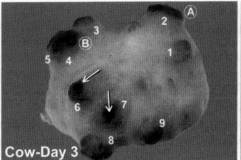 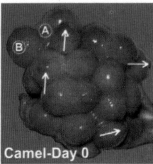

This cow ovary was hyperstimulated with gonadotropins. Ovariectomy was performed on the day of estrus. There are 9 preovulatory follicles visible (all numbered). (Specimen courtesy of Dr. Brad R. Lindsey).

This superovulated cow ovary has 9 corpora hemorraghica (all numbered) indicating individual ovulation sites. Ovariectomy was performed 3 days after estrus. Notice the points of follicular rupture and the blood clots at the apex (arrows). Two corpora hemorrhagica (A and B) are larger than the others because the follicles ovulated sooner. (Specimen courtesy of Dr. Brad R. Lindsey).

This hyperstimulated camel ovary was exteriorized through an incision in the lumbar fossa. The camel was in estrus. There are 13 follicles approaching ovulation. Four follicles recently ovulated as judged by the small points of rupture (arrows) at the apex of the follicle. Notice the thinning at the apex of follicles A and B. These are very near ovulation. (Photograph courtesy of Dr. Ahmed Tibary, Washington State University, College of Veterinary Medicine).

> **The four phases of oocyte maturation are:**
> - **mitotic division of primordial germ cells (prenatal)**
> - **nuclear arrest (dictyotene)**
> - **cytoplasmic growth**
> - **resumption of meiosis**

8

Mitotic divisions occur prenatally (See Chapter 4) and ensure that the female is born with a complete supply of germ cells that will provide a future follicular reservoir. Further mitotic activity does not take place postnatally except for a few postnatal days in the rabbit. The last mitotic division from the oogonia to the primary oocyte constitutes an important step because the primary oocyte enters the first meiotic prophase (See Figure 8-16). The meiotic prophase is then arrested and the nucleus of the oocyte becomes dormant and will remain so until stimulated by gonadotropins after puberty. The oocyte remains arrested for a prolonged period of time from late fetal life through birth and puberty. Oocytes remain in the period of arrest until ovulation occurs or even later in some species. The purpose of this nuclear arrest is to inactivate the DNA in the female gamete so that it may not be vulnerable to possible insult during the lifetime of the female. Insults, or damage to DNA of the female gamete could compromise reproduction because embryo death would likely occur after fertilization.

Oocyte Growth Involves Formation of a Large Cytoplasm and the Zona Pellucida

The neonatal female enters a period during which body growth increases but the gonad remains relatively dormant. During this period of growth, however, some of the primary oocytes begin to accumulate larger volumes of cytoplasm and develop a translucent band around this cytoplasm known as the **zona pellucida** that is formed during the secondary follicle stage. An important development during this stage of maturation is the establishment of **junctional complexes** between neighboring follicular cells and the oocyte that permit ionic and electronic coupling between different cell types. These cell contacts are important for communication between the oocyte and the adjacent granulosal cells. These junctions are known as **gap junctions**. Their presence is especially important after the formation of the zona pellucida because it would serve as a barrier limiting diffusion of materials needed for growth of the oocyte. Junction complexes between the granulosal cells and the oocyte plasma membrane helps overcome this transport problem.

Oocyte growth is believed to be mediated primarily by granulosal cells of the follicle. Indeed, *in vitro* experiments have shown that oocytes cannot develop unless follicular cells and functional gap junctions are present. Gap junctions between granulosal cells and the plasma membrane of the oocyte remain intact until the time of the preovulatory LH surge. During the growth phase, the volume of oocyte cytoplasm increases about 50 times. Presumably, the ability of the oocyte cytoplasm to develop is a direct function of the ability of the cell to maintain functional contact with the granulosal cell.

It was once thought that the zona pellucida was formed exclusively by the follicle cells adjacent to the oocyte. It is now evident that the oocyte is primarily responsible for the synthesis of the zona pellucida. The precursors for this **mucopolysaccharide** material are synthesized by the oocyte and then transferred out of the oocyte to form the thick, translucent layer surrounding the cytoplasm. At the time of antrum formation in the follicle, the oocyte has attained its full cytoplasmic size and these oocytes presumably have the potential to undergo a nuclear maturation provided that atresia has not been initiated.

Final Maturation and Resumption of Meiosis Occur Near the Time of Ovulation

Once the follicle has entered the dominance phase, the oocyte becomes poised to resume meiosis. It is believed that when the oocyte reaches a critical minimum size, it gains the ability to resume meiosis when the ovulatory LH surge occurs. Shortly after the LH surge, the gap junctions between the granulosal cells and the oocyte deteriorate. This deterioration precedes meiotic resumption and it is thought that this disruption of communication between the granulosal cells and the oocyte cytoplasm may remove the inhibition upon meiosis. The timing of the deterioration of gap junctions varies among species. Therefore, the resumption of meiosis cannot be explained totally by the breakdown of these cellular junctions.

The nuclear arrest must be interrupted to permit final oocyte maturation. The preovulatory discharge of gonadotropins is necessary to release the oocyte from inhibitors, presumably provided by the granulosal cells. Cyclic AMP (cAMP) provided by granulosal cells is proposed as the primary inhibitor of meiotic resumption. When granulosal projections dissociate from the cytoplasm of the oocyte, cAMP is no longer available to inhibit the oocyte. Another substance called **oocyte meiotic inhibitor** (OMI) has been implicated in controlling the resumption of meiosis. However, this substance has not been purified and its exact role remains uncertain. Once these inhibitors have been

Figure 8-13. The Major Steps of Oogenesis

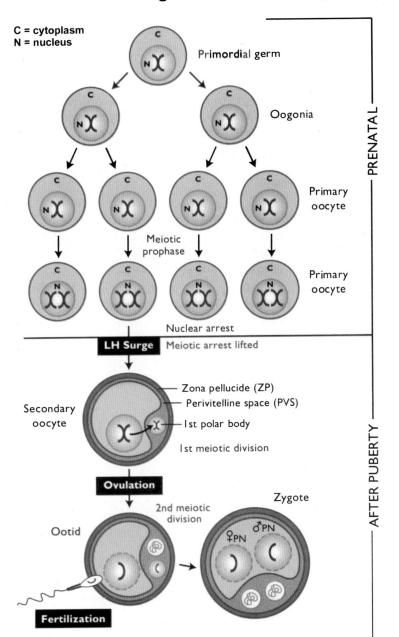

C = cytoplasm
N = nucleus

Primordial germ

Oogonia

Primary oocyte

Meiotic prophase

Primary oocyte

Nuclear arrest

LH Surge Meiotic arrest lifted

Secondary oocyte

Zona pellucide (ZP)
Perivitelline space (PVS)
1st polar body

1st meiotic division

Ovulation

Ootid

2nd meiotic division

Zygote

♀PN   ♂PN

Fertilization

PRENATAL

AFTER PUBERTY

Prenatal
Oogenesis begins with the development of primordial germ cells in the embryo. Primordial germ cells divided mitotically into oogonia. Oogonia divided into primary ooyctes that enter the first meiotic prophase. At the end of meiotic prophase the nuclear material is arrested. This arrest is called the dictyate, a form of nuclear "hibernation".

After Puberty
At puberty, the female begins to cycle and ovulate. The LH surge allows the meiotic arrest to be lifted in the first meiotic division takes place. This division results in the formation of a secondary ooycte that possesses the first polar body. The first polar body contains one-half of the genetic material. Around the time of ovulation, the second polar body is voided and the ootid is formed. Fertilization occurs slightly before or slightly after the second meiotic division. At fertilization the sperm delivers the other half of the genetic material and a zygote is formed. At this time the zygote contains a male and a female pronucleus. When the pronucleii fuse, early embryo development begins.

8

removed, the oocyte is free to proceed with the first meiotic division. For example, in the sheep, pig, mouse and hamster the relationship between the follicle cells and the oocyte is the main factor controlling resumption of meiosis. It is clear that this event takes place in the dominant follicle just prior to ovulation in most mammals. In the dog and the fox, ovulation occurs before meiosis is resumed.

The resumption of meiosis is complex and can be described using a number of criteria. In the dominant follicle, the nucleus of the oocyte begins to migrate towards the periphery and flattens against the oocyte plasma membrane. The peripheral migration of the nucleus constitutes an early morphologic sign of the initiation of final oocyte maturation. This migration takes place after the preovulatory surge of LH in rodents and carnivores. In ruminants, the nucleus becomes polymorphic with many folds. This lobulation is then followed by a dissociation of the nuclear membrane. The bivalent chromosomes then line up and the chromatids are then separated by a microtubule system that pulls the chromosome apart, forming the **first polar body**. This meiotic division generally occurs slightly before ovulation. After fertilization, the second meiotic division will occur, producing the **second polar body**. In some cases, the first polar body will divide, producing two additional "daughter" polar bodies. In this case, three polar bodies can be observed.

Further PHENOMENA for Fertility

Aristotle reported that "Camels copulate with the female in a sitting posture and the male straddles over and covers her...and they pass the whole day long in the operation." The practical significance of this relates to the use of camels as pack animals during military operations. Aristotle reported that camels were spayed (removal of ovaries) to prevent pregnancy. An equally important reason for spaying the female camel was to prevent estrus so that excessive time spent copulating would not interfere with military operations. Tribesmen also discovered that placing stones in the uterus prevented copulation during traveling and wars.

During estrus (2 to 4 days), lions can copulate more than a hundred times, with mating occurring every 15 minutes. It has been estimated that lions copulate 3,000 times for every cub that survives to the yearling stage. One male copulated 157 times in 55 hours with 2 different females. (Lions are induced ovulators.)

In the domestic chicken, ovarian progesterone induces the preovulatory surge of LH, not estradiol.

The elephant shrew and tenrec are natural superovulators. In fact, in the tenrec more than 40 follicles may ovulate, but litters of greater than 10 have not been observed. About 75% of the embryos die and are reabsorbed during gestation.

Female elephants in estrus attract males by releasing a pheromone that is excreted in the urine. This pheromone is potent and can attract bull elephants from miles away.

The Guinness Book of World Records reported that Mrs. R.A. Kistler gave birth to a baby girl when she was 57 years, 4 months and 5 weeks old.

The alpine black salamander has the longest gestation period known. Interestingly, it depends on altitude. When they live more than 4,600 feet above sea level, the infant develops within the mother for over three years.

When comparing the size of bird eggs to the sizes of the birds that produce them, ostrich eggs are among the smallest and hummingbird eggs are among the largest.

The female pigeon can't lay eggs when she's alone. She needs either another pigeon or her own reflection in a mirror to do that task.

8

Key References

Berek, J. ed. 1996. *Novak's Gynecology*, 13th Edition. Williams and Williams. Baltimore. ISBN 0-7817-3262-X.

Crowe, M.A. 1999. "Gonadotrophic control of terminal follicular growth in cattle." *Reprod. Dom. Anim.* 34:157-166.

Crozet, N. 1993. "Fertilization *in vivo* and *in vitro*" in *Reproduction in Mammals and Man*. p327-348. C. Thibault, M.C. Levasseur and R.H.F. Hunter, eds., Ellipses, Paris. ISBN 2-7298-9354-7.

Driancourt, M.A., A Gougeon, A. Royere and C. Thibault. 1993. "Ovarian function" in *Reproduction in Mammals and Man*. p281-306. C. Thibault, M.C. Levasseur and R.H.F. Hunter, eds, Ellipses, Paris. ISBN 2-7298-9354-7.

Johnston, S.D., M.V. Root Kustritz and P.N.S. Olson. 2001. *Canine and Feline Theriogenology*. W.B. Saunders Co., Philadelphia. ISBN 0-7216-5607-2.

Lucy, M.C., J.D. Savio, L. Badinga, R.L. De La Sota and W.W. Thatcher, 1992. "Factors that affect ovarian follicular dynamics in cattle." *J. Anim. Sci.* 70:3615-3626.

McGee, E.A. and A.J.W. Hsueh. 2000. "Initial and cyclic recruitment of ovarian follicles." *Endocrine Reviews.* 21(2):200-214.

Netter, A. 1993. "The menopause" in *Reproduction in Mammals and Man*. p627-642. C. Thibault, M.C. Levasseur and R.H.F. Hunter, eds., Ellipses, Paris. ISBN 2-7298-9354-7.

Szöllösi, D. 1993. "Oocyte maturation" in *Reproduction in Mammals and Man*. p307-326. C. Thibault, M.C. Levasseur and R.H.F. Hunter, eds., Ellipses, Paris. ISBN 2-7298-9354-7.

Udolff, L.C. and E.Y. Adashi 1998. "Menopause" in *Encyclopedia of Reproduction*, Vol. 3 p183-188. Knobil and Neill, eds. Academic Press, San Diego. ISBN 0-12-227023-1.

8

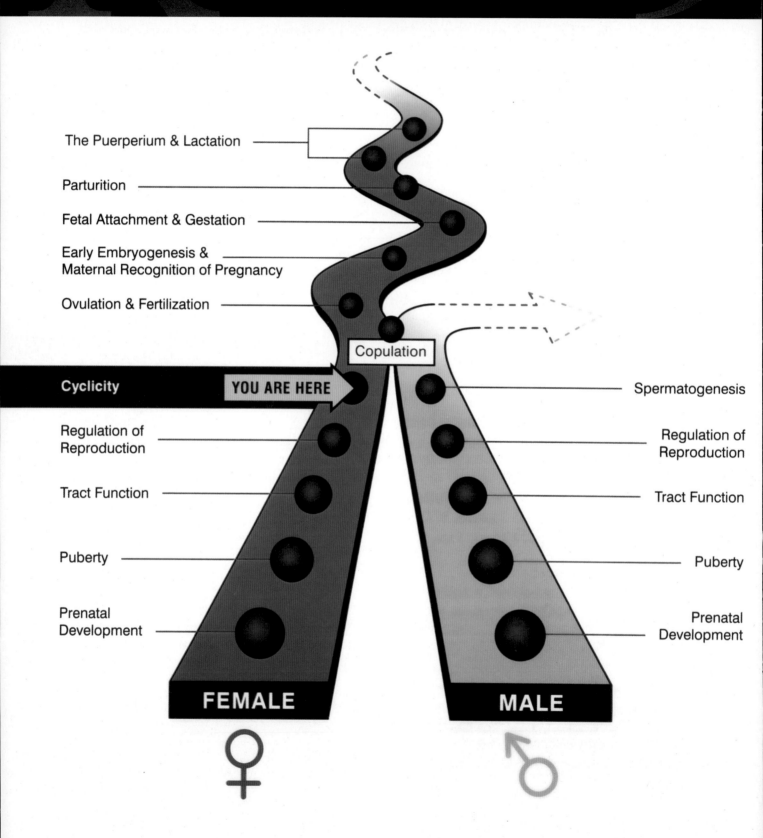

The Puerperium & Lactation

Parturition

Fetal Attachment & Gestation

Early Embryogenesis &
Maternal Recognition of Pregnancy

Ovulation & Fertilization

Copulation

Cyclicity

YOU ARE HERE

Regulation of
Reproduction

Tract Function

Puberty

Prenatal
Development

FEMALE

Spermatogenesis

Regulation of
Reproduction

Tract Function

Puberty

Prenatal
Development

MALE

Take Home Message

The luteal phase consists of three major processes. They are: 1) luteinization (the transformation of follicular cells into luteal cells after ovulation), 2) synthesis and secretion (growth and development of the corpus luteum accompanied by increasing quantities of progesterone) and 3) luteolysis (destruction of the corpus luteum) accompanied by rapidly declining blood progesterone that results in a subsequent follicular phase. Regression of the corpus luteum is brought about by prostaglandin $F_{2\alpha}$ that is synthesized and secreted by the uterine endometrium in most mammals and by the ovary in women. The negative feedback.exerted by progesterone on the hypothalamus is removed and the female enters a new follicular phase because the pulse frequency and amplitude of GnRH increases thus allowing FSH and LH to increase. In women, luteolysis causes the initiation of menstruation that is followed by another follicular phase.

The luteal phase lasts from the time of ovulation until **luteolysis** of the **corpus luteum (CL)** near the end of the estrous cycle. It includes **metestrus** and **diestrus** (See Figure 9-1). The dominant ovarian hormone during the luteal phase is progesterone.

> *The luteal phase consists of:*
> - *luteinization (formation of the CL)*
> - *synthesis and secretion of large quantities of progesterone*
> - *luteolysis*

When the follicle ruptures at ovulation, blood vessels within the follicular wall also rupture. This vascular breakage results in a structure with a "bloody" clot-like appearance. This structure is called the **corpus hemorrhagicum** because of its hemorrhagic (bloody) appearance when viewed from the surface of the ovary. Corpora hemorrhagica can be observed from the time of ovulation until about day 1 to 3 of the estrous cycle (See Figures 9-3 through 9-6). Immediately after ovulation, corpora hemorrhagica appear as small, pimple-like structures on the surface of the ovary. At about day 3 to 5, the corpus luteum (CL) begins to increase in size and lose its hemorrhagic appearance. It increases in mass until the middle of the cycle, when its size is maximal and coincides with the maximum secretion of progesterone during diestrus. Near the end of the luteal phase, luteolysis occurs and the CL loses its functional integrity and decreases in size. Luteolysis results in an irreversible structural degradation of the corpus luteum. A regressed corpus luteum will become a corpus albicans (white body).

Figure 9-1. The Luteal Phase

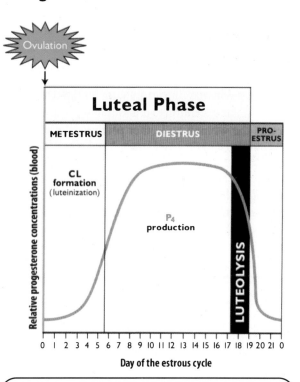

The luteal phase begins immediately after ovulation. During the early luteal phase, the corpus luteum (CL) develops (luteinization) and progesterone increases. During the mid-luteal phase (diestrus) the corpus luteum is fully functional and progesterone (P_4) plateaus. During the last 2-3 days of the luteal phase, destruction of the corpus luteum occurs (luteolysis) and the luteal phase terminates. Following luteolysis, proestrus is initiated.

9

In general, a corpus albicans can be observed for a substantial period of time (several estrous cycles) after luteolysis. The corpus albicans appears as a white scar-like structure because the connective tissue remains after the glandular tissue disappears.

The corpus luteum originates from an ovulatory follicle.

After ovulation the **theca interna** and the **granulosal cells** of the follicle undergo a dramatic transformation known as **luteinization**. Luteinization is the process whereby cells of the ovulatory follicle are transformed into luteal tissue. This transformation is governed by LH. Shortly before ovulation the basement membrane of the follicle undergoes partial disintegration and the physical separation of the thecal and granulosal cells disappears (See Figure 9-2). During ovulation, follicular fluid leaks from the follicle. At the same time, the wall of the follicle collapses forming many folds (See Figure 9-2). These folds begin to interdigitate, allowing thecal cells and the granulosal cells to mix, thus forming a gland consisting of connective tissue cells, thecal cells and granulosal cells. In general, the cells of thecal origin and the cells of granulosal origin mix uniformly with one another (See Figure 9-2). An exception to this is found in the corpora lutea of the woman and other primates, where thecal and granulosal cells are clustered into distinct "islets". It is easy to distinguish microscopically between luteal cells that originate from the granulosal cells and those that originate from the thecal cells. Large luteal cells are derived from granulosal cells while small luteal cells are derived from thecal cells. Portions of the basement membrane that separated the thecal cells from the granulosal cells remain and constitute the connective tissue network of the corpus luteum (See Figure 9-2).

Luteal tissue consists of large and small luteal cells:

• *large cells originate from the granulosal cells*

• *small cells originate from the cells of the theca interna*

Large luteal cells (sometimes called granulosal-lutein cells) vary in diameter from 20-70 micrometers (μm), depending on species. In some species (ruminants), there are a large number of dense secretory granules close to the plasma membrane. These secretory granules contain **oxytocin** in the corpus luteum of the cycle and are believed to contain **relaxin** in the corpus luteum of pregnancy.

Small luteal cells (sometimes called thecal-lutein cells) are less than 20 μ m in diameter, have an irregular shape and possess numerous lipid droplets in their cytoplasm. They do not contain secretory granules as do the large luteal cells. Both small and large luteal cells are **steroidogenic** (possessing the ability to produce steroids), in this case progesterone.

In general, the corpus luteum increases in size until about midway through the luteal phase (See Figures 9-3 through 9-6). For example, a skilled examiner can almost always determine whether a corpus luteum is present or absent in cows. In mares, it is almost impossible to ascertain the presence or absence of the corpus luteum because it does not protrude from the surface of the ovary.

In the cow, palpation cannot accurately predict the functional status of the corpus luteum. In four separate studies, cows were transrectally palpated by experienced diagnosticians. Corpora lutea were classified as functional (secreting high quantities of progesterone) or nonfunctional (regressing or secreting low levels of progesterone) by the diagnosticians. Using measurements of blood progesterone as the indicator of corpus luteum function, it was found that 25% to 39% of cows classified as having a functional corpus luteum were not secreting high quantities of progesterone. Furthermore, 15% to 21% of cows classified as having a nonfunctional corpus luteum had high blood progesterone. Clearly, the use of transrectal palpation to assess the functional status of the corpus luteum has limitations. From a practical reproductive management perspective, this problem limits the effectiveness of treating animals with luteolytic agents to induce estrus and ovulation. In other words, administering luteolytic agents (prostaglandin $F_{2\alpha}$) on the basis of transrectal palpation of the ovaries alone will provide suboptimal results.

The use of real-time ultrasonography has proven effective for the examination of corpora lutea, as well as ovarian follicles. In cattle, progesterone concentration in blood is correlated with the diameter of the corpus luteum as measured by ultrasonography.

Large luteal cells rarely multiply after ovulation. Therefore, the total number of granulosal cells "donated" by the follicle determines the number of large luteal cells in the newly-formed CL. Luteal function may in-part be related to the vigor (as judged by the number of granulosal cells) of the follicle prior to ovulation. In the ewe (and presumably other species), an increase in corpus luteum size and weight is due to a threefold increase in <u>volume</u> of large luteal cells coupled with a fivefold increase in the <u>number</u>

Figure 9-2. Formation of the Corpus Luteum

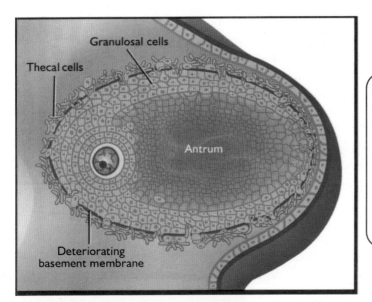

Preovulatory Follicle
The preovulatory follicle consists of granulosal cells that line the antrum. The basement membrane, separating the granulosal cells from the cells of the theca interna begins to deteriorate prior to ovulation because of the action of collagenase. Complete separation between the granulosal cells and the theca interna no longer exists and the cells can begin to intermingle.

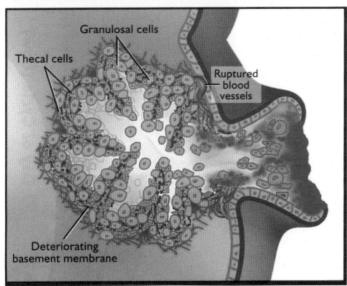

Corpus Hemorrhagicum (CH)
During ovulation, many small blood vessels rupture causing local hemorrhage. This hemorrhage appears as a blood clot on the surface of the ovary that sometimes penetrates into the center of the follicle after ovulation (See Figures 9-3, 1A and B and 9-4,1A and B). Following evacuation of the follicular fluid and oocyte, the follicle collapses into folds. The cells of the theca interna and the granulosa begin to mix. The basement membrane forms the connective tissue substructure of the corpus luteum.

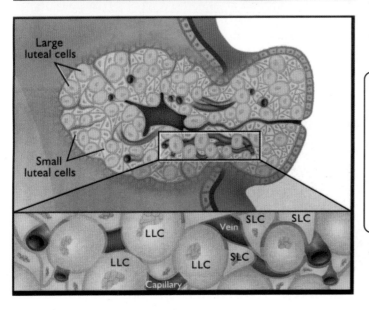

Functional Corpus Luteum (CL)
The corpus luteum is now a mixture of large luteal cells, LLC (formerly granulosal cells) and many small luteal cells, SLC (formerly thecal cells). In some cases, there is a remnant of the follicular antrum that forms a small cavity in the center of the corpus luteum (See Figures 9-3, 3B and 9-4, 2B; 9-6, 3B).

9

Figure 9-3. Luteal Anatomy in Relation to Progesterone Secretion During the Estrous Cycle in the Cow

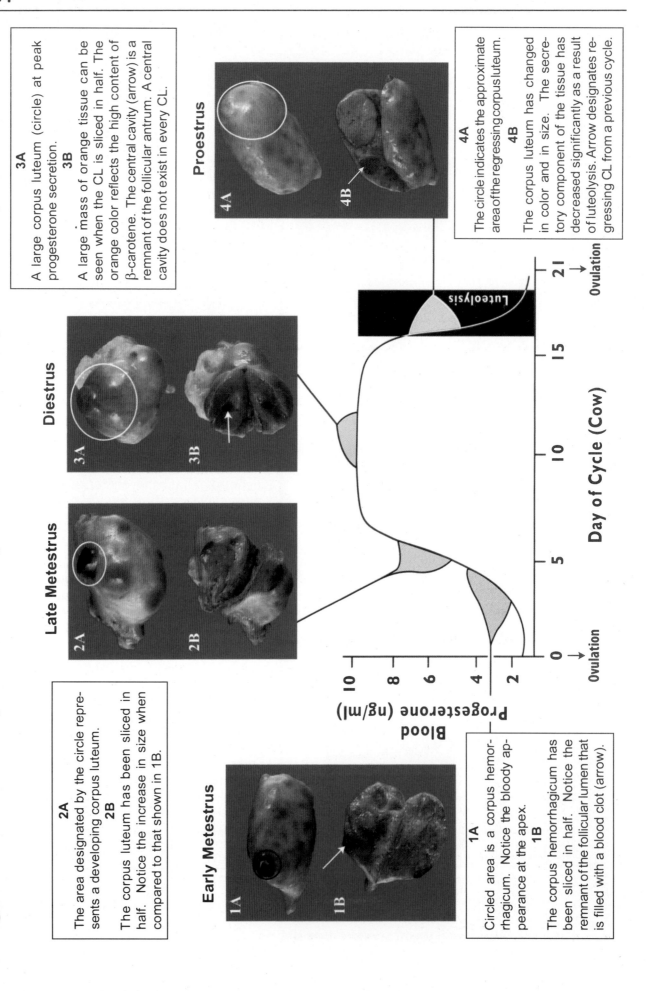

3A

A large corpus luteum (circle) at peak progesterone secretion.

3B

A large mass of orange tissue can be seen when the CL is sliced in half. The orange color reflects the high content of β-carotene. The central cavity (arrow) is a remnant of the follicular antrum. A central cavity does not exist in every CL.

Proestrus

4A

The circle indicates the approximate area of the regressing corpus luteum.

4B

The corpus luteum has changed in color and in size. The secretory component of the tissue has decreased significantly as a result of luteolysis. Arrow designates regressing CL from a previous cycle.

Diestrus

Late Metestrus

2A

The area designated by the circle represents a developing corpus luteum.

2B

The corpus luteum has been sliced in half. Notice the increase in size when compared to that shown in 1B.

Luteolysis

Day of Cycle (Cow)

Ovulation   0   5   10   15   21   Ovulation

Blood Progesterone (ng/ml)   2   4   6   8   10

Early Metestrus

1A

Circled area is a corpus hemorrhagicum. Notice the bloody appearance at the apex.

1B

The corpus hemorrhagicum has been sliced in half. Notice the remnant of the follicular lumen that is filled with a blood clot (arrow).

Figure 9-4. Luteal Anatomy in Relation to Progesterone Secretion During the Estrous Cycle in the Ewe

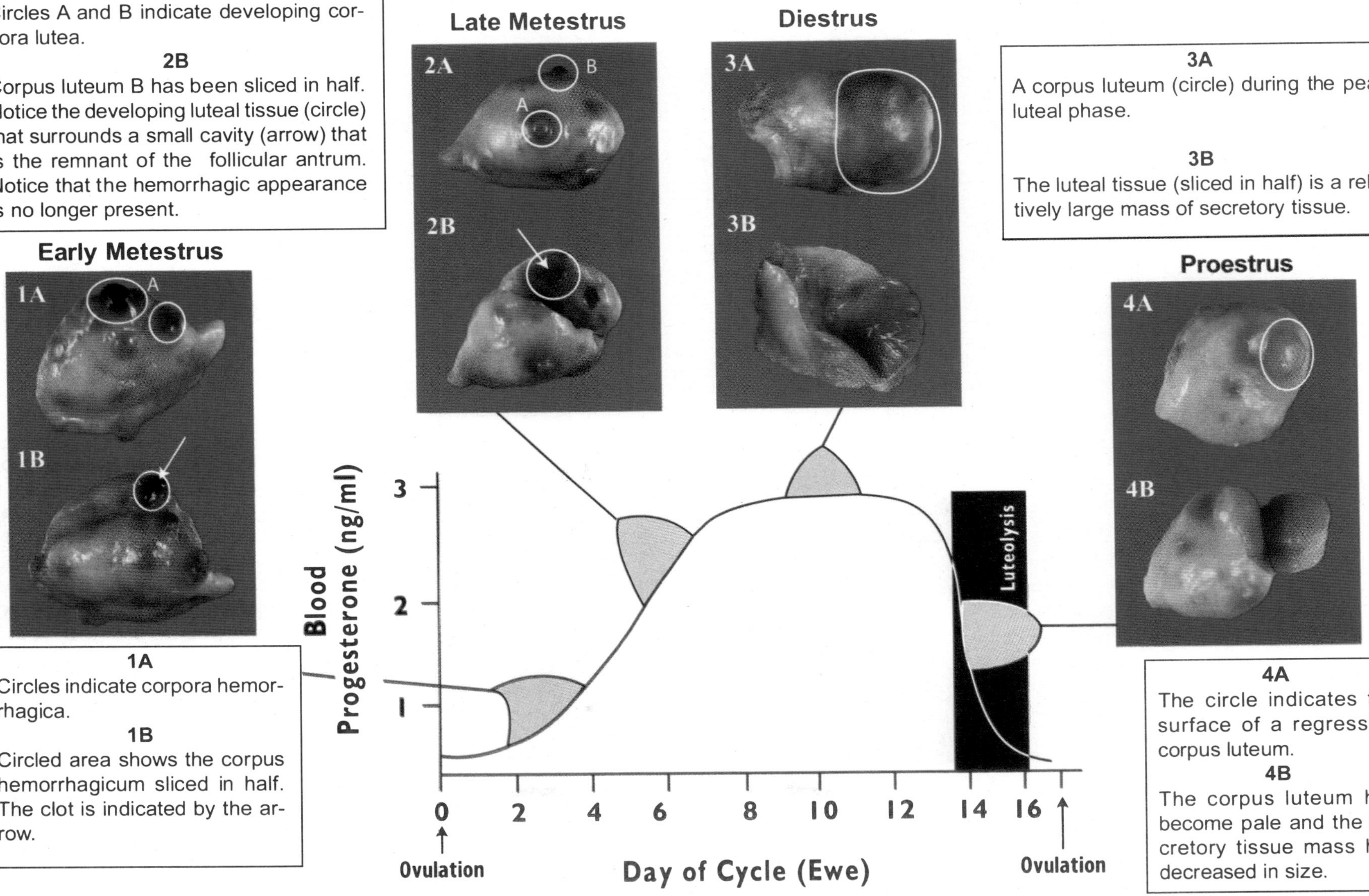
Early Metestrus
1A
A
1B
Late Metestrus
2A
A
B
2B
Diestrus
3A
3B
Proestrus
4A
4B
Blood Progesterone (ng/ml)
3
2
1
Luteolysis
0
2
4
6
8
10
12
14
16
Ovulation
Ovulation
Day of Cycle (Ewe)

2A
Circles A and B indicate developing corpora lutea.

2B
Corpus luteum B has been sliced in half. Notice the developing luteal tissue (circle) that surrounds a small cavity (arrow) that is the remnant of the follicular antrum. Notice that the hemorrhagic appearance is no longer present.

1A
Circles indicate corpora hemorrhagica.

1B
Circled area shows the corpus hemorrhagicum sliced in half. The clot is indicated by the arrow.

3A
A corpus luteum (circle) during the peak luteal phase.

3B
The luteal tissue (sliced in half) is a relatively large mass of secretory tissue.

4A
The circle indicates the surface of a regressing corpus luteum.

4B
The corpus luteum has become pale and the secretory tissue mass has decreased in size.

Figure 9-5. Luteal Anatomy in Relation to Progesterone Secretion During the Estrous Cycle in the Sow

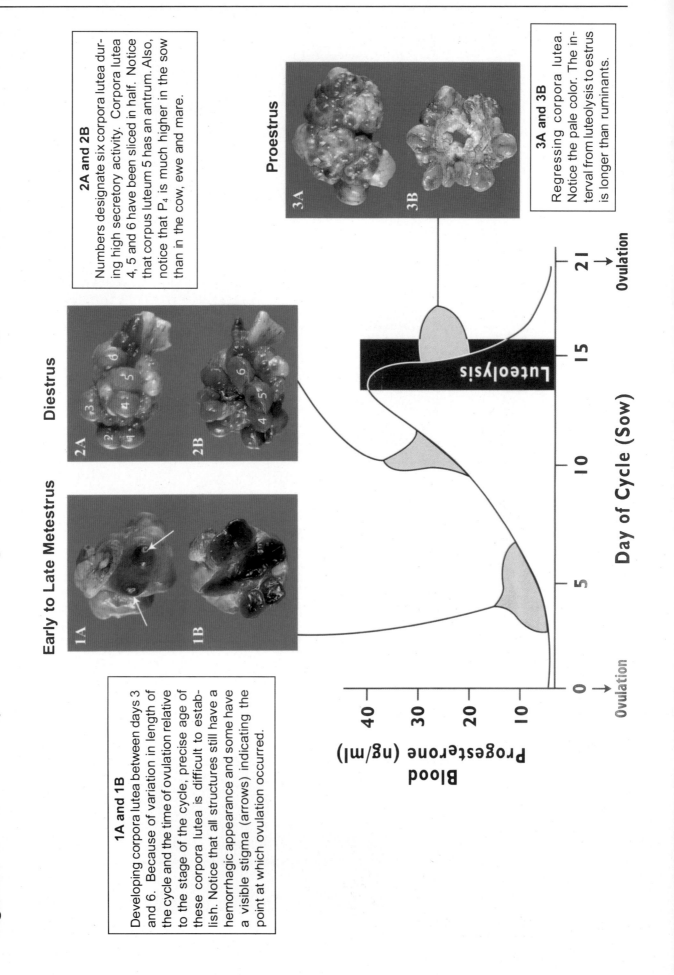

1A and 1B

Developing corpora lutea between days 3 and 6. Because of variation in length of the cycle and the time of ovulation relative to the stage of the cycle, precise age of these corpora lutea is difficult to establish. Notice that all structures still have a hemorrhagic appearance and some have a visible stigma (arrows) indicating the point at which ovulation occurred.

2A and 2B

Numbers designate six corpora lutea during high secretory activity. Corpora lutea 4, 5 and 6 have been sliced in half. Notice that corpus luteum 5 has an antrum. Also, notice that P₄ is much higher in the sow than in the cow, ewe and mare.

3A and 3B

Regressing corpora lutea. Notice the pale color. The interval from luteolysis to estrus is longer than ruminants.

Early to Late Metestrus   Diestrus   Proestrus

Figure 9-6. Luteal Anatomy in Relation to Progesterone Secretion During the Estrous Cycle in the Mare

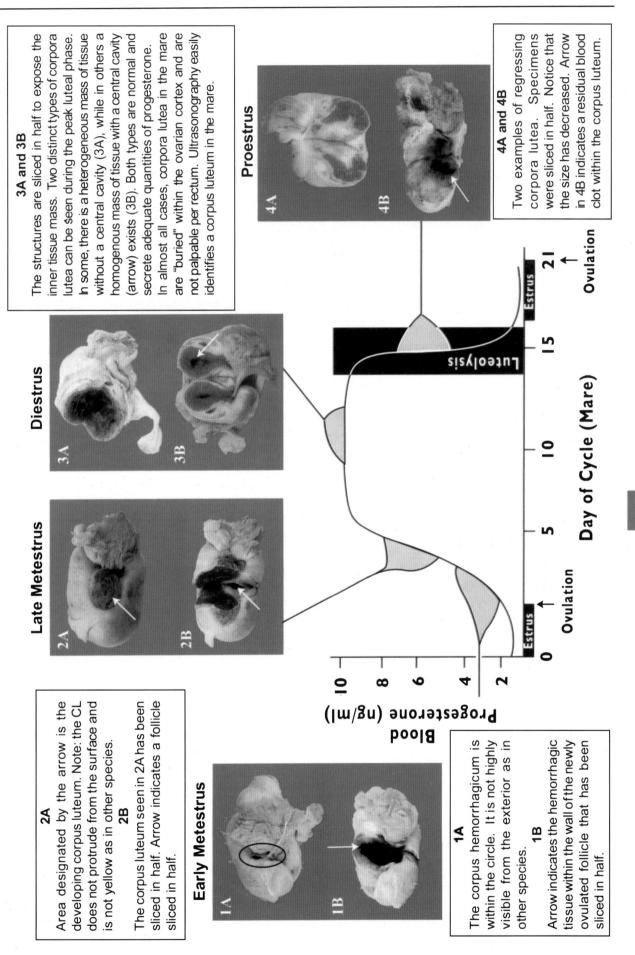

3A and 3B

The structures are sliced in half to expose the inner tissue mass. Two distinct types of corpora lutea can be seen during the peak luteal phase. In some, there is a heterogeneous mass of tissue without a central cavity (3A), while in others a homogenous mass of tissue with a central cavity (arrow) exists (3B). Both types are normal and secrete adequate quantities of progesterone. In almost all cases, corpora lutea in the mare are "buried" within the ovarian cortex and are not palpable per rectum. Ultrasonography easily identifies a corpus luteum in the mare.

Diestrus

Late Metestrus

2A

Area designated by the arrow is the developing corpus luteum. Note: the CL does not protrude from the surface and is not yellow as in other species.

2B

The corpus luteum seen in 2A has been sliced in half. Arrow indicates a follicle sliced in half.

Early Metestrus

1A

The corpus hemorrhagicum is within the circle. It is not highly visible from the exterior as in other species.

1B

Arrow indicates the hemorrhagic tissue within the wall of the newly ovulated follicle that has been sliced in half.

Proestrus

4A and 4B

Two examples of regressing corpora lutea. Specimens were sliced in half. Notice that the size has decreased. Arrow in 4B indicates a residual blood clot within the corpus luteum.

Blood Progesterone (ng/ml)

Day of Cycle (Mare)

Estrus — Ovulation — Luteolysis — Estrus — Ovulation

9

of small luteal cells. Thus, large luteal cells undergo **hypertrophy** (increase in size), while small luteal cells undergo **hyperplasia** (increase in cell numbers) as the CL develops. In addition to changes in steroidogenic cells, non-steroidogenic cells (fibroblasts, capillary cells and eosinophils) increase in number during the estrous cycle. The net effect of these cellular changes is a marked enlargement of the corpus luteum.

> *The "vigor" of the corpus luteum*
> *probably depends on:*
> • *the number of luteal cells*
> • *the degree to which the CL*
>   *becomes vascularized*

The functional capability (ability to secrete progesterone) of the newly developed corpus luteum may also depend on the degree of vascularity in the cellular layers of the follicle. The ability of the corpus luteum to vascularize may relate to its ability to synthesize and deliver hormones. As presented in the previous chapter, follicular fluid contains angiogenic factors. The degree to which these angiogenic factors promote vascularization of the corpus luteum is probably related to the quantity of angiogenic factors present in the follicular tissue.

Insufficient luteal function (poor progesterone synthesis and secretion) is believed to be a possible contributor to reproductive failure in mammals. A corpus luteum secreting suboptimal concentrations of progesterone probably results in the inability of the dam's uterus to support development of the early embryo.

The primary target organs for progesterone are the hypothalamus, the uterus and the mammary gland (See Figure 9-7). The uterus has two target components: 1) the glandular endometrium and 2) the muscular myometrium. Progesterone stimulates maximal secretion by the endometrial glands. Secretory products from the endometrial glands contribute to an environment that supports the development of the "free-floating" conceptus after it enters the uterine lumen. An important inhibitory role of progesterone is to reduce the motility (contractions) of the myometrium. Such a role causes a "uterine quiescence" effect on the myometrium in the cow, pig and ewe. In the mare, myometrial motility is not inhibited to the same degree so that the conceptus is transported around the uterus but not expelled. Myometrial inhibition is thought to be important because it provides "calming" conditions for attachment of the conceptus to the uterine endometrium. In the mare, the conceptus

is transported about in the uterine lumen by contractions of the myometrium. This phenomenon will be discussed in more detail in Chapter 13. Progesterone causes final alveolar development of the mammary gland during pregnancy, thereby allowing initiation of lactation.

Progesterone Synthesis Requires Cholesterol and LH

The presence of basal (tonic) LH and cholesterol is necessary for progesterone to be secreted by luteal cells. The mechanism whereby LH causes secretion of progesterone in luteal cells is illustrated in Figure 9-8. In order to fully understand progesterone synthesis, you should carefully read the explanation of each step in the boxes provided in Figure 9-8.

Progesterone is of major importance in the endocrine control of reproduction because it exerts a strong **negative feedback** on the hypothalamus (See Figure 9-7). Elevated progesterone reduces the pulse frequency of GnRH by the tonic GnRH center in the hypothalamus. However, the amplitude of the LH pulses is still relatively high. Such a pattern of LH secretion along with tonic FSH secretion allows follicles to develop during the luteal phase. These follicles do not reach preovulatory status until progesterone decreases and the frequency of LH pulses increases. High progesterone therefore prevents development of steroidogenic preovulatory follicles, secretion of estradiol, behavioral estrus and the preovulatory surge of GnRH and LH.

> *Progesterone is an inhibitor because it:*
> • *reduces GnRH pulse frequency*
> • *prevents behavioral estrus*
> • *stops the preovulatory LH surge*
> • *reduces myometrial tone (except in*
>   *the mare)*

Progesterone almost totally inhibits estrual behavior. In general, females under the influence of progesterone do not display estrus and will not copulate with the male. However, as pointed out in Chapter 7, progesterone exerts a positive priming effect on the brain to enhance the behavioral effects of estradiol after progesterone is reduced. For example, if females are **ovariectomized** (removal of ovaries) and treated with estradiol, they will display behavioral characteristics of estrus. These traits will be amplified in both intensity and duration if cows are treated with progesterone for about 5 to 7 days before they receive estradiol.

Lysis of the Corpus Luteum Must Occur Before the Female Can Enter the Follicular Phase

Luteolysis is the loss of progesterone secretion by the CL followed by loss of luteal tissue mass. It occurs during a one-to-three day period at the end of the luteal phase. Luteolysis is a process whereby the corpus luteum undergoes irreversible degeneration characterized by a dramatic drop in blood concentrations of progesterone (See Figures 9-1, 9-3 through 9-6). The hormone inducing luteolysis is $PGF_{2\alpha}$ secreted by the uterine endometrium. Communication between the corpus luteum and the uterine endometrium is necessary in order to bring about successful luteolysis. The uterus functions as an endocrine organ and is responsible for secreting $PGF_{2\alpha}$ that causes luteolysis. If luteolysis does not occur, the animal remains in a sustained luteal phase because progesterone inhibits gonadotropin secretion (See Figure 9-7). The importance of the uterus in controlling the life-span of the corpus luteum is illustrated in Figure 9-9. In mammals, other than primates, complete removal of the uterus (**uterectomy**) after ovulation causes the corpus luteum to be maintained just as if the

---

Figure 9-7. Progesterone (P_4) has Many Physiological Effects

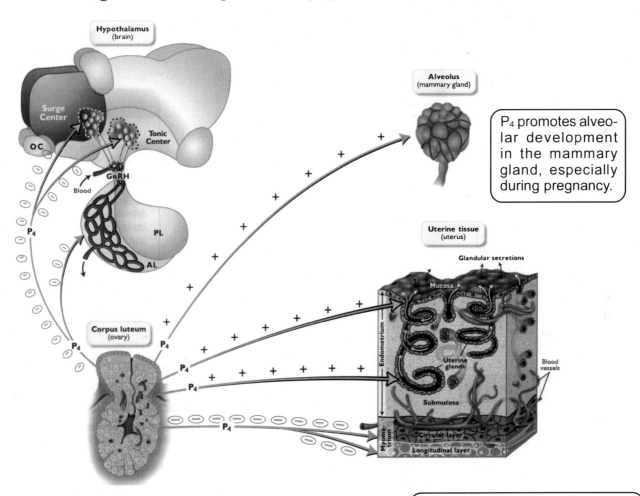

P_4 promotes alveolar development in the mammary gland, especially during pregnancy.

P_4 produced by the CL exerts a negative (-) feedback on the GnRH neurons of the hypothalamus. Therefore, GnRH, LH and FSH are suppressed and little estrogen is secreted. Progesterone is thought to decrease the number of GnRH receptors on the anterior pituitary.

P_4 exerts a strong positive (+) influence on the endometrium of the uterus. Under the influence of P_4, the uterine glands secrete materials into the uterine lumen. Progesterone inhibits the myometrium and thus reduces its contractility and tone.

Figure 9-8. Mechanism of Progesterone Synthesis by Luteal Cells

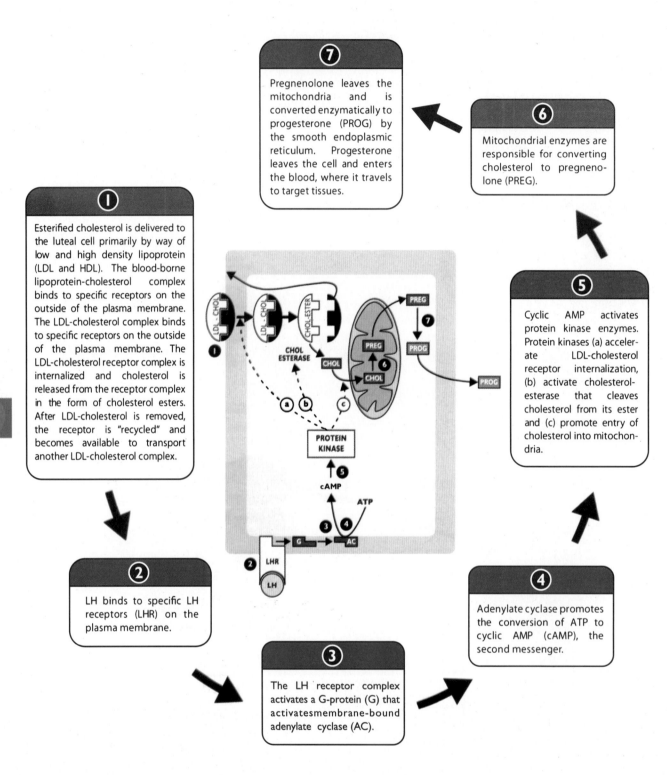

⑦ Pregnenolone leaves the mitochondria and is converted enzymatically to progesterone (PROG) by the smooth endoplasmic reticulum. Progesterone leaves the cell and enters the blood, where it travels to target tissues.

⑥ Mitochondrial enzymes are responsible for converting cholesterol to pregnenolone (PREG).

① Esterified cholesterol is delivered to the luteal cell primarily by way of low and high density lipoprotein (LDL and HDL). The blood-borne lipoprotein-cholesterol complex binds to specific receptors on the outside of the plasma membrane. The LDL-cholesterol complex binds to specific receptors on the outside of the plasma membrane. The LDL-cholesterol receptor complex is internalized and cholesterol is released from the receptor complex in the form of cholesterol esters. After LDL-cholesterol is removed, the receptor is "recycled" and becomes available to transport another LDL-cholesterol complex.

⑤ Cyclic AMP activates protein kinase enzymes. Protein kinases (a) accelerate LDL-cholesterol receptor internalization, (b) activate cholesterol-esterase that cleaves cholesterol from its ester and (c) promote entry of cholesterol into mitochondria.

② LH binds to specific LH receptors (LHR) on the plasma membrane.

④ Adenylate cyclase promotes the conversion of ATP to cyclic AMP (cAMP), the second messenger.

③ The LH receptor complex activates a G-protein (G) that activates membrane-bound adenylate cyclase (AC).

9

female were pregnant. For example, in ewes with an intact uterus the life-span of the corpus luteum is identical to that seen in the normal cycle (17 days). However, when the entire uterus is removed (total uterectomy), the life-span of the corpus luteum is prolonged for months and is similar to a normal gestation period (148 days). Clearly, removal of the entire uterus extends the life-span of the corpus luteum dramatically.

> ## The uterus is required for successful luteolysis in many species.

When partial uterectomy is performed, a less dramatic effect can be seen. For example, when the uterine horn **ipsilateral** (on the same side) to the corpus luteum is removed, the life-span of the corpus luteum is almost twice as long (about 35 days) as the normal cycle. In contrast, when the **contralateral** (opposite side) uterine horn is removed, there is little, if any, effect on the life-span of the corpus luteum. The response to complete and partial uterectomy is summarized in Figure 9-9. Several important findings have emerged from the classic experiments illustrated in Figure 9-9. First, the uterus is required for lysis of the corpus luteum. Therefore, the uterus secretes a substance(s) that causes luteolysis. Second, removal of the uterus ipsilateral to the corpus luteum increases the life-span of the corpus luteum, while removal of the uterine horn contralateral to the corpus luteum does not. A local effect of the uterus directly upon the ipsilateral ovary containing the corpus luteum is obvious. A local effect can be further supported by the fact that when the ovary is transplanted into the neck of the female, but the uterus remains intact, the corpus luteum life-span is prolonged by many weeks. Collectively, what these experiments have told us is: 1) the uterus is responsible for luteolysis and 2) the uterus must be near the ovary.

You should now understand from the above discussion that the uterus is required for luteolysis. Clearly then, the uterus must secrete a substance that causes destruction of the corpus luteum. After years of intensive and heavily focused research, it has been conclusively demonstrated that prostaglandin $F_{2\alpha}$ is the luteolysin in domestic animals. Prostaglandin $F_{2\alpha}$ is also the luteolytic agent in primates but is secreted by the corpus luteum. Among domestic animals, the uterectomized bitch cycles normally and has a luteal phase of normal duration suggesting that the uterus has little or no influence upon luteal function in canids.

> ## A vascular countercurrent transport system ensures that PGF$_{2\alpha}$ will reach the ovary in sufficient quantities to cause luteolysis in the ewe, cow and sow.

How does $PGF_{2\alpha}$ get from the uterus to the ovary, where it causes luteolysis? Prostaglandin $F_{2\alpha}$ from the uterus is transported to the ipsilateral ovary through a **vascular countercurrent exchange mechanism**. A countercurrent exchange system involves two closely associated blood vessels in which blood from one vessel flows in the opposite direction to that of the adjacent vessel. Low molecular weight substances in high concentrations in one vessel diffuse into the adjacent vessel, where they are in low concentrations. The $PGF_{2\alpha}$ secreted by the endometrium enters the uterine vein and the uterine lymph vessels, at relatively high concentrations. The ovarian artery lies in close association with the utero-ovarian vein (See Figure 9-10). By countercurrent exchange, transfer of $PGF_{2\alpha}$ is accomplished by a prostaglandin transport protein that facilitates movement of $PGF_{2\alpha}$ across the wall of the uterine vein into the blood of the ovarian artery. This special anatomical relationship ensures that a high proportion of the $PGF_{2\alpha}$ secreted by the uterus will be transported directly to the ovary and the corpus luteum <u>without dilution</u> by the systemic circulation. This mechanism is particularly important because much of $PGF_{2\alpha}$ is denatured during one circulatory pass through the pulmonary system in the ewe and the cow (around 90%). In the sow, only about 40% of the $PGF_{2\alpha}$ is denatured in the pulmonary circulation. By entering the ovarian artery, $PGF_{2\alpha}$ can exert its lytic effect directly on the corpus luteum. The countercurrent transport system is present in the cow, sow and ewe, but not in the mare. The mare does not metabolize $PGF_{2\alpha}$ as rapidly as other species, so the need for a local transport specialization is not as important in the mare. In addition, the mare CL is thought to be more sensitive to $PGF_{2\alpha}$ than the CL of the cow, sow and ewe.

Exogenous $PGF_{2\alpha}$ causes luteolysis during about 60% of the cycle in most species. For example, it exerts its most potent effect after day six of the cycle and will almost always cause luteolysis if administered after this time in the cow. In contrast, $PGF_{2\alpha}$ has a negligible effect during the first two to four days after ovulation. In the pig, the corpus luteum does not become responsive to the luteolytic action of a single dose of $PGF_{2\alpha}$ until day 12 to 14 of the cycle. Prostaglandin $F_{2\alpha}$ and its analogs are used widely to cause regression of the corpus luteum and thus synchronize estrus and ovulation, to induce abortion and sometimes to induce parturition.

9

Figure 9-9. Effect of Uterectomy upon Estrous Cycle Duration in the Ewe

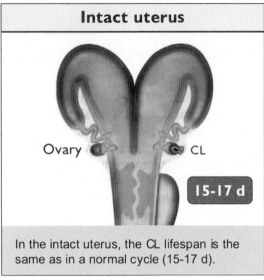

Intact uterus

Ovary — CL

15-17 d

In the intact uterus, the CL lifespan is the same as in a normal cycle (15-17 d).

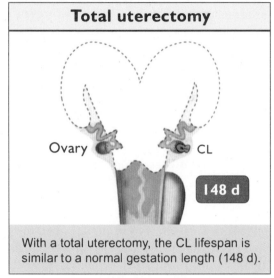

Total uterectomy

Ovary — CL

148 d

With a total uterectomy, the CL lifespan is similar to a normal gestation length (148 d).

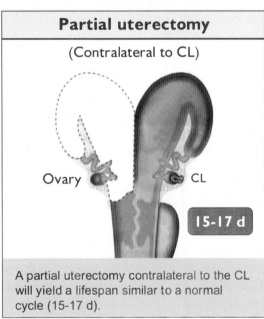

Partial uterectomy
(Contralateral to CL)

Ovary — CL

15-17 d

A partial uterectomy contralateral to the CL will yield a lifespan similar to a normal cycle (15-17 d).

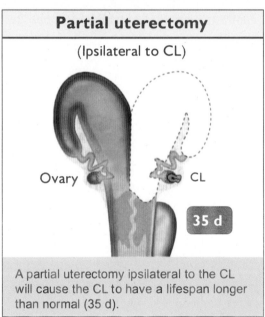

Partial uterectomy
(Ipsilateral to CL)

Ovary — CL

35 d

A partial uterectomy ipsilateral to the CL will cause the CL to have a lifespan longer than normal (35 d).

9

The requirements for luteolysis (in subprimate mammals) are:

• *presence of oxytocin receptors on endometrial cells*

• *presence of a critical level of oxytocin*

• *PGF$_{2\alpha}$ synthesis by the endometrium*

What stimulates the secretion of PGF$_{2\alpha}$ during the late luteal phase? In addition to progesterone, large luteal cells synthesize and secrete oxytocin. In fact, in the cow and the ewe the corpus luteum contains very large quantities of oxytocin. Luteal oxytocin is stored in secretory granules analogous to those observed in the nerve terminals of the posterior pituitary gland. When oxytocin is injected into ewes near the end of the luteal phase, PGF$_{2\alpha}$ appears in the circulating blood in response to these injections.

During the first-half of the luteal phase, prostaglandin secretion by the endometrium of the uterus is almost nonexistent. However, during the late luteal phase, secretion of PGF$_{2\alpha}$ begins to occur in pulses (See Figure 9-11). The pulses increase in frequency and amplitude as the end of the luteal phase approaches.

Figure 9-10. The Utero-Ovarian Vascular Countercurrent Transport System

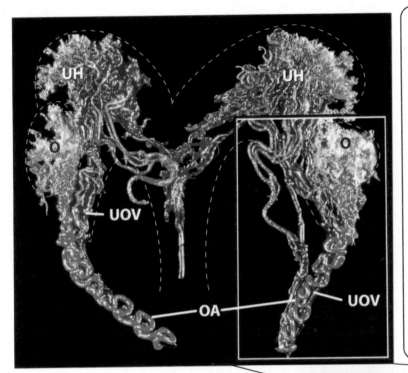

In the two photographs, a blue latex medium was injected into the utero-ovarian vein (UOV) and a red latex medium into the ovarian artery (OA). The latex was allowed to polymerize and solidify. The tissue was then dissolved with repeated treatments of saturated sodium hydroxide followed by washings with water until all of the tissue was removed (From Cody <u>et al</u>. 1999. *Biol. Reprod.* 60(Suppl 1): 90). The dashed lines in the photo at left approximate the boundaries of the uterine horns (UH) and the ovary (O). The uterus secretes prostaglandin $F_{2\alpha}$ that enters the venous drainage at high concentrations. In the photo below $PGF_{2\alpha}$ diffuses from the utero-ovarian vein into the ovarian artery and is transported directly to the ovary (artery-arrows) where it causes luteolysis.

Schematic illustration of the countercurrent transport system in the cow, sow and ewe. A portion of uterine $PGF_{2\alpha}$ is transported directly from the utero-ovarian vein into the ovarian artery where it has a direct lytic effect on the corpus luteum.

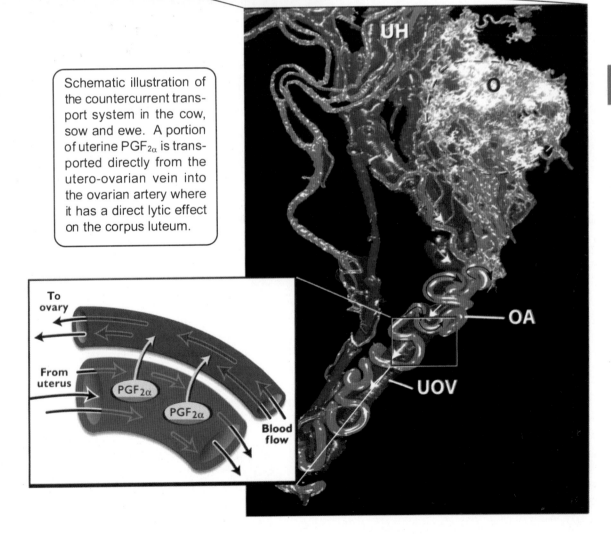

Figure 9-11. Changes in PGF Metabolite (PGF-M) During Late Diestrus and Proestrus

PGF-M (brown line) is an accurate estimate of PGF$_{2\alpha}$. As the graph shows, PGF$_{2\alpha}$ is low.

The amplitude and frequency of episodes of PGF$_{2\alpha}$ secretion increase at about day 16. About 5 pulses of PGF$_{2\alpha}$ in a 24 hour period are required to cause luteolysis and a dramatic drop in P$_4$.

Episodic secretion of PGF$_{2\alpha}$ remains high for about 2 days after luteolysis.

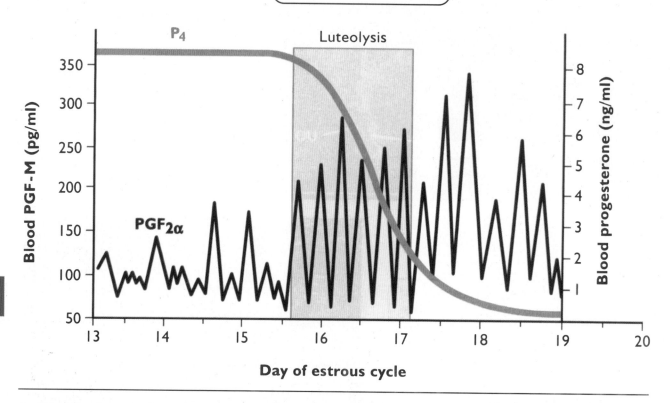

A critical number of PGF$_{2\alpha}$ pulses within a given time-span are required to induce complete luteolysis. The exact number of pulses required has not been defined for all species. However, based on data from the ewe, about five pulses in a 24 hour period are required to induce complete luteolysis. Pulsatile release of PGF$_{2\alpha}$ is apparently not required under conditions of exogenous PGF$_{2\alpha}$ administration. For example, one injection of PGF$_{2\alpha}$ is sufficient to cause luteolysis.

The exact stimulus that initiates PGF$_{2\alpha}$ secretion is controversial. One school of thought maintains that the uterus must be exposed to elevated progesterone for a period of days before it can synthesize and secrete PGF$_{2\alpha}$ in sufficient quantities to cause luteolysis. During the first half of the estrous cycle, progesterone prevents secretion of PGF$_{2\alpha}$ by blocking the formation of oxytocin receptors in the uterus. After 10 to 12 days progesterone loses its ability to block formation of oxytocin receptors, although it is not known how this

occurs. During the late luteal phase injections of exogenous oxytocin cause secretion of PGF$_{2\alpha}$ by the uterus. Injections of PGF$_{2\alpha}$ during the late luteal phase lead to a rapid release of ovarian oxytocin. Thus, oxytocin and PGF$_{2\alpha}$ stimulate each other in a positive feedback manner. In the ewe, oxytocin episodes precede PGF$_{2\alpha}$ episodes.

It should be emphasized that our understanding of the precise luteolytic mechanism is not complete. Progesterone is believed to play a major role in regulating the timing of PGF$_{2\alpha}$ secretion. For example, as progesterone increases during the luteal phase, progesterone receptors decrease in the endometrium. The decrease in progesterone receptor numbers in the endometrium is followed by episodes of PGF$_{2\alpha}$ secretion by the endometrium later in the cycle. The exact interaction between progesterone concentrations, progesterone receptors, oxytocin secretion and PGF$_{2\alpha}$ secretion needs further clarification.

Figure 9-12. Proposed Steps Resulting in the Loss of Progesterone Secretion from Luteal Cells

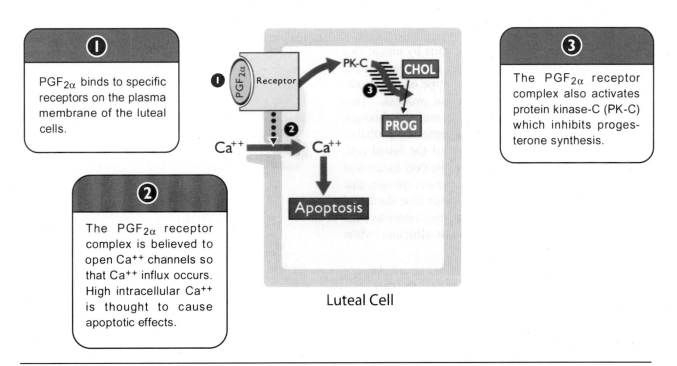

Luteal Cell

---

①	PGF$_{2\alpha}$ binds to specific receptors on the plasma membrane of the luteal cells.
②	The PGF$_{2\alpha}$ receptor complex is believed to open Ca^{++} channels so that Ca^{++} influx occurs. High intracellular Ca^{++} is thought to cause apoptotic effects.
③	The PGF$_{2\alpha}$ receptor complex also activates protein kinase-C (PK-C) which inhibits progesterone synthesis.

> **Luteolysis results in:**
>
> • **cessation of progesterone secretion**
>
> • **structural regression to form a corpus albicans**
>
> • **removal of negative feedback by progesterone upon GnRH secretion resulting in a new follicular phase**

The intracellular mechanisms that cause luteolysis have been the subject of intense research during the last 20 years. One of the original theories to explain the demise of the corpus luteum was that PGF$_{2\alpha}$ caused reduction in blood flow to the corpus luteum by causing vasoconstriction (contraction) of arterioles supplying the luteal tissue. While blood flow to the corpus luteum does decrease during luteolysis, blood flow to the corpus luteum is still 5 to 20 times greater than to the surrounding ovarian tissue. Thus, **ischemia** (reduced blood flow) as a primary mode for luteolysis seems unlikely. It is known that capillaries in the corpus luteum undergo degeneration during luteolysis. It is possible that this capillary degeneration is more responsible for reducing blood flow than vasoconstriction associated with PGF$_{2\alpha}$. Nevertheless, a degree of circulatory disruption is associated with the luteolytic process. However, it is unlikely that disruption to the luteal vasculature can totally account for luteolysis.

A second line of thinking is the theory that PGF$_{2\alpha}$ binds to specific receptors on large luteal cells and triggers a cascade of events resulting in the death of these cells and thus, cessation of steroidogenesis. These events are presented in Figure 9-12.

The Immune System May Be Involved in Regression of the Corpus Luteum

It is well-known that immune cells are present in the corpus luteum at the time of luteolysis. These cells are capable of performing phagocytosis of luteal cells. Phagocytic cells increase prior to the onset of luteolysis. Lymphocytes secrete **cytokines**. Cytokines are non-antibody proteins secreted by a variety of immune cells that activate macrophages that then phagocytize damaged dead luteal cells and cellular debris. Examples of cytokines are interferons, interleukins and tumor necrosis factors (TNF). Cytokines have been shown to cause luteal cell death *in vitro*. They also inhibit progesterone synthesis by luteal cells. While the mechanism involving the roles of cytokines in luteolysis is far from clear, it appears that normal morphologic and functional integrity of the corpus luteum can be reduced when cytokines are present.

9

In addition to a direct effect on the luteal cell, cytokines may serve as triggering agents for a process called apoptosis. **Apoptosis** (pronounced "a-pa-toe-sis") is a phenomenon known as "programmed cell death". It is quite normal for cells throughout the body to die on a daily basis. Cell death occurs by one of two processes. The first, cell **necrosis,** is brought about by pathologic damage. The second type of cell death, apoptosis, is an ordered biochemical process. This process involves distinct biochemical and morphologic changes in the cell. The process of apoptosis is probably the final step resulting in the death of the luteal cell. Final destruction and "clean-up" of the non-functional luteal cells is probably performed by macrophages that phagocytize damaged luteal cells. Over time the luteal cells disappear completely, leaving only connective tissue behind. Thus, the scar-like **corpus albicans** (white body) is formed.

Luteolysis in Women is an Intra-Ovarian Event. The Uterus is Not Required.

Uterectomy in the woman does not influence ovarian cyclicity. In other words, the normal pattern of folliculogenesis, luteal development and luteolysis occurs in a rhythmic fashion about every 28 days after the removal of the uterus. A proposed mechanism for luteolysis in primates is presented in Figure 9-13. Even though traces of luteal oxytocin have been identified, it is thought that oxytocin from the posterior pituitary acts on ovarian oxytocin receptors to generate small amounts of intraovarian $PGF_{2\alpha}$. Luteolysis is thought to be a local effect and therefore only small amounts of $PGF_{2\alpha}$ are required to lyse the CL. As a result of oxytocin receptors binding oxytocin, the synthetic pathway for $PGF_{2\alpha}$ is activated and this causes luteolysis. Luteolysis therefore causes a marked reduction in progesterone that is thought to cause endometrial synthesis of $PGF_{2\alpha}$. Endometrial $PGF_{2\alpha}$ is important because it causes local vasoconstriction of the endometrial arterioles and initiates menstruation. This significant reduction in blood flow brought about by vasoconstriction in the luminal region of the endometrium causes necrosis and sloughing of the endometrial tissue. A more detailed description of the mechanism of menstruation is presented in Chapter 16.

Administration of Progesterone Results in Manipulation of the Estrous Cycle

Now that you understand the mechanisms that control progesterone synthesis, secretion and luteolysis, an understanding of how progesterone is used to control/manipulate cyclicity will provide you with practical knowledge that is based on the physiologic principles.

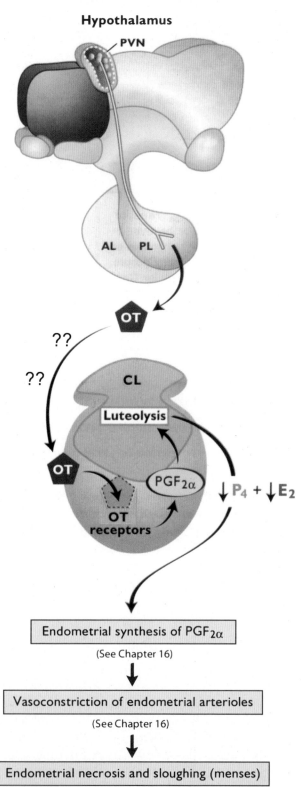

Figure 9-13. Proposed Mechanism of Luteolysis in Primates

As you know, progesterone provides negative feedback to the hypothalamus to suppress GnRH. This fact has been applied to the development of many applications designed to manipulate the reproductive cycles in domestic animals. The administration of progesterone serves as an "artificial corpus luteum".

Exogenous progesterone suppresses estrus and ovulation. However, when the exogenous progesterone is removed or withdrawn, the animal will enter proestrus and estrus within two to three days after progesterone removal. This approach enables estrus to be synchronized in large groups of females so that artificial insemination can be accomplished within a few days. This application is intended to increase the convenience of artificial insemination programs and to facilitate fertility (higher pregnancy rates). In contrast, the use of exogenous progesterone in women is intended to block ovulation and minimize the likelihood of pregnancy. Mechanisms of this application are presented in Chapter 16.

Intravaginal Progesterone is Effective at Synchronizing Estrus in Cattle

The EAZI-BREED™ CIDR® Cattle Insert is an intravaginal progesterone-releasing device used for synchronization of estrus in beef cattle and dairy heifers. CIDR® is an acronym for "Controlled Internal Drug Release". The product has also been approved for advancing first estrus in anestrus postpartum beef cows and in prepubertal beef heifers. The CIDR® is inserted into the vagina of the cow/heifer and remains there for 7 days.

While in the vagina, progesterone diffuses out of the CIDR® Insert, crosses the vaginal mucosa and enters the vasculature of the vagina. The blood profiles of progesterone in ovariectomized cows immediately following insertion, during a 7 day administration and immediately after CIDR® Insert removal are shown in Figure 9-14.

For synchronization of estrus the CIDR® Insert is administered for 7 days with an injection of 5ml Lutalyse® Sterile Solution (25mg prostaglandin $F_{2\alpha}$) on the sixth day. Progesterone from the CIDR® Insert suppresses GnRH release, gonadotropin release, follicular development and ovulation in those cows and heifers that have corpora lutea that regress spontaneously during the 7 day administration period. Lutalyse® is administered to initiate luteal regression in those cows and heifers that have a functional corpus luteum at the end of the CIDR® Insert administration period. Upon removal of the CIDR® Insert and injection of Lutalyse®, cows and heifers will experience a rapid decline in the concentration of progesterone followed by elevated GnRH, elevated gonadotropins and follicular development and will enter proestrus and estrus within two to three days (a synchronized estrus).

Figure 9-14. Blood Progesterone Profiles After the CIDR® Insertion and Removal

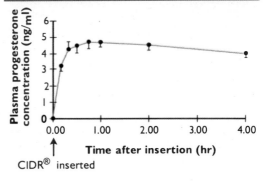

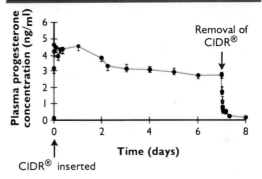

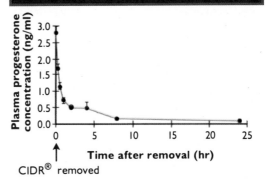

Another use of an exogenous progesterone-like compound is in mares. A material with the trade name Regu-Mate® is used to control cyclicity. The active ingredient in Regu-Mate® is a synthetic progestin called altrenogest. The physiologic action of altrenogest is the same as progesterone. It is used in mares for the following reasons: 1) to induce regular cyclicity in mares making the transition from winter anestrus to the breeding season, 2) to suppress undesired estrous behavior and 3) allow for scheduled breeding during the breeding season.

Altrenogest is administered by placing the appropriate dose on the posterio-dorsal surface of the mare's tongue or is applied to the grain ration. It is given daily for 15 consecutive days. During the time that altrenogest is being administered GnRH is suppressed, and behavioral estrus does not occur. After cessation of the treatment, mares will display estrus four to five days later.

Exogenous Prostaglandin $F_{2\alpha}$ is a Potent Luteolysin and Can Synchronize Estrus

Following the discovery that $PGF_{2\alpha}$ was the luteolysin, a major research emphasis was placed on using this hormone to shorten the estrous cycle and induce estrus in cattle. Injections of $PGF_{2\alpha}$ between day seven and day 18 will cause the cow to begin to show estrus in about three days (60-80 hours after the injection). Figure 9-15 illustrates the effect of prostaglandin for inducing estrus. It must be emphasized that the corpus luteum of the cow is not sensitive to $PGF_{2\alpha}$ between days one and six of the cycle. In other words, injecting the cow with $PGF_{2\alpha}$ during this time will not have an effect (See Figure 9-15).

Reproductive physiologists at the University of Wisconsin and Michigan State University have developed an innovative use of GnRH and $PGF_{2\alpha}$ that synchronizes ovulation. This protocol is named Ovsynch (See Figure 9-16, green section). When GnRH and $PGF_{2\alpha}$ are used together in the proper timed-sequence, visual detection of estrus can be eliminated and timed artificial insemination (TAI) can be performed. This program is being used routinely as a reproductive management tool in the dairy industry. The Ovsynch innovation incorporates the mechanisms of follicular dynamics described in Chapter 8 and the mechanisms of luteolysis (described earlier in this chapter) into a practical application of physiologic principles. A solid understanding of these mechanisms will translate into understanding of the Ovsynch protocol described later.

The basic strategy for the Ovsynch program is presented in the steps that follow. **Step 1**- GnRH is injected into cows that are eligible to be inseminated (fully recovered from their last parturition). The GnRH injection causes one of two events to take place. First, if there is a dominant follicle on the ovary (a follicle that is greater than 10mm and has an adequate population of LH receptors) the cow will ovulate in response to GnRH. A CL will then form. Second, if the cow does not have a dominant follicle (an immature follicle that has few LH receptors), GnRH will promote continued follicular growth. In this case, there is a CL present from the previous ovulation; **Step 2**- An injection of $PGF_{2\alpha}$ seven days after GnRH causes luteolysis and the cow will enter the follicular phase; **Step 3**- A second injection of GnRH 48 hours later causes the cow to ovulate. **Step 4**- The cow can then be inseminated without detection of estrus 16 hours after the second GnRH injection.

This strategy, when properly applied in commercial dairy herds has resulted in acceptable conception rates without detection of estrus in lactating dairy cows. The Ovsynch strategy will enable almost 100% of the cows to be inseminated after the designated postpartum waiting period (typically 60 days and called the "voluntary wait period"). The first GnRH injection in the Ovsynch program is given at random (without knowledge of the specific day of the cycle). This can result in several problems. If cows are not cyclic, GnRH will not initiate cyclicity in all of them. Those that do ovulate in response to GnRH have reduced conception. Some GnRH-treated cows will recruit follicles from the second or third follicular wave and the follicle may not ovulate. Therefore, the $PGF_{2\alpha}$ injection is not totally effective (because there is no CL present) in these cows.

In order to help minimize the above problems, a strategy has been developed that is called Presynch (See Figure 9-16, brown section). The Presynch program begins 26 days prior to the first GnRH injection. At random, all cows are given $PGF_{2\alpha}$. Fourteen days later a second $PGF_{2\alpha}$ injection is given. Remember, the first $PGF_{2\alpha}$ will regress an existing corpus luteum if it is between days 7 and 17. Obviously, all cows will not fall into this range and the second $PGF_{2\alpha}$ regresses all corpora lutea that are present because they are in the "sensitive window" between days 7 and 17. Twelve days after the prostaglandin injection, GnRH is injected. GnRH may cause a new follicle to ovulate, forming a new CL as per the original Ovsynch protocol. More detail about each method can be obtained from the **Key References** section at the end of the chapter.

Figure 9-15. Influence of Prostaglandin $F_{2\alpha}$ Upon Cycle Length in the Cow

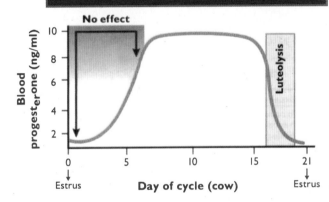

In the normal cyclic cow estrus and ovulation occurs every 21 days. Luteolysis (induced naturally by $PGF_{2\alpha}$ from the uterus) causes the animal to enter a new follicular phase and subsequent estrus.

If a single injection of $PGF_{2\alpha}$ is given between day zero and about day six, luteolysis will not occur and the cycle will be of normal length. This is because the corpus luteum must reach a certain stage of development before it is sensitive to $PGF_{2\alpha}$.

9

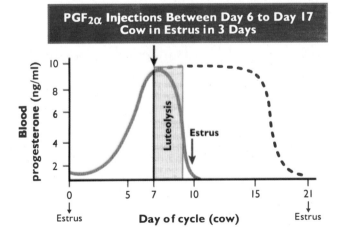

If $PGF_{2\alpha}$ is injected on day 7-17, luteolysis will occur. Progesterone will drop and the animal will come into estrus in about three days after the injection. Such a strategy is used to synchronize estrus in large groups of animals.

Figure 9-16. Presynch and Ovsynch as Methods to Synchronize Ovulation in Cows

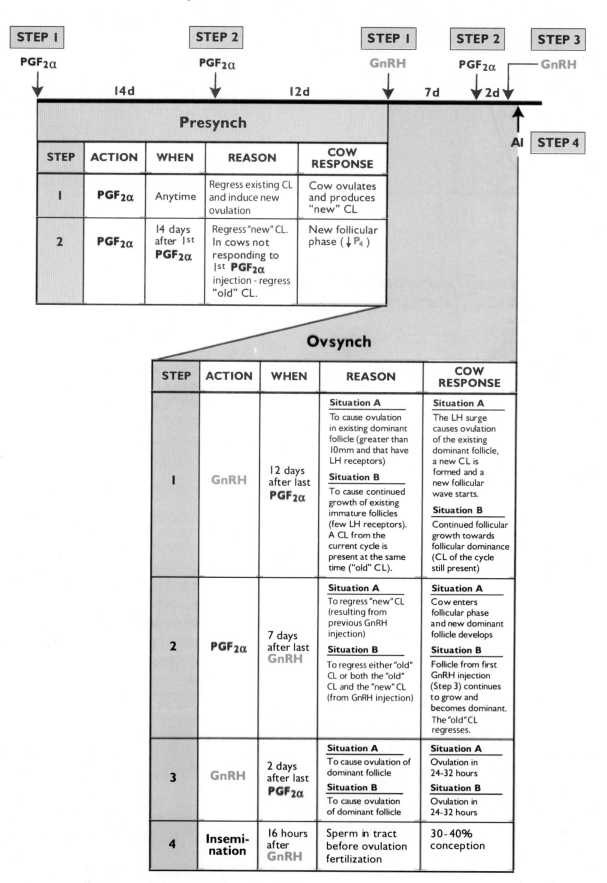

Further PHENOMENA for Fertility

Female elephants have a uniquely long estrous cycle (16 weeks) and a gestation of 22 months. What does this say about elephant CL?

The regression of the corpus luteum in humans and other primates is not controlled by the uterus. However, $PGF_{2\alpha}$ will induce luteolysis in primates. It is believed that $PGF_{2\alpha}$ of ovarian origin is responsible for causing luteal regression.

The corpus luteum of most rodents (rats, mice, hamsters and gerbils) does not develop unless copulation occurs. Penile stimulation of the cervix causes prolactin release from the female. Prolactin is luteotropic and causes the formation of corpora lutea.

Some spiders have no penis. They eject sperm from their abdomen onto their web. The male spider picks up the ejaculate with a special set of antennae and searches for a receptive female who produces a pheromone. The male has to be very careful and deposit the semen by surprise because the female will eat him if she catches him.

The luteal phase of the estrous cycle of the kangaroo is longer than pregnancy.

Researchers at N.C. State University observed a sow that had 128 corpora lutea on both of her ovaries. This is ten times the normal number of corpora lutea. The cause of such a high number of ovulations is unknown.

Key References

Leymarie, P. and Martal, J. 1993. "The corpus luteum from cycle to gestation" in *Reproduction in Mammals and Man*. p 413-434. C. Thibault, M.C. Levasseur and R.H.F. Hunter, eds., Ellipses, Paris. ISBN 2-7298-9354-7.

McCracken, J.A. 1998. "Luteolysis" in *Encyclopedia of Reproduction*. Vol. 2. p1083-1094. Knobil, E. and J.D. Neill, eds. Academic Press, San Diego ISBN 0-12-227022-3.

Niswender, G.D. and T.M. Nett. 1994. "Corpus luteum and its control in infraprimate species" in *The Physiology of Reproduction*, 2nd Edition. Vol. 1 p781-816. E. Knobil and J.D. Neill, eds., Raven Press, Ltd., New York. ISBN 0-7817-0086-8.

Pate, J.L. and D.H. Townson. 1994. "Novel local regulators in luteal regression." XXI Biennial Symposium on Animal Reproduction. *J. Anim. Sci.* 72 (Suppl. 3):31-42.

Pursley, J.R., M.R. Kosorok and M.C. Wiltbank, 1997. "Reproductive management of lactating dairy cows using synchronization of ovulation" in *J. Dairy Sci.* 80:301-306.

Salamonsen, L.A. 2003. "Tissue injury and repair in the female human reproductive tract." *Reprod.* 125(3):301-311.

9

Endocrinology of the Male
& SPERMATOGENESIS

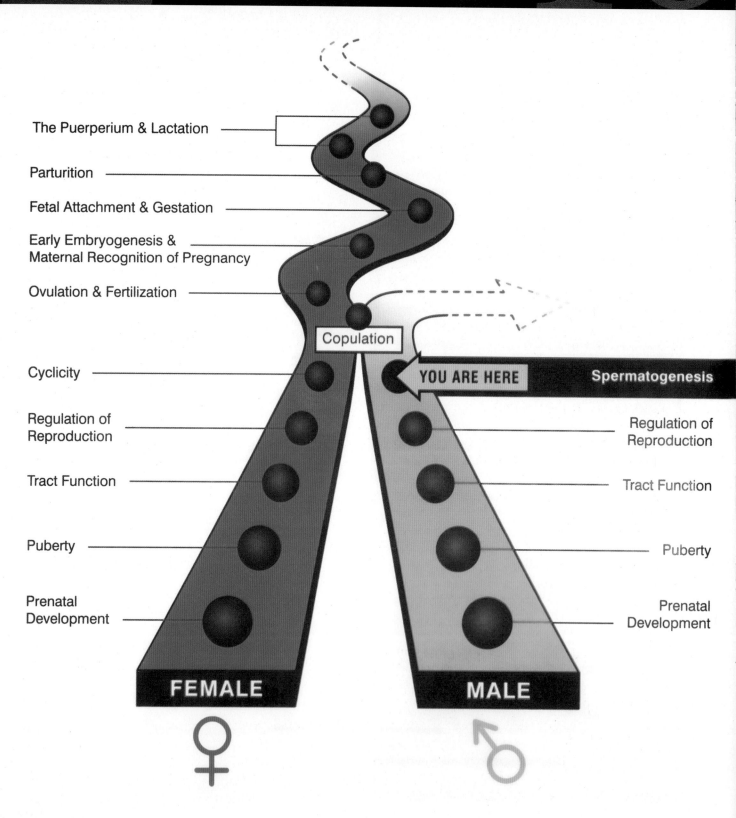

The Puerperium & Lactation

Parturition

Fetal Attachment & Gestation

Early Embryogenesis &
Maternal Recognition of Pregnancy

Ovulation & Fertilization

Copulation

Cyclicity

Regulation of
Reproduction

Tract Function

Puberty

Prenatal
Development

FEMALE

YOU ARE HERE   Spermatogenesis

Regulation of
Reproduction

Tract Function

Puberty

Prenatal
Development

MALE

Take Home Message

In the adult male, GnRH, LH and testosterone are secreted in pulses that occur every several hours. Follicle stimulating hormone is released in smaller pulses of longer duration. Spermatozoa are produced by the testes by a process called spermatogenesis that requires 5 to 9 weeks, depending on the species. The number of sperm produced each day is independent of the number ejaculated. Spermatogenesis is a process involving sequential mitotic and meiotic divisions and concludes after differentiation of spherical spermatids into highly specialized spermatozoa. Spermatozoa are released continually from the seminiferous epithelium in post-pubertal males.

Endocrine Control/Regulation is Different than in the Female

Before spermatozoa can be produced, certain endocrine requirements must be met. They are: 1) adequate secretion of GnRH from the hypothalamus; 2) FSH and LH secretion from the anterior lobe of the pituitary and 3) secretion of gonadal steroids (testosterone and estradiol). Recall from Chapter 6 that the hypothalamus in the male does not develop a surge center. The discharge of GnRH from the hypothalamus in the male occurs in frequent, intermittent episodes that occur throughout the day and night. These short-lived bursts of GnRH last for only a few minutes and cause discharges of LH that follow almost immediately after the GnRH episode. The episodes of LH last from 10 to 20 minutes and occur between 4 to 8 times every 24 hours. Concentrations of FSH are lower, but the pulses are of longer duration than LH because of the relatively constant secretion of inhibin by the adult testis and the longer half-life of FSH (See Figure 10-1).

Luteinizing hormone acts on the **Leydig cells** within the testes. These cells, named after the German anatomist Franz von Leydig, are analogous to the cells of the theca interna of antral follicles in the ovary. They contain membrane-bound receptors for LH. When LH binds to their receptors, Leydig cells synthesize progesterone, most of which is converted to testosterone. Blood LH is elevated for about 30 to 75 minutes. The Leydig cells synthesize and secrete testosterone less than 30 minutes after the onset of an LH episode. The

response (testosterone secretion) by Leydig cells is short and secretion is pulsatile, lasting for a period of 20 to about 60 minutes (See Figure 10-2).

> *Successful testis function requires:*
> * *pulsatile GnRH secretion (every 3-6 hrs)*
> * *high concentrations of testosterone in the seminiferous tubule*
> * *low concentrations of testosterone in a systemic blood*
> * *adequate LH receptors in Leydig cells*

Pulsatile discharge of LH is important for normal testicular function. The pulsatile nature of LH secretion prevents sustained concentrations of LH to which the Leydig cells become refractory (unresponsive or not yielding to treatment). A refractory condition is thought to be caused by reduction in the number of LH receptors in the Leydig cells. As a result of low receptor numbers, reduced secretion of testosterone by Leydig cells follows. Pulsatile LH secretions optimize LH receptor numbers and testosterone secretion by Leydig cells.

Normally, intratesticular concentrations of testosterone are 100-500 times higher than that of systemic blood. High concentrations of testosterone are required for normal spermatogenesis. When testosterone from the testis mixes with peripheral blood,

10

> *Production of normal numbers of fertile spermatozoa requires:*
> * *endocrine regulation of the testis*
> * *mitotic divisions of spermatogonia*
> * *meiotic divisions resulting in haploid spermatids*
> * *morphologic transformation of spermatids into spermatozoa*

Figure 10-1. Relationship Between GnRH, LH and FSH in the Male

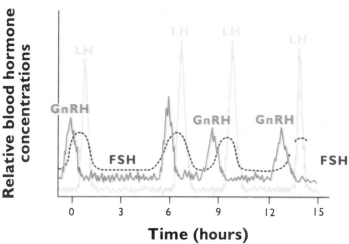

GnRH causes the release of LH and FSH. Episodes of all three hormones occur between 4 and 8 times in 24 hours. The lower FSH profile, when compared to LH, is due to inhibin secretion by Sertoli cells. Also, the greater duration of the FSH episode is probably due to its longer half-life (100 min) when compared to LH (30 min).

it is diluted over 500 times. This is important because it keeps systemic concentrations well below that which would cause down-regulation of the GnRH/LH feedback system. For example, if LH pulses were long (hours), Leydig cells would secrete testosterone for hours rather than minutes. This would likely result in a metabolic overload for testosterone clearance and testosterone would exert a sustained negative feedback on the GnRH neurons in the hypothalamus. The net effect would be significantly reduced LH secretion, followed by severely reduced testosterone secretion.

The role of the pulsatile nature of testosterone is not fully understood. It is thought that a chronically high systemic concentration of testosterone removes the negative feedback on FSH. Sertoli cell function is FSH dependent. Thus, their function is compromised when FSH is reduced. The periodic reduction in testosterone removes the negative feedback on FSH (See Figure 10-3).

In addition to secretion of testosterone by the Leydig cells, the testes also secrete estradiol and other estrogens. The stallion and the boar secrete large amounts of estrogens (both free and in conjugated form). In fact, urinary estrogens in the male are significantly higher than urinary estrogens in pregnant mares and sows. These high concentrations of estradiol seem to be of little consequence, since they are secreted as molecules with low physiologic activity.

Leydig cells are the male equivalent of the follicular theca interna cells.

Sertoli cells are the male equivalent of the follicular granulosal cells.

Figure 10-2. Typical Peripheral Concentrations of Blood LH and Testosterone (T) in the Male

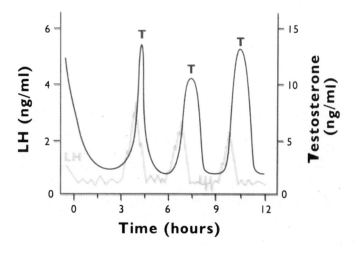

LH is elevated for a period of 0.5 to 1.25 hours, while the subsequent testosterone (T) episode lasts for 0.5 to 1.5 hours.

Figure 10-3. Interrelationships Among Hormones Produced by Sertoli Cells, Leydig Cells, the Hypothalamus and the Anterior Lobe of Pituitary

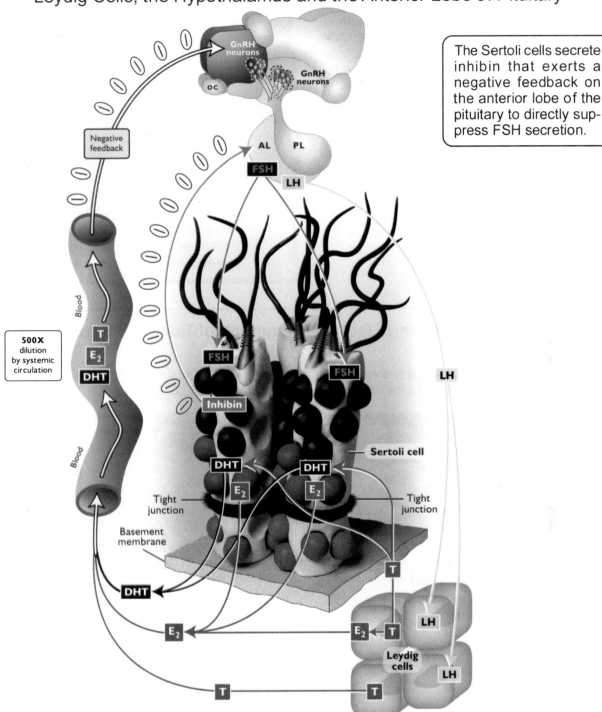

The Sertoli cells secrete inhibin that exerts a negative feedback on the anterior lobe of the pituitary to directly suppress FSH secretion.

Blue spheres = spermatogonia; Red spheres = primary spermatocytes; Brown spheres = secondary spermatocytes; Black spheres = spermatids

Testosterone (T) secreted by the Leydig cells is transported into the Sertoli cells where it is converted to dihydrotestosterone (DHT) and also estradiol (E_2). Testosterone and E_2 are transported by the blood to the hypothalamus where they exert a negative feedback on the GnRH neurons.

LH binds to receptors in the interstitial cells of Leydig and FSH binds to Sertoli cells. Leydig cells secrete testosterone that is transported to the adjacent vasculature and the Sertoli cells where T is converted to DHT.

Sertoli cells convert testosterone to estradiol utilizing a mechanism identical to the granulosal cells of the antral follicle in the female. The exact role of estradiol in male reproduction is poorly understood, but there is little doubt that this hormone has a negative feedback role on the hypothalamus. Testosterone and estradiol in the blood act on the hypothalamus and exert a negative feedback on the secretion of GnRH and, in turn, LH and FSH are reduced. Therefore, high concentrations of estradiol result in suppression of GnRH and LH discharges (See Figure 10-3). In addition to converting testosterone to estradiol, Sertoli cells also secrete inhibin that, as in the female, suppresses FSH secretion from the anterior lobe of the pituitary. The importance of inhibin and suppressed FSH release is not clear in the male.

> *The goals of spermatogenesis are to:*
> - *provide a continual supply of male gametes (up to decades) through stem cell renewal*
>
> - *provide genetic diversity*
>
> - *provide billions of sperm each day (domestic animals) to maximize reproduction by both natural service and artificial insemination*
>
> - *provide an immunologically privileged site where developing germ cells are not destroyed by the male's immune system*

Figure 10-4. Scanning Electron Micrograph of Testicular Parenchyma in the Stallion

(Courtesy of Dr. Larry Johnson, Texas A&M University, The American Society for Reproductive Medicine. *Fertil. and Steril.*, 1978. 29:208-215)

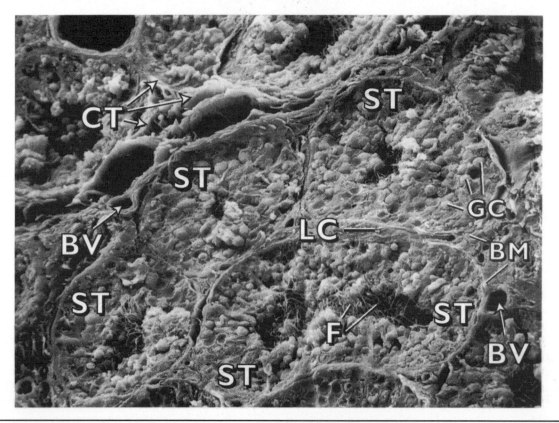

Seminiferous tubules (ST) containing developing germ cells (GC) are surrounded by a basement membrane (BM). Flagella (F) from developing spermatids can be observed protruding into the lumen of some tubules. The interstitial compartment contains Leydig cells (LC), blood vessels (BV) and connective tissue (CT).

Spermatogenesis = proliferation + meiosis + differentiation

Spermatogenesis is the Process of Producing Spermatozoa

Spermatogenesis takes place entirely within the seminiferous tubules (See Figure 10-4) and consists of all cell divisions and morphologic changes that occur to developing germ cells. (See Figures 10-5 and 3-16).

The process of spermatogenesis can be subdivided into three phases. The first phase, designated the **proliferation phase**, consists of all mitotic divisions of spermatogonia. Several generations of A-spermatogonia undergo mitotic divisions, generating a large number of B-spermatogonia (See Figure 10-5). An important part of the proliferation phase is **stem cell renewal**. Loss of intercellular bridges allows some spermatogonia to revert to stem cells (spermatogonial stem cells) providing continual renewal of these stem cells from which new spermatogonia can develop.

The **meiotic phase** begins with primary spermatocytes. During meiosis I, genetic diversity is guaranteed by DNA replication and crossing over during the production of secondary spermatocytes. From a genetic perspective no two sperm are identical. Conclusion of the meiotic phase (the second meiotic division) produces haploid (1N) **spermatids**.

The third or final phase of spermatogenesis is the **differentiation phase**. No further cell divisions take place during this phase. The differentiation phase has commonly been referred to as **"spermiogenesis"** in reproductive physiology literature. During the differentiation phase, a spherical undifferentiated spermatid

Figure 10-5. Typical Sequence of Spermatogenesis in Mammals

Spermatogonia (A$_1$-A$_4$, I and B) undergo a series of mitotic divisions (Mit) and the last mitotic division gives rise to primary spermatocytes that enter meiosis. This series of mitotic divisions allows for continual proliferation of spermatogonia and replacement of A$_1$ spermatogonia.

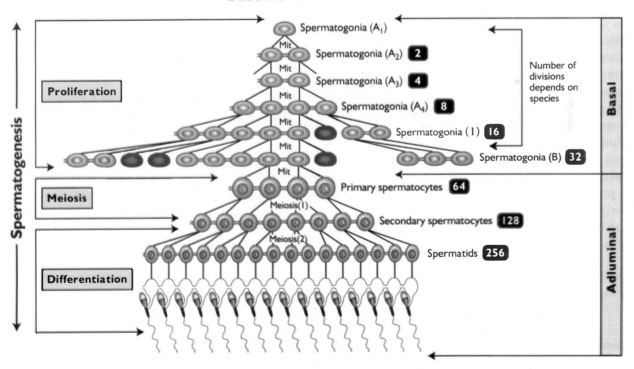

After meiosis, haploid spherical spermatids differentiate into spermatozoa. Meiosis and differentiation take place in the adluminal compartment. Notice that each generation of cells is attached by intercellular cytoplasmic bridges. Thus, each generation divides synchronously in cohorts. Some cells (black) degenerate during the process. Numbers indicate the theoretical number of cells generated by each division.

undergoes a remarkable transformation that results in the production of a fully differentiated, highly specialized spermatozoon containing a head (nuclear material), a flagellum including a midpiece (with a mitochondrial helix) and a principal piece.

The most immature germ cells (spermatogonia) are located at the periphery of a seminiferous tubule near the basement membrane. As these germ cells proliferate, they move toward the lumen. The cell types in the seminiferous epithelium are illustrated in Figure 10-5. Developing germ cells are connected by **intercellular bridges**. Groups of spermatogonia, spermatocytes or spermatids are connected by intercellular bridges, so that the cytoplasm of an entire cohort (groups of cells of the same type) is interconnected. The exact number of germ cells that are interconnected is not known, but might approach 50. The significance of these intercellular bridges is not fully understood. However, they undoubtedly provide communication between cells that contributes to synchronized development of a cohort.

Proliferation Generates Spermatogonia That are Committed to Become More Advanced Cell Types

The most primitive cells encountered in the seminiferous epithelium are the spermatogonia. These specialized diploid (2N chromosomal content) cells are located in the **basal compartment** of the seminiferous epithelium. Spermatogonia undergo several mitotic divisions with the last division resulting in primary spermatocytes (See Figure 10-5). There are three types of spermatogonia: **A-spermatogonia, I-spermatogonia** (intermediate) and **B-spermatogonia**. A-spermatogonia undergo several mitotic divisions in which they progress mitotically from A_1 through A_4. A pool of stem cells is also maintained so that the process can continue indefinitely. Stem cells divide mitotically to provide a continual source of A-spermatogonia allowing spermatogenesis to continue without interruption for years. The mechanism for the renewal of stem cells is not understood.

Meiotic Divisions Produce Haploid Spermatids

During spermatogenesis the number of chromosomes in the gamete is reduced to the haploid state. This is accomplished by meiosis. The mitotic divisions of B-spermatogonia result in the formation of primary spermatocytes. These primary spermatocytes immediately enter the first meiotic prophase. As you will recall from your previous courses, the meiotic prophase consists of five stages: preleptotene, leptotene, zygo-

tene, pachytene and diplotene. Each of these stages represents a different step in the progression of DNA synthesis and replication. Primary spermatocytes must progress through these five steps before the first meiotic division can occur. The important event of the preleptotene phase is complete DNA replication forming tetrads without separation. These tetrads then fuse at random points known as chiasmata and **crossing-over** of DNA material later takes place. The term "crossing-over" refers to segments of one chromosome crossing-over to a homologous chromosome when the chromatids separate. Crossing-over results in a random assortment of different segments of each chromosome. Thus, prophase of the first meiotic division insures genetic heterogeneity and that each secondary spermatocyte and subsequently each spermatid will be genetically unique. Prophase of the first meiotic division is a relatively long process. In fact, the lifespan of the primary spermatocyte is the longest of all germ cell types found in the seminiferous epithelium. For example, in the bull the lifespan of the primary spermatocyte is 18 to 19 days. The total duration of spermatogenesis in bulls is 61 days. Thus, prophase of the first meiotic division (primary spermatocyte) is about 30% of the time required for the entire spermatogenic process.

The secondary spermatocyte resulting from the first meiotic division of a primary spermatocyte is short-lived. It exists for only 1.1 to 1.7 days depending on the species. The secondary spermatocyte rapidly undergoes the second meiotic division, resulting in haploid spherical spermatids.

Differentiation Produces a Highly Sophisticated, Self-Propelled Package of Enzymes and DNA

The role of a spermatozoon is to deliver the male's genetic material to an oocyte during fertilization. To form cells that are capable of fertilization, spherical spermatids undergo a series of changes in which the nucleus becomes highly condensed, the acrosome is formed and the cell becomes potentially motile. The ability to swim (motility) requires the development of a **flagellum** and a metabolic "powerplant" known as the **mitochondrial helix**.

> *Differentiation consists of the:*
> * *Golgi phase*
> * *cap phase*
> * *acrosomal phase*
> * *maturation phase*

Figure 10-6. The Golgi Phase of Spermatid Differentiation

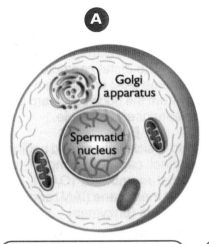
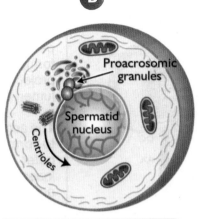
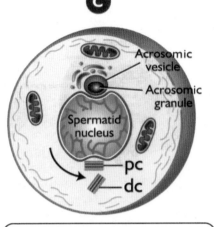

The newly formed spermatid is almost perfectly spherical and has a well developed Golgi apparatus.

Small vesicles of the Golgi fuse, giving rise to larger secretory granules called pro-acrosomic granules. The centrioles start to migrate to a position beneath the nucleus that is opposite the acrosomic vesicle.

Vesicle fusion continues until a large acrosomic vesicle is formed containing a dense acrosomic granule. The proximal centriole (PC) gives rise to the attachment point of the tail. The distal centriole (DC) gives rise to the developing axoneme (central portion of the tail) inside the cytoplasm of the spermatid.

The Golgi phase = acrosomic vesicle formation

The **Golgi phase** is characterized by the first steps in the development of the **acrosome**. The newly formed spermatid contains a large, highly-developed Golgi apparatus located near the nucleus that consists of many small vesicles (See Figure 10-6). The Golgi apparatus is not unique to the spermatid, but is the intracellular "packaging" system in all secretory cells. In a spermatid, the Golgi will give rise to an important subcellular organelle known as the acrosome. First, proacrosomic vesicles are formed and these fuse, generating a larger vesicle that resides on one side of the nucleus. This vesicle is called the **acrosomic vesicle** and contains a dense **acrosomic granule** (See Figure 10-6). Smaller Golgi vesicles are continually added to the larger vesicle increasing its size.

While the acrosomic vesicle is being formed, the centrioles migrate from the cytoplasm to the base of the nucleus (See Figure 10-6). The proximal centriole will give rise to an implantation apparatus that allows the flagellum to be anchored to the nucleus (See Figure 10-9). The distal centriole gives rise to the developing **axoneme**. The axoneme is the central portion of a flagellum, in this case the sperm tail.

The cap phase = acrosomic vesicle spreading over the nucleus

During the **cap phase** the acrosome forms a distinct, easily recognized cap over the anterior portion of the nucleus (See Figure 10-7). The Golgi now has performed its function by packaging the acrosomal contents and membranes and moves away from the nucleus toward the caudal end of the spermatid and eventually disappears. The primitive flagellum (tail), formed from the distal centriole, begins to project from the spermatid toward the lumen of the seminiferous tubule.

The acrosomal phase = nuclear and cytoplasmic elongation

During the **acrosomal phase** the acrosome continues to spread until it covers about two-thirds of the anterior nucleus (See Figures 10-7 and 10-8). The nucleus begins to elongate. A unique system of microtubules known as the **manchette** develops near the area of the posterior nucleus. Portions of the manchette attach to the region of the nucleus just posterior to the

Figure 10-7. The Cap, Acrosomal and Maturation Phases of Spermatid Differentiation

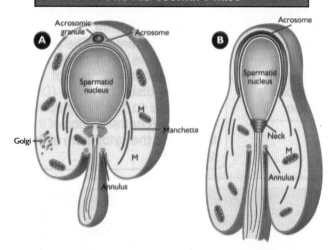

The Cap Phase

A
The Golgi migrates toward the caudal part of the cell. The distal centriole (DC) forms the axoneme (AX) or flagellum that projects away from the nucleus toward the lumen of the seminiferous tubule.

B
The acrosomic vesicle flattens and begins to form a distinct cap consisting of an outer acrosomal membrane (OAM), an inner acrosomal membrane (IAM) and the acrosomal contents (enzymes).

The Acrosomal Phase

A
The spermatid nucleus begins to elongate and the acrosome eventually covers the majority of the anterior nucleus. The manchette forms in the region of the caudal half of the nucleus and extends down toward the developing flagellum.

B
The neck and the annulus are formed and the latter will become the juncture between the middle piece and the principal piece. Notice that all components of the developing spermatid are completely surrounded by a plasma membrane. M = mitochondria.

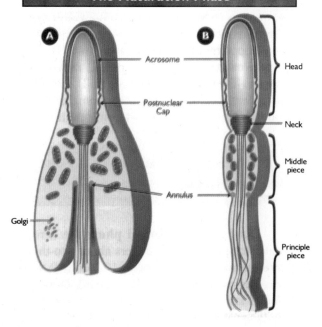

The Maturation Phase

A and B
Mitochondria form a spiral assembly around the flagellum that defines the middle piece. The postnuclear cap is formed from the manchette microtubules. The annulus forms the juncture between the middle piece and the principal piece.

Spermatogenesis **211**

Figure 10-8. The Head of the Bovine Spermatozoon

(Courtesy of Dr. R.G. Saacke, Virginia Polytechnic Institute and State University with permission from John R. Wiley and Sons, Inc. *Am. J. Anat.* 115:143)

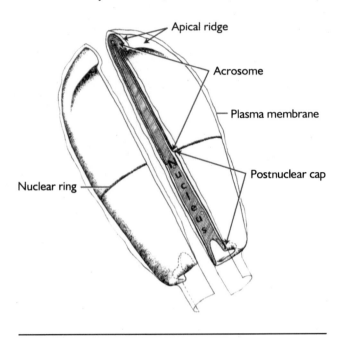

Spermatozoa = head + tail

Head = nucleus + acrosome + post-nuclear cap

Tail = middle piece + principal piece + terminal piece

Finally, release of spermatozoa from the Sertoli cells into the lumen of the seminiferous tubule occurs. This release is referred to as **spermiation** and is analogous to ovulation in the female, except that spermiation occurs continuously throughout the testis.

The head of a mammalian spermatozoon has a shape characteristic for each species. In domestic mammals the nucleus is oval and flattened and is surrounded by a nuclear membrane. The chromatin is compacted and is almost inert because it is highly **keratinized**. Keratinoid proteins (hair, claws, hoofs and feathers) have a high degree of disulfide cross-linking and are quite insoluble. During spermiogenesis, nuclear histones of the haploid sperm nucleus are replaced by **protamines**. Protamines are small, arginine-rich nuclear proteins thought to be essential for DNA condensation. The sulfhydryl groups of protamines form disulfide bonds. These bonds are the basis for nuclear condensation that results in a highly compact, stable nucleus that forms the sperm head. At this point in spermiogenesis, transcription and translation stops because the "transcriptional machinery" can no longer access nuclear DNA. Most of the "translational machinery" has been partitioned and lost within the residual cytoplasm of the spermatid. The DNA within the sperm head remains fundamentally inert until the time of fertilization. The inert nature of the DNA is thought to be a mechanism to prevent damage to the DNA between spermiation and fertilization. At fertilization, the process is reversed because the disulfide cross-links within the sperm nucleus are reduced by glutathione in the cytoplasm of the oocyte. The protamines are replaced with histones from the oocyte cytoplasm resulting in nuclear decondensation and formation of the male pronucleus (See Figure 12-8). Thus, the process of nuclear condensation, characterized by a high degree of keratinization and DNA stability is reversed only after the sperm enters the oocyte cytoplasm.

The anterior two-thirds of the nucleus is covered by the acrosome. The acrosome is a membrane-bound lysosome that contains hydrolytic enzymes. These enzymes, **acrosin**, **hyaluronidase**, **zona lysin**, **esterases** and **acid hydrolases**, are required for penetration of the cellular investments and the zona pellucida of the ovulated oocyte. During fertilization the acrosome undergoes an ordered, highly specialized exocytosis, known as the **acrosome reaction**, that allows release of the enzymes that are packaged in it to digest or penetrate

acrosome (See Figure 10-7). Some of the **microtubules** of the manchette will become the **postnuclear cap**. During the acrosomal phase, spermatids become deeply embedded in Sertoli cells with their tails protruding toward the lumen of the seminiferous tubule (See Figure 10-4).

> *The maturation phase = final assembly that forms a spermatozoon*

During the **maturation phase** microtubules of the manchette direct the formation of the postnuclear cap. Mitochondria migrate toward and cluster around the flagellum in the region posterior to the nucleus. Mitochondria are quickly assembled around the flagellum from the base of the nucleus to the anterior one-third of the tail. They are assembled in a spiral fashion (See Figure 10-9) and form the middle piece in fully differentiated spermatozoa. Dense outer fibers of the flagellum and the fibrous sheath are produced and final assembly is complete. It should be emphasized that, as in any cell, the entire spermatozoon is covered with a plasma membrane. Integrity of the plasma membrane is required for the survival and function of spermatozoa as you will see later in the chapter.

10

Figure 10-9. The Tail of the Bovine Spermatozoon

(Courtesy of Dr. R.G. Saacke, Virginia Polytechnic Institute and State University with permission from John R. Wiley and Sons, Inc. *Am. J. Anat.* 115:163)

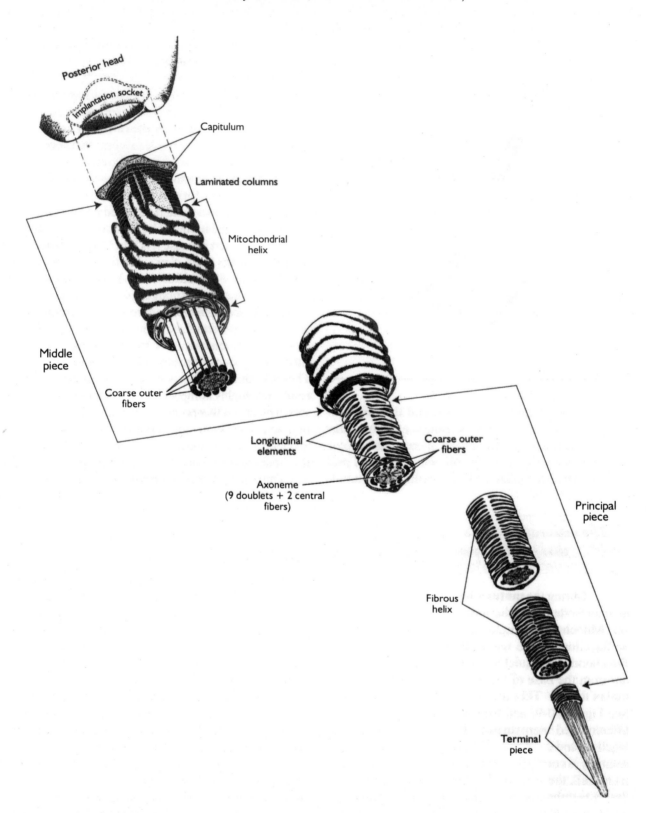

10

the zona pellucida. These reactions will be described in more detail in Chapter 12. Acrosomal morphology varies among species, but in the boar, ram, bull and stallion the acrosome is similar to that shown in Figure 10-8. The membrane component posterior to the acrosome is the postnuclear cap.

> ## The sperm tail is a self-powered flagellum.

The tail is composed of the **capitulum**, the **middle piece**, the **principal piece** and the **terminal piece**. The capitulum fits into the implantation socket, a depression in the posterior nucleus. The anterior portion of the tail consists of laminated columns that give the neck region flexibility when it becomes motile, so the tail can move laterally from side-to-side during the flagellar beat. The axonemal component of the tail originates from the distal centriole and is composed of 9 pairs of microtubules that are arranged radially around two central filaments. Surrounding this 9 doublets + 2 central fiber arrangement of microtubules are 9 coarse fibers that are unique to the flagellum of spermatozoa. This arrangement of tubules in the tail of spermatozoa is illustrated in Figure 10-9.

The mitochondrial sheath is arranged in a helical pattern (See Figure 10-9) around the outer coarse fibers of the tail and contributes to the middle piece. The annulus demarcates the juncture between the middle piece and the principal piece. The principal piece makes up the majority of the tail and continues almost to the end of the flagellum, where only the microtubules end in the terminal piece.

Spermatozoa are Released Continually into the Lumen of the Seminiferous Tubules

One of the major differences between gamete production in the female and the male is that the female's gamete supply is produced entirely before birth. After puberty, she begins to produce oocytes that will undergo meiosis and ovulate every 3-4 weeks. Thus, maturation, meiosis and release of female gametes is pulsatile. In contrast, the male produces gametes continually and uniformly throughout his reproductive lifespan. An exception to this is the seasonal breeder that produces spermatozoa during the breeding season only. Understanding the mechanisms responsible for the continual production of spermatozoa by the seminiferous epithelium represents a major challenge for students of reproductive physiology.

Appreciating the spermatogenic process is necessary for a complete understanding of reproductive physiology. But the importance of this understanding goes beyond the academic. From a clinical perspective, evaluation of sperm numbers in the ejaculate does not always accurately reflect normal or abnormal spermatogenesis. Therefore, the fate of males being evaluated is often fraught with error and thus bad decisions are made. One needs to understand that there is a 2 to 4 week delay before the effects of deleterious events (heat stress, shipping, fever, exposure to certain toxins) can be observed by monitoring changes in ejaculated sperm. Furthermore, 6 to 12 weeks are required before restoration of normal spermatogenesis can be accomplished after these events. Therefore, clinical interpretations of ejaculate characteristics requires specific knowledge of the timing of spermatogenesis in the species being evaluated. Seasonal spermatogenesis requires that the germinal epithelium "turn-on" and "turn-off" as a function of environmental influences. More and more emphasis is being placed on "saving and managing" endangered species. For these efforts to be successful, the timing of spermatogenesis and sperm producing potential must be understood so that sufficient male gametes are available for reproductive manipulation (artificial insemination, *in vitro* fertilization, etc.). As of yet, a practical, cost-effective contraceptive is not available for men. We need to learn how to temporarily "turn-off" and later "turn-on" spermatogenesis without altering the behavior of the male. Our ability to manipulate male gamete production will play a major part in the ability to manipulate reproduction in the future.

> *In order to comprehend the cycle of the seminiferous epithelium you must first understand:*
> - *cellular generations*
> - *stages of the cycle*
> - *duration of one cycle*
> - *how the cycle is repeated*

10

The **cycle of the seminiferous epithelium** is the progression through a complete series of cellular associations (stages) at one location along a seminiferous tubule. The time required for this progression is the duration of the cycle of the seminiferous epithelium and is unique for each species.

> *Germ cell generations are cells of the same type located at one site within the seminiferous epithelium.*

Within any given microscopic cross-section of a seminiferous tubule, one can observe four or five concentric "layers" of germ cells. Cells in each layer comprise a generation. A generation is a cohort of cells that develops as a synchronous group. Each generation of cells (each concentric layer) has a similar appearance and function. Cross-sections along the length of a seminiferous tubule will have a different appearance but the entire cross-section at a given location will usually appear similar. For example, while viewing cross-section I (stage I) in Figure 10-10, you will observe four generations of germ cells. Each generation will give rise to a succeeding, more advanced generation. Observe in Figure 10-10 that there is a generation of A-spermatogonia near the basement membrane in the

section of the tubule labeled Stage I. Just above the A-spermatogonia is a young generation of primary spermatocytes. Above it lies a third generation consisting of more mature primary spermatocytes. Finally, near the lumen, is a fourth generation of cells. This generation consists of spherical immature spermatids. Remember that the more immature cell types are generally located near the basement membrane (basal compartment) and the more advanced cell types reside in the adluminal compartment.

In cross-section IV (stage IV) of Figure 10-10, there are five generations of germ cells. You will observe a generation of A-spermatogonia, one generation of intermediate spermatogonia, one generation of primary spermatocytes, one generation of secondary

Figure 10-10. Associations of Developing Germ Cells That Represent Various Stages of the Cycle of the Seminiferous Epithelium

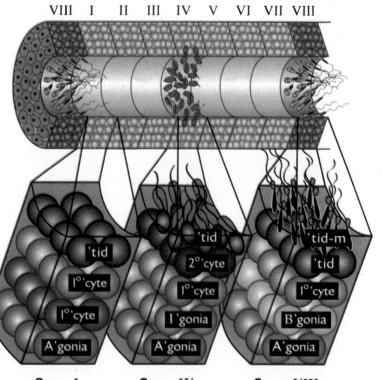

VIII I II III IV V VI VII VIII

At any given cross-sectioned location along a seminiferous tubule, one can observe different stages of the cycle of the seminiferous epithelium. In this example, we see three stages (I, IV, and VIII).

'gonia = spermatogonium
1° cyte = primary spermatocyte
2° cyte = secondary spermatocyte
'Tid = immature spermatid
'Tid-m = mature spermatid

Stage I

Stage IV

Stage VIII

A stage I tubule consists of 1 generation of A-spermatogonia, 2 generations of primary spermatocytes (1° cyte) and 1 generation of immature spermatids ('Tid).

A stage IV tubule consists of 2 generations of spermatogonia (A+I), 1 generation of primary spermatocytes (1° cyte), 1 generation of secondary spermatocytes (2° cyte) and 1 generation of immature spermatids ('Tid).

A stage VIII tubule consists of 2 generations of spermatogonia (A+B), 1 generation of primary spermatocytes (1° cyte) and 2 generations of spermatids ('Tid). The young generation of spermatids ('Tid) have formed only a few days earlier and are quite immature. The second generation of spermatids are mature ('Tid-m) and are about to be released into the lumen.

Figure 10-11. Cycle of the Seminiferous Epithelium in the Bull
(Modified from Amann, R.P. *Am. J. Anat.* 110:69)

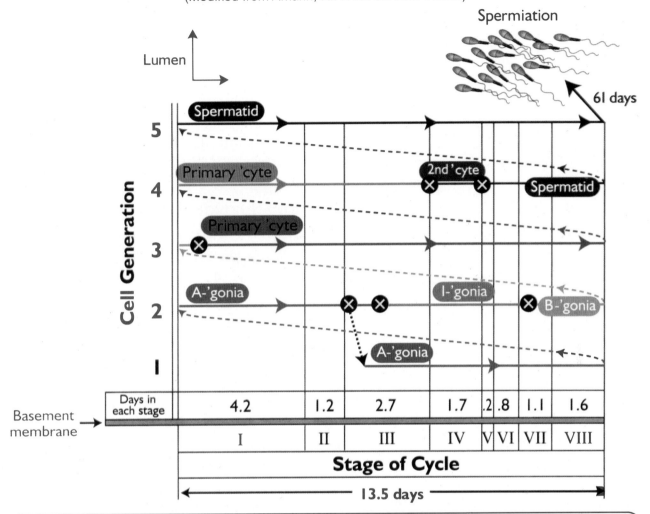

- **Horizontal axis** = Stage of cycle and days spent in each stage.
- **Vertical axis** = Cell generations in each stage i.e. type of cell seen from the basal level to the luminal level within a cross section of a seminiferous tubule.
- **Horizontal line** = Developmental pathway from spermatogonia to spermatozoa (61 days).
- The release of spermatozoa from the Sertoli cells occurs in stage VIII and is called spermiation. It occurs 61days after A-spermatogonia are formed at the beginning of Stage III.
- ⊗ Cell division (mitotic for 'gonia, meiotic for primary and secondary 'cytes).
- In the bull, it takes about 4.5 cycles of the seminiferous epithelium to complete spermatogenesis (4.5 cycles x 13.5 days/cycle = 61 days).

spermatocytes and one generation of spermatids. The spermatids in stage IV are elongated and, thus are more advanced than the spermatids in stage I.

In cross-section VIII (stage VIII), there are also five generations of germ cells. Observe two generations of spermatogonia (one generation of A and one generation of B-spermatogonia), one generation of primary spermatocytes and two generations of spermatids. One generation of spermatids is rather immature and spherical, while the more advanced generation consists of mature spermatids ready for release from Sertoli cells into the lumen of the seminiferous tubule.

At one instance in time, three cross-sections at different locations along the seminiferous tubule show different generations of cells. Cells in each section are actively engaged in spermatogenesis, but only one cross-section (VIII) is ready to release spermatozoa into the lumen. Thus, along the length of any seminiferous tubule there are only certain zones (cross-sections) where spermatozoa are released at any given point in time. All other zones or stages are preparing to release spermatozoa, but the cells in those zones have not reached the appropriate stage of maturity for spermiation to occur.

Stage = specific cellular associations

Stage duration = time required for completion of one stage (cell association)

Cycle = progression through sequence of all stages

Cycle duration = time required to complete one cycle

Figure 10-12. The Cycle of Seminiferous Epithelium is Analogous to a University
(Modified from Johnson, 1991)

Every year, freshmen (spermatogonia) enter and seniors (spermatozoa) graduate. However, four years are required for a freshmen to progress through the various classes to become a graduating senior. Each class is analogous to a generation of germ cells found in the seminiferous epithelium.

Graduation
(Spermiation)

4 years

Senior
('tid)

Junior
(Secondary 'cyte)

Sophomore
(Primary 'cyte)

Freshman
('gonia)

Fall semester

Spring semester

"Flunk-out"

I year

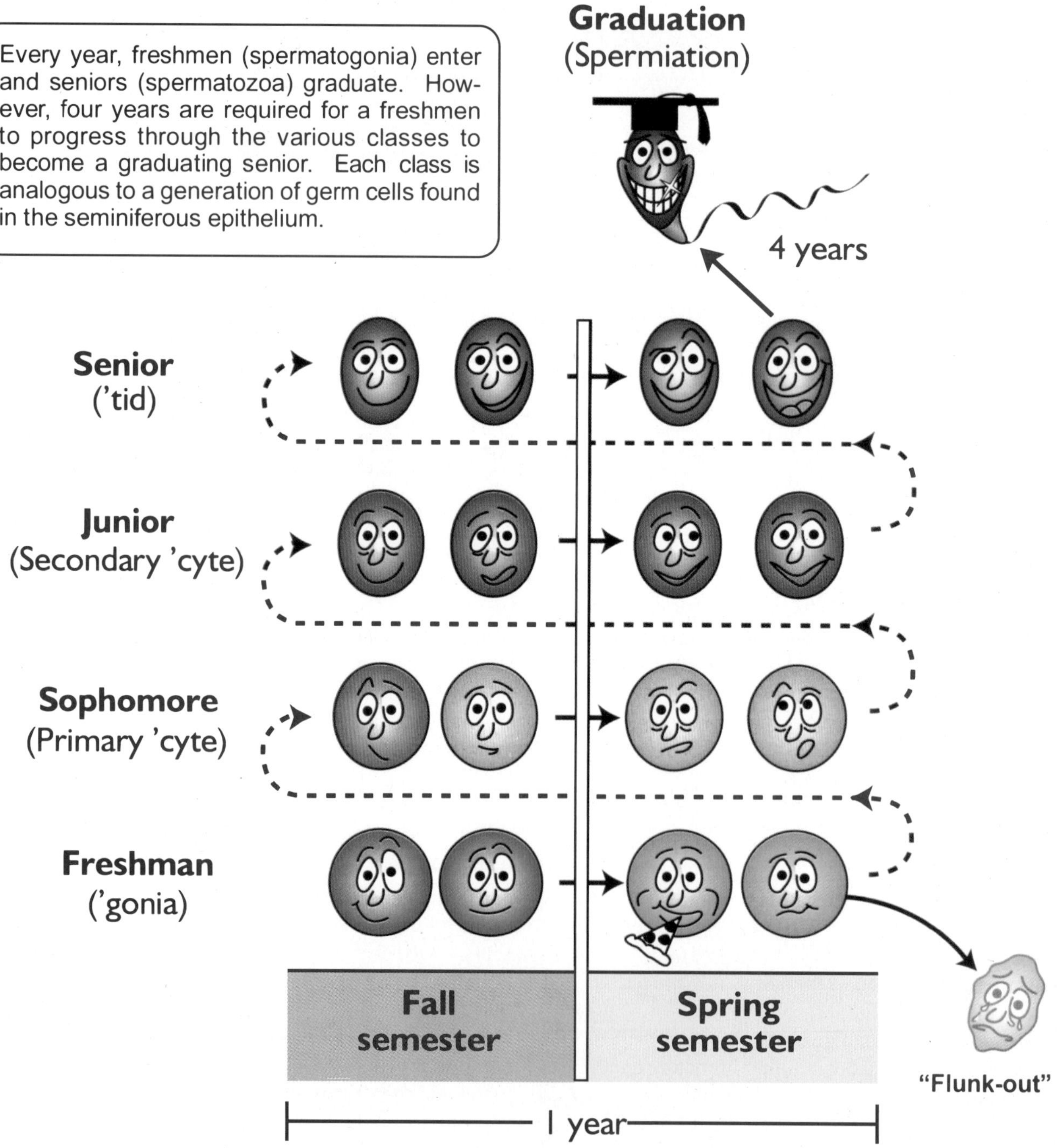

> ### *Stages of the cycle are arbitrarily defined cellular associations that transition one to the next at predictable intervals.*

As previously explained, sections or zones along a seminiferous tubule contain different cellular associations. These cellular associations, or **stages of the cycle of the seminiferous epithelium**, have been defined arbitrarily by researchers who have made thousands and thousands of observations of the seminiferous epithelium using light microscopy.

If you were to microscopically scan a number of tubules in the testicular parenchyma, you would see tubule cross-sections that contain exactly the same cell types and relationships as other tubules. In fact, with enough observation you would begin to encounter different cross-sections with definable cellular compositions at predictable frequencies. For the purposes of this text, we will describe eight stages in the cycle of the seminiferous epithelium, even though other schemes are available with as many as 14 stages.

Figure 10-11 illustrates the cellular composition of each stage of the seminiferous epithelium. For example, stage I contains one generation of A-spermatogonia, two generations of primary spermatocytes and one generation of spermatids. By scanning from the basement membrane (bottom of diagram) toward the lumen, you can quickly determine which cell types are present at each of the eight stages.

> ### *Lifespan of cells and duration of the cycle vary among species.*

The entire progression of one cycle of the seminiferous epithelium from stage I through stage VIII requires 13.5 days in the bull (for other species see Table 10-1). That is, if you could observe one cross-section of a seminiferous tubule continually, starting at the beginning of stage I, it would require 13.5 days before you would observe spermiation (the end of stage VIII). After spermiation (end of stage VIII), the cross section you were observing would again have the same cellular association as it did on the day you started watching (stage I). Thus, one cycle of the seminiferous epithelium would have been completed.

The complete process of spermatogenesis from A-spermatogonia to the formation of fully differentiated spermatozoa takes 61 days in the bull. During the 61 days, cells at a given area of the seminiferous epithelium proceed through 4.5 cycles of the seminiferous epithelium (13.5 days/cycle X 4.5 cycles = 61 days).

This process is analogous to a traditional university. Every year a new class of freshmen enters the university in the fall. These freshmen are analogous to committed A-spermatogonia entering the spermatogenic pathway. The freshmen (A-spermatogonia) undergo noticeable changes during the first year, and after one year they become sophomores. Sophomores are analogous to primary spermatocytes. The sophomores (primary spermatocytes) also undergo maturational changes and become juniors (secondary spermatocytes; although they actually are short-lived). Finally, they become seniors (spermatids) and graduate after four years (See Figure 10-12).

The cycle of the seminiferous epithelium is almost identical in concept to the university situation, except the school year is only 13.5 days (1 cycle of the seminiferous epithelium in the bull). Every 13.5 days a new generation of freshmen (A-spermatogonia) enter and a generation of seniors (spermatids) graduate. Graduation by the seniors is analogous to spermiation. Remember, it takes four years to graduate from the university. Similarly, it takes 4.5 cycles for an A-spermatogonium (freshman) to become a fully differentiated spermatozoon (senior). A major difference between the university example and the actual cycle of the seminiferous epithelium is that the germinal elements have different lifespans. For example, a primary spermatocyte exists for about 21 days while a secondary spermatocyte exists for only 1.7 days in the bull. In the university, freshmen, sophomores, juniors and seniors have similar lifespans (assuming a basal academic performance).

There is another major difference between the university analogy and what actually takes place in the germinal epithelium. Spermatogonia (freshmen), primary (sophomores) and secondary (juniors) spermatocytes all divide and generate many spermatids. For example each incoming freshmen (A-gonia) could theoretically produce 256 seniors (spermatids). Obviously, such multiplication does not take place with university students. In the university, a significant proportion of entering freshmen "flunk-out" and never graduate, so there are always more freshmen than graduating seniors. Similarly, during spermatogenesis many proliferating spermatogonia die and never become primary spermatocytes. Therefore, the number of primary spermatocytes generated per committed A-spermatogonium is closer to 20-30 than the theoretical 64 as depicted in Figure 10-5. There also is death of primary spermatocytes, although most spherical spermatids do form a spermatozoon. In contrast from a university where each student can choose their pace throughout the years, to amass 120 credits, in the testis of a given species, the pace through spermatogenesis is essentially identical and is not affected by environment.

10

Table 10-1. Duration of the Stages of the Cycle of the Seminiferous Epithelium in Various Species

Stage	Bull	Ram	Boar	Stallion	Rabbit
I	4.2	2.2	1.1	2.0	3.1
II	1.2	1.1	1.4	1.8	1.5
III	2.7	1.9	0.4	0.4	0.8
IV	1.7	1.1	1.2	1.9	1.2
V	0.2	0.4	0.8	0.9	0.5
VI	0.8	1.3	1.6	1.7	1.7
VII	1.1	1.1	1.0	1.6	1.3
VIII	1.6	1.0	0.8	1.9	0.9
TOTAL[A]	13.5	10.1	8.3	12.2	11.0
SPERMATOGENESIS[B]	61	47	39	55	48

[A]Total days required for 1 cycle of the seminiferous epithelium

[B]Approximate days to complete spermatogenesis (spermatogonia to spermatozoa)

> *The spermatogenic wave is the sequential ordering of stages along the length of the seminiferous tubule.*

The duration of each stage of the cycle of the seminiferous epithelium varies with species, as does the length of the cycle of the seminiferous epithelium. Variations in stage, cycle length and total time required for spermatogenesis are presented in Table 10-1.

The **spermatogenic wave** refers to the differences at any given instant in time along the length of the seminiferous tubule. Imagine that you could run down the lumen of the seminiferous tubule. As you run down the tubule, you will encounter zones that are near spermiation (stage VIII). The distance between these spermiation sites is relatively constant. During the wave, each stage of the seminiferous epithelium transitions to a successively more advanced stage. For example, a stage I tubule will later become a stage II and stage II will later become a III and so on. Thus, the site of spermiation along the tubule is constantly changing, creating a "wave" of sperm release down the length of the tubule. This "wave" is like the wave conducted by football fans in a stadium. When the fans stand up, they mimic spermiation. They sit back down and don't stand up again until it's their turn again. The time spent sitting (stages I-VII) is much longer than the time spent standing. As the wave in the stadium continues, repeated standing and sitting takes place at a relatively constant rate. So does spermiation. The physiologic importance of the spermatogenic wave is to provide a relatively constant supply of spermatozoa to the epididymis, creating a pool for ejaculation.

Figure 10-13. Scrotal Circumference Measurements are Good Indicators of Sperm Producing Ability

(Photograph courtesy of Select Sires, Inc. Plain City, Ohio, *www.selectsires.com*)

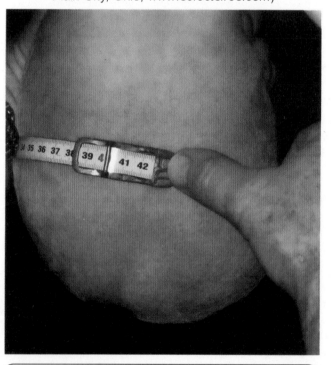

Accurate scrotal circumference measurements require that both testicles be pushed ventrally by applying pressure to the spermatic cord. A specially designed tape is then placed around the scrotum at its widest point and a measurement is taken (in this case, 40cm).

Table 10-2. Testicular Characteristics and Sperm Production Estimates of Sexually Mature Mammals

Species	Gross weight of paired testes (grams)	Sperm produced per gram of testicular parenchyma	Daily spermatozoal production
Beef Bull	650	11×10^6	6×10^9
Boar	750	23×10^6	16×10^9
Cat	21	16×10^6	32×10^6
Dairy Bull	725	12×10^6	7.5×10^9
Dog (16 kg body weight)	31	17×10^6	0.50×10^9
Man	35	4×10^6	0.13×10^9
Rabbit	6	25×10^6	0.20×10^9
Ram*	550	21×10^6	10×10^9
Rooster***	25	100×10^6	2.5×10^9
Stallion**	340	16×10^6	5×10^9

*in breeding season (shortening-day length), ** in breeding season (increasing day length), ***varies greatly with management and strain

Daily sperm production (DSP) is defined as the total number of spermatozoa produced per day by both testicles of the male. Accurate measurement of DSP requires removal of all or a portion of the testicle and thus, DSP cannot be measured using non-invasive techniques. However, noninvasive measures such as total number of spermatozoa ejaculated into an artificial vagina with daily ejaculations for 2-3 weeks gives a good estimate of DSP. Interspecies variation in testicular weights, sperm produced per gram of testicular parenchyma and daily sperm production is presented in Table 10-2. The number of spermatozoa produced per day per gram of testicular parenchyma is referred to as **efficiency of sperm production**. Daily sperm production is dependent, at least in part, on the number of Sertoli cells populating the testes. For example, the higher the number of Sertoli cells, the higher the spermatozoal production rates. Numbers of Sertoli cells also have been positively correlated with spermatogonial and spermatid numbers.

Testicular Size is a Good Estimator of Sperm Producing Ability

To determine a given male's sperm producing capability, it is necessary to collect ejaculates from the animal for a period of time. This enables one to accurately estimate how many spermatozoa the animal can produce per unit time. If collection of semen is not possible, a good estimate of sperm producing capability can be made by measuring the circumference of both testicles (See Figure 10-13). The greater the testicular circumference, the greater the sperm producing capabil-

ity, in other words, "the bigger the factory, the greater the output." Because of the non-pendular scrotum in the boar and stallion, scrotal width or length is used as the measurement.

Assuming that a male can develop an erect penis, mount and ejaculate in the female, his potential fertility is determined by:

- *his sperm producing ability*

- *the viability of his spermatozoa*

- *the number of morphologically abnormal spermatozoa that he ejaculates*

- *the number of functionally normal spermatozoa that he ejaculates*

Spermatozoal Viability is Judged by Evaluating Motility

Even though a male can produce large quantities of spermatozoa, it is important that these sperm are alive and highly motile. Motility is generally described as the ability of sperm to swim progressively forward. Motility is the most commonly used assessment of viability. It is expressed as an estimate of the percentage of sperm that are swimming in a linear fashion within a given environment as determined microscopically. Unfortunately, the relationship between percentage of motile sperm and fertility is not a good one. However, if few spermatozoa within a series of

Figure 10-14. Some Common Abnormalities in Bovine Sperm as Observed With Differential-Interference Contrast Microscopy
(Courtesy of R.G. Saacke, Virginia Polytechnic Institute and State University)

Head Abnormalities

Crater Defect
(Nuclear Vacuoles)

Tapered Heads

Ruffled Acrosome

Knobbed Acrosome

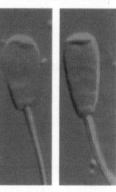

Tail Abnormalities

Coiled Tail

Double Midpiece

Folded Tail

Detached Head

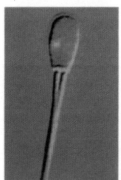

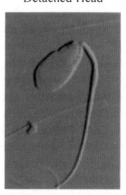

Note: A vast amount of information is available for bulls because of intense scrutiny given to abnormal sperm by commercial AI organizations. For details on the incidence, causes and their effects on fertility of abnormal sperm shown here (and other types as well) see Barth and Oko, 1998 in the **Key References** section at the end of the chapter. Most descriptions in the bull apply to other mammals as well.

---

ejaculates are motile, the assumption can be made correctly that sperm in the ejaculate are not alive and therefore cannot fertilize the egg. There are many ways to tell if a spermatozoon is alive. These include oxygen consumption, exclusion of certain dyes by the plasma membrane (live-dead stains) and examination by flow cytometry. However, the simplest and most common is to determine if a cell moves forward in a progressive manner (motile) when examined at 37°C. Evaluating motility at temperatures below 37°C is not a good practice because motility stops at about 18°C. The use of a phase-contrast microscope (essential to clearly visualize sperm) and a heated stage (to allow sperm to display their potential to swim) is the most practical way to evaluate motility of sperm. Decisions about motility should never be based solely on one ejaculate.

There are Many Types of Abnormal Spermatozoa

As you might imagine, a process that potentially produces up to 20 billion sperm per day (over 200,000 per second) will have errors. These errors are expressed as abnormal spermatozoa some of which can be detected on the basis of abnormal shape. Morphologically abnormal sperm can be defined as any shape characteristic deviating from normal. Every ejaculate will contain between 5 and 15% abnormal sperm and these levels are generally considered acceptable. Reduced fertility may result when morphologically abnormal sperm exceed 20% of sperm in the ejaculate. Some morphologic abnormalities have a severe effect on fertility while others have little or no effect. In general, morphologic abnormalities either originate in the testes because of faulty differentiation or in the epididymis because of faulty epididymal transit and/or maturation. The latter results in the presence of cytoplasmic droplets (See Chapter 3). Morphologically abnormal sperm of testicular origin are generally classified as either head abnormalities or tail abnormalities.

Potential fertility of the male can be related to the percentage of morphologically abnormal sperm within an ejaculate. Some common abnormalities in bull sperm are shown in Figure 10-14. Some abnormalities are heritable and result in sterility. Males possessing these abnormalities should be eliminated from the gene pool.

Evaluation of the proportion of abnormal sperm in an ejaculate requires a microscope. For most laboratories, a phase-contrast microscope and a skilled observer will yield satisfactory diagnoses. For laboratories examining large numbers of ejaculates, a **differential-interference contrast microscope** is preferred because of the high resolution and the cellular detail generated with this optical system. A differential-interference contrast microscope transforms gradients in intracellular density into an optical image that appears as a relief or an indentation in the cell. Thus, abnormalities of both the head and tail can be observed and quantitated with a high degree of precision. All of the micrographs presented in Figure 10-14 were generated with a differential-interference contrast microscope. A description of each type of abnormality that one can encounter within a series of ejaculates is beyond the scope of this text.

It must be recognized that morphologic abnormalities represent only one characteristic among a myriad of possibilities for abnormal function. For example, abnormal nuclear composition (faulty DNA), abnormal biochemical composition, surface protein deficiency and faulty response to stimuli within the female tract represent only a few possibilities that may limit the function of spermatozoa.

Artificial Insemination is the Single Most Important Physiologic Technology Ever Devised for Accelerating Genetic Improvement

The components of artificial insemination (AI) in the fact box, will be presented in the chapters that discuss the physiology of each process. For example, collection of semen involves behavioral issues requiring specific stimuli for mounting and ejaculation (See Chapter 11). Preservation and extension of semen is an issue associated with providing an optimum in-vitro environment to preserve sperm viability (Current Chapter). Finally, insemination of the female delivers sperm to the female reproductive tract so that adequate numbers are present and fertilization can be accomplished (See Chapter 12). Successful AI can be accomplished in any species provided the criteria below are met.

The major steps of artificial insemination are:

- *collection of semen from the male (See Chapter 11)*
- *preservation and extension of sperm (See Below)*
- *insemination of the female (See Chapter 12)*

Artificial insemination is a common practice in some species. For example, over 7 million dairy cows and about 2 million beef cows are artificially inseminated annually in the United States. All turkey hens in commercial flocks (over 300 million) are artificially inseminated because the toms have such a broad breast that they cannot mount and copulate. The use of AI in swine has exploded during the past 10 years. Approximately 85% of all female swine are artificially inseminated in the United States. This means that about 5 million females are artificially inseminated each year. Typically, each female receives about 2.3 inseminations per year in order to deliver two litters per year. This means that in the swine industry there are about 11.3 million artificial inseminations per year. This means that nearly 120 million pigs are sired by artificial insemination in the United States each year.

It should be emphasized that widespread application of artificial insemination allows for intense and relatively rapid genetic selection that significantly improves production efficiency in dairy, beef, poultry and swine. Improvements in animal efficiency result in a wide variety of highly affordable animal products to the consumer. Artificial insemination is also common for horses. In addition, many species in zoos have been artificially inseminated to avoid inbreeding and facilitate reproduction in exotic and endangered species. In 2002 the first baby elephant was produced by artificial insemination at the National Zoo in Washington D.C. Artificial insemination is used routinely in assisted reproductive techniques in humans, allowing pregnancies to occur that otherwise would not be possible (See Chapter 16).

10

> *Immediately after collection, the following information is needed:*
>
> • *ejaculate volume*
>
> • *concentration of spermatozoa in the ejaculate (sperm/mL ejaculate)*
>
> • *percentage of motile sperm*

In Vitro Preservation is Obligatory for Successful AI

After semen has been collected from the male, *in vitro* preservation of sperm for a period of time must be accomplished before successful delivery of sperm to the female can take place. Preservation and dilution of sperm requires an environment that minimizes death of sperm. It also requires knowledge about the volume of the ejaculate, the concentration of sperm in the ejaculate and their motility.

Having the above information is necessary to determine the appropriate dilution rate of the sperm so multiple females can be inseminated with sperm from the same ejaculate. Where multiple females are to be inseminated, one must know the concentration of sperm in the ejaculate so that each female can be inseminated with a threshold number (minimum number) of spermatozoa to maximize the probability of a pregnancy.

Evaluation of Semen is Needed Before Dilution

Immediately after collection of the ejaculate seminal evaluation is conducted. First, ejaculate volume must be determined. Second, the percentage of sperm displaying progressive motility (swimming in a linear fashion) is estimated by viewing live smears at 37°C with a phase-contrast microscope. Third, the concentration of spermatozoa in the ejaculate is determined by comparing optical density of a standard dilution of neat semen with a reference standard. The greater the sperm concentration, the greater the optical density. The sperm concentration is determined from a standard curve where optical density is plotted against concentration.

The ejaculate volume and concentration of spermatozoa are important elements of seminal evaluation because the volume multiplied by the concentration equals the total number of sperm in the ejaculate as shown in the equation below.

Total Sperm in Ejac. = Ejac. Vol. x Sperm/ml

Knowing the total number of sperm in the ejaculate enables the laboratory technician to determine how many insemination doses are potentially available within each ejaculate.

A high percentage of motile sperm (60% or more) indicates good quality. An ejaculate containing few motile sperm (less than 50%) is a candidate for discard especially if sperm are to be frozen and later thawed to inseminate females.

Information for determining the number of insemination doses contained in a typical ejaculate for the bull is presented below. These calculations apply in principle to other species except that the values (volume, concentration and motility) may vary significantly from species-to-species and from male-to-male.

Ejaculate volume = 6 ml

Sperm concentration = 1.0×10^9 sperm/ml (1 billion)

Total sperm in ejaculate = 6 ml x 1.0×10^9 sperm/ml = 6×10^9 (6 billion)

Progressive motility = 70%

Total motile sperm = $6.0 \times 10^9 \times .7 = 4.2 \times 10^9$ motile sperm/ejaculate

Desired concentration = 15×10^6/dose (1 insemination)

Number of doses = $4.2 \times 10^9 / 15 \times 10^6$ = **280 doses**

To determine the number of doses a single ejaculate will generate, one must divide the total number of sperm by the desired number of sperm in each dose. For example, the ejaculate illustrated above contains 4.2 billion motile sperm. If a dose of semen is intended to contain 15 million motile sperm (15×10^6) then we divide 4.2×10^9 sperm by 15×10^6 sperm. By the computation in the box above, this ejaculate will produce 280 doses (units) of semen after dilution.

> *Good seminal extenders must:*
>
> • *be isotonic*
>
> • *be good buffers*
>
> • *minimize cold damage ("cold shock")*
>
> • *provide appropriate nutrients*
>
> • *prevent microbial growth*
>
> • *maintain viability*
>
> • *be relatively low in cost*

Seminal Extenders Extend Both Sperm Viability and Numbers

After it has been determined that the ejaculate is of sufficient quality (volume, % motile spermatozoa and concentration of spermatozoa) the sperm must be preserved so that they can be used to inseminate females over an extended period of time (e.g. several days to one week). To inseminate many females with a single ejaculate the neat semen must be extended so that each inseminate dose contains less sperm than the entire ejaoulate. Typically, the solution into which spermatozoa are diluted is referred to as an **extender** because it not only "extends" the number of sperm in the original ejaculate, but it "extends" their functional life. Extenders may be purchased from commercial sources or they can be prepared in the laboratory.

The Extender Must be Isotonic

You will recall from your basic biology class that when a cell is in an isotonic solution there is no net movement of water into or out of the cell. A **hypotonic** solution is a solution in which the medium contains fewer osmotically active particles than the cell and water rushes into the cell and the cell membrane ruptures (**cell lysis**). In contrast, a **hypertonic** solution contains more osmotically active particles than does the inside of the cell and water moves out of the cell and it dehydrates. Providing the proper osmotic balance of the seminal extender is obligatory for survival of spermatozoa.

An Extender Must Buffer and Protect

A **buffer** is a material that prevents marked changes in pH (hydrogen ion concentration). Extremes in pH, both acidic and alkaline, are damaging to all cells including spermatozoa.

The cell membrane of a spermatozoon is quite sensitive to sudden drops in temperature ("cold shock"). Care must be taken to prevent sudden declines in temperature so that the cell membrane and motile apparatus of the sperm do not become damaged. In neat semen, particular care must be taken to prevent damage to the spermatozoa. The design of the artificial vagina is important so that "cold shock" can be prevented (See Chapter 11). Slow, controlled cooling of sperm is important because it lowers the temperature gradually and minimizes stresses on the cell membrane. A low storage temperature reduces metabolism by about 50% for each 10°C decline. Sperm are analogous to a battery. They have no option but to "run down." Unfortunately, recharging sperm cells after ejaculation is not possible.

Where the goal is to extend the semen for a sustained period of time (1 week to years), a **cryoprotectant** in the extender is required. Cryoprotectants are materials that protect the cells against cold damage that would occur between 0 and -50°C. These compounds protect sperm membranes by minimizing ice crystal formation within the cell. In general, cryoprotectants can be classified as cell-permeating (glycerol, DMSO) and non-permeating (milk protein and egg yolk lipoprotein). Depending on species, one or a combination of types of cryoprotectants may be optimum. Common cryoprotectants are **glycerol** and **dimethyl sulfoxide** (DMSO) with glycerol being the dominant cryoprotectant for frozen sperm. Physiologic fluids are used frequently as extender ingredients. These include hen's egg yolk and cow's milk. These provide macromolecules that minimize cold damage and provide nutrients.

The rate of temperature decline and ultimate storage temperature are important depending on species. For example, a slow decline in temperature is important in the bull and the stallion but is of much less importance to the dog and human. The influence of holding temperatures for unfrozen sperm also vary among species. For example, bull and stallion semen can be stored effectively at 5°C while boar semen requires 18°C for best preservation. These differences are due, at least in part, to differences in lipid composition of the sperm membranes.

Spermatozoa have no **anabolic** capability. In other words, spermatozoa are incapable of synthesizing materials for energy and repair. Therefore, the viability of sperm is totally dependent on the environment in which they are suspended. Nutrients need to be supplied in adequate quantities so that metabolism can be maintained for the appropriate duration of time. The major nutrients for sperm metabolism are **fructose** and **glucose**. Sperm are capable of converting glucose to fructose and metabolizing it to fuel their motility.

Ejaculated Semen is Not Sterile

Bacteria are present in the sheath and on the penis of the male and occasionally in the urethra and vesicular glands and therefore semen contains a variety of microorganisms. Seminal plasma and extender are ideal mediums for microbial growth and steps must be taken to minimize this growth. Antibiotics typically are added to the neat semen and extender to prevent microbial growth. Antibiotics such as penicillin, liquamycin, linco-spectin and streptomycin may be added in some combination to neat semen and to extenders.

Preservation of spermatozoa can be accomplished using two methods. For relatively short term use, fresh liquid semen is used after the semen has been extended. In most species, liquid semen can be cooled

10

Table 10-3. Offspring Ratios of Spermatozoa Sorted for the X and Y Chromosome

Species	Sorted for Y Chromosome		Sorted for X Chromosome	
	% Male	% Female	% Male	% Female
Cattle	81	19	11	89
Rabbit	81	19	6	94
Swine	75	25	10	90

and stored at near freezing temperature (5°C) for several days to about one week. In swine, 17-18°C is optimum. When widespread distribution and long-term usage is a requirement, frozen semen is the preferred method of preservation. When frozen semen is used, careful attention to freezing and thawing techniques must be practiced. Freezing and thawing compromises spermatozoal viability in all species. However, the degree to which viability and fertility are affected depends on the individual male and species.

Sex of the Conceptus is Determined by the Sperm Because Each Spermatozoon Contains Either an X or a Y Chromosome

As you already know, each secondary spermatocyte produces two haploid daughter spermatids. Each spermatid contains either an X or a Y chromosome. Sperm containing the **X chromosome** that fertilize an oocyte will generate a female. Sperm containing the **Y chromosome** will generate a male (See Figure 10-15).

The desire to separate the X and Y bearing sperm is driven by the fact that one sex has significantly more economic value than the other in certain species. For example, in the dairy industry, bull calves are of little value since about 80% of all cows in the U.S. (and higher on a worldwide basis) are artificially inseminated. Thus, relatively few bulls are required to inseminate the cows in the national dairy herd. The cow is the primary income generator for a dairy business. It would be advantageous to have a high percentage of female offspring since lactation is limited to the female. In other food producing animals, it might be more desirable to produce higher percentage males since these animals grow faster and have more desired meat characteristics.

The X and Y chromosome contain different quantities of DNA. For example, an X bearing sperm contains 2.8-4.2% more DNA (depending on the species) than does a Y bearing sperm. Based on this difference, it is possible to separate the X and Y bearing sperm into two subpopulations. The separation

procedure requires the uptake of a DNA stain or dye (called a **flourochrome**) into both living and dead spermatozoa. Those sperm that contain the X chromosome "take-up" more DNA dye than do sperm containing the Y chromosome. Vital dyes used to stain sperm produce emissions of light at a specific wavelength when excited or activated by light at a specific wavelength.

The technology utilized for separation of X and Y bearing spermatozoa is referred to as flow cytometry (sometimes called "cell sorting"). Figure 10-15 highlights the major steps for separation of the X and Y bearing spermatozoa using flow cytometry.

Experimental evidence clearly shows the success of this technology for separating the X and Y bearing spermatozoa from common mammals and most experiments have yielded 80-90% successful separation for either males or females in cattle, swine and rabbits (See Table 10-3). Several factors have limited the efficiency of this technology, but the application is now widespread in dairy cattle and is feasible in many other species.

Regardless of the problems associated with separating the X and Y bearing spermatozoa, the technology is now available through artificial insemination organizations. Thus, it is reasonable to expect that separation of X and Y bearing spermatozoa eventually will be commonplace. Manipulation of the sex ratio under controlled conditions could greatly impact the efficiency of food animal production.

Figure 10-15. Major Steps for Separation of X and Y Bearing Spermatozoa by Flow Cytometry

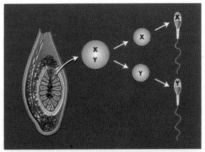

Step 1
X and Y bearing spermatozoa are produced by the testis and ejaculated by the male.

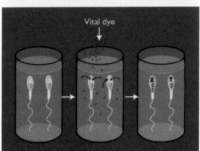

Step 2
Ejaculated spermatozoa are treated with a fluorescent DNA specific dye. X bearing sperm absorb more dye than Y bearing sperm. They therefore emit more intense light when excited by a laser. Sperm also are treated with a dye that greatly suppresses the signal from dead sperm. Dead sperm are therefore identified and rejected.

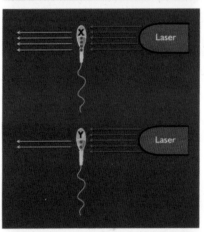

10

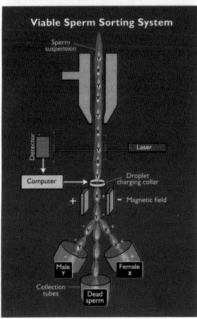

Step 3
Once spermatozoa enter the flow cytometer chamber, they pass single-file through a small nozzle. At a region just outside the nozzle, a laser beam excites the fluorescent dye in each sperm. Each live sperm emits light at a wavelength and intensity that is directly related to quantity of DNA. X-bearing live sperm produce more intensity. A light sensing device is coupled to a computer that determines the intensity of light emission by each sperm and the order of passage of each sperm through a column below the nozzle. When the sperm pass by charged plates, they are assigned either a positive or negative charge depending on their DNA content (X or Y chromosome). When the microdroplet containing a single sperm passes through an electromagnetic field the computer applies an appropriate charge and directs the droplet (and sperm) to one side or the other. Dead sperm are discarded into the center tube. Thus, at the conclusion of the separation process there are three vessels that contain sperm. One contains a high proportion of X, one contains a high proportion of Y chromosome bearing sperm and one contains dead sperm.

Further PHENOMENA for Fertility

Spermatozoa of the American opossum are ejaculated in doublets. They are formed in the seminiferous epithelium as single cells with an acrosome. During epididymal transit the acrosome of two spermatozoa attach to each other, so that a pair of spermatozoa exists. These doublets apparently have more progressive motility than do single cells. When motility ceases they apparently separate.

In Greek Mythology, when Priapus was in the womb of his mother Aphrodite, Hera put a spell on him to make him ugly. When he was born, he was of small stature and very ugly but possessed an extremely large penis that was always erect. The name Priapus gave rise to the medical term "priapism", which is defined as a persistent (sometimes painful) erection of the penis, associated with some form of pathology (blood clot in cavernous tissue) and not sexual excitation. Priapus became known as the Greek God of Fertility in most species, including plants, animals and humans. As the source of fertility, statues of Priapus were kept in gardens to ensure fertile crops and to scare away thieves. He has also been thought to be a cure for impotence.

In some regions of the world, testes are prized as gourmet treats. In Japan, testicles of dolphins are highly valued hors d'oeuvres. In Spain, bull testicles are served at social events surrounding the occasion of a bull fight. Bull testicles are also consumed by hungry American cowboys at castration time. In all cases, they are cooked.

The bulls at a leading AI organization produce a lot of sperm. The annual semen production from the bulls collected is as follows:

- *42-43,000 ejaculations per year*
- *205 trillion spermatozoa per year*
- *454 lbs. (206kg) neat semen per year*
- *10,282,759 0.5-ml straws per year*
- *12,196 lbs. (6.1 tons) of extended semen per year*

It is rumored that during the early stages of Christianity, the church had succeeded in getting the pagans to give up worship of all the old gods except Priapus (the Greek God of Fertility with a huge penis). No matter what the threats or enticements were, the loyal worshipers of Priapus would not give up reverence for their favorite god. The expression of this unwavering reverence included the baking of bread in the shape of a penis on every available celebratory occasion, including church holidays. Unable to dissuade the people from this rather un-Christian practice, the wise church fathers sanctified the loaves, providing each had three crosses carved into its top. This was the reported beginning of hot crossed buns.

The ancient Greeks thought that spermatozoa from the left testicle produced girls and spermatozoa from the right testicle produced boys. This myth apparently stood the "test of time" because as late as the 1700s, French noblemen would have their left testicle removed in an attempt to sire boys only. The author proposes that the modern day declaration by males, "I would give my left testicle for a ---", is a sexist comment that devalues the left testicle because it was once thought to produce females only. Have you ever heard a male say he was willing to give-up his right testicle for something?

Lazzaro Spallanzani was a mathematician and philosopher. He was also a priest who conducted experiments with sperm and eggs. His religious beliefs prevented him from collecting and working with human sperm. He wondered, though, if every human sperm in an ejaculate had a soul and, if so, what happened to the millions of souls in wasted semen. If every sperm had its own soul, then masturbation and contraception were serious sins. In Spallanzani's era

(1700s) many biologists believed in "remote fertilization," in which the egg could be stimulated to develop without contact with semen. They thought if an egg were exposed to invisible "spermatic vapor" it would develop into an embryo. Since "spermatic vapor," like a ghost, could not be seen there was some worry that this ghostly vapor, once released from an ejaculate, might waft-up the legs of some unsuspecting female, causing an unwanted pregnancy. No one knows how many unmarried women of Spallanzani's era may have credited their pregnancies to "spermatic vapor." Spallanzani believed in these sperm ghosts but wanted to test his belief. He attached freshly laid toad eggs to a watch glass and inverted it over another watch glass containing toad seminal fluid. He thus had an enclosed system in which the eggs and seminal fluid were separated, and where the invisible "spermatic vapor" could migrate to stimulate the eggs. Nothing happened. But when the eggs were mixed directly into seminal fluid, the physical contact produced tadpoles. How did Spallanzani obtain frog semen? He dressed male frogs in tiny taffeta trousers and placed them with a female frog (without clothes). He waterproofed the pants with a light coating of candle wax. Aroused, the males mounted the females and ejaculated in their pants. Spallanzani then collected the semen. These experiments might have been the forerunners to in vitro fertilization because tadpoles developed. Spallanzani was one of the first scientists to achieve artificial collection of semen in a laboratory under controlled conditions.

Key References

Amann, R.P. 1999. "Cryopreservation of sperm" in *Encyclopedia of Reproduction* Vol. 1 p 773-783. Knobil, E. and J.D. Neill (eds). Academic Press, San Diego. ISBN 0-12-227021-5.

Barth, A.D. and R.J. Oko. 1989. *Abnormal Morphology of Bovine Spermatozoa*. Iowa State University Press, Ames. ISBN 0-8138-0112-5.

Dadoune, J.P. and A. Demoulin. 1993. "Structure and functions of the testis" in *Reproduction in Mammals and Man*. C. Thibault, M.C. Levasseur and R. H. F. Hunter, eds. Ellipses, Paris. ISBN 2-7298-9354-7.

Ericsson, R.J. and S.A. Ericsson. 1999. "Sex ratios" in *Encyclopedia of Reproduction*. Vol. 4 p 431-436. Knobil, E. and J.D. Neill (eds.) Academic Press, San Diego ISBN 0-12-227024-X.

Hess, R.A. 1999. "Spermatogenesis overview" in *Encyclopedia of Reproduction*. Vol. 4 p 539-545. Knobil, E. and J.D. Neill (eds). Academic Press, San Diego. ISBN 0-12-227024-X.

Johnson, L. 1991. "Spermatogenesis" in *Reproduction in Domestic Animals* 4th Edition, P.T. Cupps, ed. Academic Press, Inc. San Diego. ISBN 0-12-196575-9.

Johnson, L. T.A. McGowen, G.E. Keillor. 1999. "The Testis, overview" in *Encyclopedia of Reproduction*, Vol. 4 p 769-783. Knobil and Neill, eds. Academic Press, San Diego. ISBN 0-12-227024-X.

Lamming, G.E. ed. 1990. *Marshall's Physiology of Reproduction*. Fourth Edition Vol. 2: Reproduction in the Male. Churchill Livingstone, New York. ISBN 0-443-01968-1.

Russel, L. D. and M. D. Griswold, eds. 1993. *The Sertoli Cell*. Cache River Press, Clearwater. ISBN 0-9627422-0-1-X.

10

CHAPTER 11

REPRODUCTIVE BEHAVIOR

The Puerperium & Lactation

Parturition

Fetal Attachment & Gestation

Early Embryogenesis & Maternal Recognition of Pregnancy

Ovulation & Fertilization

YOU ARE HERE — Copulation — **YOU ARE HERE**

Cyclicity — Spermatogenesis

Regulation of Reproduction — Regulation of Reproduction

Tract Function — Tract Function

Puberty — Puberty

Prenatal Development — Prenatal Development

FEMALE **MALE**

Take Home Message

Reproductive behavior is an obligatory component of the reproductive process. It consists of precopulatory, copulatory and postcopulatory stages. In the female, sexual receptivity occurs only during estrus and is characterized by distinct behavior and mating posture (lordosis). In the male, reproductive behavior can occur potentially any time. Sexual arousal in the male involves a cascade of endocrine and neural events that result in erection of the penis, mounting of the sexually receptive female, intromission and ejaculation. Erection of the penis involves specific neural and biochemical events that culminate in penile vasodilation. Ejaculation is a reflex that is initiated by stimulation of the glans penis and concludes with expulsion of semen.

Reproductive behavior has evolved as one of the strongest drives in the animal kingdom and usually takes precedence over all other forms of activity such as eating, resting and sleeping. The purpose of reproductive behavior is to promote the opportunity for copulation and thus increase the probability that the sperm and the egg will meet. The ultimate goals of copulation are pregnancy, successful embryogenesis and parturition.

> *Reproductive behavior in the male consists of three distinct stages:*
> - *the precopulatory stage*
> - *the copulatory stage*
> - *the postcopulatory stage*

Reproductive behavior in the male can be divided into three distinct stages. These stages are: the **precopulatory stage**; the **copulatory stage**; and the **postcopulatory stage**. The specific events that occur during each of these stages are presented in Figure 11-1.

> *Reproductive behavior in the female can be considered to serve the following functions:*
> - *attractivity*
> - *proceptivity*
> - *receptivity*

Figure 11-1. Stages of Male Reproductive Behavior and Specific Events in Each Stage

Precopulatory Behavior

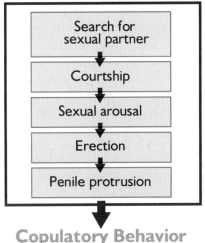

Copulatory Behavior

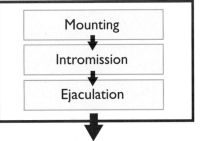

Postcopulatory Behavior

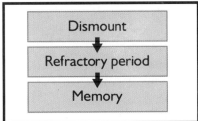

11

Precopulatory, copulatory and postcopulatory behaviors in the female can be considered as serving the functions of: attractivity, proceptivity and receptivity. **Attractivity** refers to behaviors and other signals that serve to attract males. This can include postures, vocalizations, behaviors and chemical cues such as pheromones that attract the male to approach and engage in precopulatory behavior. **Proceptivity** refers to the behaviors exhibited by females toward males that stimulate the male to copulate or that reinitiate sexual behavior after copulation. For example, head butting of the male and mounting the male are two of the most common proceptive behaviors exhibited by females. Proceptivity may also include behaviors among females, such as female-female mounting that sexually stimulate males. Finally, **receptivity** is the copulatory behavior of females that ensures insemination. This may include the immobility or standing response (lordosis) as well as tail deviation or backing-up toward the male.

As you have already learned, sexual activity of the postpubertal female is confined to estrus (heat). This short period of sexual receptivity limits the time during which precopulatory behavior occurs in most females. In contrast, the male is potentially capable of initiating reproductive behavior at any time after puberty. The initiation of courtship-specific behavior is generally under the influence of the female. She will send subtle, or sometimes overt signals to the male (attractivity) to initiate courtship behavior. Factors such as sexual signaling pheromones, vocalization, increased physical activity and subtle postural changes are signals provided by the female that will initiate more intense courtship behavior on the part of the male. In addition, it has been hypothesized that female-female (proceptivity) interactions such as homosexual mounting activity among cattle may serve as signals to initiate male-female courtship behavior. In general, the postpubertal male is almost constantly searching for signals sent by the female to indicate that she is sexually receptive.

Identification of a sexual partner probably requires most of the senses (olfactory, visual, auditory and tactile). The relative importance of these sensory stimuli has not been described critically in most species.

Females of almost all species appear to show a marked increase in general physical activity as they come into estrus (See Figure 11-2). Elevated physical activity is generally manifested by increased locomotion. In addition, milling around, exploration, increased vocalization and agonistic behavior towards other females can be observed. In almost all species studied, including humans, there is a marked increase

11

Figure 11-2. Relationship Between Physical Activity and Reproductive Cycles in Various Female Mammals

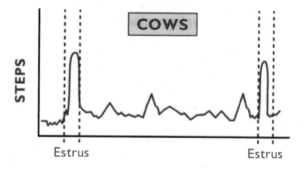

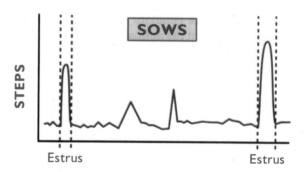

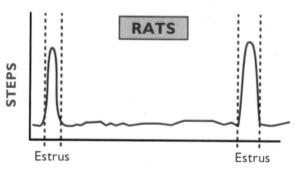

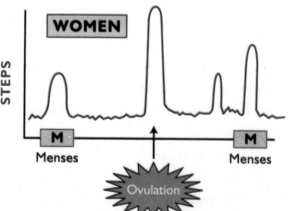

Physical activity increases significantly around the time of estrus and/or ovulation.

in physical activity that accompanies the time of ovulation. Presumably, this physical activity is associated with searching for a mate. This increased physical activity can be measured by equipping females with pedometers. Pedometers are devices that monitor and quantitate steps taken by the animal and are currently used in commercial dairy enterprises for detection of estrus.

> *Courtship-specific behavior is initiated after a sexual partner has been identified.*

Once a sexual partner has been identified, a series of highly specific courtship behaviors begin. Courtship-specific behaviors include sniffing of the vulva by the male, urination by the female in the presence of the male, exhibiting **flehmen** behavior (See Figure 11-5), chin resting, circling and increased phonation. In many species the sense of vision appears to be the most important with regard to sexual arousal in the male. This should not be interpreted to mean that other stimuli, such as auditory or olfactory are not important.

> *Copulatory behavior varies significantly among species with regard to duration.*

Lordosis (mating posture) by the female (receptivity) triggers significant sexual arousal behavior on the part of the male. Once the male discovers that the female will display lordosis, he becomes sexually stimulated. It should be emphasized that lordosis is a highly specific female motor response associated with the "willingness" to mate.

> *Sexual arousal is followed by erection and penile protrusion.*

Following exposure to the appropriate stimuli, erection and protrusion of the penis occur. These highly specific motor events are controlled by the central nervous system. The mechanisms of penile protrusion and erection will be presented later. Typical behavior during search, courtship and sexual arousal for domestic animals is presented in Table 11-1.

After significant sexual stimulation, mounting, intromission and ejaculation follow. In general, mammals can be classified as sustained copulators or short copulators. The bull, ram, buck and tom are short copulators while the boar, dog and camelids are sustained copulators. The stallion is intermediate with regard to duration of copulation.

Mounting behavior generally requires immobilization of the female and elevation of the front legs of the male to straddle the caudal region of the female (See Figure 11-10). **Intromission** is entrance of the penis into the vagina. **Ejaculation** is expulsion of semen from the penis into the female reproductive tract.

Copulatory behavior on the part of the male is learned. Past sexual experiences are important in order for the male to develop appropriate reproductive behavior. For example, negative experiences during the precopulatory and copulatory stages will generally result in less enthusiasm on the part of the male. From a practical standpoint, management of the breeding male should always be directed towards providing the male with totally positive stimuli. Utilizing non-estrus females to collect semen from stallions, boars, rams and bulls should be avoided because these females do not willingly stand to be mounted. Injury to both the female and the male can occur under these circumstances.

> *Postcopulatory behavior is a period of refractivity.*

Postcopulatory behavior involves dismounting and a period during which either the male, the female or both will not engage in copulatory behavior. This **refractory period** is a period of time during which a second copulation will not take place. Memory is important in both a positive and negative way. Positive mating experiences promote reproductive behavior and negative inhibit reproductive behavior. When semen is collected for artificial insemination, it is important to reduce the duration of the refractory period when multiple ejaculations need to be collected in the shortest possible time. Techniques to reduce the refractory period will be presented later in the chapter. Both males and females often display specific postcopulatory behavior such as vocal emissions, genital grooming, changing postural relationships and various tactile behaviors, such as licking and nuzzling.

11

Table 11-1. Typical Behavior During Search, Courtship and Consummation by Female and Male Domestic Animals

FEMALE		
Species	**Search**	**Courtship**	**Consummation**

Species	Search	Courtship	Consummation
Cow	Increased locomotion, increased vocalization, twitching & elevation of the tail	Increased grooming, mounting attempts with other females	Homosexual mounting & immobile stance (standing to be mounted)
Mare	Increased locomotion, tail erected ("flagging")	Urination stance, urination in presence of stallion	Presents hindquarters to male, clitoral exposure by labial eversion, pulsatile contractions of labia
Ewe	Short period of restlessness ram "seeking"	Urination in presence of ram	Immobile stance
Sow	Mild restlessness	Immobile stance	Immobile stance
Bitch	Roaming	Immobile stance	Tail deflected to one side Urination in presence of male affectionate head rubbing
Queen	Vocalization (calling)	Crouching, affectionate head rubbing, rolling	Elevation of rear quarters and hyper-extension of back (lordosis), presentation of vulva, tail deviation

MALE		
Species	**Search**	**Courtship**	**Consummation**

Species	Search	Courtship	Consummation
Bull	Approach sexually active group of females testing for lordosis, flehmen	Nuzzling and licking of perineal region: chin resting, testing for lordosis	Penile protrusion with dribbling of seminal fluid with few spermatozoa, erection and attempted mounts
Stallion	Visual search, flehmen	High degree of excitement	Penile protrusion with no preejaculatory expulsion of seminal fluid
Ram	Sniffing and licking of ano-genital region, nudging ewe, flehmen	Neck outstretched and head held horizontally	Repeated dorsal retraction of scrotum, penile protrusion with no dribbling of seminal fluid
Boar	Moving among females	Nuzzling, grinding of teeth, foams at mouth	Penile protrusion, shallow pelvic thrusts, attempted mounting
Dog	Roaming around territory	Sniffing, licking of the vulva	Erection, protrusion of penis, mounting
Tom	Prowling	Biting queen on dorsal neck	Mounting

11

Reproductive Behavior is Programmed During Prenatal Development

During embryogenesis, sexual differentiation occurs, during which the brain is programmed to be either male or female. Recent findings suggest that the very early embryo is neutral with regard to sex (gender). Under the influence of extremely small quantities of estradiol the brain becomes feminized. **Feminization** is the development of female-like behavior. As you learned in Chapter 6, during fetal development, α-fetoprotein is produced that prevents most fetal and maternal estradiol from crossing the blood-brain barrier and entering the brain. When α-fetoprotein prevents estradiol from entering the brain, the embryo becomes "fully feminized," because it has not been exposed to estrogen (See Chapter 6). Alpha-fetoprotein does not bind to testosterone, which can then enter the brain and be converted to estradiol. In developing males this high concentration of estradiol in the brain causes **defeminization** and **masculinization** of the brain. Defeminization reduces the likelihood that the animal will express female-like behavior postpubertally. Masculinization results in the potential of the animal to develop male-like behavior after puberty.

Sex differences in specific brain structures for the control of reproductive behavior have been observed. For example, in the male, the preoptic area of the hypothalamus is larger than in females. In the male, the size of neurons, the neuron nuclei and the dendritic arborizations are greater. In the female, the ventromedial hypothalamus is more important with regard to reproductive behavior.

In most mammals, reproductive behaviors are sexually differentiated. For example, mounting, erection and ejaculation are typically male behaviors, while standing to be mounted (lordosis), crouching and increased locomotion are typically female behaviors. These behaviors are endocrine controlled. For example, sequential treatment with progesterone and estradiol induces sexual receptivity in ovariectomized females and testosterone will restore reproductive behavior in castrated males. In some species, injections of testosterone into castrated females will even induce male-like reproductive behavior. Female fetuses exposed to androgens prenatally will display significantly reduced female behavior (defeminized) and acquire male-like behavior postnatally (masculinized). In contrast, males exposed to estrogen or progesterone prenatally are unaffected. A classic example illustrating the behavioral manifestations of prenatal exposure to androgens is the freemartin heifer. As previously discussed (See Chapter 4), this animal has abnormal development of the reproductive tract for two reasons. First, from a genetic perspective, freemartins are chimeras that are XX/XY and therefore they have an ovotestis. Second,

Figure 11-3. Influence of Various Steroid Treatments Upon Reproductive Behavior

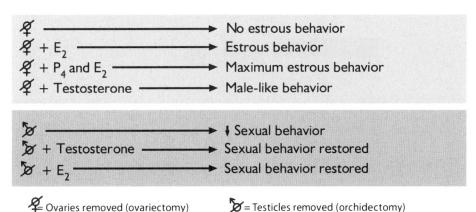

androgen exposure per se causes abnormal development of the female tract. In addition, the freemartin displays more male-like behavior than do her normal heifer counterparts. Figure 11-3 summarizes the influence of reproductive steroids on behavior in the male and the female.

The presence of gonadal steroids (estradiol and testosterone) is obligatory for normal reproductive behavior in both the male and the female. For example, ovariectomized females display no estrous behavior (See Figure 11-3). Likewise, castrated males have significantly reduced reproductive behavior. However, the abolition of reproductive behavior depends on the duration of time between castration and the opportunity to copulate. For example, males that have reached puberty and established a sustained pattern of reproductive behavior require a longer period of time between abolition of sexual behavior after castration than do males that have not established a sustained pattern of reproductive behavior.

> *Females will display male reproductive behavior following injections of testosterone.*

When ovariectomized females receive injections of estradiol, estrous behavior is reestablished, but at a less than maximum level. Among farm animals, ovariectomized females that are treated first with progesterone (to mimic the luteal phase of the cycle) and then treated with estradiol display maximum estrous behavior. In other species, estradiol must precede progesterone to produce maximal behavior. It is not clear why progesterone "priming" of the central nervous system for maximal stimulation is necessary. It would be logical to propose that progesterone promotes upregulation of estradiol receptors in the brain. Ovariectomized females that are treated with testosterone develop male-like behavior. They will even develop secondary sex characteristics (reduced pitch of voice, hump on the back of the neck and atrophy of the female reproductive tract).

Figure 11-4. Hypothetical Nervous Pathway Eliciting Reproductive-Specific Motor Behavior

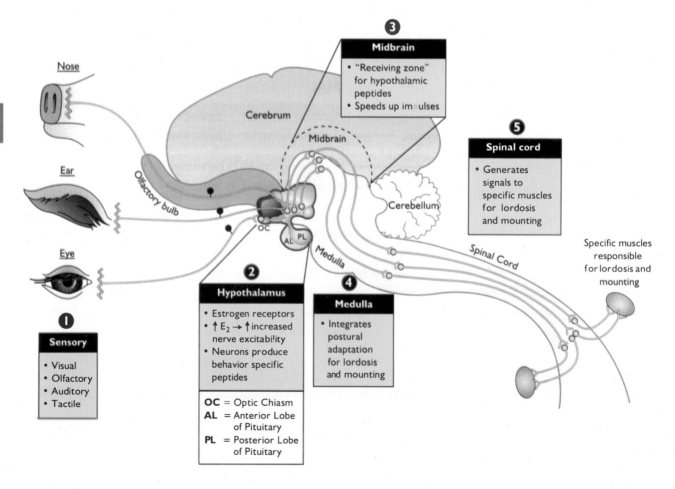

Reproductive Behavior is Controlled by the Central Nervous System

The neural pathways and key anatomical components for the control of reproductive behavior are presented in Figure 11-4. Reproductive behavior can take place only if the neurons in the hypothalamus have been sensitized to respond to sensory signals. Testosterone in the male is aromatized to estradiol in the brain and estradiol promotes reproductive behavior. Recall that testosterone is produced in small episodes every 4 to 6 hours. Therefore, there is a relatively constant supply of testosterone and thus estradiol, to the hypothalamus in the male. This allows the male to initiate reproductive behavior at any time. In contrast, the female experiences high estradiol during the follicular phase only and will display sexual receptivity during estrus only.

Figure 11-4 outlines a generic neural pathway for sexual behavior. Under the influence of estrogen, sensory inputs such as olfaction, audition, vision and tactility send neural messages to the hypothalamus. These neurons synapse directly on neurons in the ventromedial hypothalamus as well as the preoptic and anterior hypothalamic regions. These sensory inputs cause neurons in the hypothalamus to release behavior specific peptides that serve as neurotransmitters. These neurotransmitters act on neurons in the midbrain. The neurons in the midbrain serve as receiving zones for the peptides produced by the hypothalamic neurons. The midbrain translates neuropeptide signals released by hypothalamic neurons into a fast response. Neurons in the midbrain synapse with neurons in the brain stem (medulla). These nervous signals are integrated in the medulla. From the medulla, nerve tracts extend to the spinal cord where the nerves synapse with motor neurons that innervate muscles that cause lordosis and mounting. It should be emphasized that the model presented in Figure 11-4 does not account for all of the nerve pathways involved in reproductive behavior.

> *Reproductive behavior is initiated by:*
> * *olfaction*
> * *vision*
> * *audition*
> * *tactility*

The primary sensory inputs for reproductive behavior are olfaction, audition, vision and tactility. The degree to which these sensory inputs influence reproductive behavior, particularly precopulatory behavior, varies significantly among species.

Figure 11-5. Flehmen Response in the Stallion and Bull and the Vomeronasal Pathway

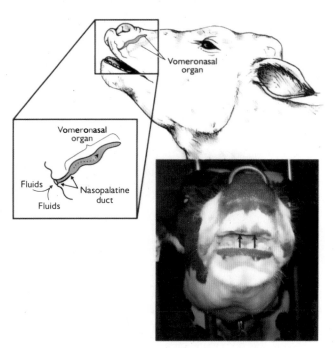

The flehmen response involves curling of the upper lip so that airflow through the nasal passages is restricted. A subatmospheric pressure is thus created in the nasopalatine duct. Therefore, fluids can be aspirated through the duct and into the sensory surfaces of the vomeronasal organ. Arrows in the bull indicate the approximate openings of the nasopalatine ducts. (Photo of stallion courtesy of Dr. A. Tibary, Washington State University, College of Veterinary Medicine; Photo of bull courtesy of Select Sires, Inc. *www.selectsires.com*)

The Olfactory and Vomeronasal Systems Respond to Pheromones that Trigger Reproductive Behavior

Secretions from the female reproductive tract serve to sexually stimulate and attract the male to the female. Vaginal and urinary secretions from females in estrus smell different to the male than secretions from females not in estrus. There is good scientific evidence that females produce pheromonal substances that are identifiable both within species and among species. However, their action is species specific. Recall that a **pheromone** is a volatile substance secreted or released to the outside of the body and perceived by the olfactory system and/or activated by the vomeronasal organ. Releasing pheromones can cause specific behavior in the recipient. Pheromones can also be priming pheromones that have physiologic rather than behavioral effects on the recipient.

Males also produce sex pheromones that attract and stimulate females. Among food producing animals, the best documentation for a male sex pheromone is in swine. Boars produce specific substances that cause sows and gilts to become sexually aroused when they are in estrus. Two sexual attractants are produced by boars. One of these attractants is a preputial pouch secretion. The second pheromonal-like substance is present in saliva secreted by the submaxillary salivary glands. During sexual excitement and precopulatory interactions, the boar produces copious quantities of foamy saliva. The active components in saliva are the androgen metabolites 3α-androstenol and 5α-androstenone. Both compounds have a musk-like odor.

It has been demonstrated that dogs have the ability to identify cows in estrus by olfactory discrimination. In addition, rats can be trained to press a lever in response to air bubbled through urine from cows in estrus. Rats did not press the lever when air was bubbled through urine from nonestrous cows. Clearly, urine from cows in estrus contains a material that can be identified by olfaction by other species (dogs and rats).

Figure 11-6. "Warm-Up" Stalls Used for Stimulating Sexual Behavior in Bulls Providing Semen for Artificial Insemination

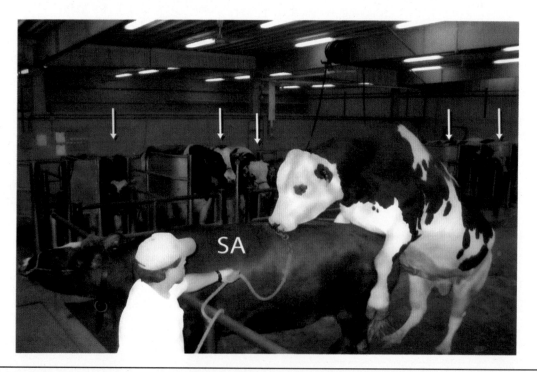

Bulls waiting to be ejaculated (arrows) watch mounting and ejaculatory behavior of another bull. Such a practice "prestimulates" bulls and reduces stimulation time when they enter the collection arena. It also increases sperm harvest. A false-mount is being performed by the bull mounting the stimulus animal (SA). (Photo courtesy of Select Sires, Inc., *www.selectsires.com*)

Flehmen Behavior is a Close-Range Investigative Behavior

Some pheromones appear to be less volatile and need to be detected by the **vomeronasal organ** in the bull, ram, stallion and to some extent, the boar. The male needs to closely approach the source of pheromones and he will nuzzle the genital region of the female. The vomeronasal organ (See Figure 11-5) is an accessory olfactory organ. It is connected to two small openings in the anterior roof of the mouth just behind the upper lip. Fluid-borne, less volatile chemicals can enter the vomeronasal organ through the oral cavity by means of the **nasopalatine** (incisive) **ducts**. Many species, such as bulls, rams and stallions, perform a special investigative maneuver when in close proximity to a female. Vaginal secretions and urine evoke an investigative behavior known as the **flehmen response**. Flehmen behavior allows less volatile materials to be "examined" by sensory neurons in the vomeronasal organ. Flehmen behavior is characterized by head elevation and curling of the upper lip (See Figure 11-5). Curling of the upper lip closes the nostrils and allows a negative pressure to form in the nasopalatine duct. Thus, less volatile materials (like mucous and urine) can be aspirated through the duct into the vomeronasal organ where they can be "evaluated" by sensory neurons in the organ. Olfactory bulbectomy in goats inhibits the flehmen response. Flehmen behavior in males is likely to be performed whether the material is from an estrus or nonestrus female. It is believed that the flehmen behavior is used to help a male identify mating opportunities. Flehmen is occasionally performed by females during sexual encounters with males. Cows will frequently perform the maneuver when sniffing other cows that are in estrus or proestrus. As in the male, females will display flehmen to novel compounds, including fluids associated with the placenta, newborn animals and other volatile materials. Flehmen is frequently displayed by post-parturient females as they make identity discriminations between their own versus other's neonates.

> ### *Auditory stimulation can serve as a long-range signal.*

In many species, sexual readiness is accompanied by some form of unique vocalization or "mating calls". For example, cows are known to increase their bellowing during the time of estrus. Sows display a characteristic grunting sound associated with estrus. Queens often "yeow" repeatedly to call the tom. By comparison, mares and ewes are relatively silent. Elevated vocalization serves to alert or send a signal to males that sexual readiness is imminent. The auditory stimulus is more useful in long-range discrimination, rather than close discrimination. The classic example of reproductive driven vocalization is bugling of the bull elk during rut (the breeding season).

> ### *Visual signals are valuable for close encounters.*

All females display a form of sexual posturing that can be perceived by males. While posturing can be quite subtle, especially to human observers, the identification of postures probably takes place easily among members of the same species.

> ### *Tactile stimulation is generally the final stimulus before copulation.*

Almost all males experience a degree of sexual stimulation when they observe mating behavior among other individuals of the same species. It is well documented that in bulls, visual observation of mating behavior enhances sexual stimulation. This observation has led to the common practice of placing bulls used for artificial insemination in "warm-up" stalls (See Figure 11-6). Bulls are brought to the "warm-up" stalls and are allowed to observe the mounting behavior and collection of semen from other bulls prior to entering the collection area themselves. This causes an elevated level of sexual excitement and reduces the time required for final sexual stimulation and collection of semen. This is important because labor requirements for semen collection are significant. This procedure is also important because it tends to increase sperm concentration in the ejaculate.

Tactile stimuli from males appears to be important in evoking sexual postures or standing postures by females. For example, biting on the neck and the withers of mares by stallions appears to be important for sexual stimulation. Biting of the neck of the queen by the tom is also a characteristic reproductive behavior among cats. Rubbing of the flanks and genitalia of mares, whether done by the stallion or by a human handler, evokes behavior signals of estrus from the mare that otherwise would not be displayed. Chin resting by a bull on the back of a cow just prior to mounting may have some stimulatory effect on the cow.

11

Penile Erection and Protrusion Completes the Precopulatory Phase of Reproductive Behavior

When sexual receptivity of a female is established and sufficient arousal is accomplished in the male, erection and protrusion of the penis ensue. Successful penile erection requires a complex series of neural and vasomotor (blood vessel) reactions. Erection of the penis is necessary for copulation and deposition of semen in the female reproductive tract. Erection is characterized by a marked increase in the rigidity of the penis. The increased rigidity is the result of a marked increase in arterial inflow of blood when compared to the venous outflow of blood. Erection requires that blood be trapped within the cavernous sinuses of the penis. Increased blood flow to the penis is brought about by vasodilation of the arterioles supplying it. In the bull, ram and boar erection not only involves increased blood flow and a subsequent

Figure 11-7. Steps in Penile Erection as They Relate to Cavernous Blood Pressure and Contraction of the Bulbospongiosus and Ischiocavernosus Muscles
(Modified from Beckett, et al. 1972. *Biol. of Reprod.* 7:359)

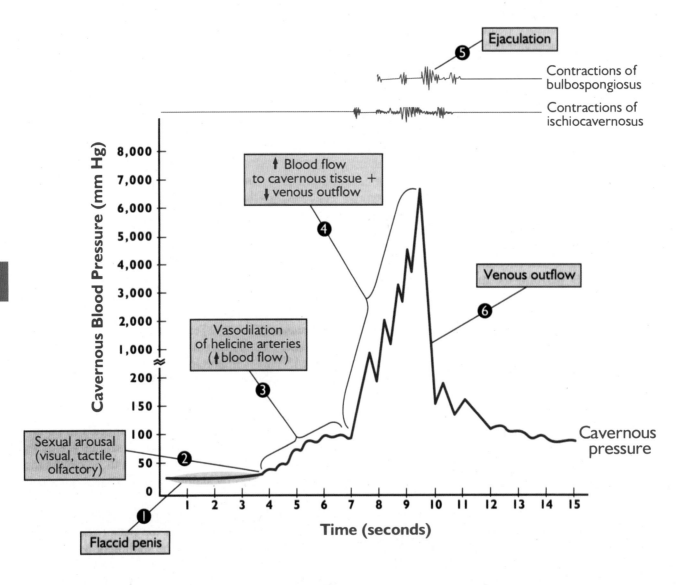

increase in pressure, but a simultaneous relaxation of the retractor penis muscles. Thus, erection and protrusion also involve straightening of the penis to eliminate the sigmoid flexure. The penis of the bull, boar and ram is fibroelastic in nature and therefore does not increase significantly in diameter during erection and protrusion. In contrast, the penis of the stallion increases significantly in diameter during erection. The stallion has a retractor penis muscle that, as in other species, relaxes during erection. However, the stallion does not have a sigmoid flexure. Engorgement with blood plays a much more significant role in the highly vascular penis of the stallion, dog and man than in the bull, ram, boar and camelids.

> *Erection of the penis requires:*
> * *elevated arterial blood inflow*
> * *dilation of corporal sinusoids*
> * *restricted venous outflow*
> * *elevated intrapenile pressure*
> * *relaxation of the retractor*
>   *penis muscle*

Contractions of the ischiocavernosus muscles cause compression of the penile veins. This compression causes blockage of venous return thus enabling the cavernous tissue to retain blood for maintenance of an erection. As you will recall, the ischiocavernosus muscles surround the two crura. Intermittent contractions of the muscles creates a pump-like action at the base of the penis. These contractions result in a buildup of blood within the corpus cavernosum of the penis and exceptionally high pressures result. For example, during the final stages of erection, the pressures within the cavernous tissue of the goat penis can reach 7,000 mm Hg (See Figure 11-7). When the penis is flaccid, pressures within the corpus cavernosum are only 19 mm Hg. Pressures in the bull penis are around 1,700 mm Hg during peak erection and about 30 mm Hg when the cavernous spaces are collapsed. Figure 11-7 summarizes the steps of penile erection and intrapenile pressures as they relate to contraction of the ischiocavernosus and bulbospongiosus muscles.

One of the most publicized pharmaceuticals ever introduced is a material called Sildenafil Citrate (Viagra®). This pharmaceutical provides a therapy for erectile dysfunction in men. Erectile dysfunction is defined as the inability to achieve and maintain a penile erection (**tumescence**). Reports indicate that 10% of men between the ages 40 and 70 years old are afflicted

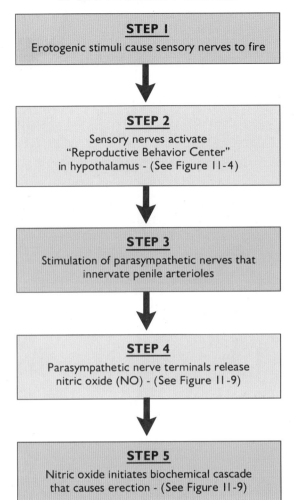

Figure 11-8. Basic Steps in the Erectile Process

STEP 1
Erotogenic stimuli cause sensory nerves to fire

STEP 2
Sensory nerves activate "Reproductive Behavior Center" in hypothalamus - (See Figure 11-4)

STEP 3
Stimulation of parasympathetic nerves that innervate penile arterioles

STEP 4
Parasympathetic nerve terminals release nitric oxide (NO) - (See Figure 11-9)

STEP 5
Nitric oxide initiates biochemical cascade that causes erection - (See Figure 11-9)

by complete erectile failure. Other reports have estimated that up to 30 million men in the United States may have some form of erectile dysfunction. Erectile dysfunction is rare among domestic animals because such males are rapidly eliminated from the gene pool by artificial selection (culling) or by natural selection (no erection-no copulation-no offspring).

Erection of the Penis Requires Sensory Input and a Local Vascular Response

As mentioned earlier in the chapter, penile erection is a complex series of neural and vasomotor events. These events can be broadly subdivided into a nervous component (cerebral and spinal) and a local vascular component within the penis. The nervous component is arousal-driven. For example, there must be appropriate sensory stimuli (tactile, visual, auditory and olfactory) in order for the central nervous system to be appropriately stimulated so that efferent neural events

11

Figure 11-9. Vascular and Biochemical Control of an Erection
(Modified from Korenman. 1998. *Am. J. Med.* 105:135.)

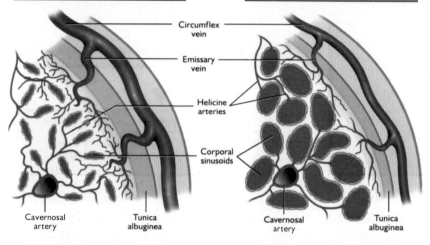

Flaccid Penis — Superficial dorsal vein, Tunica albuginea, Dorsal artery, Deep dorsal vein, Cavernosal artery, Bulbourethral artery, Helicine artery, Buck's fascia

Erect Penis — Venous outflow, Arterial inflow, Internal pudendal, Circumflex vein

Anatomy
The shaft of the penis consists of two dorso-lateral corpora cavernosa and the corpus spongiosum. Arterial blood is supplied by the internal pudendal artery that supplies the dorsal and deep cavernosal arteries. Corporal sinusoids are supplied by helicine arteries. The deep dorsal vein and superficial dorsal vein drain the erectile tissues.

Flaccid Penis / Erect Penis — Circumflex vein, Emissary vein, Helicine arteries, Corporal sinusoids, Cavernosal artery, Tunica albuginea

Flaccid penis
The sinusoids are flattened because adrenergic nerves secrete norepinepherine that causes vasoconstriction. Blood flow to the cavernous tissue therefore is quite low for the majority of the time. Since no erotogenic stimuli are present, nonadrenergic noncholinergic (NANC) parasympathetic neurons do not fire and thus do not release nitric oxide (NO). Therefore, vasoconstriction takes precedence over vasodilation.

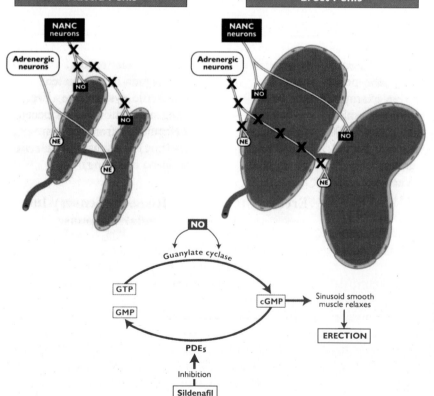

NANC neurons, Adrenergic neurons, NO, NE

NO → Guanylate cyclase, GTP, GMP, cGMP → Sinusoid smooth muscle relaxes → ERECTION, PDE₅, Inhibition, Sildenafil

Erect penis
When erotogenic stimuli are present the NANC neurons fire and release nitric oxide (NO) from their terminals. When NO is released, it activates an enzyme called guanylate cyclase. This enzyme converts guanylate triphosphate (GTP) to cyclic guanyosine monophosphate (cGMP) and causes the smooth muscle of the corporal sinusoids to relax (vasodilatation). The cavernous sinusoids engorge with blood and intracorporal pressure increases dramatically. This compresses the venules through which blood exits the penis. Blood is then trapped within the penis causing an erection.

11

can cause an erection. These extrinsic stimuli are called **erotogenic stimuli**. As shown in Figure 11-4, these stimuli cause afferent sensory nerves to fire. Their terminals synapse with neurons in the so-called "behavior center" in the hypothalamus. These hypothalamic neurons synapse with parasympathetic and sympathetic efferent neurons that control penile vascular smooth muscle (vascular tone). The basic steps in the erectile process are outlined in Figure 11-8.

Erection is caused by the firing of nonadrenergic, noncholonergic (NANC) parasympathetic neurons that release nitric oxide (NO), a gas, from their terminals. Nitric oxide is the principal neurotransmitter that "drives" the erectile process. Nitric oxide causes its effect by stimulating an enzyme, guanylate cyclase, to convert guanylate triphosphate (GTP) to cyclic guanosine monophosphate (cGMP). Cyclic guanosine monophosphate causes corporal smooth muscle relaxation (vasodilation) and an erection results.

Under nonerotogenic conditions, cGMP is acted upon by PDE_5 (Phosphodiesterase 5) and this enzyme promotes the conversion of cGMP to GMP. This breakdown causes increased vascular tone resulting in outflow of blood from the corpora cavernosa and loss of an erection. Sildenafil blocks the action of PDE_5 thus prolonging the vasodilation effect of cGMP and an erection develops that can be maintained for a sustained period of time. It should be emphasized that without nitric oxide production by the parasympathetic nerve terminals Sildenafil can have no effect because nitric oxide must be present for cGMP to be produced. The usual flaccid state of the penis (contracted corporal arteries) results from a tonic contraction of the arterial and corporal smooth muscles mediated by sympathetic adrenergic neurons. Such vasoconstriction keeps penile blood flow to a minimum under non-erotogenic conditions.

When the corporal smooth muscles relax because of cGMP, the resistance to blood flow by the penile arterioles and corporal sinusoids decreases and blood flow to the penis triples or quadruples when the appropriate erotogenic stimuli are present. When an erection occurs, the sinusoid pressure is so great that the emissary veins are collapsed. Therefore, blood cannot return through them because venous outflow is blocked. Penile erection can be maintained for as long as vasodilation of the corporal smooth muscle takes place. These reactions are summarized in Figure 11-9.

> **Copulatory behavior includes:**
> * *mounting*
> * *intromission*
> * *ejaculation*

Mounting postures and characteristics of copulatory behavior for various species are presented in Figures 11-10 and 11-11. The purpose of mounting is for the male to position himself so that **intromission** can occur. Intromission is the successful entrance of the penis into the vagina. Following intromission, ejaculation takes place in response to sensory stimulation of the glans penis. The time of ejaculation relative to intromission varies significantly among species (See Figures 11-10, 11-11 and 11-12). For example, in the bull and the ram ejaculation occurs within one or two seconds after intromission. In these species ejaculation is stimulated by the warm temperature of the vagina. Vaginal pressure is relatively unimportant in inducing ejaculation in the ram and bull. In contrast, the boar may have a sustained ejaculation for periods of up to 30 minutes. The stallion has a mating duration of between 30 seconds and one minute. The llama and the dog are perhaps the most sustained copulators with reports of copulation occuring continually for up to 50 minutes.

> *Ejaculation is a simple neural reflex caused by:*
> * *intromission*
> * *stimulation of the glans penis*
> * *forceful muscle contraction*

11

Ejaculation is defined as the reflex expulsion of spermatozoa and seminal plasma from the male reproductive tract. The basic mechanism for ejaculation of semen is quite similar among all mammals. Expulsion of semen is the result of sensory stimulation, primarily to the glans penis, that causes a series of coordinated muscular contractions. Once intromission has been achieved, reflex impulses are initiated. These neural impulses are derived mainly from sensory nerves in the glans penis. Upon threshold stimulation, impulses are transmitted from the glans penis by way of the internal pudendal nerve to the lumbosacral region of the spinal cord (See Figure 11-13). The sensory impulses result in firing of nerves in the spinal cord and the forcing of semen into the urethra is accomplished by nerves in the hypogastric plexus that innervate the target muscles. Of primary importance for ejaculation are the urethralis muscle (that surrounds the pelvic urethra), the ischiocavernosus and the bulbospongiosus muscles.

Figure 11-13 summarizes the nerve pathways resulting in **emission** and ejaculation. It should be emphasized that emission is defined as the movement of seminal fluids from the accessory sex glands into the pelvic urethra so they can mix with spermatozoa. Emission occurs before and during ejaculation. In some

Figure 11-10. Characteristics of Copulation, Site of Seminal Deposition and Number of Ejaculations to Satiation and Exhaustion in the Ram, Bull, Stallion and Boar

Mating pair	Duration of Copulation	Volume of Ejaculate (Range)	Site of Semen Deposition	Average Number of Ejaculations to Satiation	Maximum Number of Ejaculations to Exhaustion
	1 to 2 seconds (1 pelvic thrust with foreleg clasp)	.8 to 1ml (.1 to 2ml)	external cervical os	10	30 to 40
	1 to 3 seconds (1 pelvic thrust with foreleg clasp)	3-5ml (.5 to 12ml)	fornix vagina	20	60 to 80
	20 to 60 seconds (multiple pelvic thrusting, flagging o tail followed by inactive phase)	75-120ml	external cervical os but semen enters uterus at high pressure	3	20
	5 to 20 minutes (rapid pelvix thrusting to engage penis in cervix) When penis is engaged, thrusting stops and ejaculation commences that is accompanied by somnolence)		cervix and uterus		8

Photos of:

Ram/Ewe-courtesy of Drs. G.S. Lewis and J.B. Taylor, U.S. Sheep Experimental Station *http://pwa.ars.usda.gov/dubois/index*

Bull/Cow-courtesy of Dr. L.S. Katz, Rutgers University

Stallion/Mare-courtesy of Dr. A. Tibary, Washington State University, College of Veterinary Medicine

Figure 11-11. Characteristics of Copulation, Site of Seminal Deposition and Number of Ejaculations to Satiation and Exhaustion in the Camel and Llama

Mating pair	Duration of Copulation	Volume of Ejaculate (Range)	Site of Semen Deposition	Average Number of Ejaculations to Satiation	Maximum Number of Ejaculations to Exhaustion
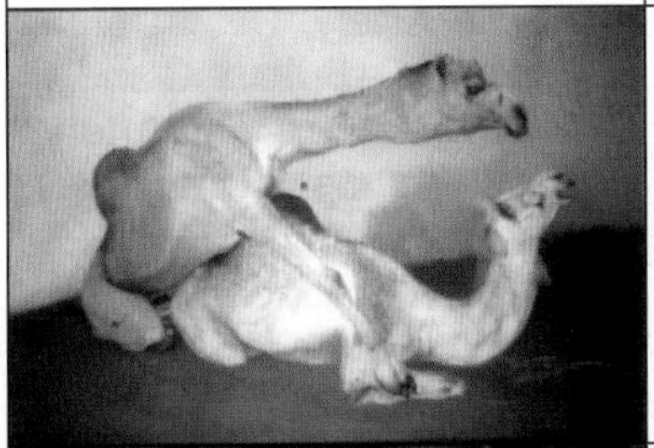	6-20 minutes, extension of neck, straining of the body, multiple ejaculations per copulation	3-8ml	Partly intrauterine, partly intracervical, some intravaginal	23 matings in 24 hr	Data not available
	20-30 minutes, body tremors and pelvic thrusts	1-5ml	intrauterine	Data not available	Data not available

(Photos courtesy of Dr. A. Tibary, Washington State University, College of Veterinary Medicine)

species, such as the boar, stallion and dog, emission occurs in a sequence resulting in an ejaculate that consists of various fluid fractions (See Chapter 12).

> *Postcopulatory behavior involves refractivity and recovery.*

Following ejaculation, all males experience a refractory period before a second ejaculation can occur. The length of time of this refractory period depends on several factors. These factors are: degree of sexual rest prior to copulation, age of the male, species of the male, degree of female novelty and number of previous ejaculations. The postcopulatory refractory period is sometimes erroneously referred to as sexual exhaustion. The refractory period should be considered as part of satiation rather than exhaustion. With natural service, it is quite normal for a male to copulate repeatedly with the same female. For example, a stallion will breed a mare in heat 5 to 10 times during one estrus period. Rams are noted to remate with the same ewe 4 to 5 times. Bulls also remate with estrous cows repeatedly. In fact, it has been noted in most species that if more than one female is in heat at the same time, some males will generally copulate preferentially with one and sometimes will not copulate with a second female. Boars normally serve sows several times over a period of 1 to 2 days.

Sexual satiation refers to a condition in which further stimuli will not cause immediate responsiveness or motivation under a given set of stimulus conditions. Restimulation may occur after the refractory period. Figures 11-10 and 11-11 compare the normal number of ejaculations to satiety and the number of ejaculations to exhaustion among species. Exhaustion is the condition whereby no further sexual behavior can be induced even if sufficient stimuli are present. As you can see from Figures 11-10 and 11-11, there is a large variation in the behavioral reserves (the behavioral capacity, or **libido**) among species. There is also a large variation in libido within species. For example, beef bulls have significantly lower behavioral reserves than dairy bulls. While the factors that control the degree of reproductive behavior among males are poorly understood, they are almost certainly governed by genetic factors as well as environmental factors.

11

> *Reproductive behavior can be enhanced by:*
> - *introducing novel stimulus animals*
> - *changing stimulus settings*

Figure 11-12. Copulation in the Dog

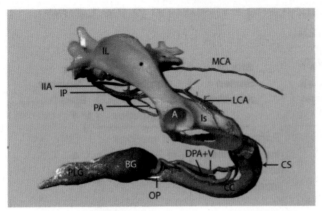

The vasculature of the dog penis has been injected with latex and the tissue dissolved away leaving cast of the vasculature. Red vessels are arteries and the blue vessels are veins. IL=Ileum, MCA=Medial Caudal Artery, LCA=Lateral Caudal Artery, IS=Ischium, A=Acetabulum, CS=Corpus Spongiousum, CC=Corpus Cavernosum, DPA=Dorsal Penile Artery, DPV=Dorsal Penile Vein, OP=Os Penis, BG=Bulbus Glandis, PLG=Pars Longa Glandis, PA=Prostatic Artery, IP=Internal Pudendal Artery, IIA=Internal Iliac Artery (Specimen courtesy of the Worthman Veterinary Anatomy Teaching Museum, College of Veterinary Medicine, Washington State University. Specimen prepared by Dr. R.P. Worthman)

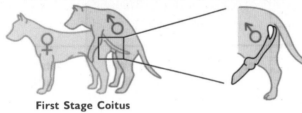

First Stage Coitus
(1-2 min)

First Stage Coitus

The male mounts the female in a manner typical of a quadraped. The female holds the tail to one side and the penis is introduced into the vagina by a few thrusting movements. This stage of copulation lasts for only 1-2 minutes. The first and second fractions of semen are ejaculated during the first stage coitus.

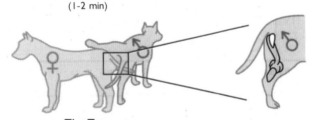

The Turn
(2-5 sec)

The Turn

This is the transition between first stage and second stage coitus. Shortly after ejaculation, the dog dismounts and turns around while lifting one hind leg over the bitch.

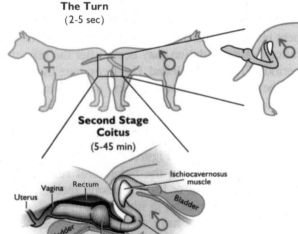

Second Stage Coitus
(5-45 min)

Second Stage Coitus

After the turn, the animals stand with their hind quarters in contact and their heads facing opposite directions. The third fraction of semen is ejaculated during this stage. Second stage coitus may last from 5-45 minutes. It is believed that the purpose of second stage coitus is to encourage uterine rather than vaginal insemination. Turning around discourages detumescence of the penis and therefore maintains high intravaginal pressure. The dog steadily ejaculates up to 30-ml of seminal fluid that is delivered through the cervix into the uterus. This phenomenon tends to force the sperm-rich fraction into the uterus. The copulatory behavior described here is perfectly natural. Unfortunately this behavior is often interpreted as being unnatural and attempts to break the "tie" are often made by the uninformed. Such intervention compromises fertility because delivery of semen to the uterus over a sustained period of time is reduced.

The male and female remain "tied" together because the bulbus glandis of the penis remains engorged with blood after the turn. Contractions of the muscles near the base of the penis prevent venous outflow of blood from the bulbus glandis. Also, the sphincter muscles of the vulva constrict thus compressing the dorsal veins of the penis preventing blood from leaving. (Figures modified from Grandage. 1972. *Vet. Rec.* 91:141)

11

Figure 11-13. Major Steps in Ejaculation

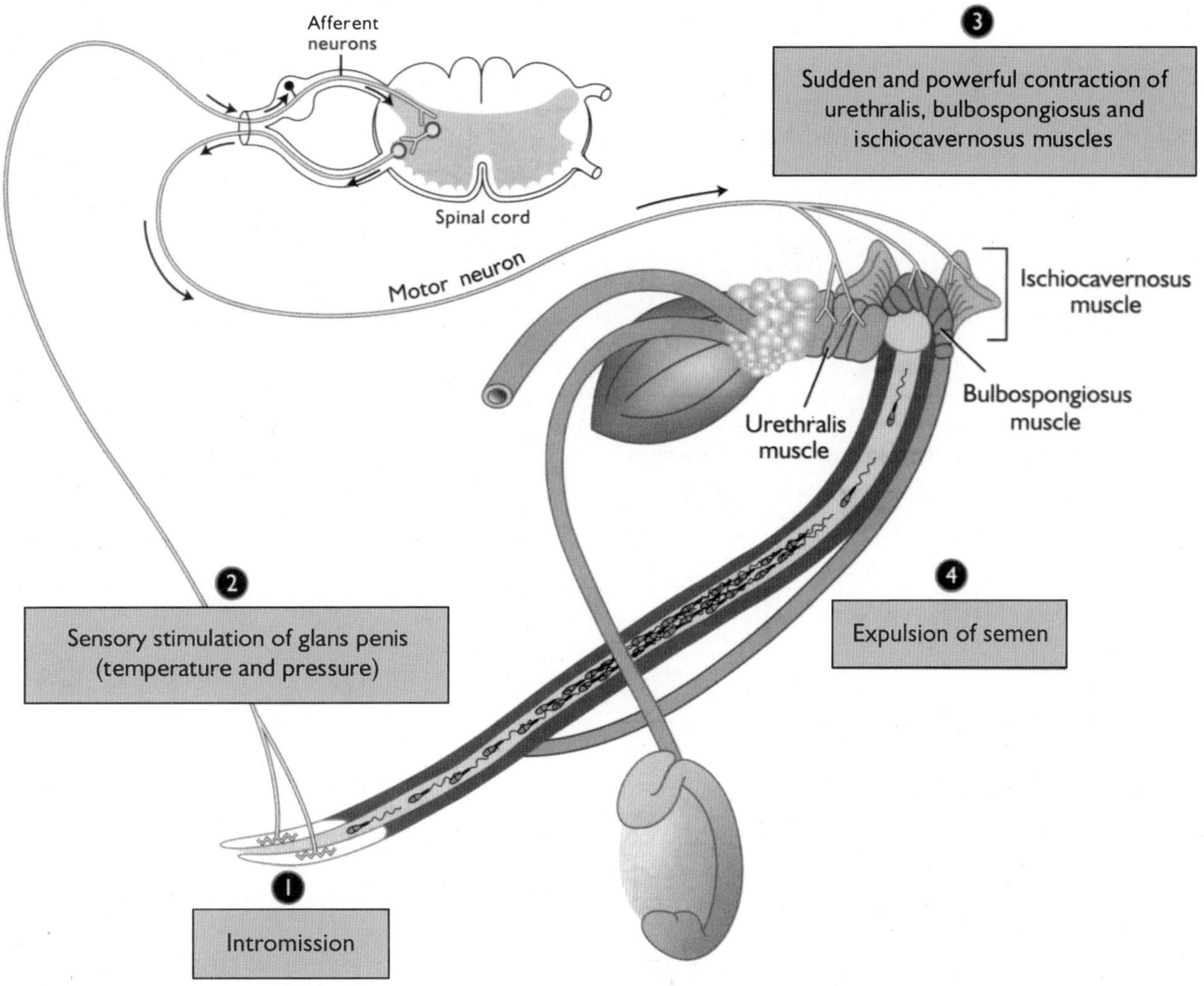

11

Reproductive Behavior and Spermatozoal Output can be Manipulated

The degree of novelty of both the copulatory partner and the copulatory environment can be of great importance when managing reproductive behavior in breeding males. Under conditions of artificial insemination, where repeated seminal collection is necessary to maximize the harvest of spermatozoa, understanding the influence of novelty and mating situations is important. The "**Coolidge Effect**" is defined as the restoration of mating behavior in males (that have reached sexual satiation) when the original female is replaced by a novel female. In other words, a sexually satiated male can be restimulated if exposed to a novel female. (For derivation of the term "Coolidge Effect" see *Further Phenomena for Fertility*)

Semen collection in bull studs can occur as frequently as 4 to 6 ejaculations per week. In order for this collection frequency to be successful, the male must first be sexually stimulated. **Sexual stimulation** is defined as the presentation of a stimulus situation that will achieve mounting and ejaculation. The purpose of sexual stimulation is to obtain ejaculation or mating in the shortest time possible so that manpower involved in managing the mating of animals can be minimized. There are three approaches used to re-induce sexual stimulation in bulls used for artificial insemination. These approaches are: to introduce a novel stimulus animal; to change the stimulus setting; or both. Presentation of novel stimulus animals reinitiates sexual behavior after sexual satiation in bulls (See Figure 11-14, "Novel Females"). A second approach to achieve sexual stimulation after satiation is to present familiar stimulus animals in new stimulus situations. In other words, changing the location or setting has a stimulatory effect on the satiated male (See Figure 11-14 "New Location"). In cases where sexual stimulation is difficult to achieve, presenting a novel stimulus animal, coupled with changing locations, often has positive effects.

Figure 11-14. Introduction of Novel Females and a Change of Locations has a Positive Effect on Mounting Behavior
(Hypothetical examples, not experimental data)

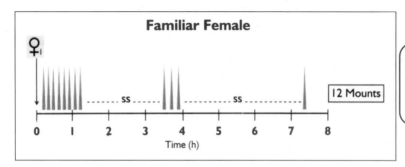

A familiar female may stimulate a bull to mount about 12 times in an 8 hour period.
SS= sexual satiation

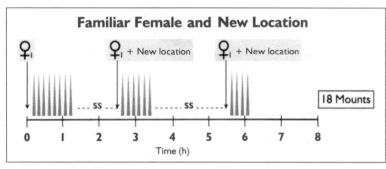

Bulls can be restimulated to mount (after satiation) by changing the stimulus setting (new location). This induces more total mounts (18 mounts) than the familiar female (12 mounts).

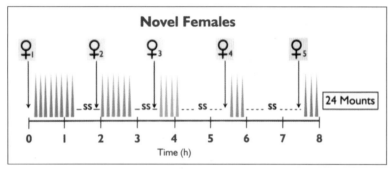

When the novel females (1-5) are introduced after a period of sexual satiation, mounting behavior is stimulated beyond that realized with change of location and exposure to a single familiar female (24 mounts vs. 18 and 12 respectively).

11

There has been little research conducted on the effect of introducing novel animals upon stimulation of mounting behavior in the female. However, it has been shown that dairy cows will mount novel cows with a greater frequency than they do familiar cows. As you might expect, the effect of novelty is confounded with the stage of the cycle.

> *Sexual preparation prolongs sexual stimulation and increases spermatozoa per ejaculation.*

In order to maximize the output of spermatozoa per ejaculate, sexual preparation is necessary. **Sexual preparation** is extending the period of sexual stimulation beyond that needed for mounting and ejaculation.

Sexual preparation prolongs the precopulatory stage of reproductive behavior. The purpose of sexual preparation is to collect semen containing the greatest possible number of spermatozoa per ejaculation. Figure 11-15 illustrates the physiologic mechanisms believed to be responsible for enhancing spermatozoal numbers in the ejaculate. Three approaches are used to sexually prepare a male. These are: false-mounting, restraint and false-mounting plus restraint.

> *Sexual preparation may include:*
> * *false-mounting*
> * *restraint*
> * *false-mounting plus restraint*

Figure 11-15. Major Steps in Sexual Preparation Resulting in Transport of Spermoatozoa from the Tail of the Epididymis into the Pelvic Urethra

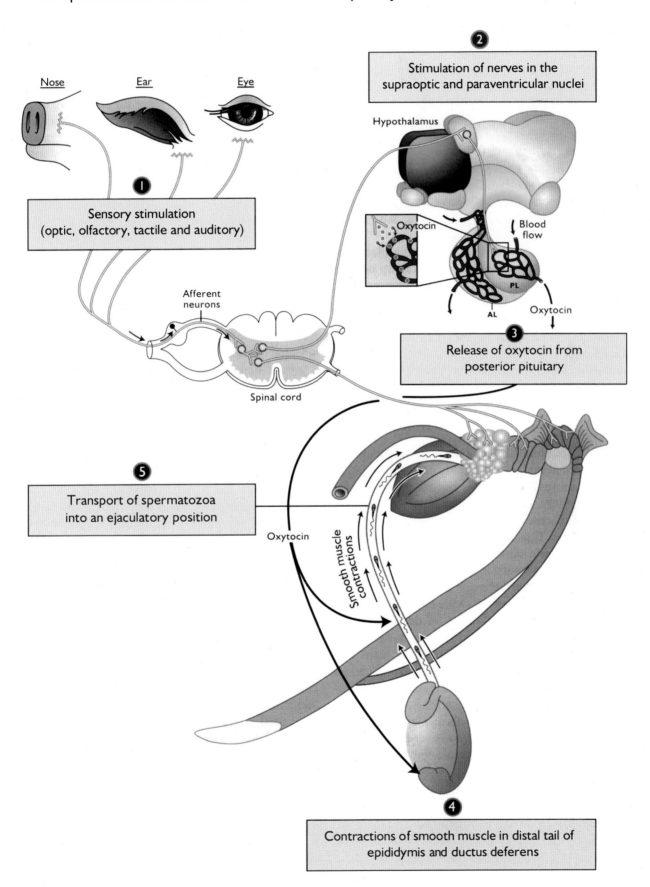

11

False mounting consists of manually deviating the penis during a mount so that intromission cannot occur. If intromission does not occur, ejaculation usually does not occur. **Restraint** prevents the male from mounting even though he wishes to do so. Generally, restraint is for two to three minutes within two or three feet of the stimulus animal. A combination of false mounting and restraint will result in the greatest improvement of spermatozoal output.

In dairy bulls, the recommended procedures for sexual preparation are: one false mount followed by two minutes of restraint, followed by two additional false mounts before each ejaculation. In beef bulls, sexual preparation involves three false mounts with no restraint. In general, beef bulls have lower behavioral reserves (libido) than dairy bulls and thus have a less rigorous sexual preparation regimen.

While sexual preparation is taking place, release of oxytocin from the posterior pituitary occurs. Oxytocin causes contraction of the smooth musculature surrounding the tail of the epididymis and the ductus deferens. These contractions transport spermatozoa from the tail of the epididymis into the ductus deferens and eventually into the pelvic urethra. Once sperm gain entrance into the pelvic urethra, they begin to mix with secretions from the accessory sex glands.

Homosexual-like Behavior

Homosexual-like behavior is common among domestic animals and is particularly common in cattle. The term homosexuality implies a sexual preference for same-sex partners. In animals, there is not a preference, but rather indiscriminate orientation or same-sex directed behavior. Thus, an alternative term that is applicable to sub-primate animals would be homosexual-like behavior. Cows and bulls exhibit strong homosexual-like behavior. Similar behavior is seen in sheep and dogs and to a lesser extent in swine and horses. Such behavior has profound usefulness for detecting cattle in estrus. When a female stands to be mounted by another cow, this alerts the management team that the cow is in estrus and artificial insemination can be performed. A favorite question of managers and students of reproductive physiology alike is, "What is the evolutionary advantage of animals displaying this kind of behavior?" While a definitive answer is not known, two theories exist to explain female-female mounting behavior in cattle.

The first explanation theorizes that cows mounting each other provide a visual signal that attracts a bull to the cow in estrus. In other words, when a bull sees cows mounting each other he will investigate and if the cow is in standing estrus, he will breed her.

The second theory explaining the evolution of homosexual-like behavior among cows involves inadvertent genetic selection by man for this behavior. It has been proposed that cattle of European descent were selected by humans for their estrous behavior. In Medieval Europe, cattle husbandry involved the use of a few cows by each peasant farmer for three purposes: draft, milk and meat. Peasant farmers could not afford to maintain a bull for breeding purposes since the bulls gave no milk, gave birth to no calves and had obnoxious behavior that made them unsuitable for everyday management. In addition, most bulls apparently were owned by wealthy land holders who probably controlled the breeding, as well as the financial aspects of cattle management. Since most cows were kept in groups without intact males, the herdsmen needed some sign to tell him when his cows should be bred. Obviously, the cow that showed the most intense mounting behavior was the one most likely to be observed by the peasant and most likely to be bred by the nobleman's bull. Those that showed little mounting behavior did not become pregnant in a reasonable amount of time. This theory suggests that cows with a high degree of mounting behavior were inadvertently selected because they were noticed by man and offered a greater opportunity to become pregnant. Thus, this behavioral trait was transmitted to their offspring.

Artificial Insemination Requires an Understanding of Reproductive Behavior and Physiology

There are two fundamental ways to collect semen from the male. The preferred method utilizes an **artificial vagina** or a device that simulates vaginal conditions of a female in estrus. The second method relies on electrical stimulation of the accessory sex glands and the pelvic urethra and this method is called **electroejaculation**. Electroejaculation is generally used in males of high genetic value that cannot physically perform mounting and ejaculation. In the beef industry, electroejaculation is used in range bulls.

Typical artificial vaginas for domestic animals are shown are Figure 11-16. In general, artificial vaginas consist of an outer casing fashioned of reinforced rubber and a liner that is generally made of rubber that can be lubricated. Temperature and pressure are controlled by the water that is placed between the casing and the liner. One end of the artificial vagina is attached to a funnel-like cone that in turn is attached to a collection vessel, usually a nonbreakable graduated test tube.

From a behavioral perspective, males that are to be collected with an artificial vagina need some form of training. Males with previous sexual experience will readily mount a surrogate animal (artificial animal or "dummy"). The degree to which animals will mount

Figure 11-16. Artificial Vaginas for Various Animals

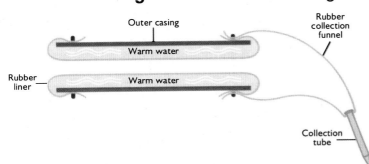

The typical artificial vagina consists of a sturdy outer casing, a rubber liner, a chamber filled with warm water, a rubber collection funnel and a collection tube.

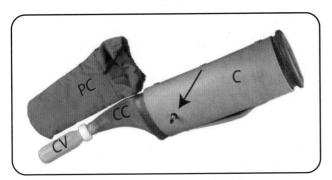

The artificial vagina for the stallion consists of a leather outer casing (C) equiped with a port to drain water (arrow). The collection vessel (CV) and the protective covering (PC) are shown. Ideally, ejaculation takes place in the collection cone (CC) so that most of the semen will drain directly into the collection vessel. (Artificial vagina courtesy of Northwest Equine Reproduction Laboratory, University of Idaho, *www.avs.uidaho.edu/nerl*)

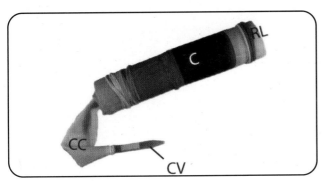

The artificial vagina for the bull consists of a black casing (C), a rubber liner (RL) a collection cone (CC) and a collection vessel (CV). Water is placed between the casing and the liner. The proper temperature is critical for successful ejaculation in the bull. While not shown in the photograph a protective covering is placed over the cone and collection vessel to prevent cold shock of the semen.

The artificial vagina for the boar consists of a bulb that can apply pressure to the artificial vagina. High pressure is obligatory for stimulation of the glans penis and ejaculation in the boar. The artificial vagina for the boar also consists of an outer casing (C), a liner (L) and a protective covering (PC) that houses the collection vessel. (Photograph courtesy of Minitüb Germany, *www.minitüb.de*)

11

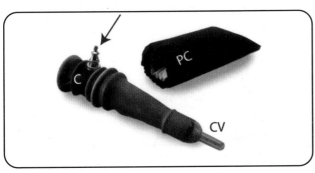

The artificial vagina for collection of semen from rams and bucks consists of a rubber casing (C) with a valve (arrow) through which water can be added or emptied, a rubber liner and a collection vessel (CV). The protective covering (PC) is shown above the artificial vagina. (Photograph courtesy of Minitüb Germany, *www.minitüb.de*)

Figure 11-17. Surrogate Stimulus Animals for Semen Collection

"Phantom" for Stallion Semen Collection

In general, males of most species can be trained to mount and ejaculate using surrogate stimulus animals. A surrogate stimulus animal provides ease of cleaning and minimizes the risk of injury and disease transmission. Further, surrogate stimulus animals do not require feed, housing and labor for maintenance as does a live stimulus animal. The use of artificial stimulus animals requires previous training of the male. Once the male has been trained he will generally mount the "dummy" readily. The size can be adjusted easily to accomodate various males. Mobile surrogate stimulus animals are used for collection of semen in bulls because the location can be changed with ease.

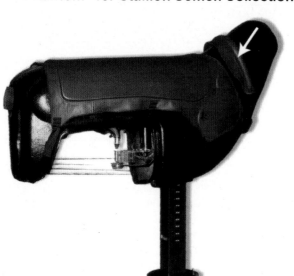

The surrogate stimulus animal used to collect semen from the stallion is generally referred to as a "phantom". The "phantom" contains a biting belt (arrow) to provide the stallion with a surface to bite during mounting thus providing a means for natural behavior. All of the devices shown have a built-in artificial vagina in which the temperature and pressure can be controlled. (Photographs courtesy of Minitüb Germany, *www.minitüb.de*)

11

dummies depends on the amount of training provided. A surrogate stimulus animal provides the advantage of safety, reduced expense and they can be designed to accomodate males of various stature. The disadvantage of using surrogate stimulus animal is that changing locations and teasers is difficult. Figure 11-17 illustrates examples of surrogate animals for semen collection.

Sometimes it is difficult to train animals to mount either a stimulus animal or a surrogate stimulus animal. In this event, semen can be collected by placing a condom-like structure inside the vagina of the female in estrus. When the male mounts the female and ejaculates, the semen is deposited inside the vessel. Such techniques are valuable when animals have not been adequately trained.

The design of an artificial vagina should accomplish the following:
- *provide a suitable environment for stimulation of the glans penis*
- *provide an environment that prevents damage to the penis*
- *provide an environment that maximizes sperm recovery and minimizes sperm insult*

Further PHENOMENA for Fertility

One day President and Mrs. Coolidge were visiting a government farm. Soon after their arrival they were taken off on separate tours. When Mrs. Coolidge passed the chicken pens, she paused to ask the man in charge if the rooster copulated more than once each day. "Dozens of times," was the reply. "Please tell that to the President," Mrs. Coolidge requested. When the President passed the pens and was told about the rooster, he asked, "Same hen every day?" "Oh no, Mr. President, a different one each time." The President nodded slowly and then said, "Please tell that to Mrs. Coolidge."

The praying mantis has unusual reproductive behavior. As soon as the male mounts the female and accomplishes intromission, the female bites his head off. She immediately eats the top half of his body while intromission is still taking place. The reason for this behavior is because ejaculation is permanently inhibited in the male and can take place only after the head has been removed. It is not known whether the slang phrase "bite-your-head-off" was derived from this behavior.

Roman snails shoot love darts at one another before copulation to determine if they are both members of the same species.

Some male insects (certain flies and mosquitoes) have evolved unusual adaptations to insure that their genetics will be passed on. Males have a sharp, specialized penis that can enter a pupa. The male inseminates the unborn female.

When a grey squirrel comes into estrus, up to a dozen males noisily chase her through the trees. This chase is necessary, because the female will not ovulate without it.

To mate, the queen bee leaves the hive and performs a mating flight in an area where drones are congregated. The fastest drone is the first to copulate with the queen. Copulation is an in-flight event that lasts from 1 to 3 seconds. When the copulating bees separate, the entire male genitalia is ripped from the male and stays with the queen. The male soon dies and another male will then mate with the queen. Up to 17 matings in one mating flight have been observed.

Females of some species are quite choosy about who gets to fertilize their eggs. In these cases, mate choice is determined by nuptial gifts presented by the male. The female black-tipped hangfly accepts nuptial gifts in the form of food in exchange for copulation. When edible food is presented by the male, the duration of copulation is dependent on the size of the gift. If the gift is small and can be consumed in 5 minutes or less, the female will not allow mating. If the gift is large (cannot be consumed in 20 minutes), the female will allow mating to take place. If the gift provides a meal of only 12 minutes she will leave the gift-giver prematurely and seek another gift-giver as a mate.

Satin bowerbirds build their nests only with blue objects. Males gather blue flowers, pen caps, berries and ribbons and arrange them under bushes or in other cozy spots. If a female "likes" what she sees, she will choose the nest's decorator as her mate.

A male newt begins his courtship by jumping on the back of the female and rubbing his jaw against her snout. This releases a scent that drives the female newt "crazy with desire."

When female rhinoceri are in heat they will run away from a male, then suddenly turn and fight him horn-to-horn, sometimes for longer than a day. Only if he is fit enough to pursue will she submit. There are no "wimp genes" in the rhinocerous gene pool.

11

During courtship the female balloon fly will eat the male if given the chance. To achieve copulation and keep from getting eaten, the male will present the female with a balloon-shaped cocoon as a "present". Unwrapping this "present" keeps the female occupied long enough for the male to mate her and fly off.

When box turtles copulate, the male mounts the female and remains in an upright position in order to facilitate insemination. The pair may remain in this position for hours to ensure adequate insemination. At the conclusion of the event the female will suddenly move away, sometimes causing the male to fall precariously on his back where he may remain until his death if he can't right himself.

Most frogs and toads copulate in the dark. They are often so eager to mate that the male will try to mount anything that passes by. They have been observed keeping a firm grip on strange objects and even other small animals in the hope that they might turn out to be females.

The long neck of the giraffe plays an important role in their reproductive behavior. First the male samples the female's urine to ascertain whether she is in estrus. If so, the two giraffes then indulge in a form of sexual preparation by entwining and rubbing their necks together. Physiologically, this behavior is like a false-mount and no doubt causes the release of oxytocin that moves sperm in the distal tail of the epididymis into an ejaculatory position.

The pressure within the penis of the bull at the time of ejaculation is equivalent to 10 times the pressure within a normal vehicle tire.

11

Key References

Albright, J.L., and C.W. Arave. 1997. *The Behaviour of Cattle*. CAB International, Wellingford, UK. ISBN 0-85199-196-3.

Craig, J.V. 1981. *Domestic Animal Behavior: causes and implications for animal care and management*. Prentice-Hall, Inc. New Jersey. ISBN 0-13-218339-0.

Evans, H.E. 1993. *Miller's Anatomy of the Dog*, 3rd Edition. W.B.Saunders Co. Philadelphia. ISBN 0-7216-3200-9.

Grandage, J. 1972. "The erect dog penis: a paradox of flexible rigidity." *Vet Rec:* 91:141-147.

Hart, Benjamin L. 1985. *The Behavior of Domestic Animals*. W.H. Freeman and Co., New York. ISBN 0-7167-1595-3.

Houpt, K.A. 1998. *Domestic Animal Behavior for Veterinarians and Animal Scientists*. 3rd Edition. Iowa State University Press, ISBN 0-8138-1061-2.

Katz, L.S. and T.J. McDonald. 1992. "Sexual Behavior of farm animals" in Repoduction in Farm Animals: Science, Application and Models. *Theriogenology* 38:240-254.

Korenman, S.G. 1998. "New insights into erectile dysfunction: a practical approach." *Am. J. Med.* 105:135-144.

Signoret, J.P. and J. Balthazart. 1993 "Sexual behavior" in *Reproduction in Mammals and Man*. C. Thibault, M.C. Levasseur and R.H.F. Hunder, eds. Ellipses, Paris. ISBN 2-7298-9354-7.

Tibary, A. and A. Anouassi. 1997. *Theriogenology in Camelidae*. United Arab Emirates. Ministry of Culture and Information. Publication authorization No. 3849/1/16. ISBN 9981-801-32-1.

11

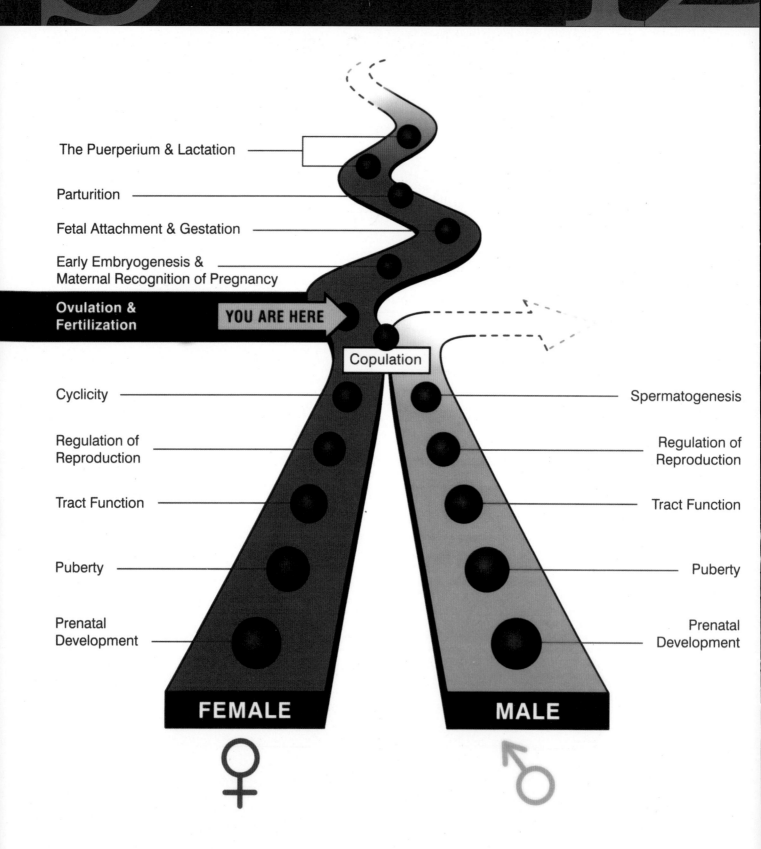

The Puerperium & Lactation

Parturition

Fetal Attachment & Gestation

Early Embryogenesis & Maternal Recognition of Pregnancy

Ovulation & Fertilization

YOU ARE HERE

Copulation

Cyclicity

Regulation of Reproduction

Tract Function

Puberty

Prenatal Development

Spermatogenesis

Regulation of Reproduction

Tract Function

Puberty

Prenatal Development

FEMALE

MALE

Take Home Message

Following insemination, viable spermatozoa that are retained in the female reproductive tract must: 1) transverse the cervix, 2) be transported through the uterus to the oviduct, 3) undergo capacitation, 4) bind to the oocyte, 5) undergo the acrosome reaction and 6) penetrate the zona pellucida and fuse with the oocyte plasma membrane. After fusion with the plasma membrane, the fertilizing spermatozoon enters the oocyte cytoplasm and its nucleus decondenses. The male pronucleus is formed. This signifies successful fertilization.

Following deposition of semen during copulation, spermatozoa are exposed to a series of different environments that significantly alter their numbers and their function. After their deposition, spermatozoa are lost from the female reproductive tract by retrograde transport and many are phagocytized by leukocytes within the female tract. The remaining spermatozoa must traverse the cervix, enter and traverse the uterus and enter the oviduct. They must undergo capacitation before they can fertilize the oocyte. When sperm encounter the egg they undergo the acrosome reaction and fertilization takes place. This series of events is summarized in Figure 12-1.

Figure 12-1. Major Sequence of Events Following Deposition of Spermatozoa in Female Tract

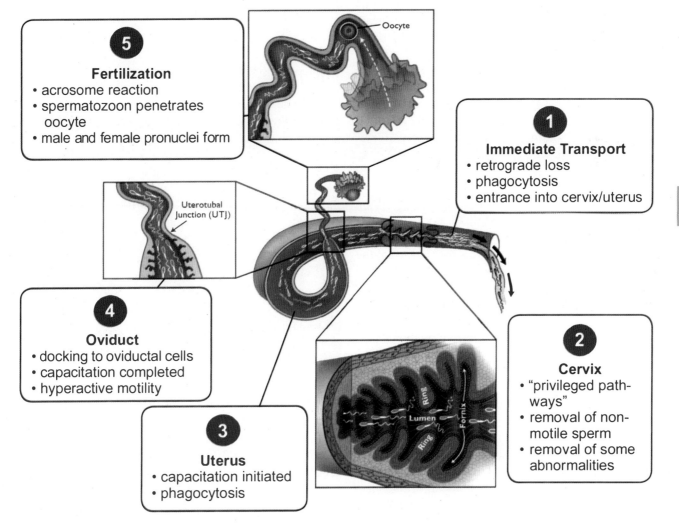

5 Fertilization
- acrosome reaction
- spermatozoon penetrates oocyte
- male and female pronuclei form

1 Immediate Transport
- retrograde loss
- phagocytosis
- entrance into cervix/uterus

4 Oviduct
- docking to oviductal cells
- capacitation completed
- hyperactive motility

3 Uterus
- capacitation initiated
- phagocytosis

2 Cervix
- "privileged pathways"
- removal of non-motile sperm
- removal of some abnormalities

In some animals (cow, sheep, rabbit, primates, dog and cat), the male ejaculates the semen into the cranial vagina. In others, (pigs, horses and camelids) semen is either deposited directly into the cervix (pig) or is squirted through the cervical lumen during copulation (horse). In the dog, pig and the horse most of the ejaculate gains entrance into the uterine lumen.

The stallion ejaculates in a series of "jets" in which a sperm-rich fraction is ejaculated first in 3-4 high pressure squirts. This fraction contains about 80% of the spermatozoa. The last 5 to 8 "jets" are of lower pressure and contain fewer sperm. The seminal plasma in the final "jets" is highly viscous and may serve to minimize retrograde sperm loss from the mare's tract.

Because of the large volume (200 to 400 ml) of boar ejaculate, most of the semen flows from the cervix into the uterine lumen. As in the stallion, the boar ejaculates a series of seminal fractions with different characteristics as ejaculation progresses. The first fraction consists of accessory fluids and gelatinous coagulum. This fraction contains few sperm. The second fraction is rich in spermatozoa and this sperm-rich fraction is followed by a final fraction that forms a gelatinous coagulum that resembles rice pudding. This coagulum reduces retrograde sperm loss. Immediately after insemination, semen undergoes varying degrees of retrograde transport (from the cervix towards the vulva).

In the dog, semen is ejaculated in three fractions. The first, is a pre-sperm fraction that is thought to originate from the prostate. The volume of the pre-sperm fraction is usually small but can range from 0.5 to 5ml. This pre-sperm fraction (clear and acellular) is ejaculated in conjunction with pelvic thrusting by the male during "first stage coitus." The second, a sperm rich fraction, is between 1 and 4 ml and is opalescent in color and contains between 300 million and 2 billion sperm. The final fraction originating from the prostate ranges in volume from 1 to 80ml. The first two fractions are ejaculated without visible force. However, the third fraction is ejaculated in surges of prostatic fluid that squirt into the vagina of the bitch during "second stage coitus." Because of the "tie" (See Chapter 11) most of this fraction is forced cranially into the uterus and is believed to "push" the sperm-rich fraction ahead of it into the uterus.

Ejaculate volumes in the tom turkey average only 0.2 to 0.3ml with a range of 0.1 to 0.7ml and it is therefore difficult to evaluate whether the ejaculate consists of multiple fractions.

The degree to which spermatozoa are lost from the female tract depends upon the physical nature of the ejaculate and the site of seminal deposition. In some species, the seminal plasma contains coagulating protein(s) that form a conspicuous vaginal plug to prevent spermatozoa from undergoing retrograde flow to the exterior. Female rodents (mice and rats) have a relatively solid vaginal plug that is externally visible following copulation. The presence of the vaginal plug can be used to determine when mating occurred. Domestic animals do not have a conspicuous vaginal plug.

> *Spermatozoa are lost from the female tract by:*
> * *phagocytosis by neutrophils*
> * *retrograde transport*

When the female reproductive tract is under the influence of estradiol during estrus, neutrophils (powerful phagocytic white blood cells) sequester in the mucosa of the tract, especially in the vagina and uterus. These neutrophils are poised to attack foreign materials that are introduced into the female reproductive tract at insemination. It should be recognized that, in addition to spermatozoa, microorganisms are introduced into the tract during copulation. Thus, the neutrophil population is important in preventing these microorganisms from colonizing the female tract. From an immunologic perspective, spermatozoa are foreign to the female. As a result, neutrophils actively phagocytize spermatozoa. They do not discriminate between live and dead sperm. In fact, a single neutrophil is capable of engulfing several motile spermatozoa (See Figure 12-2).

Studies have shown that within 6 to 12 hours after the introduction of spermatozoa into the uterus, there is a large migration of neutrophils from the uterine mucosa into the uterine lumen (See Figure 12-2). While leukocyte infiltration is an important contributor to post-insemination spermatozoal losses, this infiltration is important for the prevention of reproductive tract infection.

> *Spermatozoal transport consists of a rapid phase and a sustained phase.*

Among the least understood phenomena in reproductive physiology are factors that regulate loss of spermatozoa from the female tract. The ability of the female to retain viable spermatozoa may influence the fertility of a given mating. Transport of spermatozoa following copulation can be divided into two phases. These are the **rapid transport phase** and the **sustained**

transport phase. Within a few minutes after copulation, spermatozoa can be found in the oviducts. The rapid phase of transport was once considered to be important because it delivered spermatozoa to the site of the fertilization very shortly after copulation, where they "postured" themselves for the arrival of oocytes. However, further research has shown that spermatozoa arriving in the oviducts within minutes after copulation were not viable. The functional importance of the rapid phase of sperm transport is not obvious. It may simply represent a burst of transport activity brought about by contraction of the muscularis of the female tract in conjunction with copulation.

Figure 12-2. Leukocyte Infiltration Helps Prevent Reproductive Tract Infections

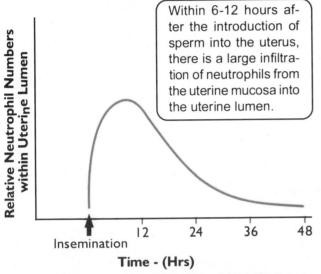

Within 6-12 hours after the introduction of sperm into the uterus, there is a large infiltration of neutrophils from the uterine mucosa into the uterine lumen.

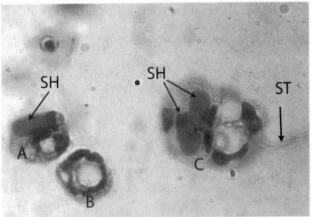

Three leukocytes (A,B and C) phagocytizing sperm. Sperm heads (SH) can be observed in the cytoplasm of the leukocytes. A sperm tail (ST) can also be seen protruding from the leukocyte (Micrograph courtesy of R.G. Saacke, Virginia Polytechnic Institute and State University, Blacksburg)

The more important component of transport is the sustained phase in which spermatozoa are transported to the oviducts in a "trickle-like" effect from so-called reservoirs in the cervix and the uterotubal junction. During the sustained transport phase, sperm move into the isthmus and attach to the oviductal epithelium. Sperm can attach to the epithelium along the entire oviduct. However, sperm temporarily "dock" to the epithelium of the lower isthmus near the uterotubal junction because this is the first oviductal region they encounter. Sperm "docking" is crucial to sperm survival because it elicits a signal cascade in the sperm that promotes viability. Without "docking", sperm die within 6-10 hours after insemination.

> *Rapid transport of spermatozoa is primarily the result of elevated tone and motility of the muscularis of the female tract.*

As you already know, estradiol is high during the follicular phase when insemination occurs. Estradiol stimulates contractions of the muscularis, particularly the myometrium. Also, prostaglandins in semen ($PGF_{2\alpha}$ and PGE_1) cause increased tone and motility of the uterus and/or the oviduct. Intermittent contractions of the muscularis propel spermatozoa in both a cranial and a caudal direction. Fluids secreted into the lumen of the female tract also serve as a vehicle for transport. Control of directionality, while not understood, is probably under the collective influence of muscular contractions and fluid distribution and characteristics.

In addition to alteration of tract motility, seminal plasma from boars has been shown by German researchers to advance the time of ovulation in gilts. For example, when seminal plasma was infused into the right uterine horn, ovulation occurred about 11 hours earlier in the right ovary than in the left ovary. The left uterine horn did not receive seminal plasma. The specific material in boar seminal plasma inducing early ovulation has not been identified, but it appears to be a protein. Identification of these factors could provide an avenue to control more precisely the time of ovulation in swine. A similar phenomenon occurs in camelids where seminal plasma components have been shown to cause ovulation.

12

> *The cervix is a major barrier to spermatozoal transport and it can also serve as a reservoir for spermatozoa.*

Figure 12-3. Spermatozoa Travel Through "Privileged Pathways" in the Cow

During estrus secretion of sulfo-mucins from the apical portion of the cervical mucosa produces sheets of viscous mucus. Secretion is toward the lumen and flows in a caudal direction. Less viscous sialomucins are produced in the basal crypts of the cervix. Spermatozoa found in the basal regions are orientated in the same direction and traverse the cervix toward the uterus through these "privileged pathways" (PP) of low viscosity sialomucin. (Modified from Mullins and Saacke 1989, *Anat. Rec.* 225:106)

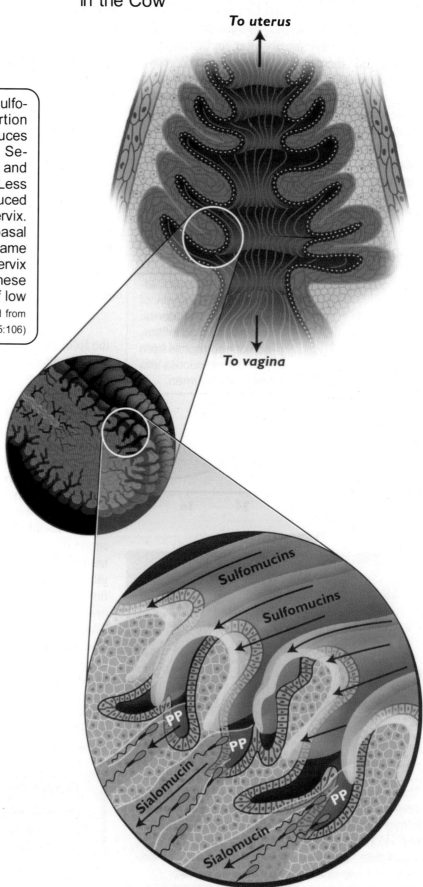

12

Following copulation in the cow and ewe and, to some degree, the mare, spermatozoa must negotiate the highly convoluted system of grooves within the cervix (See Figure 12-3). During estrus, the cervix produces mucus. In the cow cervical mucus consists of two types. One type is a **sialomucin**, a mucus of low viscosity. It is produced by cells in the basal areas of the cervical crypts (See Figure 12-3). A second type, **sulfomucin** is produced in the apical portions of the cervical epithelium covering the tips of the cervical folds. This type of mucus is quite viscous. The production of two types of mucus (one of low viscosity and one of high viscosity) creates two distinct environments within the cervix. Spermatozoa encountering the viscous sulfomucin are washed out of the tract. Those that encounter the low viscosity sialomucin in the environment of the crypts of the cervix swim into it. Thus, the low viscosity environment of the deeper cervical crypts creates "privileged pathways" through which spermatozoa can move.

The ability of spermatozoa to traverse these "privileged pathways" is thought to depend on their ability to swim through the basal channels (crypts) of the cervix and the associated low viscosity mucus. In this context, the cervix may be a filter that eliminates non-motile spermatozoa. The specific role of the cervix in spermatozoal transport and/or retention awaits further clarification in the sow and the mare, where a high proportion of spermatozoa are ejaculated into the uterus.

> *Spermatozoa must reside in the female tract before they acquire maximum fertility.*

As you recall from Chapter 3, spermatozoa acquire maturity during epididymal transit. However, the maturational changes that occur in the epididymis do not render spermatozoa completely fertile. For maximum fertility to be achieved, spermatozoa must reside in the female reproductive tract for a minimum period of time. During the time in the female reproductive tract, some spermatozoa will undergo changes that allow them to become fertile. These changes are referred to as spermatozoal **capacitation** (See Figure 12-4). The site for capacitation varies among species. In species where spermatozoa are deposited in the cranial vagina, capacitation may begin as sperm ascend and pass through the cervix. In species where semen is

---

12

Figure 12-4. Conceptual Version of Mammalian Capacitation

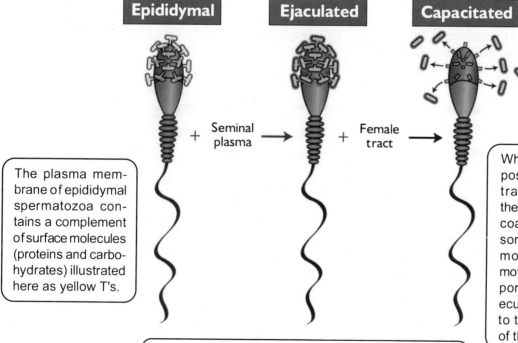

Epididymal   **Ejaculated**   **Capacitated**

+ Seminal plasma →   + Female tract →

The plasma membrane of epididymal spermatozoa contains a complement of surface molecules (proteins and carbohydrates) illustrated here as yellow T's.

The surface molecules in epididymal sperm become coated with seminal plasma proteins (orange halos) that mask portions of the membrane molecules.

When sperm are exposed to the female tract environment, these seminal plasma coatings, along with some of the surface molecules, are removed, thus exposing portions of the molecules that can bind to the zona pellucida of the oocyte.

deposited into the mid-cervix (sow) or caudal cervix (mare) and immediately enters the uterus, capacitation is probably initiated within the uterus and completed in the isthmus of the oviduct as is the case with all species. All spermatozoa are not capacitated at the same rate. Instead, they are capacitated over a relatively long period of time (several hours).

Capacitation can occur in fluids other than those found in the luminal compartment of the female reproductive tract. For example, *in vitro* capacitation has been accomplished in a wide variety of species using blood serum, a variety of commercial tissue culture media, Krebs Ringer solution and Tyrodes solution. No single *in vitro* environment will support capacitation for all species.

There is little doubt that the plasma membrane of the sperm (particularly the head) undergoes marked biochemical changes during capacitation. During mixing of sperm with seminal plasma the sperm become coated with various proteins. The coating of seminal plasma proteins is "stripped" away by the female tract environment. The exact nature of the "stripping process" of capacitation is not understood.

An important concept with regard to capacitation is that the process can be reversed by returning capacitated spermatozoa to seminal plasma. For example, when capacitated spermatozoa are removed from the female reproductive tract and returned to seminal plasma, they become **decapacitated** and require additional capacitation time in the female reproductive tract before they can regain their fertility. It appears that the seminal plasma components coat the plasma membrane with surface substances that prevent or inhibit interaction of spermatozoa with the egg.

Fertilization is a Complex Process and Involves a Cascade of Events

The process of fertilization involves a series of specific interactions between spermatozoa and the oocyte. These are outlined in Figure 12-5.

> ***Acquisition of hyperactive motility occurs in the oviduct.***

In the oviduct, as capacitation is completed, the motility patterns of spermatozoa become hyperactive. The motility pattern changes from a progressive, linear motility in which they swim in a relatively straight line (like an Olympic swimmer), into a frenzied, dancing motion that is not linear and is localized

Figure 12-5. Postcapacitation Sequence of Events Leading to Fertilization

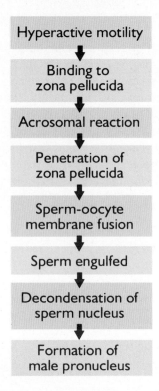

in a small area (like dancers in a disco). Hyperactive motility occurs throughout the oviduct and is thought to be brought about by specific molecules produced by the epithelium there. Hyperactive motility is thought to facilitate sperm-oocyte contact.

> ***Binding to the zona pellucida requires specific zona-binding proteins on the spermatozoal membrane.***

Spermatozoa are known to contain specific proteins on their plasma membrane surfaces overlying the acrosome that bind specifically to zona pellucida proteins. These zona binding proteins on the plasma membrane must be exposed during the capacitation process before binding to the zona pellucida can occur. Before zona binding can be understood fully, the molecular makeup of the zona must be described.

The zona pellucida of the oocyte consists of three glycoproteins. These glycoproteins have been named **zona proteins 1, 2** and **3 (ZP1, ZP2** and **ZP3)**. Zona proteins 1 and 2 are structural proteins providing the structural integrity of the zona. Zona protein 3 is much like a receptor for a hormone. It binds to proteins on the spermatozoal membrane. Binding of spermatozoa to the zona pellucida is believed to require between 10,000 and 50,000 ZP3 molecules. The current understanding is that the sperm plasma membrane contains two zona binding sites. The first binding site, referred to as the **primary zona binding region** is responsible for adherence of spermatozoa to the zona pellucida. The second binding site on the spermatozoal plasma membrane is believed to be **acrosome reaction promoting ligand**. When binding occurs between this region and the ZP3 molecule, a signal transduction occurs. This is much like a typical hormone-receptor binding complex. Binding initiates the acrosomal reaction. The relationship between ZP3 and the spermatozoal plasma membrane during binding is illustrated in Figure 12-6.

> *The acrosomal reaction is an orderly fusion of the spermatozoal plasma membrane and the outer acrosomal membrane.*

The purpose of the acrosomal reaction is twofold. First, the reaction enables spermatozoa to penetrate the zona pellucida. Second, it modifies the equatorial segment so that it can later fuse with the plasma membrane of the oocyte.

The acrosomal reaction begins when the plasma membrane of the spermatozoon forms multiple fusion sites with the outer acrosomal membrane. When the two membranes fuse, many small vesicles are formed (See Figure 12-7) and this process is called **vesiculation**. After vesiculation has occurred, the acrosomal contents are dispersed and the sperm nucleus is left

Figure 12-6. Zona Binding by Sperm and Initiation of the Acrosomal Reaction

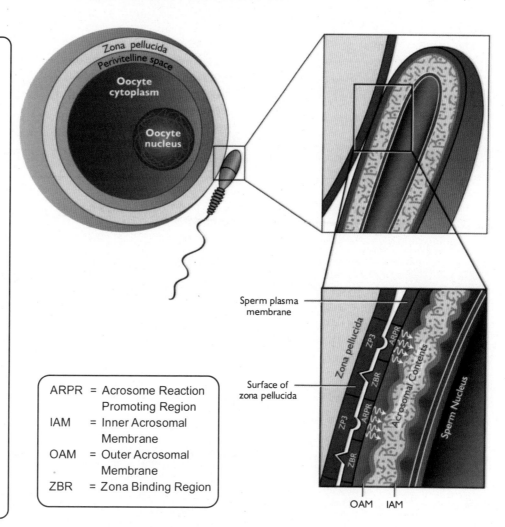

Proposed model for zona binding and the initiation of the acrosomal reaction in mammalian spermatozoa. The sperm plasma membrane overlying the acrosome contains two receptor-like regions. The first, called the zona binding region (ZBR), reacts with ZP3 to cause physical attachment of the sperm to the zona pellucida. A second membrane region, the acrosome reaction promoting region (ARPR), also binds to ZP3 and initiates the acrosome reaction by causing the sperm plasma membrane to fuse (arrows) to the outer acrosomal membrane.

ARPR = Acrosome Reaction Promoting Region
IAM = Inner Acrosomal Membrane
OAM = Outer Acrosomal Membrane
ZBR = Zona Binding Region

Figure 12-7. Schematic Illustration of the Acrosomal Reaction

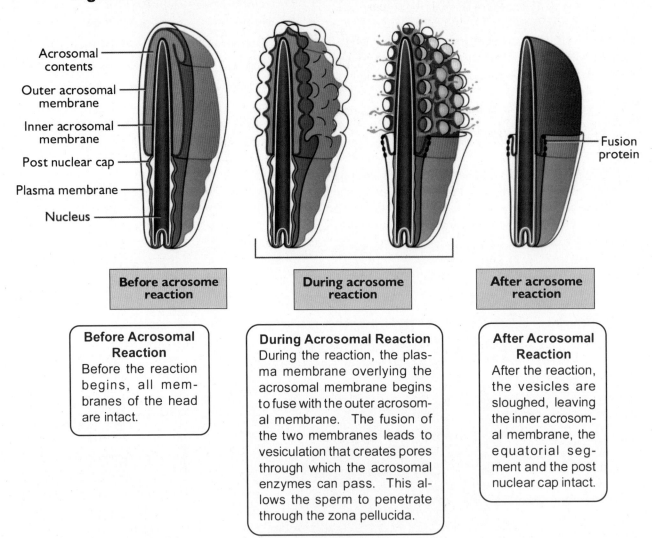

Acrosomal contents
Outer acrosomal membrane
Inner acrosomal membrane
Post nuclear cap
Plasma membrane
Nucleus
Fusion protein

Before acrosome reaction

During acrosome reaction

After acrosome reaction

Before Acrosomal Reaction
Before the reaction begins, all membranes of the head are intact.

During Acrosomal Reaction
During the reaction, the plasma membrane overlying the acrosomal membrane begins to fuse with the outer acrosomal membrane. The fusion of the two membranes leads to vesiculation that creates pores through which the acrosomal enzymes can pass. This allows the sperm to penetrate through the zona pellucida.

After Acrosomal Reaction
After the reaction, the vesicles are sloughed, leaving the inner acrosomal membrane, the equatorial segment and the post nuclear cap intact.

12

with the inner acrosomal membrane surrounding it. Vesiculation characterizes the acrosomal reaction and morphologically distinguishes it from a damaged acrosome. Damage to the acrosome membrane and plasma membrane is irreversible. Damage to these membranes is brought about by changes in osmotic pressure, sudden cooling, sudden heating or marked changes in pH. Damage to the membranes causes premature loss of acrosomal contents and such sperm cannot accomplish fertilization.

> *Release of acrosomal enzymes allows the spermatozoon to digest its way through the zona pellucida.*

The penetration of the zona pellucida by a spermatozoon is believed to be a rapid process and probably takes no more than a few minutes. Following attachment to the zona pellucida, the acrosome reaction allows the release of a variety of enzymes. **Acrosin** is one enzyme that is released from spermatozoa during the acrosomal reaction. It hydrolyzes zona proteins as well as enhances the sperm's ability to bind to the zona. In the inactive form, acrosin is known as **proacrosin** which has a strong affinity for the zona. Thus, proacrosin aids in binding the spermatozoon to the zona as the acrosomal reaction proceeds. As proacrosin is converted to acrosin, the sperm begins to penetrate and make its way through the zona pellucida. The mechanical force generated by the flagellar action of the tail may be sufficient to maintain sperm head contact with the zona pellucida. It is important to note that the acrosomal reaction allows the spermatozoon to digest a small hole through the zona through which it can pass. Placing a hot marble on the surface of a block of chilled butter would be an appropriate analogy. The hot marble would move through the butter in a small regional hole, but the butter in most of the block would be unchanged. This small regional dissolution leaves the zona predominately intact. Maintenance of an intact zona pellucida is important because it prevents blastomeres in the early embryo from separating during embryogenesis.

> ***Fertilization requires fusion of the equatorial segment and the oocyte plasma membrane.***

When the spermatozoon completely penetrates the zona and reaches the perivitelline space (the space between the zona and the oocyte plasma membrane), it settles into a bed of microvilli formed from the oocyte plasma membrane. The plasma membrane of the oocyte fuses with the membrane of the equatorial segment and the fertilizing spermatozoon is engulfed. The actual fusion of the oocyte plasma membrane with the equatorial segment is believed to be brought about by a so-called **fusion protein** located on this portion of the membrane. Prior to the acrosome reaction, this fusion protein is inactive. After vesiculation and release of the acrosomal contents, the fusion protein is

Figure 12-8. Illustration of Sperm-Oocyte Fusion

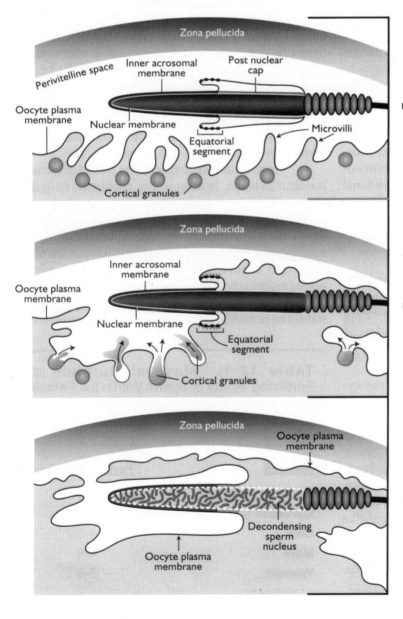

Before membrane fusion

When the spermatozoon completely penetrates the zona and reaches the perivitelline space, it settles into a bed of microvilli formed by the oocyte plasma membrane. The cortical granules have migrated to the periphery of the oocyte.

During membrane fusion

The plasma membrane of the oocyte fuses with the equatorial segment and the fertilizing spermatozoon is engulfed. The cortical granule membrane fuses with the oocyte plasma membrane and the cortical contents are released into the perivitelline space by exocytosis.

After membrane fusion

After the fusion between the membrane of the equatorial segment and the oocyte plasma membrane occurs, the nucleus of the spermatozoon is within the cytoplasm. The sperm nuclear membrane disappears and the nucleus of the sperm decondenses.

12

activated, enabling the sperm membrane to fuse or bind with the oocyte membrane. This process is illustrated in Figure 12-8.

The cortical reaction prevents penetration by additional spermatozoa.

After membrane fusion, the oocyte undergoes a series of changes that prepare it for early embryogenesis. The most easily recognizable is the **cortical reaction**. During the first and second meiotic divisions of oogenesis, small, dense granules called cortical granules move to the periphery of the oocyte cytoplasm. The contents of the cortical granules consist of mucopolysaccharides, proteases, plasminogen activator, acid phosphatase and peroxidase. After membrane fusion between the oocyte and spermatozoon, the cortical granules undergo **exocytosis** and their contents are released into the perivitelline space (See Figure 12-8). Exocytosis of the cortical granules results in the **zona block**, a process whereby the zona pellucida undergoes biochemical changes so that further sperm cannot penetrate it. **Polyspermy** is prevented by the zona block.

Polyspermy is the fertilization of an oocyte by more than one spermatozoon which results in embryo death. In addition to alteration of the zona pellucida, the cortical reaction is believed to reduce the ability of the oocyte plasma membrane to fuse with additional spermatozoa, thus causing the **vitelline block**, another mechanism that prevents polyspermy. Some species have both a zona block as well as a vitelline block, while others have either a zona or a vitelline block.

Pronuclei formation allows the male and female DNA to form a single nucleus.

After the sperm nucleus has entered the cytoplasm of the egg, it becomes the male pronucleus. Before the pronucleus can be formed, however, the nucleus of the sperm must undergo marked changes within the oocyte cytoplasm. As you will recall, one of the maturational changes that occurs in the epididymis is the acquisition of large numbers of disulfide cross-links in the sperm nucleus. Thus, the nucleus of the mammalian sperm is almost inert. The keratinoid-like quality of insolubility is considered to be important during exposure to the female tract environment, sperm transport and penetration through the zona pellucida. After the fertilizing spermatozoon enters the oocyte cytoplasm the nucleus must "decondense" so that the male

chromosomes may pair up with the chromosomes of the female pronucleus. The decondensation of the sperm nucleus requires the reduction of the many disulfide cross-links. In the cytoplasm of the oocyte, disulfide cross-links in the sperm nucleus are reduced quickly. The primary reducing agent is glutathione. When disulfide bond reduction occurs, the sperm nucleus decondenses and the nuclear material is available for interaction with the female nuclear material. The final step of fertilization is the fusion of the male and female pronuclei. This fusion is referred to as **syngamy**. Following syngamy, the zygote enters the first stages of embryogenesis that are described in Chapter 13.

The Fertile Period Varies Significantly Among Mammalian Females

The fertile life-span of sperm after deposition in the female reproductive tract varies immensely among species. For example, fertility of spermatozoa is retained for four to five years in certain reptiles. Among mammals, bat spermatozoa remain viable after insemination in the female tract for up to 4-5 months before the female ovulates. In general, retention of fertilizing capacity among domestic animals and humans lasts only a few days. Values in Table 12-1 document the variation in fertilizing ability in the female tract among various domestic species and women.

In most domestic species the period of estrus is less than 24 hours. In other words, copulation must take place within a time-period that is close to ovulation. In contrast, sperm can remain viable for as long as 5 to 6 days before ovulation in women. Another example of a sustained fertile period is the bitch. Ovulation takes place over about a three day period after the onset of sexual receptivity. Fertilization can be accomplished as long as six days after the onset of sexual receptivity. It should be pointed out that in a multiparous species like

---

Table 12-1. Maximal Duration of Fertilizing Ability of Sperm Within the Female Reproductive Tract of Various Species

Species	Fertile Life (days)
Bitch	9-11
Camelids (camel, llama, alpaca)	4-5
Cow	1.5-2
Mare	4-5
Woman	5-6

the dog, several males can sire offspring because the bitch may be bred by several males during her relatively long estrus. Spermatozoa from all males are eligible to fertilize oocytes. This phenomenon is called **superfecundation**. Thus, it is not uncommon to observe litters that have different breeds of puppies.

It should be emphasized that the long fertile period in women coupled with a high frequency of copulation predisposes humans to unwanted pregnancies and a high global birth rate. Since the woman does not have a definite period of sexual receptivity, copulation taking place within 5-6 days of ovulation can result in a pregnancy. Where a poor understanding of the cycle exists, the probability of pregnancy becomes quite high because almost 20% of the menstrual cycle has the potential to generate a pregnancy.

The question is often asked as to whether the number of copulations can influence the chance of pregnancy within a given mating period. In spontaneous ovulators the answer is "probably not". In induced ovulators (especially in felids), there appears to be a threshold number of copulations required to optimize GnRH and LH release. The chance of ovulation and therefore pregnancies are related to copulation frequency. In humans, the probability of conception (pregnancy) is about 0.33 per cycle. This means if mating takes place among fertile individuals there is a one-in-three chance that the woman will become pregnant every cycle (if sexual intercourse takes place within 2 days of ovulation as Figure 12-9 shows). It is like a batting average.

If your favorite baseball player had a batting average of 0.333 for the season, he had a one in three chance to get a base-hit during each at-bat. Each at-bat is equivalent to the fertile period of an estrous or menstrual cycle. On average, your favorite hitter needs 3 at-bats to get a hit (a pregnancy). It makes no difference how many times the batter swings (number of copulations) during each "at-bat," his batting average will still be 0.333. Similarly, assuming a threshold number of sperm are deposited during the first copulation, the number of copulations during each fertile period (an "at bat") will not influence the probability of pregnancy because the first copulation fills the oviductal reservoir and will not allow more sperm to populate the reservoir.

Batting Averages and Pregnancies are Similar:

- *Each "at-bat" = 1 opportunity to achieve pregnancy*

- *The batting average = probability of becoming pregnant*

- *A swing = 1 mating*

- *A good "at-bat" = many swings (but depletes extragonadal reserves)*

Figure 12-9. Probability of Conception When Copulation Occurred on Specific Days Relative of Ovulation in Women
(From Wilcox et al. 1995. *NEJM* 333:1517)

12

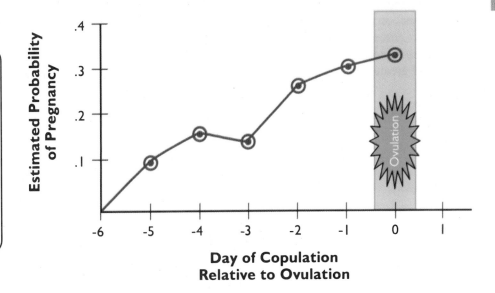

Conception can occur within a 6-day window prior to ovulation. At 5 days prior to ovulation, the probability of conception was 0.11 and the probability increases to about 0.33 two days before ovulation.

Delivery of Semen to the Proper Anatomical Region of the Female Tract is Required for Successful Artificial Insemination

It had been erroneously assumed for years that most spermatozoa ascend toward the oviduct soon after they are deposited in the cow uterus by artificial insemination. However, recent studies have shown that a high proportion of spermatozoa deposited in the uterus of the cow or ewe are lost from the tract by retrograde transport. In most cows, over 60% of spermatozoa artificially inseminated into the uterus are lost to the exterior of the tract within 12 hours after deposition. Given these findings, a logical interpretation would be that artificial insemination of spermatozoa deep into the uterus would result in reduced retrograde loss. This assumption is not true because when sperm are deposited deep into both uterine horns (as opposed to the uterine body) the degree of sperm recovered from the vagina (an indication of retrograde loss) is quite similar between the two sites of deposition (See Figure 12-10). However, when sperm are deposited in the mid-cervix, a significantly higher degree of retrograde loss of spermatozoa is encountered (See Figure 12-10).

Spermatozoa deposited into only one uterine horn of the cow experience intercornual transport. That is, when spermatozoa are deposited into one uterine horn (either right or left), they subsequently are redistributed so that both uterine horns eventually contain substantial numbers of spermatozoa. This phenomenon also occurs in swine. In cows, fertility is not compromised and in some studies is enhanced when sperm are deposited within the uterine body or in the right and left uterine horns.

The important message from the above discussion is that when artificial insemination is performed in the cow and semen is deposited into the cervix, a greater proportion of spermatozoa are lost to the exterior than when deposition is in the uterus. Thus, when the insemination procedure involves cervical deposition (a serious technique error), fertility may be compromised because of greater spermatozoal loss.

Artificial Insemination Techniques in Domestic Species

Artificial insemination technique requires that spermatozoa be deposited in the reproductive tract of the female by artificial means. In general, semen is delivered using a pipette to penetrate and bypass the cervix (See Figure 12-11). This type of insemination is referred to as **transcervical insemination**. In the sow, the insemination pipette is positioned within the cervix and semen is delivered into the cranial half of the cervix and flows directly into the uterine horns. This type of insemination is referred to as **intracervical insemination** (See Figure 12-12). In dogs and cats semen is deposited in the cranial vagina. This type of insemination is referred to as **intravaginal insemination** (See Figure 12-12).

In cases where sperm are in very limited supply, surgical insemination can be performed by exteriorizing the reproductive tract and injecting sperm directly into the uterus or uterotubal junction region. Also, use of laparoscopy enables insemination to be performed without laparotomy (an abdominal incision). In bulls, X-Y sorted semen are in short-supply. Therefore, a technique has been developed to "thread" the tip of an insemination pipette through the cervix to the uterotubal junction. Such a technique has been reported to generate excellent results.

12

Figure 12-10. Insemination into the Uterine Horns Can Reduce Sperm Loss

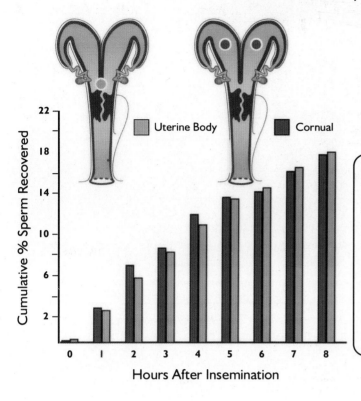

Cumulative percentage of sperm recovered from the vagina of heifers during an 8 hour period after insemination. In one group of heifers (green bar), sperm was deposited in the uterine body. In the second group (burgundy bar), sperm were deposited deep into each uterine horn. The cumulative percent of sperm recovered from the vagina did not differ between the two treatment groups.
(Modified from Gallahger and Senger, 1989, *J. Reprod. Fert.* 86:19)

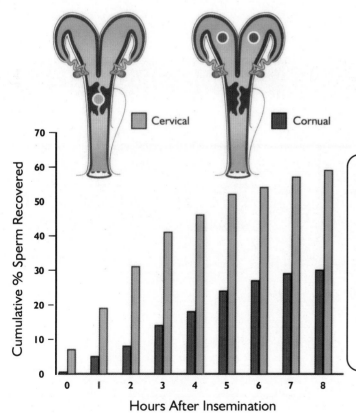

Cumulative percentage of sperm recovered from the vagina of heifers during an 8 hour period after insemination. In one group of heifers (blue bar) sperm were deposited in the cervix, while in the second group (burgundy bar) sperm were deposited in the uterine horns. A significantly higher number of sperm were found in the vagina of the animals that were inseminated at midcervix indicating retrograde sperm transport.
(Modified from Gallagher and Senger, 1989, *J. Reprod. Fert.* 86:19)

12

Figure 12-11. Artificial Insemination Technique in the Cow and Mare

Cow

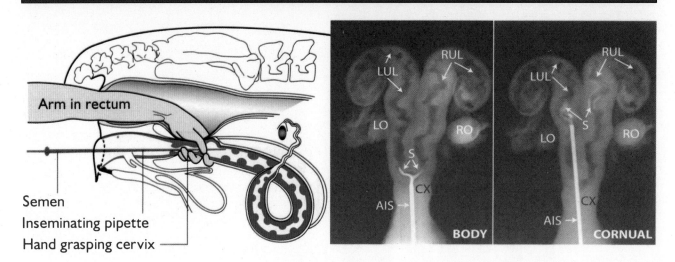

The radiographs above are from extirpated cow reproductive tracts (dorsal view). In cornual insemination, one-half of the semen is deposited in each uterine horn. In both examples, the inseminant volume is 0.5-ml. Cornual insemination minimizes the possibility of cervical deposition that results in significant retrograde loss of spermatozoa (See Figure 12-3). RUL= Right Uterine Lumen; LUL= Left Uterine Lumen; RO= right ovary; LO= left ovary; S= semen; AIS= artificial insemination syringe; CX= cervix

Mare

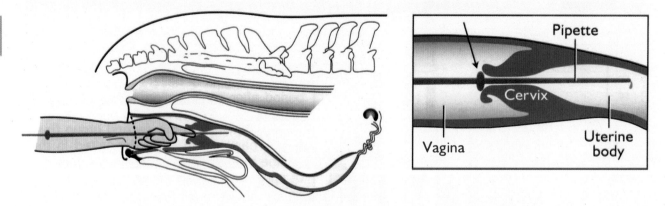

In the mare, the gloved lubricated hand is inserted directly into the vagina and the index finger is used to guide the insemination pipette into the cervical lumen. A marker (arrow) is used to gauge the depth of insemination.

Figure 12-12 Artificial Insemination Technique in the Sow and Bitch

Sow

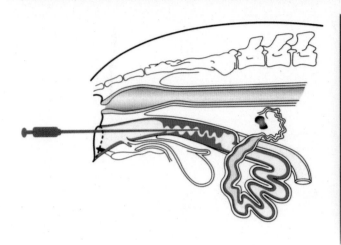
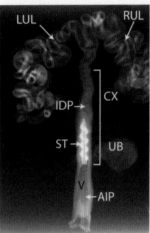
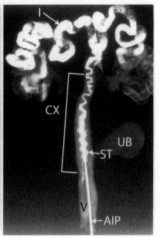

Radiographs of an extirpated sow reproductive tracts (dorsal view). An artificial insemination pipette (AIP) consists of a spiral tip (ST) that is designed so that it can snugly penetrate the interdigitating prominences (IDP) of the cervix (CX). In the photograph to the right, about 80-ml of radiopaque contrast medium was infused into the reproductive tract to mimic the inseminant (I). Notice that the semen becomes distributed within both uterine horns. High volumes (about 80-ml) are necessary to maximize pregnancies in sows. The vagina (V) and the urinary bladder (UB) can be visualized. LUL= Left Uterine Lumen; RUL= Right Uterine Lumen.

Bitch

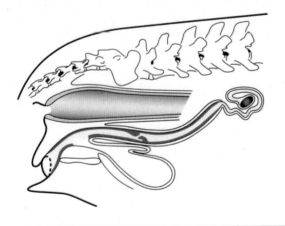
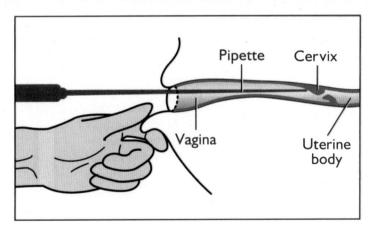

The vulva is elevated manually so that the ventral "tilt" of the vestibule is removed. This allows the insemination pipette to be inserted with relative ease. The hindquarters of the bitch should be elevated for about 5 minutes after deposition of the semen to allow pooling in the cranial vagina and caudal cervix.

12

Further PHENOMENA for Fertility

Some species have delayed fertilization. This is a process whereby the male inseminates the female and spermatozoa remain viable in the female tract for a sustained period of time. When a rooster inseminates a hen she can lay fertile eggs for over 20 days. Sperm are stored in special utero-vaginal glands. Some bats mate in the autumn before hibernation. The female does not ovulate until spring. Sperm are stored in her tract during the winter. The fertilizing life of bat sperm is reported to range from 68 to 198 days depending on the species of bat. Snakes are reported to store sperm that are fertile for up to 6 years.

The bifurcation of the glans penis of the opossum led to the widespread Appalachian folk belief that opossums mated through the nose, with one fork of the glans penis penetrating each nostril. Little scientific consideration was given to the issues of sperm transport.

Male mammals deliver sperm to the female in seminal plasma. However, many lower forms of animals make use of special packages for delivering spermatozoa to the female reproductive tract. These packages are called spermatophores. These spermatophores are produced within the male reproductive tract and are stored there until copulation. In some cephalopods (octopus and squid) the male deposits the spermatophore in the female tract or into the buccal cavity (cheek pouch), from which it can be conveniently transferred to the female tract. In some annelids, spermatophores are "injected" subcutaneously, after which the spermatozoa spread throughout the female's body before contacting eggs.

12

A Spermatozoon Race
by Cheryl A. Dudley

Half frenzied, thick and slick
and treacherous, through vast dark tunnels,
as motile and penetratingly
zona-bound as any race ever,
none other is so victim-laden,
so masked by drunken seizures
or pleasures of full-bodied assaults,
the tadpoles' mad dash
is like an escaped madman,
a drowner driven to oxygen,
the journey a seas-width heat
to life or death

When they jolted over the barrier
she didn't realize a race was on,
yet in her own primordial way
she cheered for them, provided secret
privileged pathways through crypts
too difficult for most, whose dead,
flat-floating bodies cluttered the way.
The lone victor slithered through, sensed
the trophy ahead-the zona seducing him to dip
in her warm waters, melt into her soft globe.
(The courtship was only long enough for him
to work his way through her pellucida.)

A quivering union formed
primitive cords that proliferated
time and time and time again,
swelling to fill the primed pear-palmed
womb where the victor celebrated,
And a genesis began.

Cheryl Dudley typed the 1st Edition of Path-ways to Pregnancy and Parturition from the author's dictation. She has since graduated Cum laude in English from the University of Idaho and is now a graduate student in the Department of English at that university.

Motility of trout spermatozoa is induced by the fresh water into which it is ejaculated. Motility lasts for only about 30 seconds. During this time the sperm must locate a single tiny hole in the egg (called a micropyle) through which it enters before fertilization can occur. All this happens while being swept about by moving water.

Key References

Anderson, G.B., 1991. "Fertilization, early development and embryo transfer" in *Reproduction in Domestic Animals,* 4th Edition. P.T. Cupps, ed. Academic Press. New York. ISBN 0-12-196575-9.

Crozet, N. 1993. "Fertilization *in-vivo* and *in-vitro*" in *Reproduction in Mammals and Man*. C. Thibault, M.C. Levasseur and R.H.F. Hunter, eds. Ellipses, Paris. ISBN 2-7298-9354-7.

Flowers, W.L. 1999. "Artificial insemination in animals" in *Encyclopedia of Reproduction*, Vol. 1 p291-301. Knobil, E. and J.D. Neill, eds. Academic Press, San Diego. ISBN 0-12-227021-5.

Mullins, K.J. and R.G. Saacke. 1989. "Study of the functional anatomy of bovine cervical mucosa with special reference to mucus secretion and sperm transport." *Anat. Rec.* 225:106-117.

Yanagimachi, R. 1996. "Mammalian fertilization" in *Physiology of Reproduction*, 2nd Edition. Vol. 1 p189-318. E. Knobil and J.D. Neill, eds. Raven Press, Ltd., New York. ISBN 0-7817-0086-8.

12

EARLY EMBRYOGENESIS
& Maternal Recognition of Pregnancy

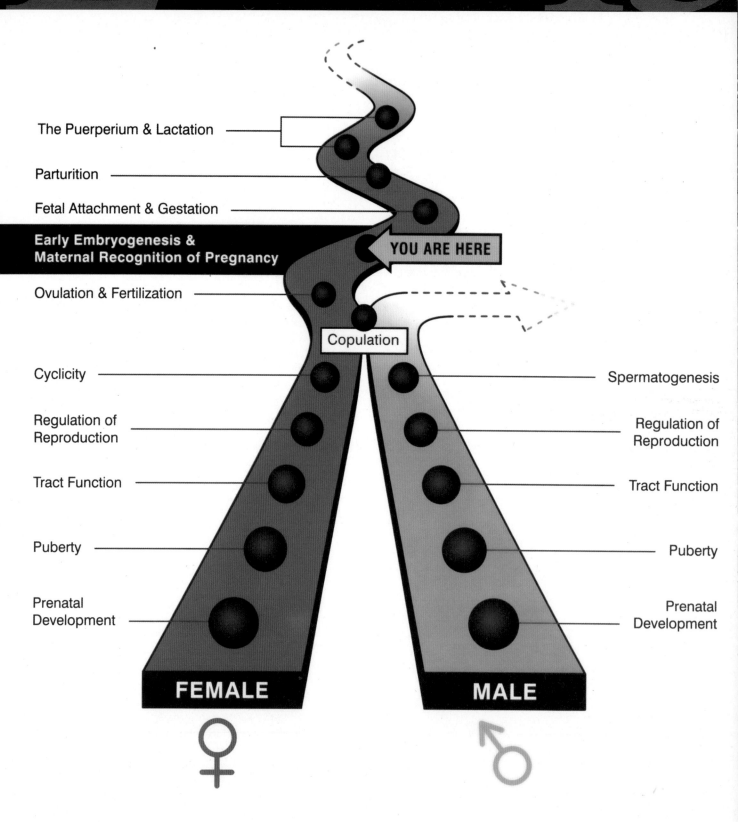

The Puerperium & Lactation

Parturition

Fetal Attachment & Gestation

**Early Embryogenesis &
Maternal Recognition of Pregnancy**

YOU ARE HERE

Ovulation & Fertilization

Copulation

Cyclicity

Regulation of
Reproduction

Tract Function

Puberty

Prenatal
Development

Spermatogenesis

Regulation of
Reproduction

Tract Function

Puberty

Prenatal
Development

FEMALE

MALE

Take Home Message

A successful pregnancy requires that the preattachment embryo develop into a blastocyst, hatch from the zona pellucida and develop a functional trophoblast. The early embryo must secrete materials that prevent luteolysis or that enhance luteal function to maintain pregnancy.

Before describing the important events of early embryogenesis, several potentially confusing terms with overlapping meanings need to be defined. These terms have subtly different uses depending on the species and the context in which they are used. After **syngamy** (fusion of the male and female pronuclei), the zygote becomes an **embryo**. An embryo is defined as an organism in the early stages of development. In general, an embryo has not acquired an anatomical form that is readily recognizable in appearance as a member of the specific species. For example, at early stages of development, the pig embryo cannot be distinguished from the cow embryo except by skilled embryologists. As a matter of fact, at certain stages, the human embryo cannot be distinguished from the embryos of lower species.

A **fetus** is defined as a potential offspring that is still within the uterus, but is generally recognizable as a member of a given species. Most physiologists think of a fetus as the more advanced form of an embryo. The terms embryo, conceptus and fetus are often used interchangeably to describe the developing organism. But, it should be recognized that each term has a distinct meaning and students of reproductive physiology are encouraged to use the term that most accurately describes the developing organism.

A **conceptus** is defined as the product of conception. It includes: 1) the embryo during the early embryonic stage, 2) the embryo and extraembryonic membranes during the preimplantation stage and 3) the fetus and placenta during the post-attachment phase.

After fertilization, four important developmental events must occur before the embryo attaches to the uterus. Only after these milestones are achieved will the embryo be eligible to develop a more intimate, semipermanent relationship with the uterus.

> **Four steps must be achieved before the embryo can attach to the uterus. They are:**
>
> - **development within the confines of the zona pellucida**
> - **hatching of the blastocyst from the zona pellucida**
> - **maternal recognition of pregnancy**
> - **formation of the extraembryonic membranes**

The presence of male and female pronuclei within the cytoplasm of the oocyte characterizes a developmental stage of the newly fertilized oocyte. When male and female pronuclei can be observed, the cell is called an **ootid** (See Figure 13-1). The ootid is one of the largest single cells in the body and is characterized by having an enormous cytoplasmic volume relative to nuclear volume. This characteristic is important, since subsequent cell divisions within the confines of the zona pellucida will involve partitioning of the cytoplasm into smaller and smaller cellular units (See Figure 13-1).

Following fusion of the male and female pronuclei, the single-celled embryo, now called a **zygote**, undergoes a series of mitotic divisions called **cleavage divisions**. The first cleavage division generates a two-celled embryo, the cells of which are called **blastomeres**. Each blastomere in the two-celled embryo is about the same size and represents almost exactly one-half of the single-celled zygote. Each blastomere undergoes subsequent divisions, yielding 4, 8 and then 16 daughter cells.

In the early stages of embryogenesis, each blastomere has the potential to develop into separate healthy offspring. Identical twins are derived from blastomeres of a two-celled embryo that divide independently to form two separate embryos. Blastomeres from the 2-, 4-,

13

Figure 13-1. Preattachment Development of the Embryo

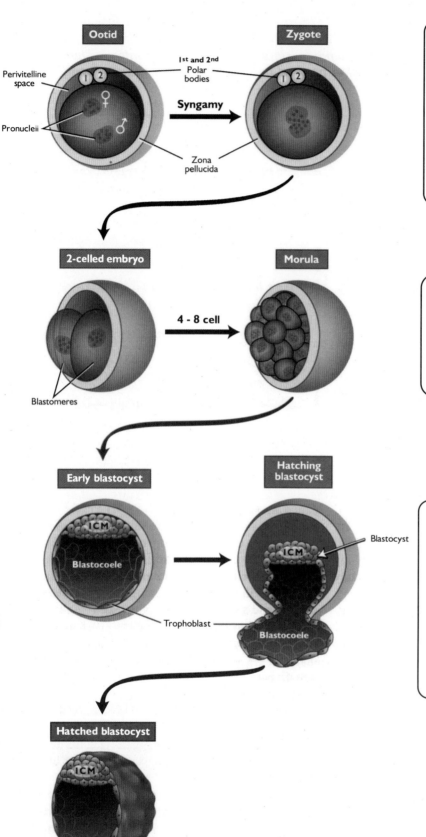

In the ootid, male and female pronuclei along with the first and second polar bodies are present. Fusion of the male and female pronuclei into a single diploid nucleus constitutes syngamy. Shortly thereafter, the zygote undergoes cleavage (mitotic divisions) and gives rise to daughter cells called blastomeres.

Cleavage divisions continue. A four-celled embryo gives rise to an eight-celled embryo. After the eight-celled stage, a ball of cells is formed and this embryonic stage is referred to as a morula.

Cells of the morula continue to divide and a blastocyst develops. It consists of an inner cell mass (ICM), a cavity called the blastocoele and a single layer of cells called the trophoblast. Finally, the rapidly growing blastocyst "hatches" from the zona pellucida and forms a "hatched" blastocyst that is free-floating within the uterus.

13

Figure 13-2. Transition of a Morula into an Early Blastocyst

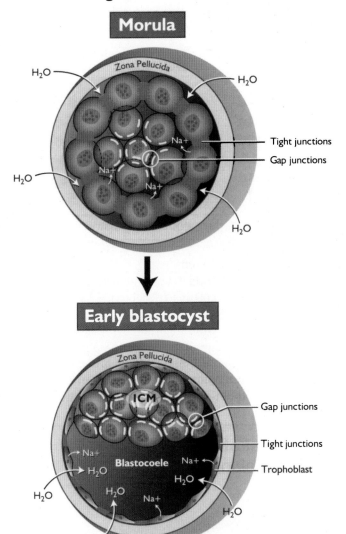

Tight junctions form between the outer cells of the morula. Gap junctions form between the inner cells thus creating two groups of cells. Sodium is pumped into the intercellular spaces by the outer cells of the morula and water follows osmotically. Therefore, fluid begins to accumulate within the morula.

As fluid accumulates, the outer cells become flattened and a cavity known as the blastocoele is formed. The gap junctions connecting the inner cells of the morula allow these cells to polarize as a group. As a result two separate cellular components emerge. These are, the inner cell mass (ICM) and the trophoblast.

8- and 16- celled embryos are **totipotent**. Totipotency is a term used to describe the ability of a single cell (blastomere) to give rise to a complete, fully formed individual. Identical twins can be artificially produced in the laboratory by separating individual blastomeres, placing each blastomere inside a surrogate zona pellucida and allowing it to develop within the uterus of a host female. The individual blastomeres isolated from 4- and 8- celled stages can develop into normal embryos in the rabbit (doe), mare, cow and ewe. Totipotency has not been demonstrated when whole blastomeres beyond the 16-cell stage are used. Recently, nuclei from somatic cells from adult cattle, sheep, goats, horses, swine, cats and dogs have been transplanted into enucleated oocytes. These oocytes have developed into normal offspring, although success rates are low (< 5%). Therefore, it appears that all cells may have the potential for totipotency if exposed to the appropriate environmental conditions.

The mitotic divisions of each blastomere generally occur simultaneously but are unique in that with each division, two cells are produced (from each blastomere) but there is no net change in cytoplasmic mass. The unique mitotic divisions are called cleavage divisions and occur between the 1-cell and the blastocyst stages. As a result of the cleavage divisions an embryo gains cell number but still contains the same total mass of cytoplasm it had when it was a 1-cell zygote. All of the cleavage divisions take place inside the zona pellucida that maintains a fixed volume throughout the process.

When a solid ball of cells is formed and individual blastomeres can no longer be counted accurately, the early embryo is called a **morula** (See Figure 13-1). When the morula is formed, the outer cells begin to be compacted more than the cells in the center. Thus, during the morula stage, cells begin to separate into two distinct populations, the inner and

13

Table 13-1. Timing of preattachment embryogenesis relative to ovulation within females of various species. Non-bolded values are in the oviduct. **Bold values in the shaded box are in the uterus; (—) = no data.**

Species	2-cell	4-cell	8-cell	Morula	Blastocyst	Hatching
bitch*	3-7d	—	—	—	—	**13-15d**
cow	24h	1.5d	3d	**4-7d**	**7-12d**	**9-11d**
ewe	24h	1.3d	2.5d	**3-4d**	**4-10d**	**7-8d**
mare	24h	1.5d	3d	**4-5d**	**6-8d**	**7-8d**
queen	—	—	—	**5d**	**8d**	**10-12d**
sow	14-16h	1.0d	**2d**	**3.5d**	**4-5d**	**6d**
woman	24h	2d	3d	**4d**	**5d**	**5-6d**

*Recall from Figure 7-4 that ovulation and fertilization occur during a 6-7 day period during estrus.

outer cells. During this transition, there is increased expression of genes involved in cell-to-cell adhesion, molecule transport (including ions) and intra/inter cell communication. This is accompanied by asymmetric divisions of cells that are thought to sequester differentiation factors in the outer layer and stem cell factors in the inner cell mass. Cells in the inner portion of the morula develop **gap junctions** (See Figure 13-2) that allow for intercellular communication and may en-

able the inner cells to remain in a defined cluster. The outer cells of the morula develop cell-to-cell adhesions known as **tight junctions** (See Figure 13-2). These tight junctions are believed to alter the permeability of the outer cells. After the tight junctions are formed, fluid begins to accumulate inside the embryo. This fluid accumulation is believed to be brought about by an active sodium pump in the outer cells of the morula that pump sodium ions into the center portion of the

13

Figure 13-3. Schematic Illustration of Preattachment Embryo Development

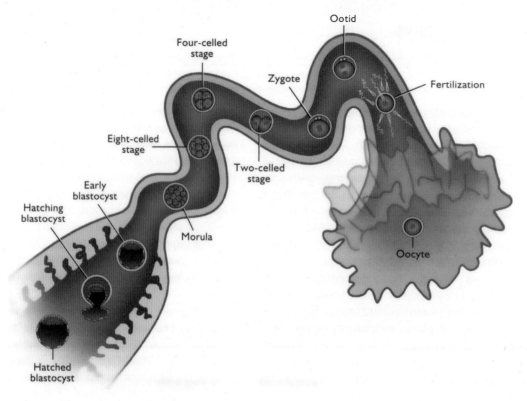

morula. This buildup of ions causes the ionic concentration of the fluid surrounding the inner cells of the morula to increase. As the ionic strength inside the morula increases, water diffuses through the zona pellucida into the embryo and begins to form a fluid filled cavity (See Figure 13-2) called a **blastocoele**.

> *Hatching of the blastocyst is governed by three forces. They are:*
>
> - *growth and fluid accumulation within the blastocyst*
> - *production of enzymes by the trophoblastic cells*
> - *contraction of the blastocyst*

When a distinct cavity is recognizable, the embryo is called a **blastocyst**. Because of the nature of the tight junctions (found in the outer cells) and the gap junctions (found among the inner cells), the embryo becomes partitioned into two distinct cellular populations. These are known as the **inner cell mass** and the **trophoblast**. The inner cell mass will give rise to the body of the embryo. The trophoblastic cells will eventually give rise to the **chorion**. The chorion will become the fetal component of the placenta that will be described later.

As the blastocyst continues to undergo mitosis, fluid continues to fill the blastocoele and the pressure within the embryo increases. Concurrent with growth and fluid accumulation is the production of proteolytic enzymes by the trophoblastic cells. These enzymes weaken the zona pellucida so that it ruptures easily as growth of the blastocyst continues. Finally, the blastocyst itself begins to contract and relax. Such behavior causes intermittent pressure pulses. These pressure pulses coupled with continued growth and enzymatic degradation cause the zona pellucida to rupture.

When a small crack or fissure in the zona pellucida develops, the cells of the blastocyst squeeze out of the opening, escaping from their confines (See Figure 13-1). The blastocyst now becomes a free-floating embryo within the lumen of the uterus and is totally dependent on the uterine environment for survival. In this context, early embryo survival is dependent on adequate luteal function, adequate progesterone synthesis and responsiveness of the uterus to progesterone. Figure 13-3 illustrates the anatomical location of the various preattachment stages of the embryo. The timing and species variation is presented in Table 13-1.

Development of the Extraembryonic Membranes Represents an "Explosion" of Embryonic Tissue Growth Prior to Attachment

After hatching, the conceptus undergoes massive growth. For example, in the cow at day 13 the blastocyst is about 3 mm in diameter. During the next four days, the cow blastocyst will become 250 mm in length (about the vertical length of the printed portion of this page) and will appear as a filamentous thread. By day 18 of gestation, the blastocyst occupies space in both uterine horns. While the blastocyst of the cow (and the ewe) grows quite rapidly during this early pre-attachment stage, the development of the pig blastocyst is even more dramatic. On day 10 of pregnancy, pig blastocysts are 2 mm spheres. During the next 24 to 48 hours, these 2 mm blastocysts will grow to about 200 mm in length (about the width of the printed portion of this page). This means that the blastocyst is growing at a rate of 4 to 8 mm per hour. By day 16, the pig blastocyst reaches lengths of 800 to 1000 mm.

Mammalian embryos can be subdivided into two primary groups. In the first group (that includes most domestic animals), the preattachment period within the uterus is long (several weeks). During this time, extensive extraembryonic membranes form by a folding process that generates the amnion, chorion and allantochorion. In the second group (primates) the blastocyst implants very soon after it enters the uterus. The extraembryonic membranes form after implantation or attachment. In this text, we will deal exclusively with the first group. For details about implantation of the human blastocyst please consult the reference by Larsen in **Key References**.

> *The extraembryonic membranes of the preattachment embryo consist of the:*
>
> - *yolk sac*
> - *chorion*
> - *amnion*
> - *allantois*

The dramatic growth of the conceptus is due largely to the development of a set of membranes called the **extraembryonic membranes**. The pig, sheep and cow are characterized as having filamentous or

13

Figure 13-4. Schematic Diagram Illustrating the Typical Development of Extraembryonic Membranes in Mammals

(This developmental sequence must occur before attachment to the endometrium can take place)

The hatched blastocyst consists of the inner cell mass (ICM), the trophoblast and the blastocoele. Very early in embryonic development, the primitive endoderm (blue layer) begins to form beneath the inner cell mass and grows downward forming a lining on the inner surface of the trophoblast. At the same time, the mesoderm (red layer) begins to develop between the primitive endoderm and the embryo.

When the primitive endoderm completes its growth, it forms a cavity called a yolk sac. This cavity does not contain yolk but is so named because it is analogous to the yolk sac in avian embryos.

The mesoderm continues to grow, forming a sac that surrounds the yolk sac and pushes against the trophectoderm (previously the trophoblastic cells). The newly formed mesodermal sac pushes against the trophectoderm and begins to fold upward forming "wing-like" structures called amnionic folds.

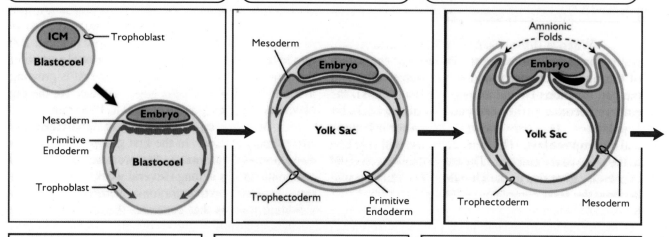

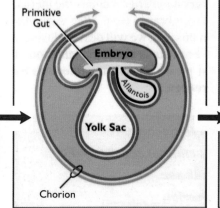

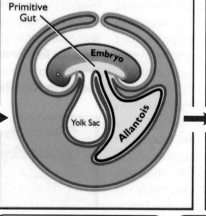

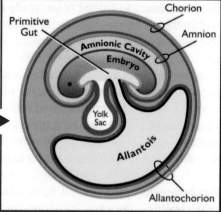

The mesoderm now completely surrounds the yolk sac and the developing allantois. The allantois is a diverticulum from the primitive gut that collects embryonic wastes. The mesoderm continues to fuse with the cells of the trophectoderm to form the chorion. The amnionic folds continue to grow upward around the embryo.

The yolk sac begins to regress but the allantois continues to grow and expand. The amnionic folds almost completely surround the embryo. The leading edges of the amnionic folds will eventually fuse.

The amnionic folds have completely fused resulting in the formation of a double sac around the embryo. The inner sac consists of trophectoderm and mesoderm and is called the amnion. It creates the amnionic cavity. The chorion completely surrounds the entire conceptus. The allantois continues to expand and begins to fill-in the spaces of the cavity. Eventually, the allantois and the chorion will fuse forming the allantochorion. The yolk sac continues to regress.

13

threadlike blastocysts prior to attachment. In the mare, however, blastocysts do not change into a threadlike structure but remain spherical.

Formation of the extraembryonic membranes is an obligatory step in the acquisition of the embryo's ability to attach to the uterus of the dam. The extraembryonic membranes are a set of four anatomically distinct membranes that originate from the trophoblast, endoderm, mesoderm and the embryo.

The trophoblast, along with the **primitive endoderm** and **mesoderm**, give rise to the **chorion** and the **amnion** (See Figure 13-4). The yolk sac develops from the primitive endoderm. The chorion will eventually attach to the uterus, while the amnion will provide a fluid-filled protective sac for the developing fetus.

As the hatched blastocyst begins to grow, it develops an additional layer just beneath, but in contact with the inner cell mass. This layer of cells is called the primitive endoderm (See Figure 13-4) and will continue to grow in a downward direction, eventually lining the trophoblast. At the same time the primitive endoderm is growing to become the inside lining of the trophoblast, it also forms an evagination at the ventral portion of the inner cell mass. This evagination forms the yolk sac (See Figure 13-4). The yolk sac in domestic animal embryos is a transient extraembryonic membrane that regresses in size as the conceptus develops. In spite of its regression, you will recall (See Chapter 4) that the yolk sac contributes the primitive germ cells that migrate to the genital ridge.

As the blastocyst continues to expand, the newly formed double membrane (the trophoblast and mesoderm) becomes the chorion. As it develops, the chorion pushes upward in the dorsolateral region of the conceptus and begins to surround it. As the chorion begins to send "wing-like" projections above the embryo, the amnion begins to form (See Figure 13-4). When the chorion fuses over the dorsal portion of the embryo, it then forms a complete sac around the embryo. This sac is the amnion. The amnion is filled with fluid and serves to hydraulically protect the embryo from mechanical perturbations. The amnionic fluid serves as an anti-adhesion material to prevent tissues in the rapidly developing embryo from adhering to each other. The amnionic vesicle can be palpated in the cow between days 30 and 45 and feels like a small, turgid balloon inside the uterus. The embryo, however, is quite fragile during this early period and amnionic vesicle palpation should be performed with caution.

During the same time that the amnion is developing, a small evagination from the posterior region of the primitive gut begins to form (See Figure 13-4). This sac-like evagination is referred to as the **allantois**. The allantois is a fluid-filled sac that collects liquid waste from the embryo. As the embryo grows, the allantois continues to expand and eventually will make contact with the chorion. When the allantois reaches a certain volume, it presses against the chorion and eventually fuses with it. When fusion takes place the two membranes are called the **allantochorion** (See Figure 13-4). The allantochorionic membrane is the fetal contribution to the **placenta** and will provide the surface for attachments to the endometrium. Details about the anatomy and function of the placenta will be presented in Chapter 14.

> *In most species, the conceptus must provide a timely biochemical signal or the pregnancy will terminate.*

In order for the events of early embryogenesis to continue into an established pregnancy, luteolysis must be prevented. Progesterone must be maintained at sufficiently high levels so that embryogenesis and attachment of the developing conceptus to the endometrium can take place. The embryo enters the uterus between days 2 and 5 after ovulation (See Table 13-1 and Figure 13-3). The critical series of events by which the conceptus initially signals its presence to the dam and enables pregnancy to continue is referred to as **maternal recognition of pregnancy**. If an adequate signal is not delivered in a timely manner, the dam will experience luteolysis, progesterone concentrations will decline and pregnancy will be terminated. Recognition factors as they relate to the critical recognition period are presented in Table 13-2.

> *Maternal recognition of pregnancy must occur prior to luteolysis.*

13

Recall from Chapter 9 that the corpus luteum of ruminants produces oxytocin that stimulates endometrial cells to synthesize $PGF_{2\alpha}$. The production of $PGF_{2\alpha}$ is dependent upon a threshold number of oxytocin receptors that are synthesized by endometrial cells at a critical time during the estrous cycle. When these receptors are available in sufficient numbers, pulsatile secretion of $PGF_{2\alpha}$ occurs in response to luteal oxytocin secretion and luteolysis follows (See Figure 13-5). Clearly, this mechanism must be prevented if a successful pregnancy is to proceed.

Figure 13-5. IFN-τ From the Conceptus Prevents Luteolysis in the Cow and Ewe

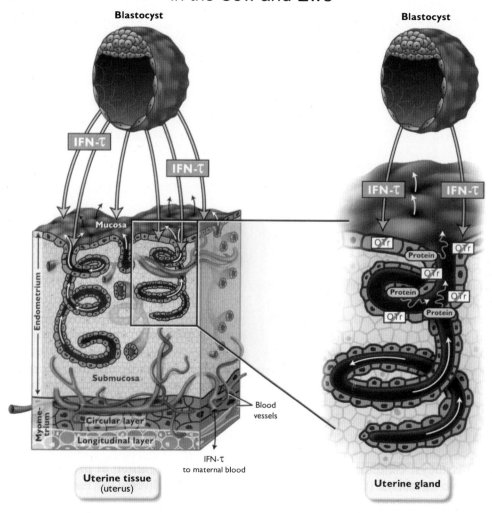

IFN-τ is secreted by the trophoblastic cells of the blastocyst (cow and ewe). IFN-τ acts on the endometrial cells of the uterus to inhibit the production of oxytocin receptors so that oxytocin cannot stimulate $PGF_{2\alpha}$ synthesis. In addition, IFN-τ causes secretion of proteins from the uterine glands. The arrows from the uterine glands indicate the movement of products that are secreted into the uterine lumen to nourish the conceptus. Finally, IFN-τ can leave the uterus via the uterine vein to affect the ovary and circulating immune cells.

13

> *In the ewe and cow, the blastocyst secretes materials that block the synthesis of uterine oxytocin receptors.*

In the ewe and the cow the free-floating blastocyst produces specific proteins that provide the signal for prevention of luteolysis. The specific proteins were once called **ovine trophoblastic protein 1** (oTP-1) and **bovine trophoblastic protein 1** (bTP-1). Both of these proteins belong to a class of materials known as **interferons**. Interferons are cytokines (immune cell hormones) secreted by many cell types, including leukocytes, fibroblasts, lymphocytes, and trophoblastic cells that are best known for their ability to inhibit virus replication. Because trophoblastic proteins (oTP-1 and bTP-1) constitute a separate class of interferons, they are now referred to as **ovine Interferon τ (oIFN-τ)** and **bovine Interferon τ (bIFN-τ)**. The use of the Greek letter τ designates the trophoblastic origin of these proteins.

A relatively small protein (18,000 to 20,000 daltons), oIFN-τ is produced by the trophoblastic cells of the blastocyst and is present in the uterus from about day 13 to 21 after ovulation. Secretion of progesterone by the corpus luteum is not enhanced by oIFN-τ and

Figure 13-6. Estradiol Reroutes PGF$_{2\alpha}$ to Prevent Luteolysis in the Sow

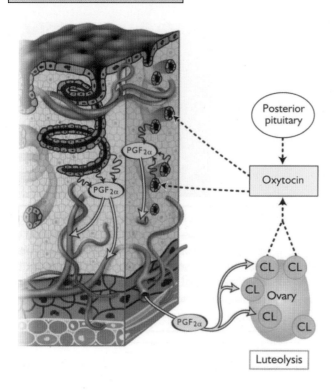

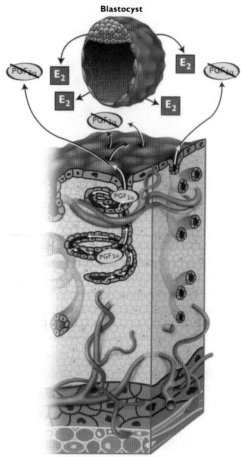

In the non-pregnant sow, oxytocin from the endometrium, posterior pituitary lobe and CL promotes PGF$_{2\alpha}$ synthesis by the uterine endometrium. PGF$_{2\alpha}$ diffuses by concentration gradient towards the endometrial capillaries where it drains into the uterine vein, is transported to the ovary and causes luteolysis.

In the pregnant sow, the blastocyst produces estradiol that causes the PGF$_{2\alpha}$ to be rerouted into the uterine lumen, where it is destroyed, thus preventing luteolysis. Like the cycling cow, oxytocin is also produced by the CL and posterior pituitary lobe in the pregnant sow.

13

therefore it is not luteotrophic. Instead, oIFN-τ binds to the endometrium and inhibits oxytocin receptor synthesis by endometrial cells. Figure 13-5 summarizes the proposed effect of oIFN-τ and bIFN-τ on endometrial production of oxytocin receptors. In addition to blocking oxytocin receptor synthesis, IFN-τ also binds to the apical portion (See Figure 13-5) of the uterine glands and promotes protein synthesis believed to be critical to preimplantation embryonic survival.

Ongoing research suggests that IFN-τ stimulates circulating immune cells of the dam to produce a family of proteins involved in immune response to invading viral pathogens. The presence of these blood proteins at days 17-20 after insemination indicates that

a conceptus is present in the uterus. Females that do not show elevated levels of these blood proteins at days 17-20 would not be pregnant. Therefore, the absence of IFN-τ induced blood proteins has potential for identifying non-pregnant cows. Identification of non-pregnant cows at days 17-20 would allow earlier re-insemination of open cows to achieve a pregnancy sooner than possible using other currently available diagnostic tests. It should be emphasized that identification of IFN-τ induced blood proteins is not a pregnancy test. An early pregnancy test (day 17-20) would be of little value because a significant proportion (20-40%) of day 17 embryos would fail to survive until term.

Figure 13-7. Transuterine Migration of the Equine Conceptus

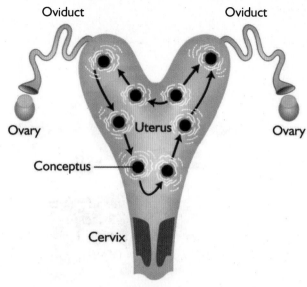

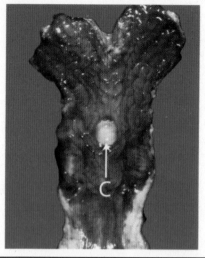

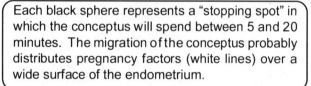

Each black sphere represents a "stopping spot" in which the conceptus will spend between 5 and 20 minutes. The migration of the conceptus probably distributes pregnancy factors (white lines) over a wide surface of the endometrium.

This uterus is from a mare at day 14 of pregnancy. The uterus has been incised on the dorsal surface to expose the spherical conceptus (C). This specimen shows the conceptus and uterus on the last day (day 14) of the uterine migration phenomenon. (Photograph courtesy of Dr. O.J. Ginther, *Reproductive Biology of the Mare*)

In the sow, estradiol reroutes PGF₂α secreted by the endometrium.

In the sow, two major differences exist in maternal recognition of pregnancy, compared to the ewe and cow. First, the conceptus of the pig produces estradiol that serves as the signal for maternal recognition of pregnancy. Second, $PGF_{2\alpha}$ is produced in significant quantities, but is rerouted into the uterine lumen. The conceptus begins to secrete estradiol between days 11 and 12 after ovulation. The production of estrogen does not inhibit the production of $PGF_{2\alpha}$, but causes the $PGF_{2\alpha}$ to be secreted in a different direction than in the cycling sow. The direction of secretion is away from the submucosal capillaries and toward the uterine lumen. Luminal $PGF_{2\alpha}$ has little access to the circulation and thus cannot cause luteolysis. The precise mechanism whereby the rerouting of $PGF_{2\alpha}$ occurs is not completely understood. However, it is believed that estrogen causes increased receptor production for prolactin in the endometrium. Prolactin changes the ionic flux for calcium. This is thought to promote the

13

Table 13-2. Pregnancy recognition factors, critical days of pregnancy recognition and time of conceptus attachment in mammals

Species	Pregnancy Recognition Factors	Critical Period for Recognition (days after ovulation)	Time of Attachment (days after ovulation)
Bitch	none needed	—	—
Cow	bIFN-τ (bTP-1)	15-16	18-22
Ewe	oIFN-τ (oTP-1)	13-14	15-18
Mare	3 Proteins/Estrogens = ?	12-14	36-38
Queen	none needed	—	—
Sow	Estradiol (E_2)	11-12	14-18
Woman	hCG	7-12	9-12

Figure 13-8. Maternal Recognition Must Occur Prior to Luteolysis

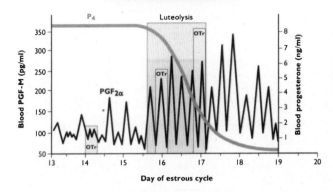

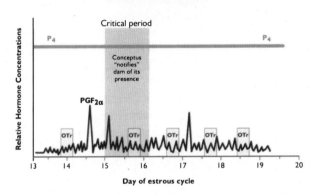

Comparison between the endocrine condition of the female (timing shown here is for the cow) with no conceptus present and with conceptus present. Notice that in the pregnant animal (conceptus present), episodes of PGF$_{2\alpha}$ that cause luteolysis do not occur. These are blocked because endometrial oxytocin receptor synthesis is blocked. This is called maternal recognition. Maternal recognition must occur prior to the onset of luteolysis if the pregnancy is to be maintained.

exocrine secretion of PGF$_{2\alpha}$ (into the uterine lumen) rather than an **endocrine** secretion (into the uterine vasculature). Porcine conceptuses produce interferons, but these materials do not affect corpora lutea longevity or function. Production of E$_2$ by the porcine conceptus not only serves as the maternal signal to prevent luteolysis, but also probably serves to stimulate contractions of the myometrium to distribute conceptuses with the proper spacing along the uterine horn.

Another important feature of maternal recognition of pregnancy in the sow is that there must be at least two conceptuses present in each uterine horn for pregnancy to be maintained. If conceptuses are not present in one uterine horn, PGF$_{2\alpha}$ will be secreted in an endocrine fashion, luteolysis will occur and the pregnancy will be terminated. Figure 13-6 summarizes the proposed mechanism for maternal recognition of pregnancy in the sow.

> *The equine conceptus must make extensive contact with the endometrial surface to initiate and complete maternal recognition of pregnancy.*

In the mare, the presence of the conceptus prevents luteolysis. Also, in the presence of the conceptus, endometrial production of PGF$_{2\alpha}$ is significantly reduced. A unique feature of maternal recognition of pregnancy in the mare is that the conceptus is translocated over the endometrial surface by uterine contractions. The conceptus is moved from one uterine horn to the other. This movement must occur between 12 and 14 times per day during days 12, 13 and 14 of pregnancy in order to inhibit PGF$_{2\alpha}$ (See Figure 13-7). The intrauterine movement of the equine conceptus appears necessary because the conceptus does not elongate as in other species. Therefore, there is less contact between the conceptus and the endometrial surface. In other words, the movement of the conceptus is probably necessary to distribute pregnancy recognition factors to the endometrial cells.

Like the other species, the conceptus of the horse produces proteins that apparently have some effect on the recognition of pregnancy (See Table 13-2). However, the specific roles are yet unknown.

> *In the woman, maternal recognition of pregnancy is provided by a hormone called human chorionic gonadotropin (hCG).*

At about the time of implantation (day 7-9 after ovulation) the human conceptus begins to secrete a hormone called human chorionic gonadotropin (hCG). This is an LH-like hormone that acts on the corpus luteum to inhibit intraovarian luteolysis (See Chapter 9). The precise mechanism whereby hCG blocks luteolysis is not known. Regardless, the luteotrophic effect of hCG is sufficient to allow for implantation and maintenance of pregnancy.

> *Maternal recognition of pregnancy in the dog and the cat probably does not require a signal from the conceptus.*

13

In the bitch, the CL of pregnancy and the CL of the cycle have similar lifespans. Therefore, under normal cyclic conditions, the CL is long-lived. When luteolysis does occur it is near the end of the normal gestation period. In other words, the period of diestrus is quite similar to the gestation period and thus, the corpus luteum is not lysed under normal conditions until the gestation period is complete.

As you recall, the queen is an induced ovulator. If mating does not occur, corpora lutea are not formed and a "post estrous" period of several days (8-10) exists before another estrus. In the queen that has been bred, a CL forms and the duration is the same as gestation (about 60 days). Like the bitch, a signal from the conceptus is not needed because corpora lutea are not lysed before a pregnancy is established. Please see Chapter 7 for graphic illustrations of this concept.

> *A successful pregnancy requires maintenance of high blood progesterone concentrations.*

Regardless of whether or not specific pregnancy recognition signals are provided, progesterone concentrations in the blood of the dam must be maintained at sufficiently high concentrations so that the conceptus will grow and develop. The extraembryonic membranes will form an attachment with the endometrium to provide a semipermanent link between the dam and the fetus. This semipermanent link is known as the **placenta** and will be discussed in the next chapter.

Embryo Transfer Technology Provides Avenues for Reproductive and Genetic Enhancement

Embryo transfer requires a set of procedures that allows removal of pre-attachment embryos from the reproductive tract of a **donor female** and transfers them into the reproductive tract of a **recipient female**. Embryo transfer is a valuable production and research technique. It is commercially available in some species to increase the productivity of females with desired traits. The first successful embryo transfer procedure was performed in a rabbit in 1890. Since that time embryo transfer techniques have been used in many species and countless offspring have been produced using this technique. In principle, embryo transfer can be performed in any mammalian species. However, its widest application is in cattle and more embryos are transferred in this species per year than in all other species combined. The main advantage of embryo transfer in cattle is to amplify the number of offspring that donor females with desired genetic traits can pro-

duce. With embryo transfer, a single donor cow is capable of producing 10 to 20 offspring annually. Embryo transfer has been a contributor to assisted reproductive technology in humans. Human embryos derived from *in vitro* fertilization currently exceed 100,000 on a worldwide basis. Futhermore, embryo transfer is an important technique used to enhance reproduction in endangered species.

> *The advantages of embryo transfer are:*
> - *circumvention of seasonal reproduction*
> - *enhanced generation of offspring in monotocous species*
> - *assisted reproduction for infertility in humans*
> - *enhanced reproductive potential of endangered species*
> - *enhanced genetic diversity across a wide geographical region (ship embryos rather than animals)*

A major advantage of embryo transfer is the ability to transport germ plasm from one geographical area to another. For example, embryos collected in North America can be shipped to any country in the world. This is particularly important in large animals (cows, horses, exotic species) because transportation of the animal over long distances is inefficient, expensive and can transmit diseases. Embryo transfer offers significant biosecurity advantages over animal transport. In addition to the above contributions, embryo transfer is an essential step in many experimental techniques in the production of clones and transgenic animals.

> *Successful embryo transfer involves:*
> - *synchronizing the cycles of donors and recipients*
> - *superovulation (hyperstimulation of the ovaries) of the donor*
> - *artificial insemination of the donor female*
> - *recovery of embryos from the donor*
> - *maintenance of viable embryos in vitro*
> - *transfer of embryos to recipient females*

13

Synchronization of Donor and Recipient Cycles is Obligatory for Successful Embryo Transfer

In order for embryos from the donor to develop within the recipient, the stage of the donor's cycle must be coincident with that of the recipient (See Figure 13-9). For example, if a 7-day embryo is to be transferred into a recipient, she must be in the seventh day of her estrous cycle. This allows for the appropriate uterine environment, maternal recognition of pregnancy and establishment of appropriate embryonic development and attachment to the uterus. Methods for synchronization of estrous are presented in Chapter 9.

Superovulation Results from Hyperstimulation of the Ovaries with Gonadotropins

Superovulation is the treatment of a female with gonadotropins (typically FSH) to increase the number of oocytes that are selected to become dominant follicles and to ovulate (See Figure 13-9). Among monotocous animals, superovulation is used to increase the number of potential offspring from donor females possessing traits of high economic value. Superovulation is also used in humans (even though only one offspring is usually desired) to compensate for low success rates with a single embryo transfer.

In monotocous species, ovulation rates of 5-10 times normal occur. In polytocous species, ovulation rates of only 2-3 times normal are achieved. There is a wide variation in the individual's response to gonadotropin stimulation. Because a commercial embryo transfer industry exists in cattle, there are significant data available describing this variation. For example, a typical response in cattle would be 8 to 10 ovulations, producing 5 to 7 viable embryos. But, about 30% of the cows respond by producing one or fewer viable embryos. About 2% of the cows may produce as many as 30 embryos or more. The physiologic reasons for this wide variation in ovarian response to hyperstimulation are not known.

> *Recovery of oocytes from ovaries can be accomplished by:*
>
> - *surgically exposing the ovary and aspirating follicles*
>
> - *non-surgically aspirating follicles utilizing ultrasonography*
>
> - *aspirating follicles postmortem in an abattoir*

Recovery of Embryos from the Donor Females may be Accomplished in Several Ways

Most frequently, donor females are bred utilizing artificial insemination with semen from a male possessing highly desired traits. After insemination, embryos can be recovered by a variety of methods.

Recovery of embryos from the oviduct requires surgery in all species. Recovery of embryos from the uterus is accomplished surgically in small species and non-surgically in large species. In cows and mares transrectal palpation and introduction of catheters for removal of embryos by flushing with various culture media is a routine procedure (See Figure 13-9).

Oocytes can be recovered directly from the ovary using aspiration with a hypodermic needle. In horses and cattle, a common technique for recovery of oocytes by aspiration involves inserting a needle through the wall of the vagina and with the use of ultrasonography, identifying dominant follicles and aspirating the oocytes into a special apparatus (See Figure 13-10). The purpose of follicular aspiration is to recover oocytes from dominant follicles and perform *in vitro* fertilization (See Figure 13-10). In the case of the postmortem recovery, large numbers of ovaries are available from cattle immediately after exsanguination from slaughter facilities. Oocytes remain viable for relatively long periods after exsanguination, typically 9-12 hours in most species. Therefore these serve as valuable sources of oocytes for experimental purposes. Even though cows have not received ovarian stimulation by gonadotropins numerous antral follicles are normally present on ovaries and provide a ready source of viable oocytes for *in vitro* fertilization procedures.

Embryo Viability Must be Maintained *In Vitro*

In order for embryos to be transferred successfully into recipient females they must be stored in an environment that maintains viability. The conditions for maintenance of viable embryos include: maintenance of appropriate temperature (near or at body temperature), exposure to the appropriate atmospheric environment (5% CO_2 and 5-8% O_2), pH slightly above neutral and the absence of microorganisms. A culture medium should also contain the appropriate ionic configuration and the appropriate energy sources for metabolism and growth by the young embryo. Embryos can be frozen successfully for long term storage.

13

Figure 13-9. Major Steps of Embryo Transfer in Mammals-Cow Model

STEP 1

Sychronization of recipients with donor

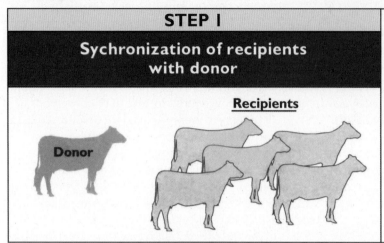

Goal: To synchronize the donor and recipient to be in the same stage of the estrous cycle.

Reason: To prepare the uterus of the recipient to support preattachment embryogenesis.

How: Treat recipient with hormonal regime that induces estrus to occur at the same time as the donor.

STEP 2

Superovulation of donor

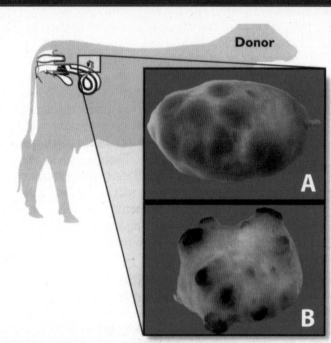

Goal: To hyperstimulate ovaries with gonadotropins.

Reason: To provide higher than normal numbers of follicles that reach dominance and ovulate.

How: Inject donor with gonadotropins to hyperstimulate follicular development. Generally, FSH (or one of its analogs) is used.

Ovary A- Hyperstimulated ovary. There are 9 follicles visible in this ovary. The donor is in estrus.

Ovary B- 1 day after estrus. There are 9 corpora hemorrhagica visible on this specimen.

STEP 3

Inseminate donor with semen from genetically superior bull

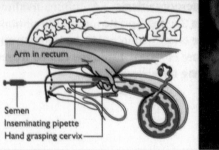 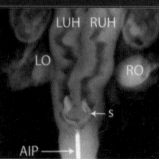

Goal: To generate the best fertilization rates and genetic combinations possible.

Reason: Enhance rate of genetic progress.

How: Utilize highly fertile semen and well-trained, experienced inseminators.

AIP = AI Pipette, S = Semen, RO = Right Ovary, LO = Left Ovary, RUH = Right Uterine Horn, LUH = Left Uterine Horn

(Ovarian specimens courtesy of Dr. B.R. Lindsey)

13

STEP 4

Recovery and indentification of viable embryos

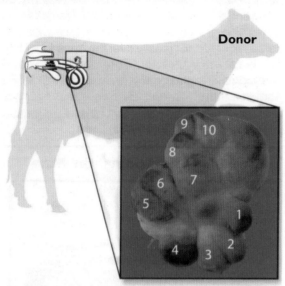

Donor

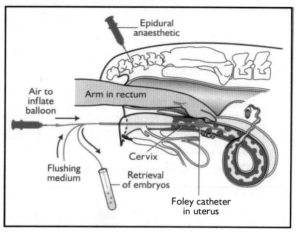

Epidural anaesthetic

Air to inflate balloon

Arm in rectum

Cervix

Flushing medium

Retrieval of embryos

Foley catheter in uterus

Goal: To nonsurgically collect (flush) embryos from the donor for transfer.

Reason: To recover viable embryos.

How: Before the procedure is started a local anesthetic is injected to cause relaxation of the rectum. At day 6-8 a specialized catheter is inserted into the uterus. The catheter has a small balloon that can be inflated to prevent retrograde flow of the flushing medium. A flushing medium is then introduced into the uterus, lavaged and then returned through the catheter to a collection vessel. The ovary in the photo has ten-7 day CL.

(Ovarian specimens courtesy of Dr. B.R. Lindsey)

STEP 5

Transfer of viable embryos into synchronized recipients

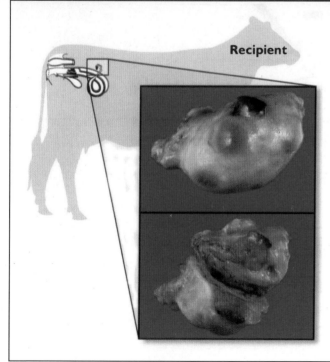

Recipient

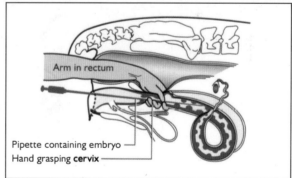

Arm in rectum

Pipette containing embryo

Hand grasping **cervix**

Goal: To deposit a potentially viable embryo into the uterine horn of each recipient.

Reason: To achieve pregnancy in each recipient.

How: A single embryo is placed into the uterine horn using a transfer pipette. Note that both the donor (step 4) and recipient here have CL at similar stages of leutinization. Thus, the uterine environment in the donor and recipient are quite similar.

13

Figure 13-10. Oocyte Collection from Ovarian Follicles for *In Vitro* Fertilization

A hypodermic needle is inserted into the follicle and the follicular fluid is aspirated and then forcefully returned to the follicle. This is repeated 2-3 times to dislodge the oocytes.

Prior to performing the procedure, mares are injected with propantheline bromide (a sedative) to relax the rectum. The lubricated ultrasound transducer is inserted into the vagina and held in the fornix vagina. The ovary is transrectally positioned against the dorsal vaginal wall directly over the transducer head so that the follicle can be visualized. The hypodermic needle is advanced through the vaginal wall into the antral follicle. Follicular fluid containing the oocyte is aspirated under constant vacuum (Graphic modified with permission from *Ultrasonic Imaging and Animal Reproduction: Horses Book 2*. 1995 by O.J. Ginther).

Direct Follicle Aspiration

Transvaginal Aspiration in the Mare

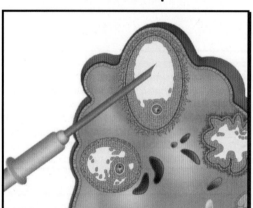
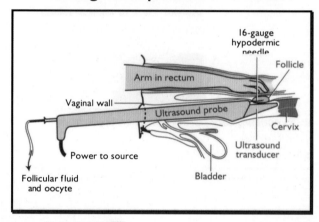

Aspirated oocytes

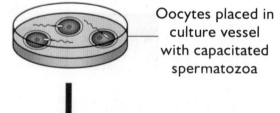

Oocytes placed in culture vessel with capacitated spermatozoa

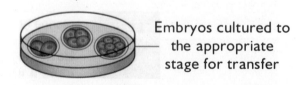

Embryos cultured to the appropriate stage for transfer

Embryos transferred to recipient female
(*See Figure 13-9*)

13

Transfer of Embryos can be Accomplished Surgically or Non-Surgically

In general, embryos can be transferred non-surgically into the recipients in almost any species. This is because the embryos can be recovered from the donor at a stage that allows them to be transferred directly into the uterus of the synchronized recipient. Transferring the embryos into the uterus involves passing a pipette through the vagina and cervix and depositing the embryos into the appropriate uterine horn (ipsilateral to the CL).

The zona pellucida is an important component of the early embryo. First, it houses the blastomeres so that they do not separate and can develop together to form an embryo. Equally important is the fact that the zona pellucida is impermeable to most viruses. This not only protects the embryo from viral infection under natural conditions but prevents disease transmission via the embryo after transfer.

Embryo transfer procedures have become very successful. In commercial embryo transfer programs with cattle, pregnancy rates of 70% with unfrozen embryos and 65% with frozen embryos have been accomplished routinely. In humans, 30% pregnancy rates are accomplished. It should be emphasized that in young human couples having regular copulatory patterns, the pregnancy rates per reproductive cycle are only about 35%. What this means is, it takes an average of 3.3 cycles for healthy, fertile couples to achieve a pregnancy.

Further PHENOMENA for Fertility

Some species have delayed implantation (attachment to the uterus) in which a viable embryo floats within the uterus for a sustained period of time. Martens (a mink-like animal) copulate in July or August and the embryo develops to the blastocyst stage, but attachment does not occur until February. The young are born about 26-30 days after attachment.

The presence of the marsupial embryo within the uterus does not interrupt the estrous cycle. Therefore, pregnancy recognition in this species is apparently not caused by a substance(s) produced by the embryo. Instead, the semipermanent attachment of the prematurely born fetus to the teat provides a pregnancy recognition mechanism, because it arrests cyclicity.

The female nine-banded armadillo has several unique features. First, the female has a simplex uterus (like primates), in spite of being a primitive life form. She has no vagina, but retains a urogenital sinus. She spontaneously ovulates a single oocyte and mates in the summer. The embryo enters embryonic diapause (delayed attachment) for about 3 to 4 months. Soon after implantation, cells of the inner cell mass give rise to four separate identical embryos. Thus, the female armadillo gives birth to identical quadruplets. The genetic implications of identical offspring in this species are not known.

The human blastocyst (along with guinea pigs, hedgehogs and chimpanzees) first attaches to the endometrial epithelium, passes through and becomes completely imbedded. Thus, the embryo is isolated from the uterine lumen. Knowledge of this phenomenon led to the term "implantation". True implantation does not occur in domestic animals.

13

13

In rodents, a successful pregnancy can be terminated if an alien male (one that did not cause the pregnancy) shows up and hangs-out with the pregnant female. This is known as the "Bruce Effect".

The Apostlebird of Eastern Australia derived its name from the fact that it does everything in groups of twelve. During the mating season, nests are built on horizontal branches of trees. The females lay eggs in each other's nests. All members share the task of incubating the eggs and rearing the young.

A pair of Indian Pythons have been observed copulating for 180 days.

After copulation, the male garter snake plugs the female's cloaca with a material made from renal secretions. This natural chastity belt prevents any further sexual activity, insuring that the offspring are sired by the first male to breed her.

Cantharidin is derived from beetles known as "blister beetles". The material has been erroneously nicknamed "Spanish Fly". This material developed a reputation as being a "medical wonder" including being a powerful sexual stimulant. Cantharidin irritates the urogenital tract, causing a tingling and burning sensation that is felt in both the male genitalia and female genitalia because of vasodilation. This vasodilation of the labia made women more aware of their genitals and it was thought to build erotic passion and cause sexual excitement. Occasionally, cantharidin caused persistent erections (priapism) in males. Priapism was generally not associated with sexual pleasure and could cause vascular damage to the penis. Cantharidin has been illegal since the 1800's and is currently not for sale over-the-counter. In significant doses, cantharidin can cause health problems. It has been reported in the French literature that "Spanish Fly" had been incorporated into a plate of pears that was consumed by the groom on his wedding night. "When the night came, the husband embraced his wife so much that she began to suffer ex-

haustion." These delights quickly changed to misfortune because "the man began to experience the effects of cantharidin inflammation by midnight. He had difficulty urinating, saw a discharge from his penis, became frightened and fainted more than once. Considerable effort was made to restore his health."

The Chinese apparently have been searching throughout the course of history for a Viagra-like compound. For example, ashes from hornets or wasps' nests were mixed with water and wine and ingested. This mixture was also applied to the penis for sexual stimulation to cure erectile dysfunction and to increase daily sperm output.

Dragonflies and silkworms were believed to increase penile turgidity and prevent ejaculation. The latter effect was believed to lengthen the duration of copulation.

Scale insects and stinkbugs were considered by the Chinese as aphrodisiacs. Consumption of scale insects was also believed to be a cure for amenorrhea.

The Chinese believed egg cases from the praying mantis had several beneficial effects such as prevention of nocturnal emissions, premature ejaculation, male weakness and impotence.

The word "aphrodisiac" is derived from the name of the Greek goddess of love, Aphrodite.

In 1848, a physician named Frederick Hollick published a book entitled, <u>The Male Generative Organs-Health and Disease from Infancy to Old Age that</u> undoubtedly received more attention than the reproductive physiology books of the day. It was marketed "For Every Man's Private Use". Not only did this book deal with the anatomy and physiology of the male genitalia, it dealt extensively with recipes and concoctions that would facilitate male genital function.

Based on clay tablets dated 12th Century B.C., it was found that castration was the punishment for several male sex offenders. Hence, they apparently knew that the testes were the source of mating behavior in human males. Castration (performed without anesthesia) was likely the first survivable surgery in humans.

Aristotle drew an analogy between the epididymis/ductus deferens, testis and a weaver's string being held tight by an attached rock. Aristotle thought that the function of the testis was only as a weight (like a rock attached to a string) to keep the "kinks" out of the ductus deferens.

Peppermint shrimp begin their life as males, but most change into a female-with a slight twist. The "female" shrimp maintain their male ducts, produce sperm and fertilize other female-phase shrimp even when incubating their own embryos. They can do it all.

On average, the bilaterally castrated man lives 12 years longer than intact men. The possible reason? There is no energy spent trying to copulate. The energy spent copulating is minuscule compared to the energy expended trying to convince the female partner to copulate. If no testes are available, there is no energy expenditure.

In Cephalopods (squids, cuttlefishes and octopi) the male deposits a special sperm package called a spermatophore in the female body cavity by way of an artificial penis. This artificial penis is known as a hectocotylus and it is a specially modified tentacle. Some species have developed a detachable penis that they can leave behind in the female's body.

Spiders (arachnids) also have an artificial penis. In their case it is a leg that doubles as a penis and is known scientifically as a maxillary palp. It is not known whether the detachable penis has the ability to grow back.

Key References

Bazer, F.W., T.L. Ott and T.E. Spencer. 1994. "Pregnancy recognition in ruminants, pigs and horses: signals from the trophoblast." *Theriogenology*. 41:79.

Flint, A.P.F. 1995. "Interferon, the oxytocin receptor and the maternal recognition of pregnancy in ruminants and non-ruminants: A comparative approach." *Reprod. Fertil. Dev*. 7:313.

Ginther, O.J. 1992. *Reproductive Biology of the Mare*. 2nd Edition. Equiservices, Cross Plains, WI. Library of Congress Catalog No. 91-075595.

Larsen, W.J. 1993. *Human Embryology*. Churchill Livingstone, New York. ISBN 0-443-08724-5.

Mirando, M.A., M.U. Zumcu, K.G. Carnahan and T.E. Ludwig. 1996. "A role for oxytocin during luteolysis and early pregnancy in swine." *Reprod. Dom. Anim*. 31:455.

Ott, T.L. and C.A. Gifford. 2010. "Effects of early conceptus signals on circulating immune cells: lessons from domestic ruminants." *Am J. Reprod. Immunol.1-9*.

Roberts, R.M., D.W. Leaman and J.C. Cross. 1992. "Role of interferons in maternal recognition of pregnancy" in *P.S.E.B.M.* 200:7.

Thatcher, W.W., C.R. Staples, G. Danet-Desnoyers, B. Oldick and E.P. Schmitt. 1994. "Embryo health and mortality in sheep and cattle." *J. Anim. Sci.*72 (suppl. 3):16.

Spencer, T.E. 1998. "Pregnancy, maternal recognition of" in *Encyclopedia of Reproduction*, Vol 3, p1006-1015. Knobil, E. and J.D. Neill, eds. Academic Press, San Diego. ISBN 0-12-227023-1.

Seidel, G.E. 1998. "Embryo transfer" in *Encyclopedia of Reproduction*, Vol 1, p1037-1042. Knobil, E. and J.D. Neill, eds. Academic Press, San Diego. ISBN 0-12-227021-5.

13

PLACENTATION GESTATION & PARTURITION

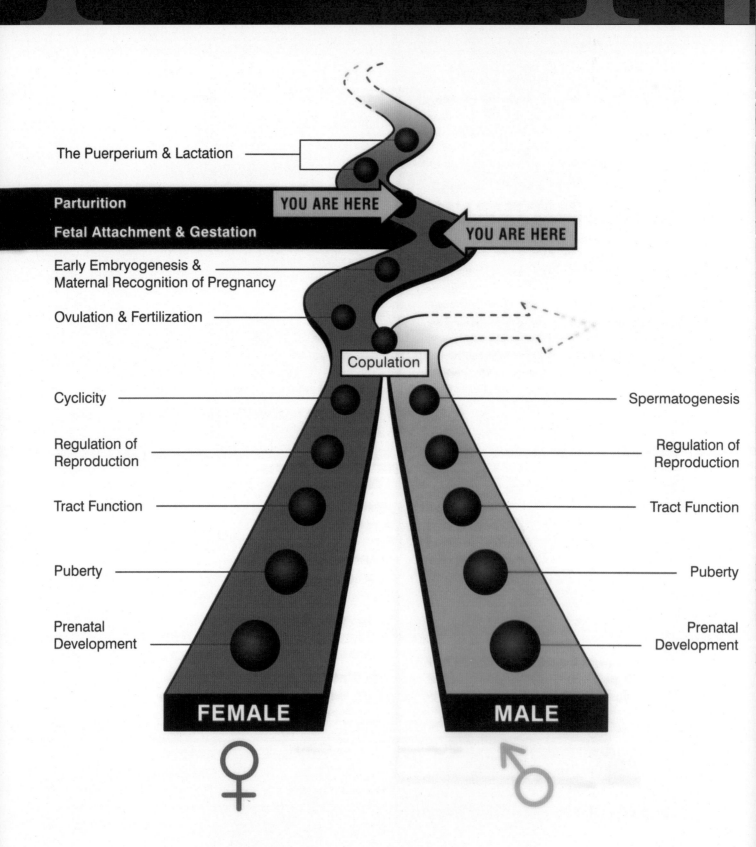

The Puerperium & Lactation

Parturition

YOU ARE HERE

Fetal Attachment & Gestation

YOU ARE HERE

Early Embryogenesis &
Maternal Recognition of Pregnancy

Ovulation & Fertilization

Copulation

Cyclicity

Spermatogenesis

Regulation of
Reproduction

Regulation of
Reproduction

Tract Function

Tract Function

Puberty

Puberty

Prenatal
Development

Prenatal
Development

FEMALE

MALE

Take Home Message

Gestation is the period of time that a female is pregnant. During gestation, the placenta forms a major organ of pregnancy that provides an interface for metabolic exchange between the dam and the fetus. Placentas are described morphologically according to the distribution of villi on the chorionic surface and the degree of separation between maternal and fetal blood. The placenta is also an endocrine organ that secretes hormones responsible for: 1) maintenance of pregnancy; 2) stimulation of the maternal mammary gland and 3) ensures fetal growth. Parturition is brought about by secretion of fetal corticoids and requires removal of the progesterone block. Parturition consists of three stages. They are: 1) initiation of myometrial contractions; 2) expulsion of the fetus and 3) expulsion of the fetal membranes.

The word gestation literally means "the act of carrying or being carried". Thus, gestation means the action or process of carrying or being carried in the uterus between conception and birth. Gestation and pregnancy are synonymous and thus, gestation length means the length of pregnancy. Attachment of the conceptus to form an intimate, but temporary, relationship with the uterus is an evolutionary step that provides significant advantage to the conceptus. The phenomenon of intrauterine development ensures that the developing conceptus will receive adequate nutrition and protection during its development. In contrast, lower forms of animals lay eggs (**oviparous**). The survival of potential offspring of oviparous animals is jeopardized because the female cannot completely protect the eggs from environmental and predatory danger. Thus, from an evolutionary perspective, **eutherian mammals** (mammals with a placenta), are "equipped" with an in-utero protection mechanism that is highly successful after the placenta is formed.

> *The final prepartum steps of reproduction are:*
> - *formation of a placenta*
> - *acquisition of endocrine function of the placenta*
> - *initiation of parturition*

The term **implantation** is often used to mean **attachment** of the placental membranes to the endometrium in most animals. Actually, true implantation is a phenomenon in humans in which the conceptus "buries" itself into the uterine endometrium. The conceptus temporarily disappears beneath the surface. In most other species, the conceptus does not truly implant, but rather attaches to the endometrial surface and never disappears from the luminal compartment.

The **placenta** is an organ of metabolic interchange between the conceptus and the dam. It is also an endocrine organ. The placenta is composed of a fetal component derived from the chorion and a maternal component derived from modifications of the uterine endometrium. The discrete regions of contact between the chorion and the endometrium form specific zones of metabolic exchange. The placenta also produces a variety of hormones. This endocrine function is important for the maintenance of pregnancy and the induction of parturition.

Parturition (giving birth to young) is the step in the reproductive process that immediately precedes lactation, uterine repair and return to cyclicity. It is initiated by the fetus and involves a complex cascade of endocrine events that promote myometrial contractions, dilation of the cervix, expulsion of the fetus and expulsion of the extraembryonic membranes.

Placentas Have Different Distributions of Chorionic Villi

As you have learned in the previous chapter, the conceptus consists of the embryo and the extraembryonic membranes (amnion, allantois and chorion). The chorion is the fetal contribution to the placenta. The functional unit of the fetal placenta is the **chorionic villus**. The chorionic villus is an "exchange apparatus" and provides increased surface area so that exchange is maximized. Chorionic villi are small, finger-like projections that are on the surface of the chorion. These tiny villi protrude away from the chorion toward the uterine endometrium. Placentas are classified according to the distribution of chorionic villi on their surfaces, giving each placental type a distinct anatomical appearance. Placentas may also be classified by number of tissue layers separating maternal and fetal blood.

> *Placentas are classified according to the distribution of chorionic villi. These classifications are:*
> - *diffuse*
> - *zonary*
> - *discoid*
> - *cotyledonary*

The diffuse placenta of the pig has a velvet-like surface with many closely spaced chorionic villi that are distributed over the entire surface of the chorion (See Figure 14-1). Initial attachment occurs around day 12 and is well established by day 18 to 20 after ovulation (See Chapter 13).

> *Diffuse placentas have uniform distribution of chorionic villi that cover the surface of the chorion.*
> *Example = pig*

The mare placenta is also classified as diffuse, however it is characterized by having many specialized "microzones" of chorionic villi known as **microcotyledons** (See Figure 14-1). These microcotyledons are microscopically discrete regions at the fetal-maternal interface. As in the pig, they are also distributed over the entire chorionic surface.

The mare placenta also contains unique transitory structures known as **endometrial cups**. These are discrete areas that range from a few millimeters to several centimeters in diameter. The endometrial cups are of both trophoblastic and endometrial origin. There are 5 to 10 endometrial cups distributed over the surface of the placenta (See Figure 14-6). Endometrial cups produce **equine chorionic gonadotropin (eCG)** and develop between days 35 and 60 of pregnancy. Following day 60, the endometrial cups are sloughed into the uterine lumen and are no longer functional. Attachment of the conceptus to the endometrium is initiated at about day 24 and becomes well established by 36 to 38 days (See Chapter 13).

> *Zonary placentas have a band-like zone of chorionic villi.*
> *Example = dogs and cats*

The **zonary placenta** (found in dogs and cats) includes a prominent region of exchange that forms a broad zone around the chorion near the middle of the conceptus (See Figure 14-2). A second region consists of a highly pigmented ring at either end of the central zone. This pigmented zone consists of small hematomas (blood clots). The pigmented zone is also referred to as the **paraplacenta** and is thought to be important in iron transport from the dam to the fetus. The function of this zone is not well understood. A third region is the transparent zone on the distal ends of the chorion that has poor vascularity. This zone may be involved in absorption of materials directly from the uterine lumen.

> *Discoid placentas form a regionalized disc.*
> *Example = rodents and primates*

The **discoid** placenta (See Figure 14-2) is found in rodents and primates. It is characterized by having one or two distinct adjacent discs. These discs contain chorionic villi that interface with the endometrium and provide the region for gas, nutrient and metabolic waste exchange.

> *Cotyledonary placentas have numerous, discrete button-like structures called cotyledons.*
> *Example = ruminants*

Ruminants have a **cotyledonary** placenta (See Figure 14-3). A cotyledon is defined as a placental unit of trophoblastic origin consisting of abundant blood vessels and connective tissue. In sheep, there are between 90 and 100 cotyledons distributed across the surface of the chorion and, in cattle, 70 to 120 cotyledons have been observed. The **placentome** (point of interface) in the cotyledonary placenta consists of a **fetal cotyledon** contributed by the chorion and a **maternal cotyledon**, originating from the **caruncular regions** of the uterus. At about day 16 in sheep and day 25 in cattle the chorion initiates attachment to the caruncles of the uterus. Prior to this time the placenta is essentially diffuse. During the formation of the placentomes, chorionic villi protrude into crypts in the caruncular tissue. This relationship is not implantation but an anatomically specialized form of attachment. Attachment is well established by day 30 in ewes and day 40 in cows (See Chapter 13).

In the cow, the placentomes form a convex structure, while in the ewe they are concave (See Figure 14-3). During gestation, the cotyledons will increase many-fold in diameter. In fact, cotyledons in the cow near the end of gestation may measure 5 to 6 centimeters in diameter. Such growth provides enormous surface area to support placental transfer of nutrients from the dam and metabolic wastes from the fetus.

Placental Classification by Microscopic Appearance is Based on the Number of Placental Layers that Separate the Fetal Blood from the Maternal Blood

The nomenclature for describing placental intimacy is derived by first describing the tissues of the maternal placenta in the prefix of the word. The tissues of the fetal placenta constitute the suffix. Exchange can occur through as many as six tissue layers and as few as three. The name of the prefix and suffix of each type of placenta changes depending on the number of tissue layers that exist.

> *__Prefix__ =maternal side __Suffix__ =fetal side*
> *"epithelio"   "chorial"*
> *epitheliochorial*

> *Epitheliochorial = 6 layers*

The **epitheliochorial** placenta (See Figure 14-5) is the least intimate among the placental types. In the epitheliochorial placenta, both the endometrial epithelium (maternal side) and epithelium of the chorionic villi are intact. In other words, there is a complete intact layer of epithelium in both the maternal and fetal components. The epitheliochorial placenta is found in the sow and the mare. Recall that the placentas of the sow and the mare are diffuse and villi occupy a large proportion of the surface area of the chorion.

Ruminants also have an epitheliochorial placenta. However, the endometrial epithelium transiently erodes and then regrows, causing intermittent exposure of the maternal capillaries to the chorionic epithelium. This type of placenta has been termed **syndesmochorial**.

In addition to the feature of partial erosion of the endometrial epithelium, a unique cell type is found in the ruminant placenta. These cells are called **binucleate giant cells**. As their name implies, they are characterized as being quite large and have two nuclei. Binucleate giant cells appear at about day 14 in the sheep and between days 18 and 20 in the cow. These

cells originate from trophoblast cells and are thought to be formed continuously throughout gestation. Binucleate giant cells constitute around 20% of the fetal placenta. During development, the binucleate giant cells migrate from the chorionic epithelium and invade the endometrial epithelium (See Figure 14-4). The binucleate giant cells are believed to transfer complex molecules from the fetal to the maternal placenta. There is evidence that they secrete **placental lactogen**. Also, these cells secrete **pregnancy specific protein B (PSPB)** that are also called pregnancy associated glycoproteins (PAG). These proteins are unique to pregnancy in ruminants. The binucleate giant cells are also important sites of steroidogenesis, secreting progesterone and estradiol. These cells will no doubt emerge as increasingly important "players" in the function of the ruminant placenta with further research.

> *Endotheliochorial = 5 layers*

The **endotheliochorial placenta** is characterized as having complete erosion of the endometrial epithelium and underlying interstitium. Thus, maternal capillaries are directly exposed to epithelial cells of the chorion (See Figure 14-5). The chorionic epithelium packs around the vessels on the maternal side. Note in Figure 14-5 that this type of placenta is more intimate than the epitheliochorial placenta because the endometrial epithelium no longer exists. Dogs and cats possess endotheliochorial placentation.

> *Hemochorial = 3 layers*

The **hemochorial placenta** (See Figure 14-5) is characterized as having the chorionic epithelium in direct apposition to maternal pools of blood. Thus, nutrients and gases are exchanged directly from maternal blood and must move through only three tissue layers. This highly intimate relationship is found in primates and rodents (See Figure 14-5).

The Placenta Regulates the Exchange Between the Fetus and Dam

Placental exchange involves a number of mechanisms found in other tissues. These are **simple diffusion, facilitated diffusion** and **active transport**. Gases and water pass from high to low concentrations by simple diffusion. The placenta contains active transport pumps for sodium and potassium, as well as calcium. Glucose and other metabolically important materials such as amino acids are transported by facilitated diffusion utilizing specific carrier molecules.

14

Figure 14-1. The Diffuse Placenta

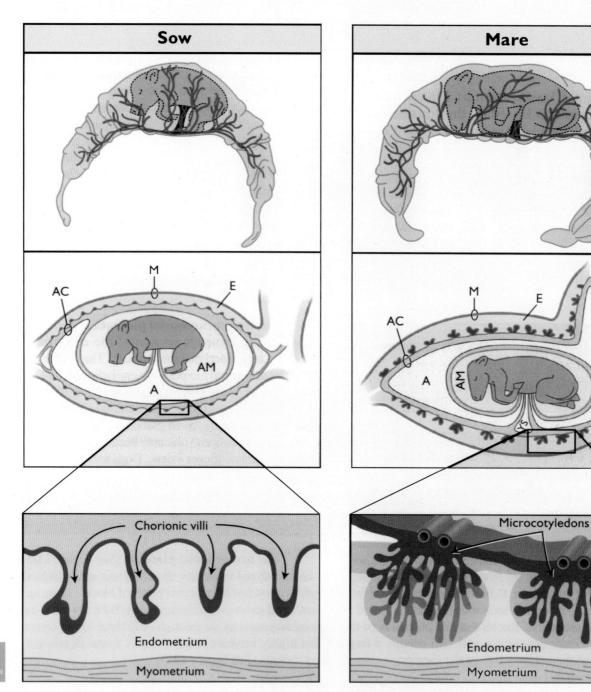

Sow

Mare

The diffuse placenta of the sow consists of many chorionic villi distributed over the entire surface of the chorion. They penetrate into the endometrium forming the fetal-maternal interface. Vessels from each chorionic villus merge and eventually form large vessels that enter the umbilical cord. A= Allantois, AC= Allantochorion, AM= Amnionic Cavity, E= Endometrium, M= Myometrium

The diffuse placenta of the mare consists of many microcotyledons distributed over the entire surface of the chorion. These microcotyledons are the site of fetal-maternal exchange. A= Allantois, AC= Allantochorion, AM= Amnionic Cavity, E= Endometrium, M= Myometrium, YS= Yolk Sac

Figure 14-2. The Zonary and Discoid Placentas

Bitch

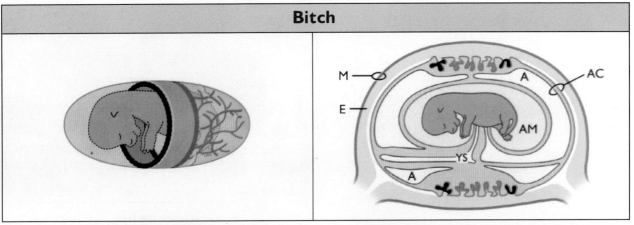

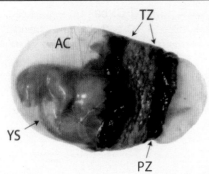

The zonary placenta consists of three distinct zones; a transfer zone (TZ), a pigmented zone (PZ) and a relatively nonvascular zone, the allantochorion (AC). In the zonary placenta, a band of tissue forms around the conceptus where nutrient transfer occurs. The pigmented zone (PZ) or paraplacenta represents local regions of maternal hemorrhage and necrosis.
A= Allantois, AC= Allantochorion, AM= Amnionic Cavity, E= Endometrium, M= Myometrium, YS= Yolk Sac

Primates

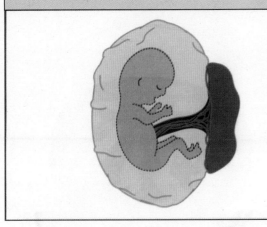

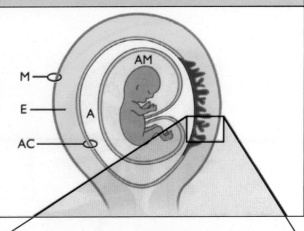

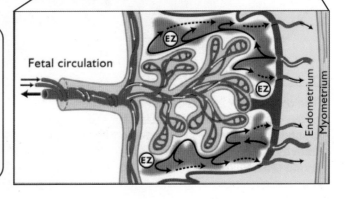

The discoid placenta consists of a round patch of chorionic tissue that forms the fetal-maternal interface. Vessels from the exchange zone merge to form the umbilical vessels that supply the fetus with blood. The vasculature of the chorion (within the disc) is immersed in pools of blood where metabolic exchange takes place.
A = Allantois, AC = Allantochorion,
AM = Amnionic Cavity, E = Endometrium,
EZ = Exchange Zone, M = Myometrium

14

Figure 14-3. The Cotyledonary Placenta

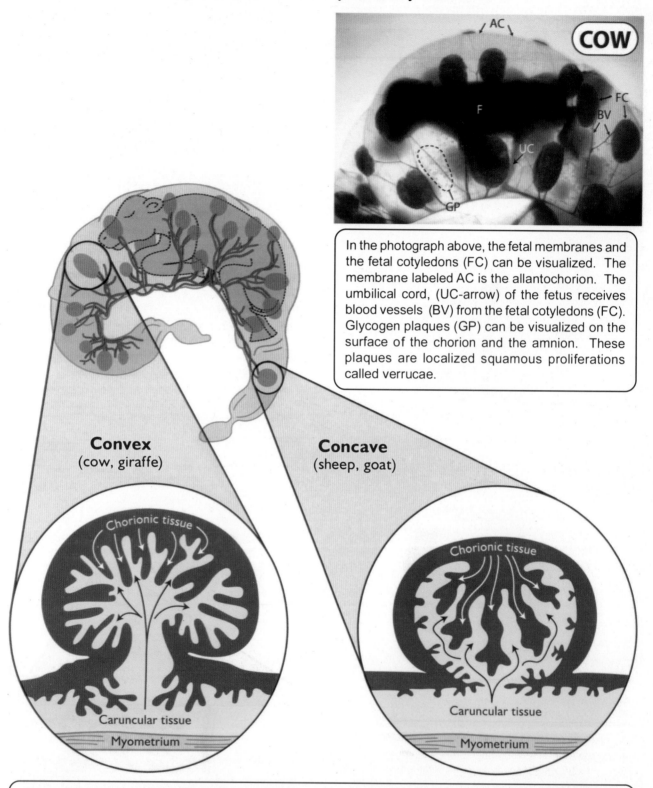

In the photograph above, the fetal membranes and the fetal cotyledons (FC) can be visualized. The membrane labeled AC is the allantochorion. The umbilical cord, (UC-arrow) of the fetus receives blood vessels (BV) from the fetal cotyledons (FC). Glycogen plaques (GP) can be visualized on the surface of the chorion and the amnion. These plaques are localized squamous proliferations called verrucae.

Convex
(cow, giraffe)

Concave
(sheep, goat)

The cotyledonary placenta is characterized by numerous "button-like" structures distributed across the surface of the chorion. These are called fetal cotyledons. When they join with the maternal caruncle they form a placentome. A convex cotyledon becomes covered with the chorion. Many finger-like villi (red) originating from the chorionic tissue protrude toward the lumen of the uterus. In the concave cotyledon, the chorionic tissue pushes inward, forming a concave interface between the chorion and the maternal caruncle.

Figure 14-3. The Cotyledonary Placenta

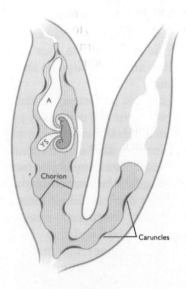

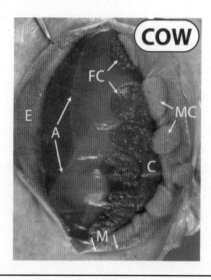

The diagram in the upper left illustrates the distribution of the extraembryonic membranes prior to complete attachment. The extraembryonic membranes consist of the amnion (blue sac), yolk sac (YS) and the allantois (A). Even though the fetus is located in one uterine horn, the chorion invades the contralateral uterine horn and forms placentomes.

Cow

Some fetal cotyledons (FC) have been partially separated from maternal cotyledons (MC). The chorion (C) is the outer fetal membrane. Arrows indicate the border of the amnion (A). The myometrium (M) is indicated by the arrows. Notice that the fetal cotyledon (FC) is attached to the surface of the caruncle creating a convex cotyledon. E= Endometrium

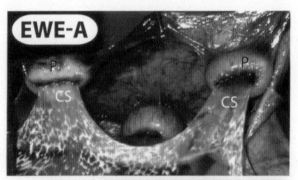

Ewe-A

The chorion can be seen entering the placentome (P). The chorionic stalk (CS) contains the fetal vasculature.

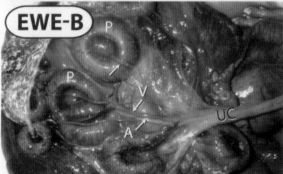

Ewe-B

A portion of the chorion has been incised so that the fetal vasculature can be visualized clearly. The fetal vessels (arrow) and chorionic tissue "push" into the caruncular tissue forming a concave cotyledon. A set of arteries (A) and veins (V) emerge from each cotyledon and eventually merge in the umbilical cord (UC). P= Placentome

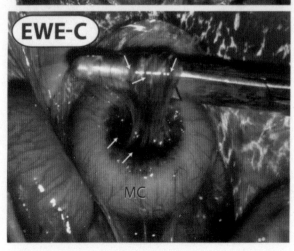

Ewe-C

A concave placentome is clearly visible. The chorionic stalk is draped over the needle holder. Notice the vessels (arrows) within the chorionic tissue. The reddish-beige tissue is the maternal cotyledon (MC) that is covered by the allantochorion. The dark tissue in the center (arrows) is the fetal component of the placentome.

14

Glucose is the major source of energy for the fetus. The majority of glucose is derived from the maternal circulation. Near the end of gestation, glucose consumption by the fetus is exceptionally high and can lead to a metabolic drain of glucose away from the dam. Such a glucose drain favors the development of ketosis in the dam. Ketosis results from the metabolism of body fat that generate ketones for energy when glucose is limited. Periparturient ketosis is common in dairy cows where postpartum metabolic demands are exceptionally high because of high milk production. Some materials cannot be transported across the placenta. With the exception of some immunoglobulins, maternal proteins do not cross the placental barrier. Immunoglobulins can be transported from the maternal to the fetal side in a hemochorial or an endotheliochorial placenta. However, the fetus synthesizes the majority of its own proteins from amino acids contributed by the dam. Nutritionally-based lipids do not cross the placenta. Instead, the placenta hydrolyzes triglycerides and maternal phospholipids and synthesizes new lipid materials to be used by the fetus. Large peptide hormones such as thyroid stimulating hormone, adrenal cortical stimulating hormone, growth hormone, insulin and glucagon do not cross the placenta. Smaller molecular weight hormones such as steroids, thyroid hormone and the catecholamines (epinephrine and norepinephrine) cross the placenta with relative ease. Vitamins and minerals are transferred to the fetus at variable rates. Fat soluble vitamins do not cross the placenta with ease, while water soluble vitamins (B and K) pass across the placenta with relative ease. Nutrients are also transferred by pinocytosis and phagocytosis. Areolae from the chorion form over the openings of the uterine glands and are thought to absorb secretions from these glands.

Of significant importance is the ability of the placenta to transfer toxic and potentially pathogenic materials. Many toxic substances easily cross the placental barrier. These include ethyl alcohol, lead, phosphorus and mercury. Also, opiate drugs and numerous common pharmaceuticals such as barbiturates and antibiotics can cross the placental barrier. Some substances may be highly **teratogenic**. Teratogenic means inducing abnormal development (birth defects). These substances include LSD, amphetamines, lithium, diethylstilbestrol and thalidomide. It is well documented that these materials induce abnormal embryonic development and cause serious birth defects.

It is known that a wide range of microorganisms can contaminate the fetus. Viruses can cross the placental barrier with ease and thus many viral diseases can be transmitted from the dam to the fetus. Such human diseases as German measles, Herpes virus and HIV can be transmitted from the pregnant mother to the fetus. Bacteria such as syphilis can also be transmitted to the fetus.

Figure 14-4. The Migration of Binucleate Giant Cells in the Ruminant Placenta

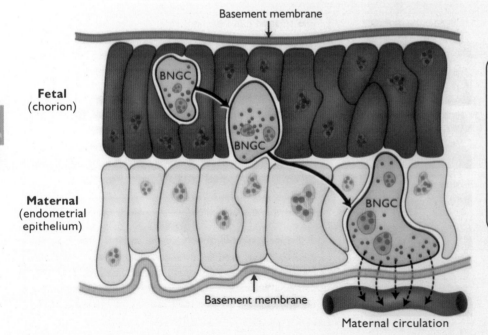

Binucleate giant cells (BNGC) migrate from the chorion to the endometrial epithelium in ruminants. These cells are thought to secrete placental lactogen and pregnancy specific protein B.
(www.biotracking.com)

Figure 14-5. Placental Classification Based on Separation Between Fetal and Maternal Blood Supplies

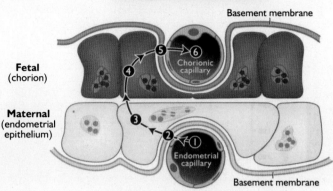

Epitheliochorial
(pigs, horses and ruminants)
6. Chorionic capillaries
5. Chorionic interstitium
4. Chorionic epithelium
3. Endometrial epithelium
2. Endometrial interstitium
1. Endometrial capillaries

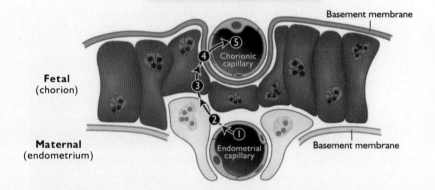

Endotheliochorial
(dogs and cats)
5. Chorionic capillaries
4. Chorionic interstitium
3. Chorionic epithelium
2. Endometrial interstitium
1. Endometrial capillaries

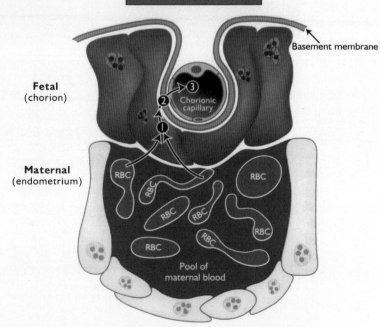

Hemochorial
(primates and rodents)
3. Chorionic capillaries
2. Chorionic interstitium
1. Chorionic epithelium
RBC= Red blood cell

14

The Placenta is a Major Endocrine Organ During Pregnancy

In addition to serving as a metabolic exchange organ, the placenta serves as a transitory endocrine organ. Hormones from the placenta gain access to both the fetal and the maternal circulation.

> *The placenta secretes hormones that can:*
> - *stimulate ovarian function*
> - *maintain pregnancy*
> - *influence fetal growth*
> - *stimulate mammary function*
> - *assist in parturition*

The placenta of the mare produces a gonadotropin called **equine chorionic gonadotropin (eCG)**. Equine chorionic gonadotropin is also called **pregnant mare's serum gonadotropin (PMSG)**. Equine chorionic gonadotropin is produced by the endometrial cups of the placenta. Endometrial cups are a transient placental endocrine gland. They begin producing eCG at the time of attachment of the conceptus to the endometrium. The relationship between the formation of the endometrial cups in the mare and the synthesis of eCG is presented in Figure 14-6. As you can see, the production of eCG is closely related to the weight of the endometrial cups.

Equine chorionic gonadotropin acts as a luteotropin and provides a stimulus for maintenance of the **primary corpus luteum**. The primary corpus luteum in the mare is defined as the corpus luteum formed from the ovulated follicle. In addition, eCG is responsible for controlling the formation and maintenance of **supplementary (accessory) corpora lutea**. As eCG increases, the pregnant mare will often ovulate, thus generating accessory corpora lutea. The eCG-induced ovulations occur between days 40 and 70 of pregnancy. Luteinization (promoted by eCG) also occurs in antral follicles that do not ovulate. Thus, eCG has a significant positive impact on the ability of the ovary to produce progesterone. Indeed, if one examines the progesterone profile, it can be seen that there is a close relationship between the concentrations of progesterone and the production of accessory corpora lutea (See Figure 14-7).

In addition to its luteotropic action, eCG has powerful FSH-like actions when administered to females of other species. In fact, eCG will cause marked follicular development in most species. It is used commonly to induce superovulation where embryo transfer is performed (cow, sheep, rabbit). In mares, however, eCG does not exert significant FSH-like action.

14

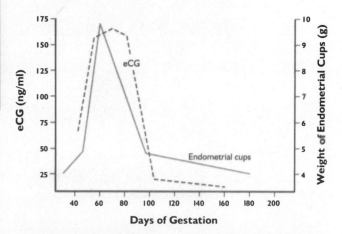

Figure 14-6. Production of Equine Chorionic Gonadotropin (eCG) is Closely Related to the Weight of the Endometrial Cups
(Modified from Ginther, *Reproductive Biology of the Mare*)

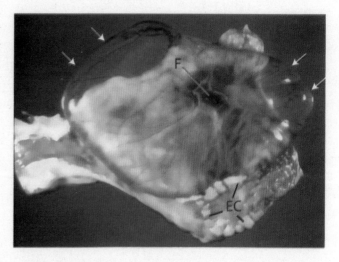

Endometrial cups (EC) are seen here in a U-shaped configuration. The fetus (F) is surrounded by the amnion (not visible). The membrane indicated by arrows is the allantochorion. This specimen was removed from a mare at 50 days of gestation.
(Photograph courtesy of Dr. O.J. Ginther from *Reproductive Biology of the Mare, 2nd Ed.*)

Figure 14-7. Luteal Progesterone Output During the First Half
of Gestation in the Mare
(Modified from Ginther, *Reproductive Biology of the Mare*)

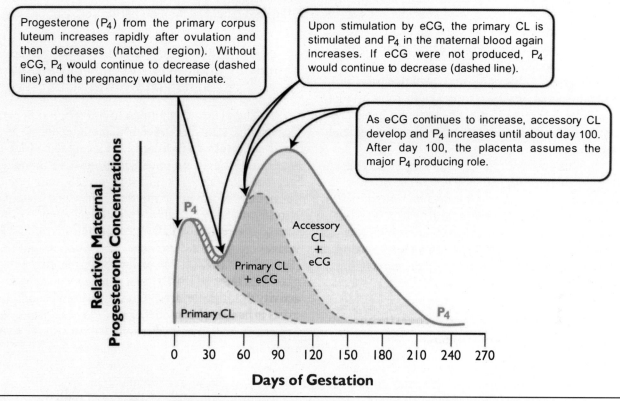

Progesterone (P_4) from the primary corpus luteum increases rapidly after ovulation and then decreases (hatched region). Without eCG, P_4 would continue to decrease (dashed line) and the pregnancy would terminate.

Upon stimulation by eCG, the primary CL is stimulated and P_4 in the maternal blood again increases. If eCG were not produced, P_4 would continue to decrease (dashed line).

As eCG continues to increase, accessory CL develop and P_4 increases until about day 100. After day 100, the placenta assumes the major P_4 producing role.

Figure 14-8. The Production of hCG and Progesterone During
Gestation in the Pregnant Woman

Human chorionic gonadotropin peaks at about 2.5 months of gestation and then declines. This period of time is critical for maintenance of pregnancy because the corpus luteum assumes primary responsibility for progesterone secretion.

At about 2.5 to 3 months of gestation the placenta begins to assume the primary responsibility for progesterone secretion and continues this role until the time of parturition. hCG increases slightly between months 6 and 9 because of the increased placental mass.

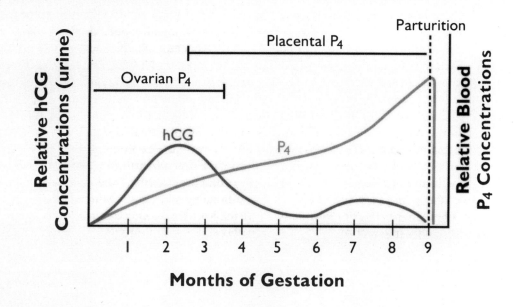

14

The second major gonadotropin of placental origin is **human chorionic gonadotropin (hCG)**. This hormone is not only found in the human but in many other primates. Often hCG (and eCG) may simply be referred to as "CG". It originates from the trophoblastic cells of the chorion and is secreted as soon as the blastocyst hatches from the zona pellucida. Human chorionic gonadotropin can be detected in the blood and urine of the pregnant woman as early as days 8 to 10 of gestation. It increases rapidly in the urine of the pregnant woman, reaching a maximum value at about 2.5 months (See Figure 14-8). Its presence in the urine constitutes the basis for over-the-counter pregnancy diagnosis kits.

The primary role of hCG during early pregnancy is to provide a luteotropic stimulus for the ovulatory corpus luteum as it transitions into the CL of pregnancy. Luteal LH receptors also bind hCG resulting in sustained progesterone production. Administration of hCG to non-primate females can cause ovulation. In fact, hCG is used commonly to induce ovulation in superovulation protocols.

The Placenta Secretes Progesterone and Estrogens

Progesterone is obligatory for early embryonic development because it provides the stimulus for elevated secretion by the endometrial glands. High progesterone is also responsible for the so-called "**progesterone block**" that inhibits myometrial contractions. Progesterone increases in the blood of the pregnant female and peaks at different stages of gestation for different species. The absolute levels of progesterone also vary significantly among species (See Figure 14-9). While progesterone is always produced by the corpus luteum in early pregnancy, the role of the corpus luteum in maintenance of pregnancy varies among species. In some species (ewe, mare and woman), the corpus luteum is not needed for the entire gestational period because the placenta takes over production of progesterone. For example, in the ewe the corpus luteum is responsible for initial production of progesterone, but the placenta assumes responsibility for its production after only 50 days of gestation (See Table 14-1). In other species (sow or rabbit), lutectomy (surgical removal of corpora lutea) will terminate pregnancy regardless of when this occurs during gestation. Lutectomy in the cow up to 8 months of gestation will result in abortion. It should be pointed out that even though the placenta takes over for the corpus luteum of pregnancy, the corpus luteum secretes progesterone throughout gestation.

In addition to progesterone, estradiol also is an important product of the placenta, particularly during the last part of gestation. In fact, the peak of estradiol in most species signals the early preparturient period. The profiles of estradiol during gestation are presented in the subsequent section on parturition.

Certain Placental Hormones Stimulate Mammary Function of the Dam and Fetal Growth

The placenta is known to produce a polypeptide hormone known as **placental lactogen** that is also called **somatomammotropin**. Placental lactogens have been found in rats, mice, sheep, cows and humans. They are believed to be similar to growth hormone, thus promoting the growth of the fetus. Placental lactogen also stimulates the mammary gland (lactogenic) of the dam. The degree to which fetal somatotropic (growth) versus lactogenic effects occur depends on the species (See Figure 14-10). For example, in the ewe **ovine placental lactogen (oPL)** has a more potent lactogenic activity than somatotropic activity. A similar condition exists in humans, but not in the cow. Placental lactogens have been studied most intensely in the ewe. They are produced and secreted by the binucleate giant cells of the placenta. The secretory products of the binucleate cells are transferred into the maternal circulation.

It is hypothesized that the sire may have an effect on the degree to which the fetus can produce placental lactogen. Such an effect could cause elevated concentrations of placental lactogen by the fetus. Increased placental lactogen secretion would cause enhanced stimulation of the maternal mammary gland and thus promote elevated milk production. This theory suggests that it might be possible for the sire to influence fetal placental lactogen and enhance milk production in the dam. This **sire-on-fetus-hypothesis** has not been tested critically, but could hold promise for the genetic improvement in dairy, beef cattle and goats.

Placental relaxin is secreted in humans, mares, cats, dogs, pigs, rabbits and monkeys. Its function is to cause softening and "relaxation" of the pelvic ligaments to facilitate expulsion of the fetus. The stimulus for relaxin secretion is not known. Relaxin is not present in the bovine placenta during any stage of gestation. It is likely (with the exception of the rabbit) that relaxin, during the time of parturition, originates from both the ovary and the placenta. The role of relaxin is therefore questionable in the cow. Maternal blood relaxin levels are the basis for a commercial pregnancy diagnostic test at about 30 days of gestation in the bitch.

14

Figure 14-9. Progesterone Profiles in Various Pregnant Females

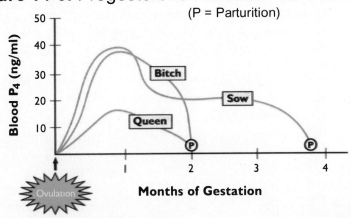

(P = Parturition)

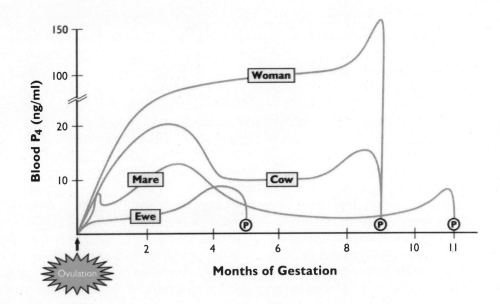

Table 14-1. Gestational Length and Time of Placental Takeover for Progesterone Production in Various Species

SPECIES	GESTATION LENGTH	TIME OF PLACENTAL TAKEOVER
Alpaca	11.4 mo	11.4 mo (none)
Bitch	2 mo (65 days)	2 mo (none)
Camel	12.3 mo	12.3 mo (none)
Cow	9 mo	6-8 mo
Ewe	5 mo	50 days
Goat	5 mo	5 mo (none)
Llama	11.3 mo	11.3 mo (none)
Mare	11 mo	70 days
Queen	2 mo (65 days)	2 mo (none)
Rabbit	1 mo	1 mo (none)
Sow	3.8 mo	3.8 mo (none)
Woman	9 mo	60-70 days

14

Figure 14-10. Placental Lactogen in Blood Near Termination of Gestation
(From Martal in *Reproduction in Man and Mammals*)

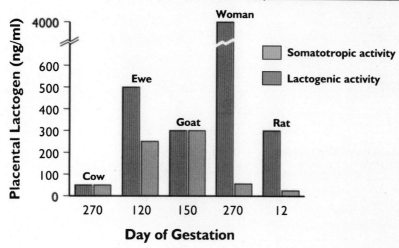

Placental lactogen has both lactogenic actions and soma-totrophic actions. The lactogenic activity of placental lactogen promotes mammary function in the dam, while the somatotropic activity promotes fetal growth.

Parturition is a Complex Cascade of Physiologic Events

The fetus triggers the onset of parturition by initiating a cascade of complex endocrine/biochemical events. The fetal hypothalamo-pituitary-adrenal axis is obligatory for the initiation of parturition. During the conclusion of gestation, fetal mass approaches the inherent space limitations of the uterus. This space limitation has been considered by some to be the stimulus that causes **adrenal corticotropin (ACTH)** to be secreted by the fetal pituitary. The fetal pituitary then stimulates secretion of adrenal corticoids from the fetal adrenal cortex. The elevation of fetal corticoids initiates a cascade of events that cause dramatic changes in the endocrine condition of the dam. These endocrine changes cause two major events to occur: 1) removal of the myometrial "progesterone block," enabling myometrial contractions to begin and 2) increased reproductive tract secretions, particularly by the cervix.

Removal of the "progesterone block" occurs because fetal cortisol promotes the synthesis of three enzymes that convert progesterone to estradiol. The conversion pathway is illustrated in Figure 14-11. Progesterone, that is high at the placental interface, is converted to 17α-hydroxyprogesterone by the enzyme 17α-hydroxylase. Fetal cortisol also triggers the enzyme 17-20 desmolase to convert 17α-hydroxyprogesterone to androstenedione. Androstenedione is converted to estrogen by activation of an aromatase enzyme. This involves aromatization of the A ring of the steroid and removal of the 19 carbon. The conversion of progesterone to estradiol accounts, at least in part, for the dramatic drop in progesterone and dramatic elevation of estradiol. The relationship between progesterone and estradiol during gestation is presented in Figure 14-12.

In addition to converting progesterone to estradiol, fetal corticoids also cause the placenta to synthesize $PGF_{2\alpha}$. The synthesis of $PGF_{2\alpha}$ helps abolish the "progesterone block." As both estradiol and prostaglandin become elevated, the myometrium becomes increasingly more active and begins to display noticeable contractions. Also, $PGF_{2\alpha}$ causes the CL of pregnancy to regress, facilitating the decline in progesterone. The drop in progesterone in some species is brought about both by the conversion of progesterone into estradiol and by the luteolytic process brought about by $PGF_{2\alpha}$. Endocrine events associated with parturition are summarized in Figures 14-13 and 14-14.

14

The three stages of parturition are:

• *Stage I: initiation of myometrial contractions (removal of progesterone block)*

• *Stage II: expulsion of the fetus*

• *Stage III: expulsion of the fetal membranes*

The fetus initiates Stage I of parturition.

Figure 14-11. Conversion of Progesterone to Estradiol as Parturition Nears

Corticoids from the fetus activate 17α-hydroxylase, 17-20 desmolase and aromatase that convert progesterone to estradiol. This conversion removes the "progesterone block" to myometrial activity.

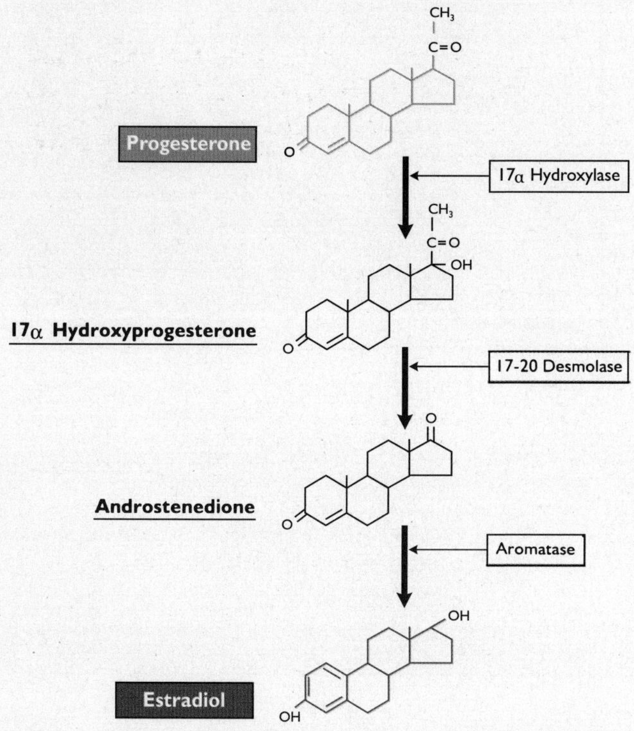

Progesterone

17α Hydroxyprogesterone ← 17α Hydroxylase

Androstenedione ← 17-20 Desmolase

Estradiol ← Aromatase

Figure 14-12. Estradiol and Progesterone Profiles During Gestation in the Mare, Cow, Woman, Ewe and Sow

(P = Parturition)

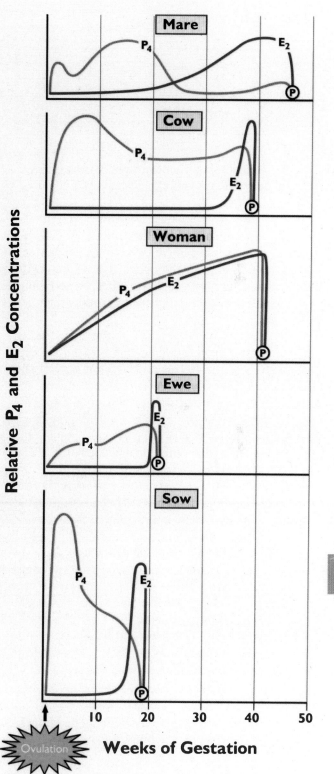

As the pressure inside the uterus continues to increase, the fetus in the cow, mare and ewe rotates so that the front feet and head are positioned to the posterior of the dam (See Figure 14-15). Such a rotation is important to insure a proper delivery. If the fetus fails to position itself correctly, **dystocia** (difficult birth) may occur.

As the levels of estradiol increase, coupled with the elevation in levels of $PGF_{2\alpha}$, the contracting uterus begins to push the fetus toward the cervix, applying pressure to the cervix. The endocrine events that promote the first stage of parturition (dilation of the cervix and entry of the fetus into the cervical canal) are summarized in Figure 14-14.

Pressure on the cervix brought about by increased myometrial contractions activates pressure-sensitive neurons located in the cervix that synapse in the spinal cord and eventually synapse with oxytocin

14

producing neurons in the hypothalamus (See Figure 14-15). Oxytocin, released into the systemic circulation, acts to facilitate the myometrial contractility initiated by estradiol and by $PGF_{2\alpha}$. As the pressure against the cervix continues to increase, so does the oxytocin secretion, and thus the force of contraction of the myometrial smooth muscle begins to peak. When this occurs, the fetus enters the cervical canal and the first stage of parturition is complete.

> *Expulsion of fetus (Stage II) requires strong myometrial and abdominal muscle contractions.*

Another important hormone involved in successful parturition is **relaxin**. Relaxin is a glycoprotein that is produced by either the corpus luteum or the placenta, depending upon the species. The synthesis of relaxin is stimulated by $PGF_{2\alpha}$. Relaxin causes a softening of the connective tissue in the cervix and promotes elasticity of the pelvic ligaments. Thus, this hormone prepares the birth canal by loosening the supportive tissues so that passage of the fetus can occur with relative ease.

One of the dramatic effects of estradiol elevation prior to parturition is that it initiates secretory activity of the reproductive tract in general and particularly the cervix. As estradiol increases, the cervix and vagina begin to produce mucus. This mucus washes out the cervical seal of pregnancy and thoroughly lubricates the cervical canal and the vagina. Mucus reduces friction and enables the fetus to exit the reproductive tract with relative ease. As myometrial contractions continue to increase, the feet and head of the fetus begin to put pressure on the fetal membranes. When the pressure reaches a certain level, the membranes rupture, with subsequent loss of amniotic and allantoic fluid. This fluid also serves to lubricate the birth canal. As the fetus enters the birth canal, it becomes hypoxic (deprived of adequate levels of oxygen). This hypoxia promotes fetal movement that, in turn, promotes further myometrial contraction. This positive feedback system creates a set of conditions where the time of parturition is reduced because an increased strength of contraction follows fetal movement. In a sense, the fetus is controlling its exit from the uterus. The uterine contractions are accompanied by abdominal muscle contractions of the dam that further aid in expulsion of the fetus.

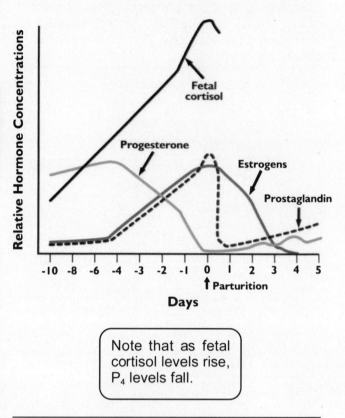

Figure 14-13. Relative Hormone Profiles in the Cow During the Periparturient Period

Note that as fetal cortisol levels rise, P_4 levels fall.

In most species, expulsion of the fetal membranes quickly follows expulsion of the fetus. Expulsion of the fetal membranes requires that the chorionic villi become dislodged from the crypts of the maternal side of the placenta. This release of the chorionic villi is believed to be brought about by powerful vasoconstriction of arteries in the villi. Vasoconstriction reduces pressure and thus allows the villi to be released from the crypts. Obviously in some forms of placentation, there must be some maternal vasoconstriction. For example, in animals that have hemochorial placentation, maternal blood is adjacent to the fetal placenta. Thus, if vasoconstriction does not occur on the maternal side, hemorrhage is likely.

The duration of parturition is variable among species and this variation is summarized in Table 14-2. Extension beyond what is considered to be the normal upper-end duration of parturition constitutes a difficult birth (**dystocia**). Such prolonged parturition can result in serious complications to both the fetus and the dam.

Figure 14-14. Cascade of Events Prompted by Fetal Cortisol

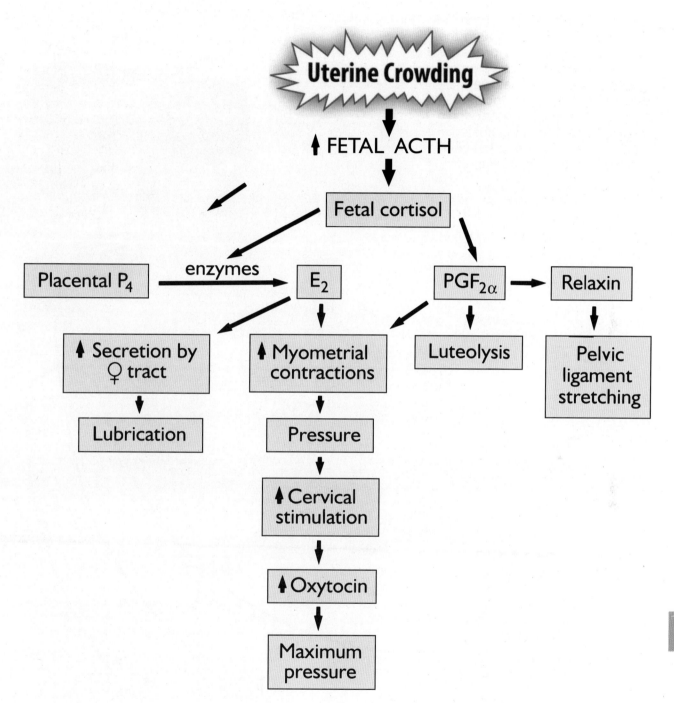

14

Figure 14-15. Pressure on the Cervix Causes Oxytocin Release and Subsequent Myometrial Contractions

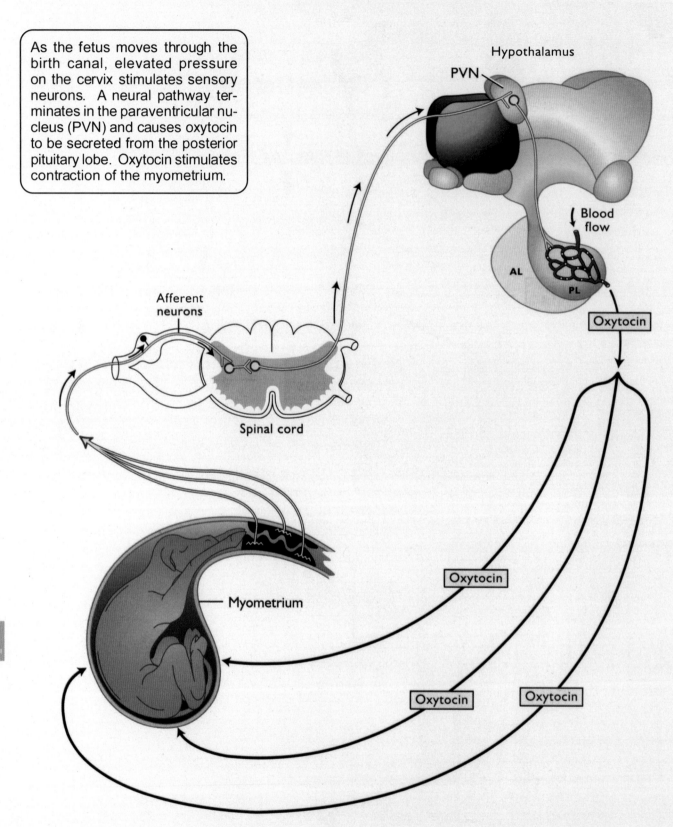

As the fetus moves through the birth canal, elevated pressure on the cervix stimulates sensory neurons. A neural pathway terminates in the paraventricular nucleus (PVN) and causes oxytocin to be secreted from the posterior pituitary lobe. Oxytocin stimulates contraction of the myometrium.

Hypothalamus

PVN

Blood flow

AL

PL

Oxytocin

Afferent neurons

Spinal cord

Oxytocin

Myometrium

Oxytocin

Oxytocin

14

Difficulties in parturition usually occur in the second stage (expulsion of the fetus). One cause of dystocia is excessive size of the fetus. Fetal size is controlled by both the dam and the sire. In primiparous dams, it is always advisable to breed females to a male of small body size so that fetal size does not exceed the ability of the female to give birth successfully.

A second cause of dystocia is failure of proper fetal rotation. About 5% of all births in cattle are characterized by abnormal positioning of the fetus during parturition. Such abnormal positioning results in difficult births and sometimes impossible presentations/ positions that require caesarean section.

A third cause of dystocia is multiple births in monotocous species. Twins generally cause dystocia. This is because: 1) both twins may be presented simultaneously, 2) the first fetus is positioned abnormally and therefore blocks the second or 3) the uterus becomes fatigued by difficult and sustained contractions. A discussion of obstetrical procedures used to correct these problems is beyond the scope of this book, but can be researched by consulting the appropriate references at the conclusion of this chapter.

> ### *Expulsion of fetal membranes (Stage III) requires myometrial contractions.*

Myometrial contractions continue after expulsion of the fetus although they are not as strong. These contractions are responsible for expelling the placenta. The time required for expulsion of the placenta varies significantly among species. This variation is presented in Table 14-2. Retention of the fetal membranes (also referred to as "retained placenta"), is not uncommon in ruminants, especially dairy cows. This condition will occur in 5-15% of parturitions in healthy dairy cows. The underlying cause of retained placenta appears to be that placental connective tissue is not enzymatically degraded by cotyledonary proteolytic enzymes. Thus, fetal cotyledons remain attached to maternal cotyledons. Retained placenta is rare in mares, sows, bitches and queens.

Table 14-2. Stages and Duration of Parturition Among Various Species

Species	Stage I (Myometrial Contractions/ Cervical Dilation)	Stage II (Fetal Expulsion)	Stage III (Fetal Membrane Expulsion)
Alpaca	2 to 6h	5 to 90 min	45 to 180 min
Bitch	6 to 12h	6h (24h in large litters)	most placentas pass with neonate or within 15 min of birth
Camel	3 to 48h	5 to 45 min	40 min
Cow	2 to 6h	30 to 60 min	6 to 12h
Ewe	2 to 6h	30 to 120 min	5 to 8h
Llama	2 to 6h	5 to 90 min	45 to 180 min
Mare	1 to 4h	12 to 30 min	1h
Sow	2 to 12h	150 to 180 min	1 to 4h
Queen	4 to 42h	4 kittens/litter, 30-60 min/kitten	most placentas pass with neonate
Woman	8+h	2h	1h or less

14

Further PHENOMENA for Fertility

The term "caesarean" was derived from the false notion that Julius Caesar was born by removing him from his mother through an incision in the abdominal and uterine wall. His family name, Caesar was derived from the belief that Julius' ancestors (centuries before him) were born in such a way. The name Caesar is derived from the Latin word "caesus" that means "to cut". The name also fits the way Julius died.

In a number of teleost fishes (fishes with a more or less ossified skeleton) the female incubates the eggs in her mouth and in some species the male does the same. The term "keep your mouth shut" has a special meaning in this species.

In pipe fishes and sea horses the female lays her eggs in a brood pouch of the male and he is responsible for gestation. In fact, several females may lay eggs in one male's brood pouch. The brood pouch offers a special environment for developing offspring and is under the control of prolactin.

Lampreys (a predatory eel) build nests in sandy bottomed streams. They assemble rock walls to slow the water running over the nest. At spawning, they stir up the sand that sticks to the eggs. The sand weights the eggs and prevents them from floating downstream. It also reduces predation. This is another form of attachment that enables successful embryogenesis.

Infant kangaroos in their mother's pouches nurse from two nipples, and two babies of different ages commonly nurse at the same time. So, the mother kangaroo produces two kinds of milk- on one side, fully rich for the younger and on the other side, a sort of skim for the elder.

The most prolific mammal in existence is the tiny rodent known as the multimammate rat. One female is capable of producing up to 120 offspring a year if conditions are favorable. This is because she has 24 teats, the most of any female mammal. It is rare that all of them are used but when they are a multimammate population explosion can occur.

The female Egyptian spiny mouse acts as a midwife to other females. She bites through the umbilical cord and licks the neonates while the mother continues to deliver the litter.

The female African elephant has a gestation period of 1.8 years. The calf weighs about 300 pounds at birth and nurses for about three years.

During the 19th Century, adultery was so feared that the chastity belt was invented. Such belts were devices that were locked around the woman's genitalia to prevent copulation. It has been recorded that a faithful wife locked into a chastity belt discovered that she was pregnant some months after her husband had left onfit crusade. Her husband had the only key. Her pregnancy progressed and eventually the village blacksmith had to be called in to remove the chastity belt.

During the Middle Ages, prostitution was considered to be an honest and essential profession. This was because prostitution was considered as a means to prevent adultery, homosexual behavior and masturbation. The Church actually condoned prostitution for this reason.

The Mayans believed in a maize god. Since corn was a nutritional staple for these people, they revered it and believed that corn was symbolic of both the male and female. From a nutritional perspective they believed that corn was nurturing like a woman's breast and that each individual kernel had powerful fertilizing capabilities like spermatozoa. Once the seeds were planted in the earth and the mature corn was produced, the cob represented the penis and the husk represented the vagina. Thus, the ear of corn was also symbolic of copulation.

14

Key References

Arthur, G.H., D.E. Noakes, H. Pearson and T.J. Parkinson. 1996. *Veterinary Reproduction and Obstetrics*. 7th Edition. W.B. Saunders Co. Philadelphia. ISBN 0-7020-1758-X.

Catchpole, H.R. 1991. "Hormonal mechanisms in pregnancy and parturition" in *Reproduction in Domestic Animals*. 4th Edition. P.T. Cupps, ed., Academic Press, San Diego. ISBN 0-12-196575-9.

Flood, P.F. 1991. "The development of the conceptus and its relationship to the uterus" in *Reproduction in Domestic Animals*. 4th Edition. P.T. Cupps, ed., Academic Press, San Diego. ISBN 0-12-196575-9.

Fuchs, A.R. and M.J. Fields. 1999. "Parturition, nonhuman mammals" in *Encyclopedia of Reproduction*, Vol. 3 p703-716. Knobil, E. and J.D. Neill, eds. Academic Press, San Diego. ISBN 0-12-227023-1.

Ginther, O.J. 1992. *Reproductive Biology of the Mare*. 2nd Edition. Equiservices, Cross Plains, WI. Library of Congress Catalog No. 91-075595.

Johnston, S.D. M.V. Root, Kustritz and P.N.S. Olson. 2001. *Canine and Feline Theriogenology*. W.B. Saunders, Philadelphia. ISBN 0-7216-5607-2.

Morrow, D.A. 1986. *Current Therapy in Theriogenology*. 2nd Edition. W.B. Saunders Co. Philadelphia. ISBN 0-7216-6580-2.

Mossman, H.W. 1987. *Vertebrate Fetal Membranes*. Rutgers University Press, New Brunswick. ISBN 0-8135-1132-1.

Thibault, C., M.C. Levasseur and R.H.F. Hunter.eds. 1993. *Reproduction in Man and Mammals*. Ellipses, Paris. ISBN 2-7298-9354-7.

14

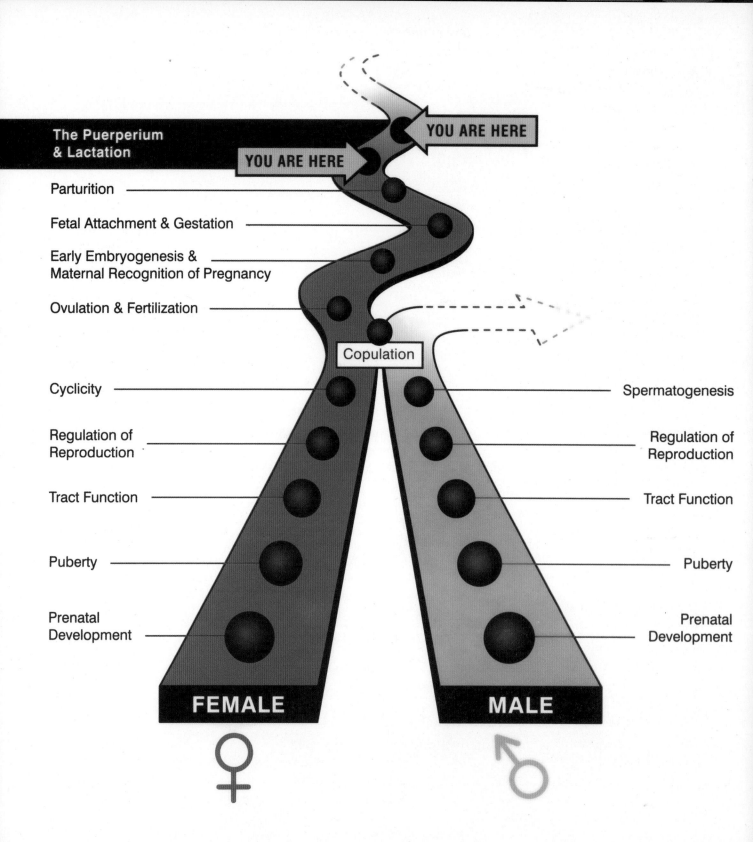

The Puerperium
& Lactation

YOU ARE HERE

YOU ARE HERE

Parturition

Fetal Attachment & Gestation

Early Embryogenesis &
Maternal Recognition of Pregnancy

Ovulation & Fertilization

Copulation

Cyclicity

Spermatogenesis

Regulation of
Reproduction

Regulation of
Reproduction

Tract Function

Tract Function

Puberty

Puberty

Prenatal
Development

Prenatal
Development

FEMALE

MALE

Take Home Message

Immediately following parturition, the female begins to lactate and enters a period of reproductive repair called the puerperium. For a period of time these two processes overlap. During the puerperium uterine involution and return of ovarian function occurs. Involution is the reduction in size and "remodeling" of the endometrium so that the uterus can initiate and sustain another pregnancy.

Mammary gland development is initiated prenatally in the female fetus and continues through puberty and pregnancy. The anatomy and distribution of mammary glands is diverse among mammals. Accumulation of secretions in the mammary gland begins about two weeks before parturition. Lactation provides the neonate with the opportunity to nurse and be nourished with minimal expenditure of energy. It also provides immunoprotection for the neonate because initial mammary secretions called colostrum contain antibodies that provide passive immunity. Lactation continues until the neonate is weaned. After weaning, the mammary glands undergo involution and return to a non-secretory state.

The puerperium and lactation are initiated immediately after parturition and for a period of time these processes occur simultaneously. **Lactation** is the synthesis, secretion and removal of milk from the mammary gland. The **puerperium** is the period after parturition when the reproductive tract returns to its nonpregnant condition so that the female may become pregnant again. This chapter will describe the basics of these two important processes. Parturition results in loss of placental function and deterioration of the maternal tissue contributing to the placenta. Tissue damage results. During the puerperium damaged reproductive tissues are repaired and ovarian function returns.

The Puerperium

The puerperium begins immediately after parturition and lasts until reproductive function is restored so that another pregnancy can occur. The time required for complete uterine involution (repair) and ovarian activity to resume in the postpartum female varies significantly among species (See Table 15-1).

> *The four major events of the puerperium are:*
> - *myometrial contractions and expulsion of lochia*
> - *endometrial repair*
> - *resumption of ovarian function*
> - *elimination of bacterial contamination of the reproductive tract*

It must be emphasized that in many polyestrous animals, the shortest possible puerperium is desirable because eligibility for a subsequent pregnancy is of high economic importance. For example, in dairy cows frequent pregnancies are required for maximum lifetime milk yield. In swine and beef cows, the shorter the interval between pregnancies the more offspring are produced and the more efficient the production of meat becomes. Conversely, the longer the puerperium, the longer the delay of a subsequent pregnancy and the less efficient the production process becomes. Figure 15-1 summarizes the events that occur from parturition to the subsequent pregnancy. These events will be described in more detail below.

Reduction in Uterine Size and Volume is Brought About by Myometrial Contractions

Immediately after parturition, the myometrium undergoes strong repeated contractions. The purpose of these contractions is threefold. First, they facilitate discharge of fluids and tissue debris from the uterus. Secondly, the contractions compress the uterine vasculature and help minimize the possibility of hemorrhage. Third, myometrial contractions reduce the overall size of the uterus. Of the species presented in this text, timely uterine involution is most important in the postpartum dairy cow. In most species, frequent postpartum suckling occurs and oxytocin is secreted (See Figure 15-13). In suckled animals, uterine contractions occur on a frequent basis. In the dairy cow however, the calf is usually removed within 24 hours after parturition and milking takes place only two or three times per day. Consequently, oxytocin episodes are

15

Figure 15-1. Major Events From Parturition to Subsequent Conception (Ruminant Model)

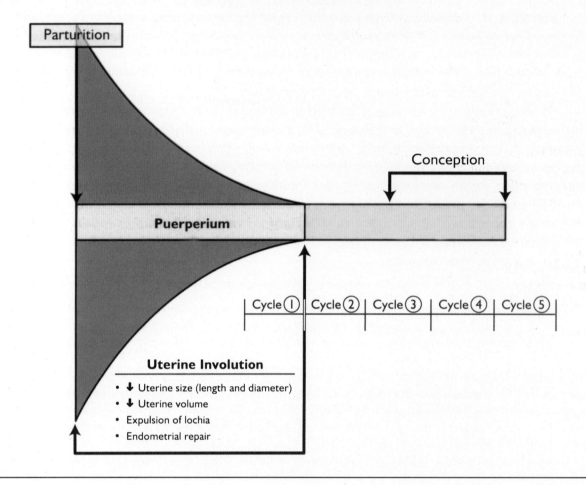

Table 15-1. Time Required for Uterine Involution and Resumption of Ovarian Activity in Various Species

Species	Time Required for Complete Uterine Involution	Time Required for Resumption of Ovarian Activity
Alpaca	20d	5-10d
Beef Cow	30d	50-60d (L)
Bitch	90d	150d (A)
Camel	30-50d	25-40d or up to 1 yr (L)
Dairy Cow	45-50d	18-25d
Ewe	30d	180d (SDB)
Llama	20d	5-10d
Mare	21-28d	5-12d
Queen	30d	30d
Sow	28-30d	7d (L)
Woman	40-45d	6-24mo (L) (See Chapter 7)

L = Lactation inhibits ovarian activity (See Chapter 7)
SDB = Short Day Breeder- ewes giving birth in the spring will not cycle until fall
A = Long natural postpartum anestrus (See Chapter 7)

reduced, myometrial contractions are not as frequent and uterine involution can be delayed. In this light, much of the material presented on uterine involution will focus on the dairy cow since delayed uterine involution is an important factor limiting fertility in this animal.

Immediately after parturition the uterus undergoes rapid but highly coordinated atrophy so that in a relatively short period of time the uterine mass is reduced to its nonpregnant size. In all species, marked size reduction occurs during the first several days after parturition. In fact, in the dairy cow, myometrial cell size decreases from 700μm on the first day after parturition to 200μm a few days later. In most species, myometrial contractions occur in three to four minute intervals for the first several postpartum days. These strong, high frequency myometrial contractions subside within several days. The exact time that these contractions stop depends on the species. The dramatic postpartum size reduction of the uterus in the dairy cow is illustrated in Figure 15-2.

physiologically normal in all species. However, it is often interpreted by observers to be the result of uterine pathology (especially in the dairy cow). Therefore, the first "instinct" of the reproductive management team is to treat the animal for nonexistent pathology. Unwarranted treatment is financially wasteful, not effective and often prolongs uterine involution especially if the uterine lumen is invaded (infusion of antibiotics, various solutions or to remove manually retained fetal membranes).

Obviously, with significant myometrial contractions occurring for the first 7 to 10 days there will be a reduction in the volume of lochia within the uterus. In the dairy cow, up to 2000ml of lochia can be expelled from the uterus during the first two to three days after parturition. By 14 to 18 days, lochial discharge is almost nonexistent in most cows (See Figure 15-3).

Figure 15-3. Changes in Lochial Volume at Various Postpartum Days

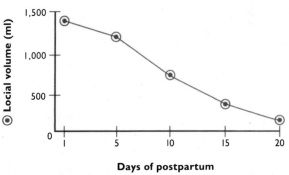

(From Gier, H.T. and G.B. Marion, 1968. *Amer. J. Vet. Res.* 29: 83-96)

Figure 15-2. Changes in Uterine Length and Weight at Various Postpartum Days

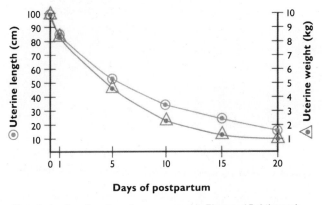

Days of postpartum

The uterine length values here are used in Figures 15-4 through 15-8 to illustrate approximate size changes. (From Gier, H.T. and G.B. Marion, 1968. *Amer. J. Vet. Res.* 29: 83-96)

During and After Myometrial Contractions a Bloody Fluid is Discharged from the Tract

Shortly after parturition, a discharge called **lochia** is expelled from the vulva. Lochia is typically a blood-tinged fluid containing remnants of the fetal placenta and endometrial tissue. Lochial discharge occurs between 2 and 9 days in postpartum dairy cows. An increase in blood and tissue debris in the lochia is normal and occurs between 5 and 10 days. This is due to the sloughing of caruncular surfaces that leaves vascular "stubs" that leak blood. Lochial discharge is

Caruncular Repair Requires Vasoconstriction, Necrosis and Sloughing of Tissues Followed by Growth of Surface Epithelium

After separation of the fetal cotyledons from the maternal caruncle (within 8-12 hours after delivery of the neonate) vasoconstriction takes place in the stalk of the maternal caruncle. Necrosis of the caruncular tissue follows. Necrosis is irreversible cell death that leads to sloughing of the caruncular mass leaving necrotic tissue in the lochial fluid inside the uterus. Some blood is released from the caruncular stalk generating a blood-tinged fluid. About 5 days after parturition, the caruncles begin to lose their cellular organization and integrity. This results in chunks of the caruncles detaching from the surface of the caruncle leaving remnants of blood vessels exposed to the surface. After the decidual tissue of the caruncle has sloughed into

15

Figure 15-4. Bovine Reproductive Organs- Day 1 Postpartum

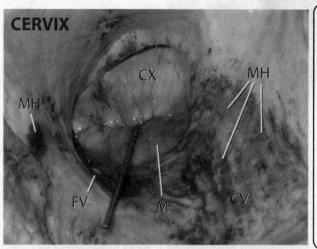

CERVIX

CX

MH

MH

FV

M

CV

Cervix (caudal view)- The brownish mucus (M) is a remnant of the cervical seal of pregnancy. Mucosal hemorrhaging (MH) has resulted from abrasive trauma to the cranial vagina (CV), fornix vagina (FV) and portions of the cervix (CX) during expulsion of the fetus. A stainless steel rod has been positioned in the cervical canal to provide spatial reference in Figures 15-4 through 15-8.

Ovaries- There are no functional structures on the right ovary. The left ovary contains two corpora lutea (arrows 1 and 2) indicating a double ovulation. Only one conceptus developed. There is no evidence of follicular development on either ovary.

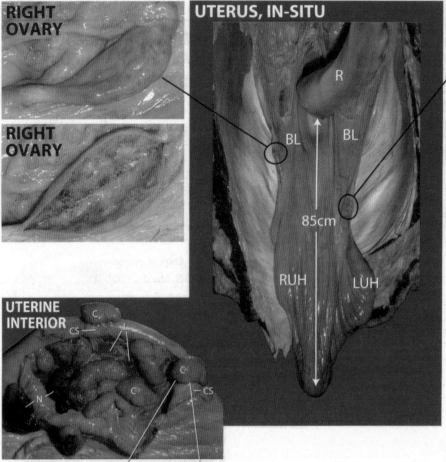

UTERUS, IN-SITU

R

BL

BL

85cm

RUH

LUH

RIGHT OVARY

RIGHT OVARY

LEFT OVARY 1 2

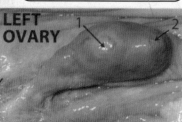

LEFT OVARY 1 2

Uterus, in-situ- This photograph and all subsequent in-situ photographs were taken from postpartum dairy cows in which the viscera was removed so that the cranial surface of the reproductive tract can be viewed. Here, the approximate overall length of the uterus is 85cm. The right uterine horn (RUH) is larger than the left uterine horn (LUH) because the right uterine horn housed the fetus. The broad ligament (BL) and rectum (R) are obvious.

UTERINE INTERIOR

C

CS

C

N

CS

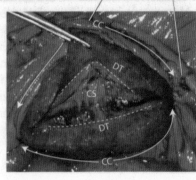

CC

DT

CS

DT

CC

Uterine Interior- The uterus contains many large caruncles (C) that consist of intact tissue. Only a few caruncles have started to undergo necrosis (N) as judged by the blackened regions. There is very little lochia (L) present. The caruncular stalks (CS) are quite long and house the vasculature that supplied the maternal cotyledon with blood during pregnancy. The enlarged photograph illustrates a caruncular crown (CC) that has been sliced open. The incision has extended into the center of the caruncular stalk (CS). The entire layer of decidual tissue (DT) will soon slough into the uterine lumen because of vasoconstriction of the caruncular arterioles.

15

Figure 15-5. Bovine Reproductive Organs- Day 4 Postpartum

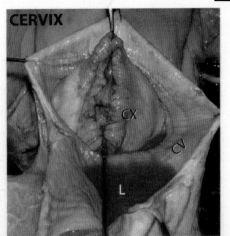

CERVIX

Cervix (caudal view)- Lochia (L) has been expelled through the cervix (CX) and it has pooled in the ventral region of the cranial vagina (CV) here. In the live cow, lochia would be discharged to the exterior.

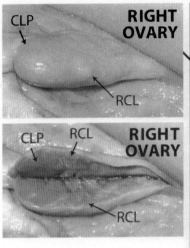

RIGHT OVARY

RIGHT OVARY

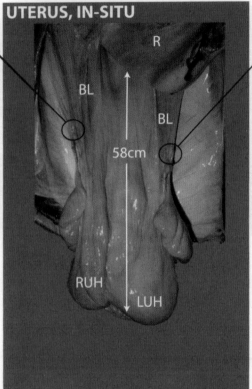

UTERUS, IN-SITU

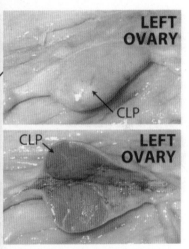

LEFT OVARY

LEFT OVARY

Ovaries- A regressing CL from the pregnancy (CLP) is present on each of the right and left ovaries indicating a double ovulation. Only one conceptus developed. A regressing CL (RCL) from a cycle prior to the pregnancy is present on the right ovary. There is no evidence of follicular development in either ovary.

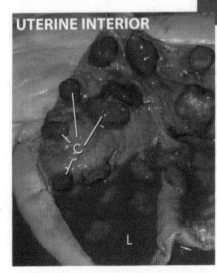

UTERINE INTERIOR

Uterus, in-situ- The most dramatic reduction in uterine size occurred between day 1 and day 5. Uterine length is reduced from about 85cm (day 1) to 58cm (day 4). The left uterine horn (LUH) housed the conceptus during pregnancy and is larger than the right uterine horn (RUH). The broad ligament (BL) and rectum (R) can be observed.

Uterine Interior- Much of the decidual tissue of the caruncles (C) has sloughed into the uterine lumen along with blood and other fluids forming lochia (L). This material is normally expelled from the uterus. The presence of lochia (L) in the uterus and its discharge from the vulva is normal.

15

Figure 15-6. Bovine Reproductive Organs- Day 10 Postpartum

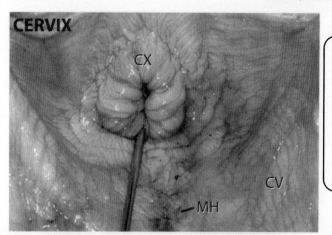

CERVIX

Cervix (caudal view)- Sites of mucosal hemorrhaging (MH) are still apparent in the floor of the cranial vagina (CV) in this cow. The cervix (CX) has decreased in diameter because its overall tone has increased.

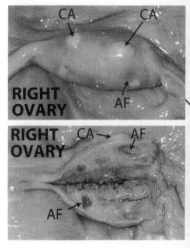

RIGHT OVARY

RIGHT OVARY

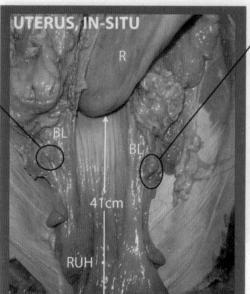

UTERUS, IN-SITU

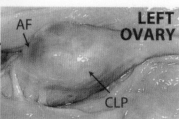

LEFT OVARY

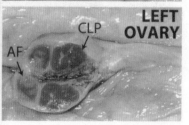

LEFT OVARY

Ovaries- The right ovary contains several corpora albicantia (CA) and a few antral follicles (AF). The left ovary contains the regressing corpus luteum of pregnancy (CLP). It also contains an antral follicle (AF) indicating that a new follicular phase is beginning.

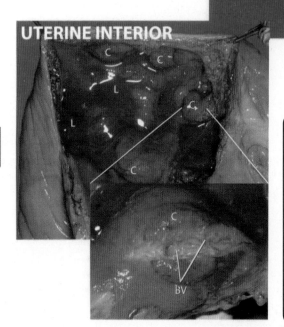

UTERINE INTERIOR

15

Uterus, in-situ- The uterus continues to undergo a reduction in size (41cm). The left uterine horn (LUH) remains larger than the right uterine horn (RUH) because the left uterine horn housed the conceptus. The rectum (R) and broad ligament (BL) are visible.
Uterine Interior- The decidual tissue of each caruncle has been sloughed into the uterine lumen. Some lochia (L) is still present but it is more viscous and mucus-like. The endometrial and caruncular epithelium is now beginning to cover the surface. The enlarged photograph illustrates the marked reduction in size of the caruncle (compare to days 1 and 4). The caruncular stalk is nonexistent. This size reduction is a function of vasoconstriction of the caruncular blood vessels (BV).

Figure 15-7. Bovine Reproductive Organs- Day 15 Postpartum

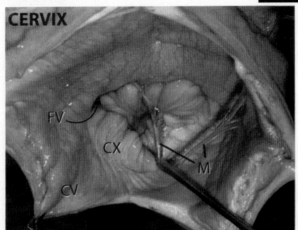

CERVIX

> **Cervix (caudal view)-** Strands of clear mucus (M) secreted by the cervix (CX) and cranial vagina (CV) indicate that this cow is entering her first follicular phase after parturition (See ovaries). FV = Fornix vagina.

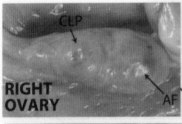

RIGHT OVARY

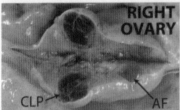

RIGHT OVARY

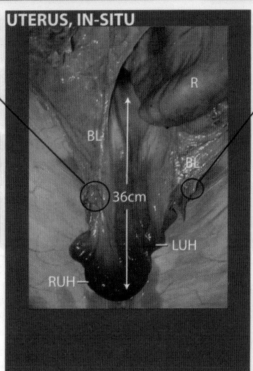

UTERUS, IN-SITU

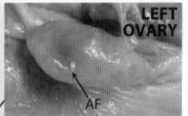

LEFT OVARY

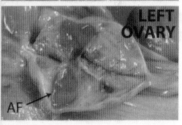

LEFT OVARY

> **Ovaries-** The right ovary contains the regressing corpus luteum of pregnancy (CLP). It also contains a developing antral follicle (AF). The left ovary contains a large antral follicle (AF) indicative of the first postpartum follicular phase. The follicles present produce estradiol that causes secretion of mucus by the cervix and cranial vagina.

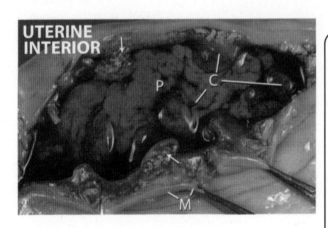

UTERINE INTERIOR

> **Uterus, in-situ-** The right uterine horn (RUH) housed the conceptus and is larger than the left uterine horn (LUH). Continued reduction in size is evident. The broad ligament (BL) and the rectum (R) can be observed. The dark coloration at the tips of the uterine horns represents pooling of blood following exsanguination of the cow.
>
> **Uterine Interior-** The caruncles (C) have decreased further in size and are almost completely covered in mucus. Lochia is almost nonexistent and a puss-like material (P) is present in localized areas. The presence of puss is normal and reflects phagocytosis of deteriorating tissue by leukocytes. Caruncular blood vessels (arrows) can be seen as small knot-like structures in the incised caruncles. M = Myometrium.

15

Figure 15-8. Bovine Reproductive Organs- Day 20 Postpartum

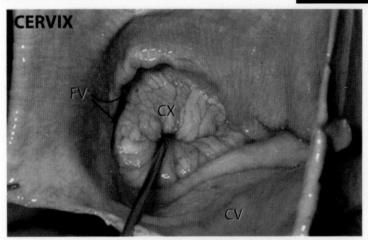

CERVIX

FV
CX
CV

Cervix (caudal view)- The cranial vagina (CV) and fornix vagina (FV) are free of hemorrhagic foci. The color, diameter and tone of the cervix (CX) are normal. Mucus is present coating the mucosal surfaces.

RIGHT OVARY

AF
CLP

RIGHT OVARY

CLP

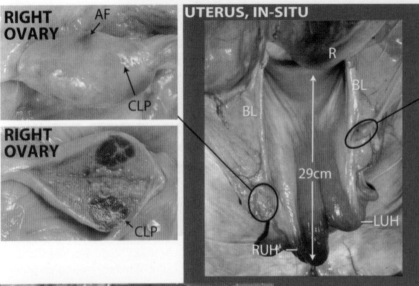

UTERUS, IN-SITU

R
BL
BL
29cm
LUH
RUH

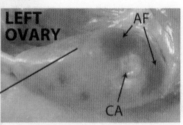

LEFT OVARY

AF
CA

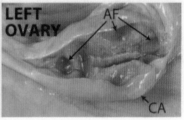

LEFT OVARY

AF
CA

Ovaries- The right ovary contains the regressing corpus luteum of pregnancy (CLP) and an antral follicle (AF). The antral follicle is not observed in the incised ovary because it is out of the plane of section. The left ovary contains several antral follicles (AF) indicating this cow is entering her first postpartum follicular phase. A corpus albicans (CA) represents a corpus luteum from a cycle prior to the previous pregnancy.

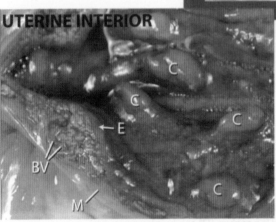

UTERINE INTERIOR

C
C
C
E
C
BV
M

The photographs in Figures 15-4 through 15-8 were part of an Honors Thesis entitled "A Full Color Photographic Description of Postpartum Uterine Involution in the Dairy Cow" submitted to Washington State University Honors College by Christina M. Davis, Spring 2002. The Honors project was sponsored by Current Conceptions, Inc.

Uterus, in-situ- The uterine horns continue to decrease in size and have almost returned to their normal nonpregnant size. The right uterine horn (RUH) remains larger than the left uterine horn (LUH) because the right uterine horn housed the conceptus. The broad ligament (BL) and the rectum (R) can be readily observed.

Uterine Interior- Caruncles (C) are approaching the size of those normally seen within the nonpregnant uterus. A cross-section of an incised caruncle shows the mass of blood vessels (BV) between the myometrium (M) and the epithelium (E) covering the caruncle. The fluid within the uterine lumen is predominantly mucus.

15

the uterine lumen the caruncle begins to undergo repair and is eventually covered again with endometrial epithelium.

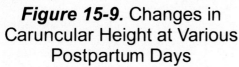

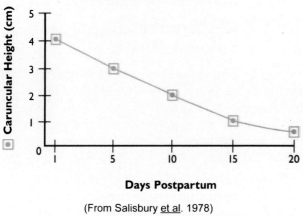

Figure 15-9. Changes in Caruncular Height at Various Postpartum Days

Days Postpartum

(From Salisbury *et al.* 1978)

At the same time caruncular repair is taking place, the intercaruncular endometrial surfaces also undergo repair. In general, the epithelium of the intercaruncular area of the endometrium repairs at a faster rate than do the caruncles. The repair of the intercaruncular endometrium is generally complete by the eighth postpartum day. The delay in caruncular repair, when compared to the intercaruncular epithelium is associated with the large mass of the caruncular tissue that must undergo necrosis and sloughing before surface epithelial repair can take place.

Postpartum Bacterial Contamination of the Uterus is Common in Most Domestic Animals

Generally, parturition in domestic animals occurs in a non-sterile environment. As a result, bacterial contamination of the reproductive tract, especially the uterus is an inevitable sequela to parturition. The postpartum reproductive tract (containing lochia) is an ideal environment for the growth of bacteria. Even though myometrial contractions tend to remove the large volume of lochia produced in some species, bacterial growth can continue. It must be emphasized that bacterial contamination is not always associated with pathology. Normal postpartum events tend to eliminate the bacterial flora within a reasonable time. As you recall, elevated estradiol promotes leukocytosis in the uterus and elsewhere in the reproductive tract. Thus, a high degree of phagocytosis can be observed in the postpartum reproductive tract as a result of relatively high postpartum estradiol concentrations that exist for a few days.

In some instances, high numbers of bacteria can overwhelm the natural defense mechanisms resulting in postpartum uterine infection. Conditions that predispose the uterus to infections are: retained fetal membranes, dystocia and delay in lochial expulsion brought about by weak myometrial contractions. Regardless of the cause, failure to eliminate bacterial contamination will: 1) prolong uterine involution; 2) prolong the puerperium and 3) delay subsequent pregnancies. Treatment of uterine infections is controversial. There is little evidence that supports the effectiveness of infusing the uterus with various pharmaceuticals in dairy cows. The single most important natural factor that aids in elimination of bacterial contamination is a return to cyclicity (estrus) so that estradiol concentrations will be elevated.

Photographic descriptions of the changes that occur in the uterus, caruncles, cervix and ovaries of the dairy cow during the first 20 days of the puerperium are presented in Figures 15-4 through 15-8. The specimens were obtained from cows that were defined as clinically normal as judged by palpation per rectum by the veterinarian servicing the herd. All cows gave birth to a single calf. To compare these various days of involution to completely involuted organs, please consult the figures in Chapter 2.

Lactation

Lactation ensures that the neonatal mammal does not have to obtain food on its own. Instead, the dam is responsible for consuming all of the nutritional raw materials and transforming these into a highly nutritious secretion called **milk**. The neonate benefits from this synthetic and secretory process because its only behavioral requirement in the early postnatal period is suckling the dam. Some animals have been domesticated and selected so they produce quantities of milk that far exceed that needed to nourish the young. The dairy cow is the dominant producer of milk for human consumption. However, goats, sheep, water buffalo, camels and mares are also considered important for their milk producing ability in some parts of the world. The immense milk producing ability of the modern dairy cow has provided a huge variety of dairy products that contribute to a multi-billion dollar industry in the western world. In this light, much of the information provided in this section will be about the dairy cow. However, the basic principles apply to most mammals. The development of the mammary gland (**mammogenesis**), anatomical diversity and **milk ejection** from the gland will be the priority topics in the remainder of this chapter.

15

Mammary Glands are Sophisticated Sweat Glands

Mammary glands arise in the developing embryo along two lateral lines on the ventral surface of the developing conceptus. These lines are slightly thickened ridges of epidermis (skin) and are called **mammary ridges** (See Figure 15-10). The mammary ridges extend from the axillary region (armpit) of the conceptus to the inguinal region. The number of mammary glands that develop from the mammary ridges depends on the species. For example, animals like the pig, dog and cat have a series of individual glands that develop at predictable positions along the entire path of the mammary ridges. In contrast, animals like the human and elephant have paired mammary glands that develop from the thoracic portion of the mammary ridges. Animals like the cow, mare and goat have mammary glands that develop from the inguinal region of the mammary ridge. The diversity among mammals in gland number, anatomic location and teat morphology is presented in Figure 15-11.

The thickened epidermal epithelium creating the mammary ridges gives rise to the **primary mammary bud** (See Figure 15-10). The primary mammary bud pushes into the underlying dermis as it grows. Continued growth results in **secondary mammary buds** that form bud protrusions away from the primary bud. These secondary buds then lengthen and branch throughout the remainder of embryonic development. Finally, these branched buds begin to **canalize** forming tiny ducts in the center of each bud. Each bud then becomes a duct with a lumen. At birth, the mammary glands consist of **lactiferous ducts** that open into larger ducts and empty to the exterior of the mammary gland through a teat or nipple (See Figure 15-10).

> *Postnatal changes in the mammary gland occur:*
>
> * *between birth and puberty*
> * *between puberty and pregnancy*
> * *during pregnancy*
> * *during lactation*
> * *during involution*

Postnatal Growth of the Mammary Gland is Endocrine Mediated

Complete anatomical development of the mammary gland coupled with the ability to synthesize and secrete milk does not occur until the female has reached puberty, becomes pregnant and gives birth to offspring.

Between Birth and Puberty, Mammary Growth is Isometric

Between birth and puberty the mammary gland experiences **isometric growth** (at the same rate as the other tissues). In other words, there is no noticeable enlargement of the mammary glands when compared to the rest of the body.

Mammary Glands Grow Significantly Between Puberty and Pregnancy

After the onset of puberty, the mammary gland begins to grow at a rate that is disproportionately faster than normal body growth. This type of growth is referred to as **allometric growth**. During repeated estrous cycles, a duct and alveolar framework is constructed within the mammary gland. This framework provides the cellular basis for future milk synthesis. During the first several estrous (or menstrual) cycles, the ducts begin to branch and their diameter increases under the influence of estradiol. Under the influence of progesterone (during the luteal phase), the terminal portions of each branch begin to form the initial portions of the alveoli. The alveoli form the functional secretory elements of the mammary gland (See Figure 15-13). Estradiol alone will cause some duct development but more complete and rapid duct development occurs in the presence of **prolactin** and **growth hormone** (somatotropin). Both of these hormones increase during the onset of puberty. Repeated cyclic exposure of the mammary cells to estrogen and progesterone can stimulate mammogenesis to proceed only so far. The mammary framework formed between puberty and pregnancy needs future endocrine input during the gestational period for complete development.

Final Mammary Development Occurs During Pregnancy

Complete alveolar development in the dam takes place during the last trimester of pregnancy. During this time the terminal alveoli begin to grow into bunches called **lobules**. A lobule would be analogous to a group of grapes on a single stem among an entire bunch of grapes (See Figure 15-13). A group of lobules that emp-

Figure 15-10. Prenatal Mammogenesis

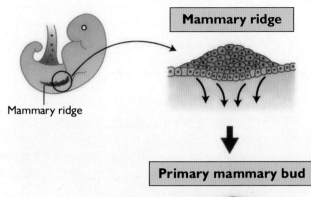

Mammary ridge

> **Mammary Ridges**
> Mammary ridges are thickened epidermal tissue that give rise to the mammary gland.

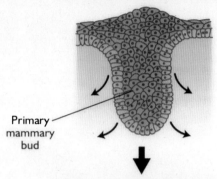

Primary mammary bud

> **Primary Mammary Bud**
> The thickened epidermal tissue begins to develop inward and penetrate into the mesenchyme (dermis).

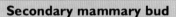

Secondary mammary bud

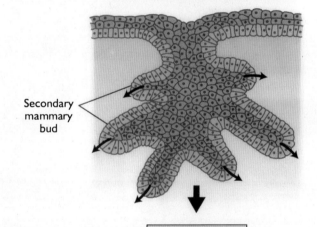

> **Secondary Mammary Bud**
> The primary mammary bud begins to send out branches that further penetrate into the dermis.

Canalization

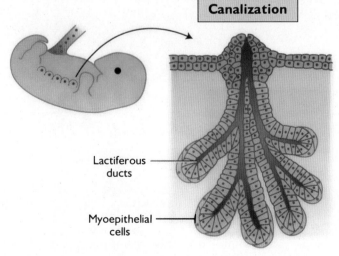

> **Canalization**
> The fingerlike secondary buds begin to lengthen and branch out. Finally they begin to form canals or channels (canalization) that will form the duct system of the gland. Myoepithelial cells surround the terminal portions of the developing gland.

15

Figure 15-11. Diversity in Anatomical Position, Number and Teat Morphology Among Mammals

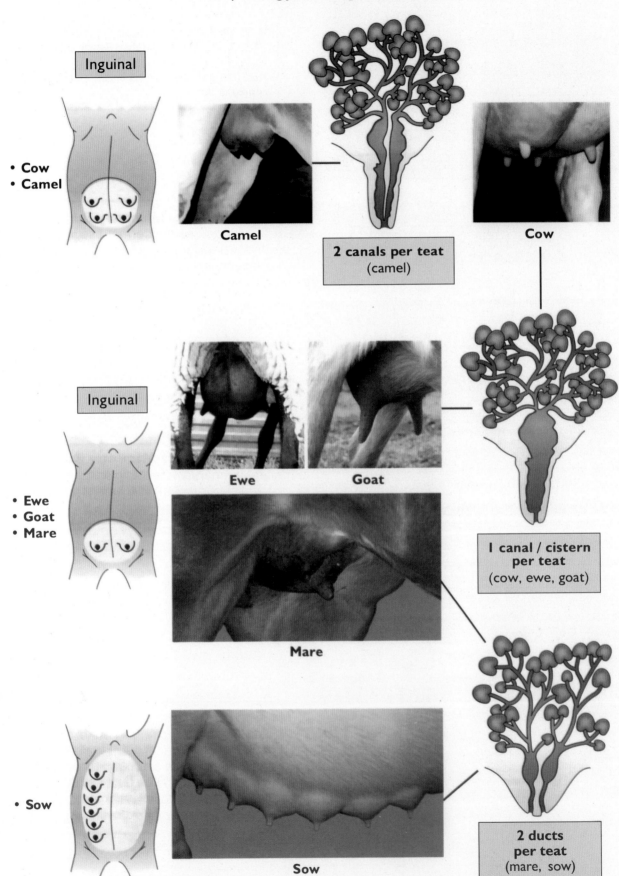

Inguinal
- Cow
- Camel

Camel

2 canals per teat
(camel)

Cow

Inguinal
- Ewe
- Goat
- Mare

Ewe   Goat

Mare

1 canal / cistern
per teat
(cow, ewe, goat)

- Sow

Sow

2 ducts
per teat
(mare, sow)

15

Figure 15-11. Diversity in Anatomical Position, Number and Teat Morphology Among Mammals

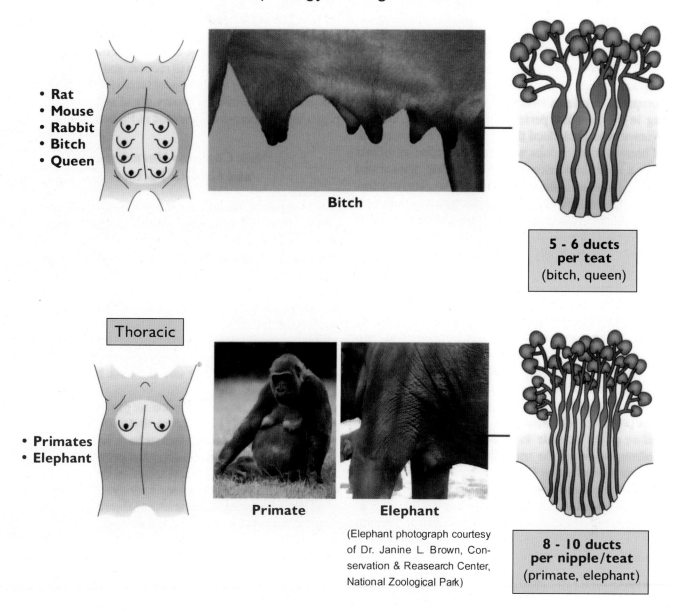

* **Rat**
* **Mouse**
* **Rabbit**
* **Bitch**
* **Queen**

Bitch

**5 - 6 ducts
per teat**
(bitch, queen)

Thoracic

* **Primates**
* **Elephant**

Primate   **Elephant**

(Elephant photograph courtesy
of Dr. Janine L. Brown, Con-
servation & Reasearch Center,
National Zoological Park)

**8 - 10 ducts
per nipple/teat**
(primate, elephant)

ties into a common duct is called a lobe. During the final trimester of pregnancy, the **lobulo-alveolar structures** develop to the point where they represent nearly 90% of the cellular mass of the mammary gland at parturition. Prolactin, adrenal cortical hormones and placental lactogen are important in allowing the mammary epithelium to synthesize milk. As seen in Chapter 14, all of these hormones increase dramatically just before the time of parturition. The induction of parturition is carefully timed with the onset of the mammary gland's ability to secrete copious quantities of milk so that the neonate has immediate access to milk.

Lactation Provides Immunoprotection and Nutrition for the Neonate

The first secretions from the mammary gland (called colostrum) are critical to neonatal survival because the milk from the dam contains immunoglobulins (antibodies). These immunoglobulins are ingested by the neonate and are transported unaltered by the cells of the gut mucosa to provide passive immunity. In ruminants (and other animals) with an epitheliochorial placenta, maternal immunoglobulins cannot be transferred in-utero because the placenta is a barrier. Thus, ingestion of colostrum soon after birth provides necessary immunologic protection for the newborn. In

15

contrast, humans and other animals with hemochorial placentation have placental transfer of immunoglobulins from the dam to the fetus. The fetus is thus born with at least partial passive immunity. Immunoglobulins in milk are still important to neonatal immunoprotection in primates.

Breastfed infants suffer fewer ear infections, respiratory infections and gastrointestinal disorders compared to infants who are formula fed. Early feeding in the neonatal period can have lifelong impact. Women who breastfeed their babies have a lower risk of breast cancer. Adults who were breastfed as infants have a lower incidence of obesity, cardiac disease and Type I diabetes compared to those who received formula. Calves fed milk have higher growth rates and lower morbidity and mortality compared to calves fed milk-replacer. In addition, calves that grow faster during the milk-feeding period can produce more milk during their lifetimes.

Colostrum is provided for a brief period (2 to 3 days) and then milk composition remains relatively constant for the remainder of the lactation. During the course of lactation, milk synthesis increases and then peaks shortly after parturition. After the secretory peak, the synthetic rate decreases and this generally coincides with the time of weaning. It is important to recognize that growth of the neonate is directly proportional to milk protein production by the dam. In some instances, failure of the neonate to grow can be due to mastitis (inflammation of the mammary gland) or agalactia (failure to synthesize milk). It should be emphasized that in some breeds of sheep and goats the reproductive goal is to produce triplets and quadruplets. This goal conflicts with the anatomy/lactation ability of the dam since these species have only two teats. Nutrition of the neonate may thus be compromised since there may not be enough milk to serve the nutritional demands of the offspring.

Involution is the Return to a Nonsecretory State

As the need for milk as the sole nutritional source begins to decrease, the neonate begins to suckle less frequently. Consequently, there is a buildup of pressure within the mammary gland causing the secretory cells to become less and less functional. This phenomenon is called **pressure atrophy**. Pressure atrophy is such a powerful force that milk synthesis can be stopped in just a few days if the intramammary pressure is allowed to buildup suddenly. The milk synthesis occurring in the alveolar epithelium decreases to the point that the cells undergo almost complete atrophy. Secretory cells will remain nonfunctional until a subsequent pregnancy. With a subsequent pregnancy, prolactin,

adrenal cortical hormones and placental lactogen will restimulate alveolar cells to produce milk for another lactation.

During involution, immune cells such as lymphocytes and macrophages invade the mammary tissue. Mammary involution is a critical process because it allows the mammary gland to recover and develop new secretory tissue for a subsequent lactation. Changes in the tissue mass of the mammary gland as a function of reproductive stage are presented in Figure 15-12.

Milk Contains Hormones and Growth Factors

Many substances that are found in blood can also be found in milk. Thus, milk naturally contains hormones and growth factors that are derived from the blood of the lactating female. Also, exogenous materials such as alcohol, drugs, antibiotics, etc. can be found in milk if they are consumed by the dam. Before the advent of controlled nutrition in dairy cattle, it was not uncommon for milk to have an onion-like flavor in the spring because cows grazed in pastures and consumed wild onions growing there. Chemicals causing the onion flavor pass directly into the milk because they are lipid soluble.

Protein hormones such as prolactin, GnRH, growth hormone (somatotropin), thyroid hormone (thyroxine) and their releasing factors have been identified in milk. It should be emphasized that protein hormones have little or no physiological effect on the neonate (or the consumer) because they are hydrolyzed into amino acids in the gastrointestinal tract and therefore lose their biologic activity.

All steroid hormones can be found in milk. The concentration of estrogen and progesterone in milk reflects cyclic hormone production by the ovaries and is highly correlated with blood concentrations. Such a phenomenon enables progesterone to be easily assayed in milk to determine the reproductive status of the female. Cowside ELISA technology enables progesterone concentrations in milk to be determined. Procedures to assay progesterone at each milking through the use of "in-line" assay technology in the milking parlor is a worthy research and development pursuit. The concept would utilize a small sensor in each milking machine that can transduce the progesterone concentration into an electrical signal that could be transferred to the computer. The development of such technology would enable the producer to determine whether a cow is cycling, the stage of the estrous cycle, the pregnancy status and some forms of ovarian pathology (e.g. cystic ovarian disease) for each cow on a daily basis. The availability of such technology would revolutionize reproductive management of dairy cows.

15

Figure 15-12. Changes in the Mammary Gland as a Function of Reproductive Stage

(Modified from Mepham. 1987. *Physiology of Lactation*)

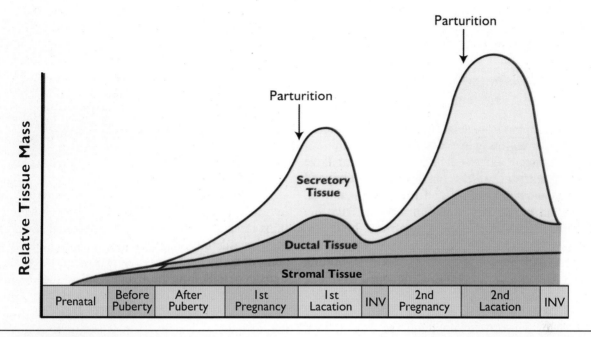

The mammary gland undergoes continuous change from prenatal life through subsequent lactations. During pubertal onset the ductal and secretory tissue of the mammary gland increases. During the first pregnancy these tissues continue to increase but at a faster rate. At the time of parturition, the secretory tissue mass is high and continues to increase until it peaks shortly after parturition during the first lactation. At the conclusion of the first lactation (either weaning or drying-off in the dairy cow) the secretory tissue mass decreases significantly (mammary involution, INV). During the second pregnancy and lactation secretory tissue and ductal tissue increases significantly. Following lactation a second involution (INV) takes place.

Growth Factors in Milk May Provide New Insights to Neonate Health

It is known that a number of growth factors are present at high levels in **colostrum**. Colostrum is the first milk produced after parturition and contains antibodies to provide the neonate with passive immunity. These growth factors mirror the profile of immunoglobulins secreted into the colostrum. Researchers have hypothesized that the accumulation of growth factors in colostrum evolved to promote neonatal growth and development. Examples of growth factors found in colostrum are Insulin Like Growth Factors 1 & 2 (IGF1&2), Epidermal Growth Factor (EGF) and Transforming Growth Factor a and b (TGF-a, TGF-b). Most of the discoveries related to the presence of these growth factors in milk are relatively recent. Since growth factors are present in milk and have significant biologic activity, two outcomes could be important. First, the discovery that these growth factors exist opens a new avenue of study implicating mammary secretions in neonatal health and development that go beyond simply meeting nutritional needs. Secondly, there must be some molecular protection mechanism for these growth factors that prevents digestion by the gastrointestinal tract. Better understanding in both areas could open doors regarding neonatal health and growth and protection mechanisms for various proteins.

Peptides are Physiologically Derived from Milk Proteins

Over 15 physiologically active peptides are derived from milk proteins. These peptides have been implicated in controlling blood pressure (**antihypertensive**), prevention of blood clots (**antithrombotic**) and activating the immune system (**immunostimulation**). Opioid peptides from milk proteins (caseins and lactalbumin) have morphine-like activity. Some of these "**casomorphins**" are believed to prolong gastrointestinal transit time by inhibiting gut motility. Such an effect is antidiarrheal. Further, the dynamics of amino acid transport and induction of **insulin** and **somatostatin** production may be a function of these casomorphins.

15

One additional proposed function of casomorphins is that they produce an analgesic effect causing drowsiness and sleep in infants. While little is known about the physiologic activity of these milk protein derived peptides, the fact that many of these materials have distinct pharmacological effects opens new doors for the potential use of milk in a therapeutic sense.

Pharmaceutical Proteins are Secreted in Milk of Transgenic Animals

By employing genetic engineering techniques, it is now possible to "genetically engineer" a mammary gland that would secrete materials that can have significant therapeutic effects on the consumer beyond the known nutritional effects of milk. For example, recombinant human antithrombin purified from the milk of transgenic goats has been approved for human use by the U.S. Food and Drug Administration and the European Medicines Agency to treat a rare clotting disorder. The amount of this drug obtained from one goat in a year is equivalent to that from 90,000 human blood donations. A second product, recombinant human C1 inhibitor, purified from rabbit milk and used to treat hereditary angioedema, has been approved for use in the European Union. Other pharmaceutical proteins secreted in milk from transgenic animals and currently in FDA clinical trials include fibrinogen, malaria antigen, albumin and several other clotting factors. Exploiting the mammary gland of transgenic animals as an organ to synthesize and secrete pharmaceutical proteins holds great promise as health promotion interventions.

Milk Ejection Transfers Milk from the Mammary Alveoli into the Ducts

Milk ejection is the active transfer of milk from the alveoli and alveolar ducts into the larger mammary ducts, the cisterns and into the teat or nipples where it can be removed by the suckling neonate. Milk ejection should not be confused with milk secretion. Milk is synthesized and secreted by the alveolar cell into alveolar lumina. Prior to suckling (or milking) milk is predominately located in alveolar lumina and the fine ducts draining the alveoli. Milk stays in these anatomical regions because there is a strong resistance to milk flow in such a small diameter network (a form of capillary action causing retention of the milk). Between sucklings (or milkings) 70% to 80% of all secreted milk is located within the lumina of the alveoli and small ducts of the mammary gland. Therefore, an active mechanism for removal of this large quantity of milk is necessary so that the neonate can have access to it through suckling.

> *Milk ejection requires:*
>
> - *sensory activation (auditory, tactile and visual)*
> - *neural activation of the hypothalamus*
> - *oxytocin release into the blood*
> - *contraction of the myoepithelial cells*
> - *mechanical transfer of milk from alveoli into ducts and finally into the teat/nipple*

Milk ejection is an active neuroendocrine reflex involving sensory neurons in the teat or nipple, release of oxytocin from the neurohypophysis and contraction of myoepithelial cells that surround each alveolus and some of the ducts. The ejection process results in a rapid transfer of milk from the alveolus and smaller ducts into the larger ducts and cisterns of the mammary gland. Myoepithelial cells are spindle shaped contractile cells that surround each alveolus in a mesh-like fashion (See Figure 15-13). Myoepithelial cells are very similar in structure to smooth muscle cells. The process of milk ejection is also referred to as "milk letdown." Efficient and timely removal of milk from the mammary gland is important not only for extraction of milk by the neonate, but also is an important part of the milk harvest to prevent pressure atrophy. In general, the more frequently milk is removed, the less the pressure atrophy and greater the quantity of milk that can be secreted.

Tactile stimulation of the teat or nipple is the primary sensory "driver" for milk ejection. In addition to direct tactile stimulation of the teat or nipple, sounds of the neonate (or the milking parlor), visual sight of the newborn or a milking facility can stimulate release of oxytocin from the neurohypophysis. Release of oxytocin is brought about by afferent nerve fibers that synapse with oxytocin synthesizing neurons in the paraventricular and the supraoptic nuclei. When sufficient frequency of stimulation has been accomplished, nerves in the two nuclei begin to fire and release oxytocin from their terminals located in the neurohypophysis. Oxytocin is then secreted into the blood and enters the systemic circulation of the dam. The physiology of milk ejection is presented in Figure 15-13.

The **myoepithelial cells** within the mammary gland have receptors for oxytocin and contract immediately upon exposure to it. When myoepithelial cells contract they cause the diameter of the alveolus to be greatly reduced. Thus, milk is ejected into larger ducts and is transferred into the larger spaces and finally into the teat or nipple.

Figure 15-13. The Anatomy and Physiology of Milk Ejection

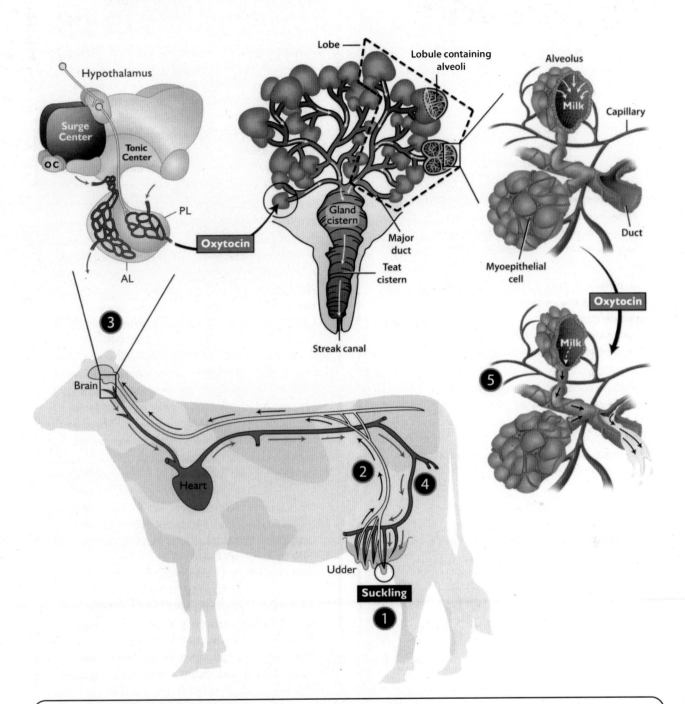

The milk ejection mechanism is initiated by suckling (1). The teat contains sensory neurons and impulses from these neurons travel through afferent nerves (2) to the hypothalamus. Nerves in the paraventricular nuclei are stimulated by these afferent neurons and the terminals in the posterior lobe of the pituitary (3) release oxytocin. Oxytocin then enters the blood and is delivered to the mammary gland (4). The target cells for oxytocin are the myoepithelial cells that surround the alveolus. Contraction of the myoepithelial cells (5) causes milk to be "squeezed" out of each individual alveolus into small ducts and then into larger ducts. The net effect of simultaneous contraction of the myoepithelial cells throughout the entire mammary gland is to deliver milk to the large ducts and the gland cistern so that it is available for removal by the neonate.

15

Further PHENOMENA for Fertility

"Bedroom Talk: Reproductive Physiology Style"
by Ruth Loomis

Hey honey, wake-up and quit your snoring
I think I can feel my E_2 levels soaring.
My ovary is primed for the LH surge,
Come on, wake-up, I've got the urge!

I'm certain this egg is ripe for fertilization,
But, in case you've forgotten, that does require
insemination!
And I recall, it's been nearly a week
Your epididymal reserves must be at peak!

Oh, I see you need a bit more stimulation.
I could continue with some more phonation?
No, don't close your eyes. Wake-up and take
notice.
I'm displaying some absolutely fabulous lordo-
sis!

What's that you say, you want me to look
On page --- of my reproduction book?
So your telling me this passage has led you to
reflect
That what would really work for you is the
Coolidge Effect?!

Is that so? Well do as you wish, my darling, my
sweets
But know this, you won't be sleeping between
these two sheets!

Ruth Loomis was a student in Animal Reproductive Physiology at Washington State University in the spring of 2002 and based the poem above on the nomenclature she learned in the reproduction course. She graduated from Washington State University with a BA in English Literature. She is now in the College of Veterinary Medicine at WSU (Class of 2006).

The 19th Century British explorer, Sir Richard Burton, developed a recipe that he believed enhanced sperm production and viability. Such a recipe would result in an increased probability of conception. He used a mixture of honey, opium, spices and a small lizard. The purpose of the lizard has not been disclosed. The author believes that Sir Burton knew something about sperm motility and related the rapid crawling motion of a lizard to that of spermatozoa.

Oysters can change from one gender to another and back again.

The tale of the mini ball pregnancy gives new meaning to the term target tissue. A surgeon in the Civil War treated two patients that had been shot near one another. One patient was a soldier who was protecting the treatment ward and suffered a gunshot that passed through his scrotum and took off the left testicle completely on its way out. The other patient was a nurse who received a serious shot to the left side of her abdomen, the bullet lost somewhere inside. Miraculously the woman survived the wound but months later she began to notice abnormal swelling of her abdomen. The surgeon was sure the woman was pregnant, but the patient and the villagers all swore to her absolute virginity. Upon examination it was found that the woman was indeed pregnant, with hymen still intact. The child was born without difficulty but soon it was noticed that the young boy had a large, hard mass contained within his right testicle. The doctor operated on the young child to remove the lump and was astounded to discover the contents of the testicle was none other than the missing mini ball that wounded the mother nine months before. The solution to this mysterious conception? The surgeon thought that this mini ball must have been the same one to have mutilated the soldier's testicle, carrying sperm with it into the uterus of the nurse after the bullet left the first victim, where it remained and functioned to fertilize one of her eggs! How could the ball get into the scrotum of the neonate? What parts of this narrative are absolutely false and which could be true? A great final exam question!

Key References

Akers, R.M. 2002. *Lactation and the Mammary Gland*. Iowa State Press, Ames ISBN 0-8138-2992-5.

Arthur, G.H. D.E. Noakes, H. Pearson, and T.J. Parkinson. 1996. *Veterinary Reproduction and Obstetrics*, 7th Edition. W.B. Saunders, Co. Philadelphia. ISBN 0-7020-1785-X.

Gier, H.T. and G.B. Marion. 1968. "Uterus of the cow after parturition: involutional changes." *Am. J. Vet. Res.* 29:83-96.

Larson, B.L. ed. 1985. *Lactation*. Iowa State Press, Ames. ISBN 0-8138-1063-9.

McEntee, K. 1990. *Reproductive Pathology of Domestic Animals*. Academic Press, Inc. San Diego. ISBN 012-483375-6.

Mepham, T.B. 1987. *Physiology of Lactation*. Open University Press, Philadelphia. ISBN 0-335-15152-3.

Morrow, D.A. 1969. "Postpartum ovarian activity and involution of the uterus and cervix in dairy cattle." *Veterinary Scope*. Vol 14.

Salamonsen, L.A. 2003. "Tissue injury and repair in the female human reproductive tract." *Reprod.* 125:301.

Salisbury, G.W., N.L. VanDemark and J.R. Lodge. 1978. *Physiology of Reproduction and Artificial Insemination in Cattle*. 2nd Edition. W.H. Freeman and Co., San Francisco. ISBN 0-7167-0025-5.

Schmidt, G.H. 1971. *Biology of Lactation*. W.H. Freeman, San Francisco. ISBN 07-1670821-3.

15

CHAPTER 16

Reproductive Physiology-
THE HUMAN FACTOR

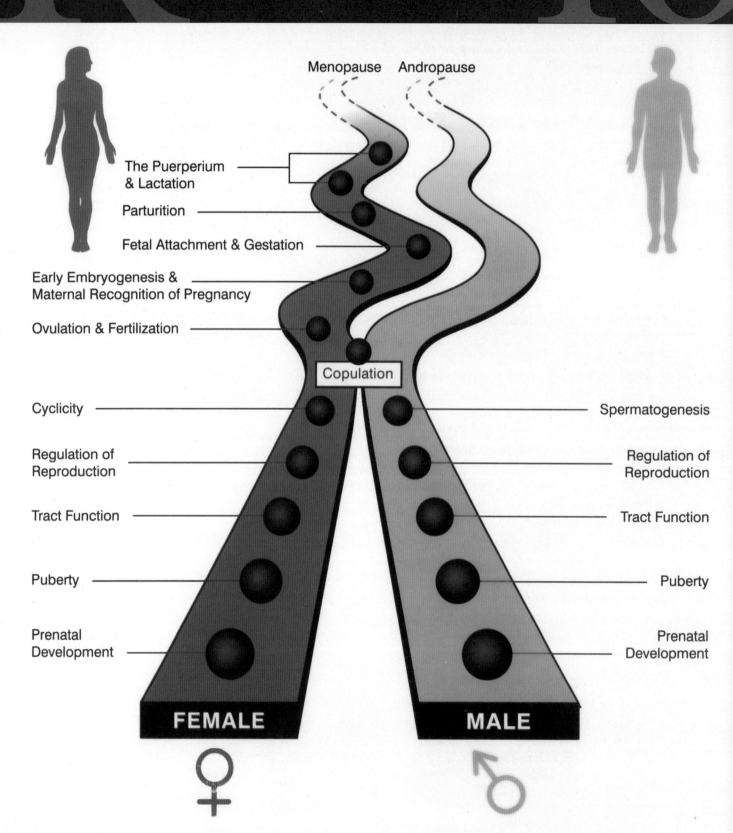

Take Home Message

Previous chapters have described the physiology of the 15 events along the pathway of the reproductive process. In this chapter, we will address human reproduction by describing four factors that distinguish reproduction in humans from other mammals.

These are:
- *The menstrual cycle that involves monthly endometrial sloughing*
- *Hormonal contraception that is used as a pregnancy management intervention*
- *Assisted reproductive technologies (ART) that are used to overcome infertility*
- *Menopause and andropause that are natural consequences of extended lifespans*

A very high percentage of the population is directly experiencing one or more aspects of the above. Understanding the physiologic basis for these factors is important for high compliance with intervention use, good reproductive health and a high quality of life.

In animals, reproductive processes can be discussed openly, manipulated without reservation and pregnancies are viewed as an essential expectation because high reproductive rates are obligatory for efficient food animal production and maintenance of wild populations of animals. Unfortunately, reproductive physiology in humans is often confused with sex and this confusion results in controversies focusing around ethical, religious, political and personal values that detract from the fundamental value of understanding how the reproductive system works. Consequently, there is a significant degree of misunderstanding about reproductive function. These misunderstandings result in untrue hearsays, myths, unfounded opinions and poor knowledge of reproductive science in general. This chapter will focus on the physiologic principles of how the reproductive system works in humans especially as it relates to contemporary interventions that directly impact reproductive function.

It is predicted that the world population will approach 10 billion by the year 2050. This will create frightening pressures on the production and allocation of food resources especially the production of animal based protein (meat, milk and eggs). The field of reproductive physiology likewise is under similar pressures because on one hand the goal is to improve and maximize reproductive performance in food-producing animals, while on the other hand to restrict and manage reproductive rate in the human population. An additional challenge is to find ways that knowledge about reproductive science can be objectively presented to different cultures, religions and political structures with the ultimate goal of improving reproductive health and the quality of life.

The Physiology of the Menstrual Cycle has a Different Starting Point Than the Estrous Cycle

Understanding the physiology of the menstrual cycle is an important prerequisite for good reproductive health, pregnancy prevention and family-planning. It should be understood by both women and men. Understanding the menstrual cycle requires basic knowledge about: 1) the female reproductive organs and their functions; 2) the major hormones and their secretory patterns during the cycle; 3) how the major hormones influence the function of the reproductive organs; 4) how the major organs impact behavioral/emotional status of the woman and 5) the major ovarian and uterine changes that occur during the cycle.

A recent study indicated that almost 40% of survey participants incorrectly identified or didn't know the menstrual cycle length and 22% did not know if their own menstrual cycles were normal or abnormal. In addition, only 2% of adolescent girls reported receiving information regarding menstruation from their health care providers. The majority of the information was obtained from their mothers (85%), friends or sisters (6.5%) or no one (6%). These data suggest the girls are not receiving scientifically accurate information about their menstrual cycles (See Houston in **Key References**).

An earlier study involving female university students found that: 1) 59% of participants could not properly describe the sequence of menstrual cycle events; 2) 30% of the women could not provide a basic definition of menstruation; 3) approximately 33% of the participants did not know how hormones fluctuated during the cycle and 4) 54% could name only one of the hormones involved, but could not describe the function of the hormone (See Koff in **Key References**).

The data above indicates a compelling lack of knowledge about the menstrual cycle among American women. This lack of knowledge undoubtedly translates into the fact that approximately 50% of the six million annual pregnancies in the United States are unintended.

> ## *The menstrual cycle consists of the following six events:*
>
> - *menstruation*
> - *follicular growth*
> - *ovulation*
> - *corpus luteum formation and growth*
> - *endometrial growth and secretion*
> - *luteolysis*

In Chapter 7, we compared the menstrual cycle with the estrous cycle. The menstrual cycle differs from the estrous cycle in two fundamental ways. First, endometrial sloughing (menses) occurs in a predictable manner during every cycle if the woman is not pregnant. Second, there is no defined period of sexual receptivity. In this chapter, we want to discuss the menstrual cycle as a series of six distinctly different events (See Figure

16-1). Remember, the menstrual cycle starts at the first day of the menstrual period (menses). This timing convention originated because the menstrual period was an observable event and marked the start of each menstrual cycle. Typically, the length of the menstrual cycle is 28 days, but can range from 25 to 34 days. This is the period of time from the start of one menstrual period to the start of the next menstrual period.

The onset of menstruation signals the start of the cycle and is it designated as day 1. Following menstruation, marked follicular growth takes place in response to FSH and LH from the anterior pituitary. At about day 14, ovulation occurs. The newly ovulated follicle then develops into a corpus luteum (CL). The CL secretes progesterone and some estrogens. These hormones promote endometrial growth. Near the end of the cycle, if a woman is not pregnant, the corpus luteum undergoes luteolysis and loses its ability to secrete progesterone (See Figure 9-14). The rapid drop in progesterone stimulates the onset of the next menstrual period. Figure 16-1 describes the events of the menstrual cycle in a circular and linear fashion.

The menstrual cycle is usually described as having two components. One component is the **ovarian cycle** that describes changes that occur in the ovary during the cycle. The **uterine cycle** describes the changes that take place in the endometrium of the uterus during the cycle.

The menstrual cycle also consists of the **follicular phase** and the **luteal phase** (See Figure 16-2). Follicular growth during and following menstruation is referred to as the follicular phase because the dominant

---

Figure 16-1. Menstrual Cycle Sequence

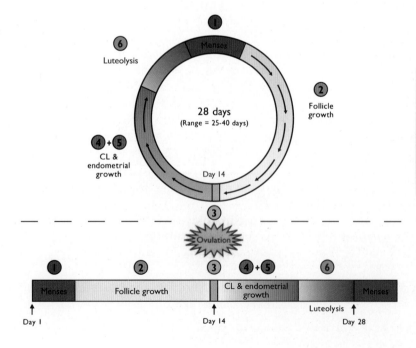

> The six major events of the menstrual cycle are shown by the circled numerals. Their relationship to the timing of the cycle is illustrated in circular form in the top portion of the graphic and in linear form in the bottom portion of the graphic.

16

ovarian structures are follicles. The dominant ovarian hormone is estradiol. After ovulation, the luteal phase begins. The dominant ovarian structure is the corpus luteum and the dominant ovarian hormone is progesterone. It should be emphasized that while both the menstrual cycle and estrous cycle are characterized by the follicular and luteal phases, follicles are constantly developing and regressing in both phases of the cycle. In other words, even during the luteal phase follicles develop and regress.

During the follicular phase, the anterior pituitary secretes FSH and LH (See Figure 16-2). These hormones promote growth of ovarian follicles and the growing follicles secrete increasing quantities of estrogens. A threshold concentration of estradiol triggers the LH surge that causes ovulation. After ovulation the luteal phase begins. The follicle that just ovulated becomes the corpus luteum and secretes high concentrations of progesterone and some estradiol. The high concentrations of progesterone inhibit GnRH secretion from the hypothalamus and FSH and LH secretion from the anterior pituitary. Therefore, follicles do not develop to the preovulatory stage during the luteal phase. At

about day 23-24, progesterone drops rapidly because luteolysis has occurred. This sudden drop in progesterone is thought to cause symptoms of **premenstrual syndrome (PMS)** in many women. Further, the drop in progesterone initiates endometrial sloughing and the next menstrual period.

The uterine cycle is subdivided into the **proliferative** and **secretory phases**. The proliferative phase is the increase in endometrial thickness in response to estradiol secreted by growing follicles. This increased thickness is referred to as the proliferative phase because the cells of the endometrium divide by mitosis (proliferate). After ovulation and formation of the CL, progesterone promotes further increased thickness in the endometrium and it develops secretory capacity. This is important because if conception takes place at around day 14, the embryo will enter an environment about three days later that is ideal for sustaining embryo development prior to implantation. If pregnancy does not occur, luteolysis is initiated, progesterone drops precipitously and a new menstrual period (and menstrual cycle) begins (See Figure 16-3.).

Figure 16-2. Relative Blood Concentrations of FSH, LH, Estradiol and Progesterone During the Follicular and Luteal Phases of the Menstrual Cycle

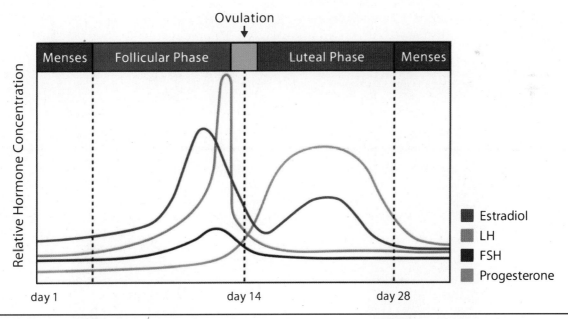

During the menstrual period, all hormones are low. During the follicular phase, FSH promotes follicular development. Developing follicles secrete increasing amounts of estradiol. The estradiol peak during the late follicular phase stimulates the preovulatory surge of LH and ovulation takes place shortly thereafter. After ovulation the corpus luteum develops and secretes progesterone and estradiol. If the woman is not pregnant, luteolysis is initiated during the late luteal phase and progesterone drops rapidly and a new menstrual period begins. Note that FSH and LH are low during the luteal phase because of the negative feedback by progesterone on the hypothalamus that inhibits GnRH and thus FSH and LH.

Figure 16-3. Major Endometrial Changes During the Menstrual Cycle

The endometrium begins to proliferate immediately after menstruation (about day 7) and continues to grow during the proliferative phase until the time of ovulation. After ovulation, a CL is formed and progesterone causes continued proliferation of the endometrium during the secretory phase. Luteolysis, caused by intraovarian $PGF_{2\alpha}$ causes progesterone and estradiol to drop dramatically. Please review Figure 9-14 for the mechanism of luteolysis mechanism and see Figure 16-3 for the hormonal profile.

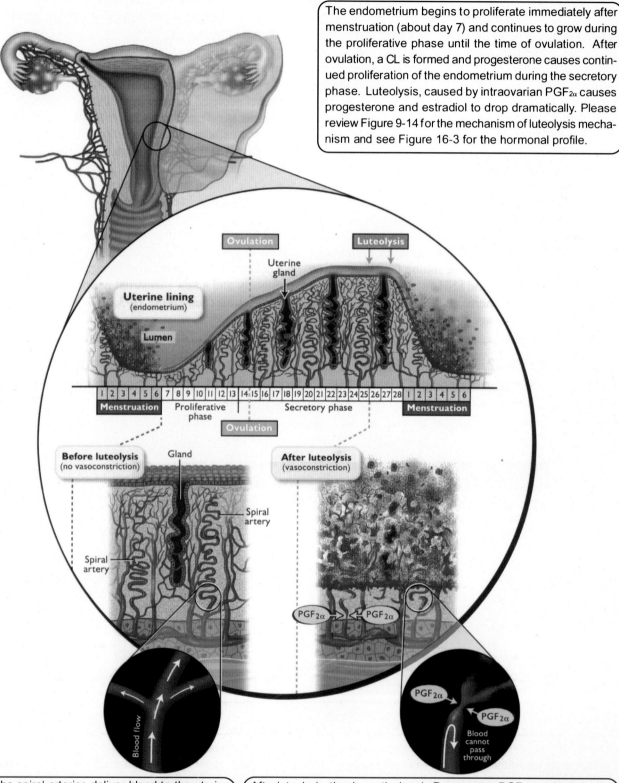

The spiral arteries deliver blood to the uterine glands during the proliferative and secretory phases before luteolysis. A high blood flow to the endometrium facilitates secretion.

After luteolysis, the dramatic drop in P_4 promotes $PGF_{2\alpha}$ synthesis by the endometrium that causes sustained vasoconstriction in the spiral arteries. Sustained vasoconstriction causes ischemia and the endometrium undergoes necrosis and sloughs into the uterine lumen. Endometrial sloughing (menstruation) lasts from 2 to 6 days.

16

Figure 16-4. Relationships Between Emotional/Mood Status and Estradiol and Progesterone During the Menstrual Cycle

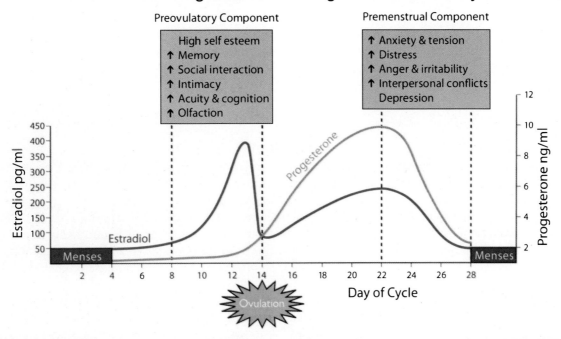

During the 5-6 days prior to ovulation ("preovulatory component"), estradiol increases and decreases dramatically. The elevated estradiol has been associated with emotional changes that reflect confidence and agressiveness.

In contrast, the 3-5 days during precipitous progesterone decline that precedes the menstrual period ("premenstrual component") is characterized by emotions reflecting tension, anger and anxiety in many women.

> ***Progesterone and estradiol undergo huge fluctuations during the menstrual cycle:***
>
> • ***estradiol increases about 5X during the 5-6 days before ovulation***
>
> • ***progesterone decreases by about 10X during the 2-3 days preceding menses***

It should be emphasized that estradiol and progesterone undergo dramatic changes in concentration during the course of one menstrual cycle. For example, during the mid-follicular phase, estradiol concentrations are about 30 pg/mL of blood. In the 5- 6 days that follow, estradiol increases to about 140 pg/mL of blood. In other words, the concentration of estradiol increases by about 5X during this 5 or 6 day period. During the luteal phase, progesterone increases from about 1-2 ng/mL of blood to 9-10 ng/mL of blood. This represents a 5-9 fold increase in progesterone during a 4-6 day period. After luteolysis, progesterone drops from a peak of 9-10 ng/mL to 1 ng/mL during a 2-3 day period, another 10X change in progesterone. No other hormone in the body changes this dramatically in such a short period of time (See Figure 16-4).

Throughout the course of history it has been known that profound emotional and behavioral changes occur during the menstrual cycle. However, only recently have we begun to understand how the hormonal fluctuations in estradiol and progesterone during the menstrual cycle influence brain function, cognition, emotions, sensory processing, appetite and probably many more as yet unidentified functions. Research involving the stages of the menstrual cycle on emotional status and other central nervous system functions has given validity to the concept that PMS is a set of physiologic-driven responses to rapid and dramatic concentration changes in estradiol and progesterone during the cycle. The fact that hormonal changes influence behavioral and emotional changes in the female should be recognized by everyone. It is particularly important that men understand the relationship between stage of the cycle and behavioral changes. This is because most women intuitively understand the emotional changes that are occurring, but men need to understand the magnitude of the hormonal "swings" and the behavioral/emotional changes that accompany them. Such an understanding would enable empathetic responses that would undoubtedly foster more positive relationships during the premenstrual component of the cycle.

16

Figure 16-4 describes some of the emotional differences that occur during the late follicular phase and late luteal phase. During the late follicular phase, estradiol promotes an overall feeling of well being, desire for intimacy, confidence and increased cognitive ability. There is evidence that during the late follicular phase, there is a significant increase in the number of synaptic junctions in the hippocampus (a region of the cerebral cortex that is thought to play a role in learning and memory). In contrast, during the late luteal phase (about 5 days prior to the onset of menstruation) significant temporary mood changes occur in a high percentage of women. These changes have been labeled as **premenstrual syndrome (PMS)**. A syndrome is a group of symptoms that occur together. The emotional symptoms associated with PMS vary significantly among women and can be characterized by feelings of anxiety or tension, sadness, irritability, anger, changes in appetite and feelings of being overwhelmed or out of control. Physical symptoms include cramps, backaches, muscle spasms, nausea, dizziness, breast tenderness and unpleasant tingling or swelling of the hands and feet. There are no precise or predictable symptoms of PMS and the degree of severity is quite variable among women. Between 70 and 90% of women experience some physical and emotional difficulties before menstruation begins. While most women experience one or more of these symptoms, only 5-10% of women experience severe and debilitating symptoms.

It is important to recognize that there is a significant amount of variation in the expression of the symptoms of PMS both within and among women. In other words, the symptomatic expressions may vary from cycle-to-cycle and from woman-to-woman. Regardless, it is clear that physical and emotional changes occur during the menstrual cycle and these are linked to the dramatic changes in estradiol and progesterone concentrations that occur during the menstrual cycle. It is important for both men and women to understand that these physical and emotional changes have a strong physiologic basis and should not be considered a "black box" of unexplained behavior.

Steroidal Birth Control is a Method to Control Ovulation

As pointed out earlier, there is no defined period of sexual receptivity associated with the menstrual cycle. Therefore, sexual intercourse can take place at any time during the cycle. Thus, frequent sexual intercourse can occur and increases the probability of pregnancy. In this context, contraception methodologies have been an important component of human reproduction throughout history, especially during the last century. Here we will address steroidal contraception because, unlike barrier methods, understanding the reproductive physiology underlying its use increases the chances of success.

Contraception means opposing conception. It is defined as the prevention of pregnancy as a consequence of sexual intercourse. There are many contraceptive methods that can be used to minimize the probability of pregnancy. Steroidal contraception is a physiologic intervention that utilizes progestins to prevent ovulation and thus prevent pregnancy. Preventing fertilization (conception) is a contraceptive approach to **birth control**. Birth control means managing or preventing birth. Fundamentally, there are three forms of birth control. These are: a) **contraception** or prevention of conception (preventing the union of sperm and the oocyte); b) **interception** (preventing implantation) and c) abortion (disruption of a pregnancy after implantation). An ethical/moral consideration should be realized by all women who use steroidal contraception. In some cases, conception can occur, but the steroidal intervention prevents optimal uterine conditions for embryo survival and implantation. The woman has no way of knowing if pregnancy was prevented by preventing ovulation (contraception) or minimizing the chance of implantation (interception). This is not to be confused with an abortive intervention. Abortion refers to the termination or loss of an embryo after implantation. It is important to recognize that even when couples are trying to conceive, 30-50% of embryos fail to implant under normal conditions. Please refer to Figure 12-13 and adjacent text for pregnancy probability relative to time of ovulation. The discussion in this chapter will focus entirely on steroidal contraception because it is a physiologic intervention that involves hormonal manipulation that prevents ovulation.

From a physiologic perspective, steroidal contraception can be used as a method of reproductive management for family-planning. It is well known that about 50% of all pregnancies in the United States are unintended. Furthermore, about 78% of all pregnancies among American teenagers are unintended. Therefore, the mechanisms responsible for the effectiveness of steroidal contraception should be understood by both women and men in order to maximize the effectiveness of this important intervention.

Regardless of the delivery method, the net effect is a sustained luteal phase. Figure 16-5 compares the estradiol and progesterone profile in an unaltered cycle with the progesterone profile of the cycle in which exogenous progesterone is administered. Notice, that women using progestin contraception have no follicular phase. Therefore, follicles do not develop to maturity and will not ovulate. Like in the normal cycle, when progestin concentrations drop, the woman will menstruate. In summary, regardless of the type of hormonal

Figure 16-5. Estradiol and Progesterone Profiles During a Normal Menstrual Cycle and With Steroidal Contraception

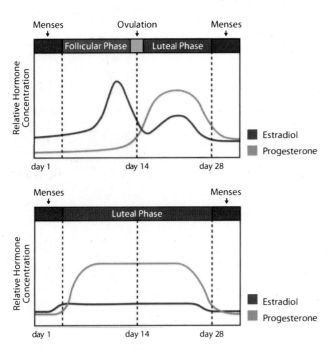

Steroidal contraception results in a sustained luteal phase when compared to a normal menstrual cycle. Shortly after administration of progesterone, blood levels increase and remain high for the remainder of the cycle until progesterone is withdrawn (placebo pill, removal of patch or vaginal ring, or metabolism of the injected progestin).

contraception used, ovulation is usually prevented because progestin and estrogens inhibit GnRH and therefore FSH and LH is inhibited. Follicles don't grow and ovulate. If ovulation does not occur, pregnancy is not possible.

The various steroidal contraception delivery methods are:

- *pill (daily)*
- *transdermal patch (weekly)*
- *intravaginal ring (monthly)*
- *injection (every 90 days)*

The primary active ingredient in steroidal contraception is progestin. Here, we use the term progestin to refer to any natural or synthetic material that has progesterone-like actions. Progestins can be administered orally, by injection, by release from a transdermal patch or release from an intra-vaginal ring. They can also be released from some **intrauterine devices (IUDs)** or from implants. Each method delivers progestins at different frequencies.

Many interventions contain an estrogen. The purpose of estradiol is two-fold. First, estrogens promote normal reproductive tract function. Second, low concentrations of estrogens cause negative feedback on GnRH neurons and thus have a negative effect on FSH and LH secretion.

Oral contraception applications are characterized by a 28-day hormonal regimen and these are summarized in Figure 16-6. The woman takes a progestin or progestin/estradiol pill for 21 consecutive days. On the following 7 days, a placebo pill containing no hormone is taken and this mimics luteolysis because progestin drops rapidly and a new menstrual period is initiated. The key to the success of this method is diligence in taking the pill every day and approximately the same time every day. This ensures that progesterone concentrations will remain high and stable. It should be emphasized that failure to take one or more pills in succession will result in decreased progestin levels in the blood and the probability of elevated FSH and LH increases, particularly if several pills are missed in succession.

The transdermal patch contains progestin that diffuses through the skin and enters the blood. Patches are replaced every week and during the patch-free week progestin concentrations drop and a new menstrual period begins. Patches can be placed at various locations in the body including the upper arm, the abdominal region, the buttocks and the shoulder blade. In order to be effective, a patch that is removed must be replaced by a new patch every week except during the patch-free week.

The vaginal ring is inserted into the vagina and steadily releases uniform concentrations of progestin that are absorbed through the vaginal tissues and enter the blood. One vaginal ring releases progestin for three weeks. After the ring is removed, blood progesterone drops and a new menstrual period is initiated.

Progestin injections provide a continual 90-day hormonal absorption from the injection site. The progestin injection is not reversible. Therefore, for a period of 90 days there will be neither ovulation nor menstrual periods. After approximately 90 days, the progesterone source is depleted and menses will occur and so will ovulation in about 2 weeks if progestin is not administered during or after the menstrual period.

16

Figure 16-6. Influence of the Pill, Patch, Vaginal Ring and Injection Upon Progestin Profile

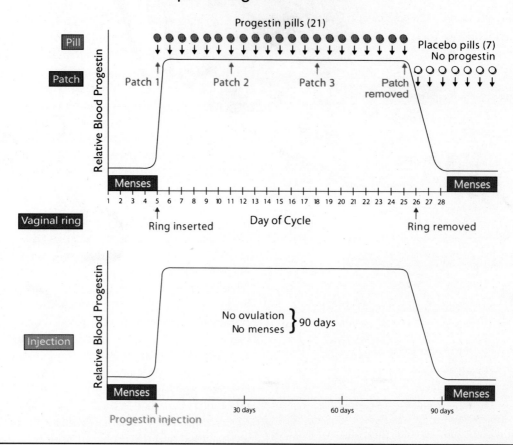

The pill, patch and vaginal ring all release progestins. In all three cases, the menstrual period is initiated after progestin administration stops. The difference between these three applications is the frequency at which they are administered. The pill is taken orally for a period of 21 days followed by 7 days of placebo pills. The patch is applied and then replaced with a new patch each week for three weeks. The vaginal ring is inserted and is removed after 21 days. Progestin injection results in elevated blood progestin for 90 days during which there will be no ovulation and no menstrual periods.

Assisted Reproductive Technology (ART) Provides Conception Opportunities For Infertile Couples

Assisted reproductive technology (ART) describes any procedure in which the sperm and oocytes are united outside the body that result in a viable zygote and embryo. One or more embryos are then transferred back into the woman's uterus to generate a pregnancy. These techniques are performed by a physician in conjunction with a reproductive biologist who is trained in embryology and andrology. The most commonly used ART method is **in-vitro fertilization (IVF)** in which oocytes are fertilized by one of two methods. First, sperm may fertilize oocytes in-vitro under "their own power". In other words, motile sperm penetrate the cu-

mulus cells, zona pellucida and the oocyte plasma membrane to form a zygote. This is called **conventional IVF** in which the man provides adequate numbers of viable sperm. In cases where the man cannot provide adequate numbers of viable sperm, a single sperm is injected into the oocyte. This technique is called **intracytoplasmic sperm injection or ICSI**.

In-vitro fertilization requires:
- *semen collection*
- *semen evalution and preparation*
- *ovarian stimulation*
- *oocyte retrieval and preparation*

16

IVF is intended to generate pregnancies in women with blocked or missing oviducts, women with endometriosis, women who fail to ovulate, men with inadequate sperm function and couples with unexplained infertility. ART procedures are conducted in fertility clinics that specialize in IVF procedures, early embryo culture and development and transfer procedures.

Now, let's look at the sequence of events (See Figure 16-7) that take place for the woman and the man during typical IVF procedures. In the woman, the ovaries are hormonally stimulated so that a higher than normal number of follicles develop. After ovarian stimulation, oocytes are retrieved from each preovulatory follicle transferred to a culture environment. In the male, semen is typically collected by masturbation and processed for fertilization. A semen analysis is performed in advance of ovarian stimulation and used to determine the method of fertilization (either conventional IVF or ICSI). If there are adequate numbers of normal sperm, the specimen can be used for conventional IVF. If there are inadequate numbers of sperm then ICSI is used. A successful fertilization results in the development of the embryo that progresses from the pronuclear stage to the 2, 4, 8 cell, morula and then to a blastocyst.

Semen Evaluation is Performed Prior to a Couple Beginning IVF Procedures

The first step in male fertility evaluation is collection of semen. Typically, a semen evaluation is conducted prior to initiation of the IVF procedure. This evaluation could be considered as a screening test to determine whether the man is producing sufficient quantities of viable sperm for conventional IVF. The three most important characteristics of the spermatozoa are: concentration of sperm in the ejaculate, adequate numbers of viable sperm (motile sperm) and low numbers of abnormal sperm. While each ART clinic has its own set of criteria, guidelines are provided by the World Health Organization (WHO). These guidelines indicate that a fertile ejaculate should contain more than 20 million sperm per milliliter, with greater than 50% motility. An ejaculate that meets these criteria is eligible for conventional in-vitro fertilization where spermatozoa fertilize oocytes under their "own power". If the ejaculate does not meet these criteria then plans are made to perform intracytoplasmic sperm injection (ICSI).

Figure 16-7. Sequence of IVF Events and Preimplantation Embryo Development

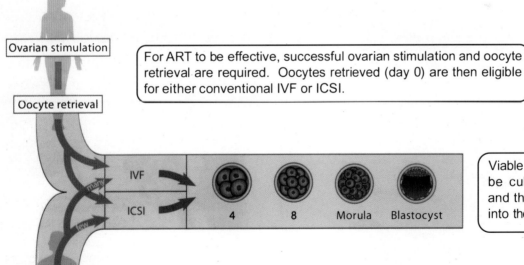

Ovarian stimulation

For ART to be effective, successful ovarian stimulation and oocyte retrieval are required. Oocytes retrieved (day 0) are then eligible for either conventional IVF or ICSI.

Oocyte retrieval

IVF

ICSI

4   8   Morula   Blastocyst

Viable embryos will be cultured in-vitro and then transferred into the uterus.

Sperm processing/preparation

Sperm quality determines which fertilization technique will be used. After semen collection and preparation, if there are sufficient viable sperm conventional IVF will be performed. If insufficient sperm are present, ICSI is used.

Semen collection

16

Ovarian Stimulation Promotes Development of Multiple Follicles

Having multiple oocytes provides increased probability for successful fertilization and embryo development. Ovarian stimulation begins with an injection of FSH, or an FSH-like hormone and concludes with human chorionic gonadotropin (hCG). It should be emphasized that there are many options for ovarian stimulation. These vary depending on the reproductive status of the woman and from clinic-to-clinic. As shown in Figure 16-8, exogenous FSH or an FSH-like hormone stimulates growth of more than one follicle. In this example, four follicles within one ovary respond to FSH and these follicles secrete estradiol like in the normal cycle. The four follicles continue to grow larger

---

Figure 16-8. Ovarian Stimulation With FSH and hCG

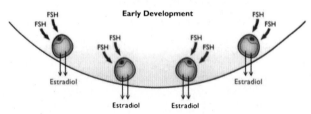

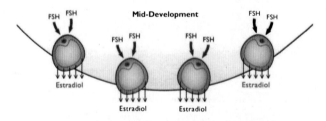

Ovarian stimulation causes development of higher than normal numbers of follicles. In this example, four follicles develop simultaneously after stimulation with FSH.

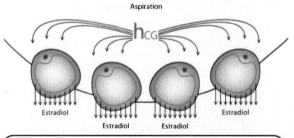

At the appropriate time, the woman is treated with human chorionic gonadotropin (hCG) to stimulate final development and maturation of the follicles. Oocytes are retreived from the follicles using transvaginal ultrasound aspiration.

into mid-development and secrete more estradiol. Final ovarian stimulation continues using hCG. Like LH, hCG promotes final follicular maturation and growth coupled with elevated estradiol secretion. When ready, oocytes are aspirated from these large follicles.

Oocyte Retrieval is Accomplished by Transvaginal Ultrasound Aspiration

Transvaginal aspiration is a technique that combines ultrasound imaging with the mechanical process of inserting a needle into each mature follicle and applying slight suction to dislodge the oocyte and remove it from the follicle. This procedure is typically conducted in the physician's office or in an outpatient clinic. Some form of mild general analgesia is generally administered. The first step in the procedure is to insert an ultrasound probe into the vagina that enables it to be positioned in close proximity to the ovary. Preovulatory follicles that are eligible for aspiration are identified. In the ultrasound images, they appear as dark circles within the ovary. Upon identification of eligible follicles, a small needle is guided along the wall of the ultrasound probe, through the wall of the vagina and into each follicle (See Figure 16-9). Once inside the follicle, slight suction is applied to the needle. This suction dislodges the oocyte and can be aspirated. In general, all eligible follicles in both ovaries can be aspirated within 30 minutes. While this procedure is minimally invasive, some women may experience cramping. This

---

Figure 16-9. Oocyte Retrieval Using Transvaginal Ultrasound Aspiration

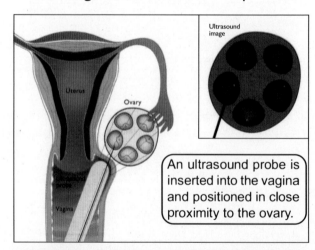

An ultrasound probe is inserted into the vagina and positioned in close proximity to the ovary.

A small needle is guided along the ultrasound probe and inserted through the wall of the vagina and into preovulatory follicles. Slight suction is applied to dislodge the oocyte and it is aspirated into a collection vessel.

16

Figure 16-10. Retrieved Oocyte, ICSI and Male and Female Pronuclei

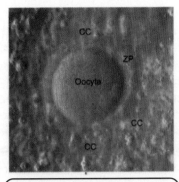
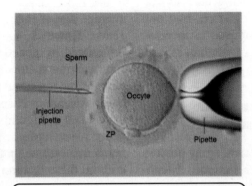
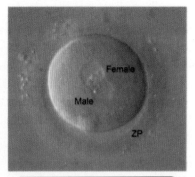

A recently retrieved oocyte with cumulus cells (CC) surrounding the zona pellucida (ZP). In conventional IVF, sperm penetrate the cumulus cells and zona pellucida before fertilizing the oocyte. *Micrograph courtesy of West Virginia University Center for Reproductive Medicine.*

With ICSI, the cumulus cells are removed by enzymatic digestion and then the denuded oocyte is inseminated. The oocyte is held in position by a pipette that applies slight suction to the zona pellucida (ZP). The sperm is injected with a glass pipette. *Micrograph courtesy of West Virginia University Center for Reproductive Medicine.*

The presence of a male and female pronuclei in the oocyte cytoplasm indicates that fertilization has taken place. Each pronucleus contains the genetic material from the woman and the man. *Micrograph courtesy of West Virginia University Center for Reproductive Medicine.*

is not serious and generally subsides within one hour. Immediately after aspiration, the oocytes are placed in a culture medium that supports their viability.

Retrieved Oocytes are Surrounded by a Layer of Cumulus Cells

Cumulus cells are remnants of granulosal cells that surround the freshly retrieved oocyte (See Figure 16-10). In the case of conventional IVF, sperm are capacitated in-vitro and added to the culture medium containing the oocyte where they penetrate the cumulus cells and eventually the zona pellucida. Typically, sperm are allowed to interact with the oocytes overnight. In cases where ICSI is used, the cumulus cells are removed by enzymatic digestion so that the zona pellucida is denuded of cells thus enabling the procedure to be more efficient.

Figure 16-10 is a composit of photomicrographs illustrating the ICSI procedure. After the cumulus cells are removed, the oocyte is held in place using a pipette that applies slight suction to the zona pellucida. At the opposite pole of the oocyte, a small glass pipette containing a single sperm is injected through the zona pellucida, the plasma membrane of the oocyte and into the cytoplasm. The ICSI procedure generally takes less than one minute per oocyte.

If fertilization is successful, the oocyte is characterized as having a male and female pronucleus (See Figure 16-10). Typically it takes about 18 hrs for the pronuclei to form after addition/injection of the sperm.

Embryo Transfer is a Non-Surgical Procedure

The transfer procedure is illustrated in Figure 16-11. A small flexible catheter is inserted into the vagina and threaded through the cervix into the uterus. The highest quality embryos are transferred into the uterus. The goal of IVF is one healthy baby. Guidelines for the number of embryos transferred as a function of

Figure 16-11. Embryo Transfer

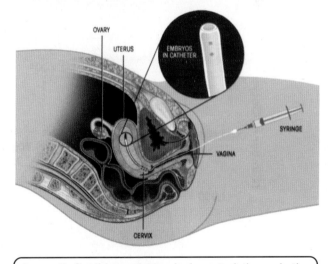

A small, flexible catheter is inserted through the vagina, cervix and into the lumen of the uterus. The catheter usually contains two embryos. It is attached to a syringe and the fluid containing the embryos is deposited. The catheter is then removed.

16

patient age, stage of embryo development and embryo a quality are available through the Society for Assisted Reproductive Technology (SART). Often, two and sometimes three embryos are transferred to increase the probability of a single birth even though twins and triplets are possible.

Reproductive Aging in Women (Menopause) and Men (Andropause)

Menopause is part of the natural aging process and is defined as lack of menstrual periods. Menopause is defined as the age of the last menstrual period.

Perimenopause refers to the timeframe (e.g., few years before and after) around the last menstrual period. The average age of menopause in western countries is 51 years. However, age of menopausal onset is heavily influenced by genetics, ethnicity and general health status. Some factors associated with early menopause include: having relatives who reached menopause early, being African or Hispanic, have a history of smoking, have lived at high altitudes for most of one's life, or being a vegetarian. Women in these categories can reach menopause up to two years sooner than women without these factors.

Figure 16-12. Changes in Oocyte Numbers Throughout the Life-span of the Human Female

(Modified from Palter and Olive in *Novak's Gynecology*, 11th Ed.)

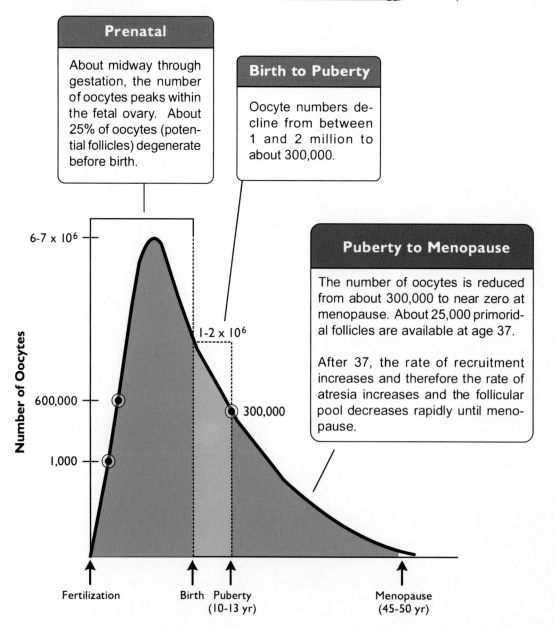

Prenatal

About midway through gestation, the number of oocytes peaks within the fetal ovary. About 25% of oocytes (potential follicles) degenerate before birth.

Birth to Puberty

Oocyte numbers decline from between 1 and 2 million to about 300,000.

Puberty to Menopause

The number of oocytes is reduced from about 300,000 to near zero at menopause. About 25,000 primoridal follicles are available at age 37.

After 37, the rate of recruitment increases and therefore the rate of atresia increases and the follicular pool decreases rapidly until menopause.

$6\text{-}7 \times 10^6$

$1\text{-}2 \times 10^6$

600,000

300,000

1,000

Number of Oocytes

Fertilization

Birth Puberty
(10-13 yr)

Menopause
(45-50 yr)

16

There are profound physiological and psychological changes that accompany menopause. Some changes that occur during the menopausal transition include: decreased cognitive function, genital atrophy, vasomotor fluctuations ("hot flashes"), bone loss, higher risk of cardiovascular disease and collagen loss. These changes are mainly due to marked decreased secretion of estradiol that will be described later in this chapter.

Depletion of Follicles is the Cause of Menopause in Women

The decline in ovarian follicle numbers over the lifetime of the female is summarized in Figure 16-12. At birth, the ovaries contain 1-2 million primordial follicles. These follicles undergo a steady rate of decline until about the age of 37, when approximately 25,000 primordial follicles remain. After age 37, the rate of atresia increases until the woman enters menopause. At this time, approximately 1000 follicles remain. It is likely that these 1000 follicles never get recruited because they are probably not sensitive to gonadotropins. Thus, further follicular development cannot occur.

Follicular Depletion Changes Many Hormone Profiles

During menopausal onset, at least 7 hormones undergo dramatic changes. These are: antiMüllerian hormone (AMH), inhibin, estradiol, testosterone, progesterone, FSH and LH (See Figure 16-13). All of the hormones are directly related to follicular depletion and will be discussed below.

AntiMüllerian Hormone

As follicles are depleted, antiMüllerian hormone (secreted by the granulosal cells of preantral follicles and early antral follicles) also declines. It is important to understand that AMH is responsible for controlling recruitment of primary follicles. AMH also inhibits the FSH sensitivity in antral follicles. Therefore, the net effect of AMH is to promote atresia in developing antral follicles. In other words, suppression of AMH also inhibits the FSH sensitivity in antral follicles. AMH begins to slowly decline with age. However, when AMH declines faster after age 37, this allows more follicles to be recruited and undergo atresia. As a result, the follicular pool is depleted at a faster rate and the number of antral follicles in each cohort decreases with age.

Figure 16-13. Hormone Profile Changes During Menopause

(Modified from F.J. Broekmans, et al., 2009)

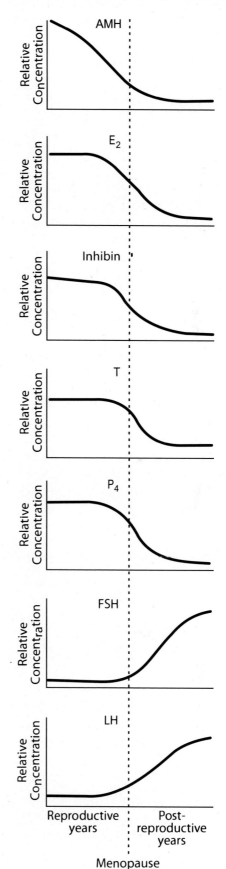

16

Testosterone, Estradiol and Inhibin

In cycling women, testosterone, estradiol and inhibin are important secretory products of antral follicles. Without antral follicles, testosterone, estradiol and inhibin drop dramatically (See Figure 16-13). Recall from Chapter 8 (Figure 8-9) that estradiol secretion takes place in a "2 cell-2 gonadotropin" model where testosterone is secreted by the theca interna cells and converted to estradiol by the granulosal cells. Without these cells neither hormone can be synthesized and secreted.

Progesterone

Progesterone significantly declines when the corpus luteum from the last cycle is lysed. Without future antral follicles and ovulations, corpora lutea cannot be formed. As you recall from Chapter 9, the human corpus luteum secretes estradiol in addition to progesterone (See Figure 9-14). Without estradiol secretions from antral follicles or the corpus lutem, circulating estradiol concentrations in the blood drop dramatically.

FSH and LH

Without AMH, testosterone, estradiol, inhibin and progesterone, negative feedback on the hypothalamus and pituitary does not exist. As a result, FSH and LH concentrations increase dramatically. Post menopausal FSH concentrations are six times greater than FSH concentrations in the normal reproductive years. Concurrently, LH concentrations are four times greater than LH concentrations in the normal reproductive years.

> *Estrogen deficiency results in:*
> - *genital atrophy*
> - *decreased secretion by the reproductive tract*
> - *modification of lipid metabolism and of the vascular walls*
> - *increase in the physiological loss of bone (osteoporosis)*
> - *vasomotor symptoms ("hot flashes")*
> - *decreased cognitive function*
> - *increased fat mass*

Regardless of the number of overall hormonal changes, the single most important hormonal change is the decrease of estradiol. Almost all negative effects associated with menopause are due to lack of estradiol. The primary physiological and psychological effects of menopause relate to estradiol deficiency.

The majority of the symptoms of menopause can be reversed with estradiol. Unfortunately, hormone replacement therapy is surrounded by controversial issues relating to the possible carcinogenic effects of estradiol. More recently, AMH has been suggested as a possible alternative to the conventional hormone replacement therapy. AMH could be used to slow the rate of follicular recruitment and atresia. In this way, the onset of menopause would be delayed. The negative health effects associated with estradiol absence such as osteoporosis, increased cardiovascular disease and decreased cognitive ability would be minimized. For more details about the risks and benefits of hormone replacement therapy, consult the references at the end of this chapter.

Reproductive Aging in Men (Andropause)

Andropause is a decline in reproductive function as it relates to advancing age. However, andropause is not a defined, finite cessation of reproductive capacity. The changes are significantly slower than in the woman. Andropause is characterized by a decline in libido, an increased incidence in erectile dysfunction, loss of muscle and bone mass, physical function, and an increase in fat mass. The biochemical causes of erectile dysfunction are presented in Figure 11-9.

> *Andropause results in:*
> - *decreased libido*
> - *decreased muscle mass*
> - *decreased bone density*
> - *increased fat mass*

Men in the seventh and eighth decade of life have about 70% of daily sperm production when compared to men in their early 30s. Circulating testosterone concentrations decrease approximately 1%-3% per year beginning at the age of 35-40, thus men aged 70-80 have about 50% of circulating testosterone concentrations when compared to younger men. Although hormones decrease with age in males, these changes are minimal compared to the hormonal changes in women (See Figure 16-14).

16

Figure 16-14. FSH and LH Profiles Associated With Gender and Age

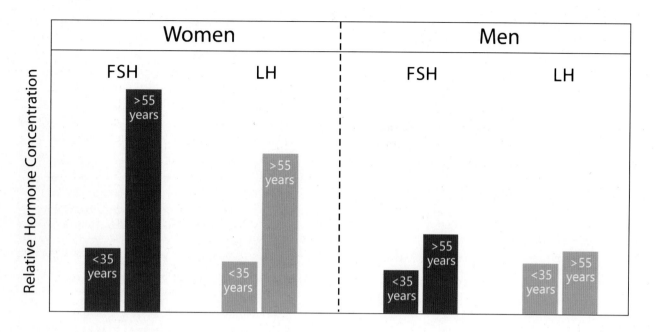

FSH concentrations in older women (post-menopausal years) are approximately six times greater than FSH concentrations when compared to women in their reproductive years. LH concentrations are approximately four times higher in older women when compared to women in their reproductive years.

FSH and LH concentrations increase with age in men as well. However, FSH and LH concentrations in older men are not as dramatic when compared to the hormone changes during and after menopause. Despite higher FSH and LH concentrations, sperm production is still possible.

16

Further PHENOMENA for Fertility

Some African tribes believed that menstrual blood kept in a covered pot for nine months had the power to turn itself into a baby.

The oldest woman to conceive naturally is Dawn Brooke. She gave birth to her son at 59 years of age.

Guiness Book of World Records reported that Jacilyn Dalenberg gave birth to her three granddaughters at age 56. She was a surrogate for her daughter.

Female pilot whales as old as 51 years of age have been observed to be lactating. One female was recorded to have lactated for approximately 11 years after the last ovulation and parturition. The last calf may be suckled until puberty (8 years for females and 11 years for males).

In the 1700s, it was reported that a peasant wife from Russia holds the record for the greatest number of children born to one mother. 27 pregnancies resulted in 16 sets of twins, 7 sets of triplets and four sets of quadruplets, for a total of 69 children. It was also reported that only two children died in their infancy. What is the probability of this story?

40 species of lizards are known to reproduce by parthenogeneis (natural cloning). These species consist of all females. Who needs a male around?

In 2007, Nanu Jogi is reported to have been the oldest known father in the world. He was 90 years old when his 21st child was born.

The typical person spends about 600 hours having sex between the ages of 20 and 70.

Shaking hands is one way to say hello to a friend. However, Walibri tribesmen from Central Australia greet each other by shaking each other's penises.

Besides the eyelid, the scrotal skin is the only part of the body with little or no subcutaneous fat.

The nesting behavior of the Silvery-Cheeked Hornbill adds new meaning to the term "cabin fever". When the time comes to incubate the eggs, the female finds a suitable hole in a tree and goes inside. The male then brings mud to his spouse who "plasters" herself inside for over three months. She leaves a narrow opening so that the male can deliver food for her and the chicks.

Two separate British courts in the 1980s reduced the sentences of women who killed their husbands on the grounds that severe PMS (premenstrual syndrome) was responsible for transforming the normally sane women into maniacs.

It has been calculated that the average man will ejaculate approximately 18 quarts of semen containing over half a trillion sperm over his lifetime.

The voice of a male frog deepens and gets louder with age.

The average speed of the ejaculate during a male orgasm is 28 mph, according to the Kinsey Institute.

A dragonfly's penis has a shovel on the end that scoops out a rival male's sperm.

16

Key References

Berek, J. ed. 1996. *Novak's Gynecology*, 13th Edition. Williams and Williams. Baltimore. ISBN 0-7817-3262-X.

Broekmans, F.J., M.R. Soules and B.C. Fauser. 2009. Ovarian aging: Mechanisms and Clinical Consequences. *Endo Rev.* 30(5) 465-493.

Driancourt, M.A., A Gougeon, A. Royere and C. Thibault. 1993. "Ovarian function" in *Reproduction in Mammals and Man*. p281-306. C. Thibault, M.C. Levasseur and R.H.F. Hunter, eds, Ellipses, Paris. ISBN 2-7298-9354-7.

Houston, A, Abraham, A, Zhihuan Huang, Z., and D'Angelo, L. (2006). Knowledge, attitudes, and consequences of menstrual health in urban adolescent females. *J Pediatr Adolesc Gynecol.* 19:271-275.

Horstman, A.M., Dillion, E., Urban, R. and M. Sheffield-Moore. 2012. The role of androgens and estrogens on healthy aging and longevity. *J Gerontol A Biol Sci Med Sci,* doi: 10.1093/gerona/gls068.

Koff, E., Rierdan, J., and Stubbs, M. (1990). Conceptions and misconceptions of the menstrual cycle. *Women & Health,* 16(3/4): 119-136.

Lobo, R. 2004. "Menopause and Aging" in *Yen and Jaffe's Reproductive Endocrinology-5th Edition,* Strauss and Barbieri, eds. Elsevier, Philadelphia. ISBN 0-7216-9546-9.

Netter, A. 1993. "The menopause" in *Reproduction in Mammals and Man*. p627-642. C. Thibault, M.C. Levasseur and R.H.F. Hunter, eds., Ellipses, Paris. ISBN 2-7298-9354-7.

Synder, P. 2004. "Male Reproductive Aging" in *Yen and Jaffe's Reproductive Endocrinology-5th Edition,* Strauss and Barbieri, eds. Elsevier, Philadelphia. ISBN 0-7216-9546-9.

Udolff, L.C. and E.Y. Adashi 1998. "Menopause" in *Encyclopedia of Reproduction*, Vol. 3 p183-188. Knobil and Neill, eds. Academic Press, San Diego. ISBN 0-12-227023-1.

16

GLOSSARY

accessory sex glands. Glands of the male reproductive system surrounding the pelvic urethra that produce seminal plasma. The accessory sex glands are the vesicular glands (seminal vesicles), prostate, bulbourethral glands (Cowper's Glands) and ampullae.

acid hydrolases. Hydrolytic enzymes within the acrosome that aid in sperm penetration of the zona pellucida.

acrosin. A proteolytic enzyme specific to the acrosome of spermatozoa. Acrosin causes zona pellucida dissociation during sperm penetration.

acrosomal granule. An intracellular granule within the young spermatid resulting from the condensation of Golgi products within the confines of the acrosomal membrane that will give rise to the acrosomal contents. (See Figure 10-6)

acrosomal phase. A specific developmental phase of spermatid differentiation in which the acrosome extends toward the posterior of the nucleus. (See Figure 10-7)

acrosomal reaction. An orderly fusion of the spermatazoal plasma membrane with the outer acrosomal membrane. This fusion initiates the release of acrosomal enzymes from the acrosome that allow the sperm to penetrate the zona pellucida. (See Figure 12-11)

acrosomal reaction promoting ligand/region. One of two binding sites found on the sperm plasma membrane that binds with the zona pellucida (ZP3). Binding of this ligand to ZP3 initiates the acrosomal reaction. (See Figure 12-10)

acrosomal vesicle. An intracellular vesicle within the young spermatid resulting from fusion of smaller Golgi vesicles; the precursor to the acrosome. (See Figures 10-6, 10-7)

acrosome. A membrane-bound organelle of the spermatozoon that covers the anterior one-third to one-half of the nucleus. It contains proteolytic enzymes required for penetration of the zona pellucida. (See Figure 10-7)

action potential. The rapid, all-or-none depolarization of a nerve cell membrane that is propagated from a nerve cell body to the axon and to another nerve or to an effector organ.

active transport. Transport of materials across a cell membrane against a concentration gradient (from low concentration to high); requires energy in the form of ATP.

activin. A protein hormone that stimulates follicle stimulating hormone (FSH) secretion. Activin belongs to a broader family of proteins that modify tumor growth and cell differentiation.

adeno-. A prefix designating a glandular organ or tissue. For example, the adenohypophysis is the glandular portion of the hypophysis.

adenohypophysis. The anterior lobe of the pituitary gland.

adenosine triphosphate (ATP). The energy source of the cell. It is synthesized from adenosine diphosphate (ADP). (See Figure 5-14)

adenylate cyclase. A membrane-bound enzyme activated by a hormone-receptor complex, and by G-protein. Adenylate cyclase promotes conversion of ATP to cyclic AMP. (See Figure 5-14)

adipocyte. A fat cell.

adluminal compartment. The compartment or zone of a seminiferous tubule defined at its lower boundary by the tight junctions of Sertoli cells and at its upper boundary by the lumen of the seminiferous tubule. (See Figure 3-16)

adrenal corticoids. A class of steroid hormones produced by the adrenal cortex that govern mineral metabolism, induce parturition and mediate response to stress.

adrenal corticotropin (ACTH). A glycoprotein hormone produced by the anterior lobe of the pituitary that controls the release of adrenal corticoids.

agonist. Any substance capable of binding to receptors for the native substance and that causes action identical to the native substance. Degree of response varies depending on the agonist.

allantochorion. The extraembryonic membrane resulting from the fusion of the chorion and the allantois. (See Figure 13-4)

allantois. One of the extraembryonic membranes formed from the embryonic ectoderm that serves as a liquid waste storage reservoir for the developing fetus. (See Figure 13-4)

allometric growth. Growth of an organ or tissue that is disproportionately faster than the growth in the remainder of the body.

alpha fetoprotein (AFP). A fetal protein that binds estradiol and prevents it from crossing the blood-brain barrier.

alpha subunit. The protein subunit of a glycoprotein hormone common to all gonadotropins. (See Figure 5-8)

amenorrhea. Absence of or abnormal cessation of cyclicity as manifested by lack of menses.

amnion. One of the extraembryonic membranes formed from the chorion that surrounds and encloses the fetus. It is filled with fluid and serves to protect the embryo against mechanical damage and to prevent tissue adhesions. (See Figure 13-4)

GLOSSARY

accessory sex glands. Glands of the male reproductive system surrounding the pelvic urethra that produce seminal plasma. The accessory sex glands are the vesicular glands (seminal vesicles), prostate, bulbourethral glands (Cowper's Glands) and ampullae.

acid hydrolases. Hydrolytic enzymes within the acrosome that aid in sperm penetration of the zona pellucida.

acrosin. A proteolytic enzyme specific to the acrosome of spermatozoa. Acrosin causes zona pellucida dissociation during sperm penetration.

acrosomal granule. An intracellular granule within the young spermatid resulting from the condensation of Golgi products within the confines of the acrosomal membrane that will give rise to the acrosomal contents. (See Figure 10-6)

acrosomal phase. A specific developmental phase of spermatid differentiation in which the acrosome extends toward the posterior of the nucleus. (See Figure 10-7)

acrosomal reaction. An orderly fusion of the spermatazoal plasma membrane with the outer acrosomal membrane. This fusion initiates the release of acrosomal enzymes from the acrosome that allow the sperm to penetrate the zona pellucida. (See Figure 12-11)

acrosomal reaction promoting ligand/region. One of two binding sites found on the sperm plasma membrane that binds with the zona pellucida (ZP3). Binding of this ligand to ZP3 initiates the acrosomal reaction. (See Figure 12-10)

acrosomal vesicle. An intracellular vesicle within the young spermatid resulting from fusion of smaller Golgi vesicles; the precursor to the acrosome. (See Figures 10-6, 10-7)

acrosome. A membrane-bound organelle of the spermatozoon that covers the anterior one-third to one-half of the nucleus. It contains proteolytic enzymes required for penetration of the zona pellucida. (See Figure 10-7)

action potential. The rapid, all-or-none depolarization of a nerve cell membrane that is propagated from a nerve cell body to the axon and to another nerve or to an effector organ.

active transport. Transport of materials across a cell membrane against a concentration gradient (from low concentration to high); requires energy in the form of ATP.

activin. A protein hormone that stimulates follicle stimulating hormone (FSH) secretion. Activin belongs to a broader family of proteins that modify tumor growth and cell differentiation.

adeno-. A prefix designating a glandular organ or tissue. For example, the adenohypophysis is the glandular portion of the hypophysis.

adenohypophysis. The anterior lobe of the pituitary gland.

adenosine triphosphate (ATP). The energy source of the cell. It is synthesized from adenosine diphosphate (ADP). (See Figure 5-14)

adenylate cyclase. A membrane-bound enzyme activated by a hormone-receptor complex, and by G-protein. Adenylate cyclase promotes conversion of ATP to cyclic AMP. (See Figure 5-14)

adipocyte. A fat cell.

adluminal compartment. The compartment or zone of a seminiferous tubule defined at its lower boundary by the tight junctions of Sertoli cells and at its upper boundary by the lumen of the seminiferous tubule. (See Figure 3-16)

adrenal corticoids. A class of steroid hormones produced by the adrenal cortex that govern mineral metabolism, induce parturition and mediate response to stress.

adrenal corticotropin (ACTH). A glycoprotein hormone produced by the anterior lobe of the pituitary that controls the release of adrenal corticoids.

agonist. Any substance capable of binding to receptors for the native substance and that causes action identical to the native substance. Degree of response varies depending on the agonist.

allantochorion. The extraembryonic membrane resulting from the fusion of the chorion and the allantois. (See Figure 13-4)

allantois. One of the extraembryonic membranes formed from the embryonic ectoderm that serves as a liquid waste storage reservoir for the developing fetus. (See Figure 13-4)

allometric growth. Growth of an organ or tissue that is disproportionately faster than the growth in the remainder of the body.

alpha fetoprotein (AFP). A fetal protein that binds estradiol and prevents it from crossing the blood-brain barrier.

alpha subunit. The protein subunit of a glycoprotein hormone common to all gonadotropins. (See Figure 5-8)

amenorrhea. Absence of or abnormal cessation of cyclicity as manifested by lack of menses.

amnion. One of the extraembryonic membranes formed from the chorion that surrounds and encloses the fetus. It is filled with fluid and serves to protect the embryo against mechanical damage and to prevent tissue adhesions. (See Figure 13-4)

B

basal compartment. The compartment of the seminiferous tubule containing spermatogonia between the basement membrane and the tight junctions of adjacent Sertoli cells. (See Figure 3-16)

base of penis. The proximal portion of the penis that is attached to the floor of the pelvis by a suspensory ligament in larger species.

beta subunit. The protein subunit of a glycoprotein hormone that gives the hormone its specificity or uniqueness. (See Figure 5-8)

bicornuate uterus. A uterus consisting of distinct uterine horns (cornua). (See Figure 2-15)

binucleate giant cells. Cells originating in the chorion of the ruminant placenta that migrate toward the endometrial epithelium and produce pregnancy-specific substances. (See Figure 14-4)

bipotential gonad. The gonad of the developing embryo that is capable of differentiating along two developmental pathways toward the development of either a testis or the ovary.

birth control. Managing or preventing birth.

blastocoele. The cavity in the central portion of the blastocyst.

blastocyst. An early embryo consisting of an inner cell mass, a blastocoele and a trophoblast.

blastomere. A cell produced by the cleavage divisions of the early embryo.

blood-testis barrier. The specialized permeability barrier consisting primarily of multiple junctional complexes (tight junctions) between Sertoli cells that divides the seminiferous epithelium into the basal compartment and the adluminal compartment. Two separate environments exist between these two compartments.

bovine interferon tau (bIFN-τ). A glycoprotein produced by the preimplantation bovine conceptus that allows maternal recognition of pregnancy by inhibiting oxytocin receptor synthesis by the endometrial cells.

bovine trophoblastic protein 1. See bovine Interferon τ.

broad ligament. The ligament (continuous with the peritoneum) that supports the female reproductive tract consisting of the mesometrium, the mesosalpinx and the mesovarium.

buffer. A mixture of an acid and its conjugate base that when present in solution, minimizes any changes in pH when acid or alkali are added and thus helps maintain the pH of physiologic fluids so that cell viability is maintained.

bulbospongiosus muscle. A thick, circular, striated muscle that is continuous with the urethralis muscle at the position of the bulbourethral glands. It covers the bulb of the penis and attaches to the proximal shaft of the penis. In the stallion, it extends on the ventrolateral surface of the penis to the glans penis.

bulbourethral glands (Cowper's glands). Paired glands that lie on the dorsal surface of the caudal end of the pelvic urethra. These glands are so named because they are associated with the bulb of the penis and the pelvic urethra.

bursa (pl. bursae). A sac or saclike cavity that may contain a fluid and usually located in areas subject to friction. The ovarian bursa is a saclike structure that will completely (bitch) or partially (sow) surround the ovary.

C

canalize. To furnish with, or convert to a canal or canals.

canalization. Formation of canals or tube-like structures within a tissue.

cap phase. The phase of spermatid differentiation in which the acrosomic vesicle begins to spread over the anterior portion of the spermatid nucleus. (See Figure 10-7)

capacitation. The process whereby spermatozoa acquire fertility in the female reproductive tract. (See Figure 12-8)

caput epididymis. The head of the epididymis.

caruncle. In ruminants, a button-like area of the uterine endometrium that will form the maternal side of the cotyledonary placenta.

caruncular regions. Highly vascular and non-glandular regions of the ruminant uterus that protrude from the endometrial surface. They will form the maternal cotyledon, the maternal contribution to the placentome.

casomorphins. Opioid peptides from milk proteins that have morphine-like activity.

cauda epididymis. The tail of the epididymis; the primary sperm storage reservoir of the extragonadal duct system.

cell lysis. Rupturing of the cell membrane resulting in cell death.

cervical seal of pregnancy. A highly viscous plug that cements the folds of the cervix together during pregnancy, thus isolating the developing fetus from the exterior environment.

cervix. A structure consisting of dense connective tissue with varying degrees of folding and protrusion of the mucosal epithelium. The cervix connects the uterus to the vagina.

chorion. The outermost extraembryonic membrane, derived from the trophoblastic ectoderm. It will develop villi that will form the fetal sites of placental attachment.

chorionic girdle. A specialized region of the chorion in the equine fetus that forms the initial attachment to the endometrium.

chorionic gonadotropins. Glycoprotein hormones produced by the trophoblastic cells of the placenta that cause stimulation of the ovary in the pregnant female.

chorionic villus (villi). Small, finger like projections found on the surface of the chorion that interface with the maternal placenta. The functional unit of the fetal placenta.

CIDR®. Controlled Intravaginal Drug Release in this case progesterone. That is used for synchronization of estrus in beef and dairy cattle (See Figure 9-17).

cistern of the teat. A holding area or reservoir for milk within the teat. (See Figure 15-13)

cleavage divisions. The series of mitotic divisions of the early embryo within the confines of the zona pellucida giving rise to equally sized daughter cells, called blastomeres.

clitoral fossa. A longitudinal depression or cavity below the surface of the vulva housing the clitoris (especially developed in the bitch and mare).

clitoris. A small body of highly innervated erectile tissue located in the posterior extremity of the ventral vaginal floor. It is the homologue of the penis.

cohort. A group united through/for a common purpose, or a group having certain similarities.

coitus (copulation). The sexual union of male and female during mating that involves intromission. Copulation.

collagenase. An enzyme that breaks down collagen.

colostrum. The first milk produced after parturition that contains antibodies to provide the neonate with passive immunity.

columnar epithelium. An epithelial type consisting of cells that are taller than they are wide, thus resembling columns. (See Figures 2-19 and 2-22)

commissure. A seam or a line resulting from the site of union of two components of an organ system. (See Figures 2-23 and 2-24)

conceptus. The products of conception, including the embryo, the extraembryonic membranes and the placenta.

constrictor vulvae. The bundles of skeletal muscle embedded in the labia that maintain closure of the labial commissure.

contraception. Prevention of conception, preventing the union of the sperm and oocyte.

contralateral. The opposite side.

Coolidge effect. Renewal of sexual stimulation in the sexually satiated male by the introduction of a novel female into the stimulus setting. (See Figure 11-14)

copulatory stage. The second stage of reproductive behavior consisting of mounting, intromission and ejaculation.

cornua. A structure resembling a horn.

cornual insemination. A technique of artificial insemination where the semen is deposited into the horns of the uterus. (See Figures 12-3 and 12-6)

corpus albicans (pl. corpora albicantia). A white scar-like fibrous ovarian structure that represents advanced regreassion of the corpus luteum. (See Figure 2-11)

corpus cavernosum. The cavernous erectile tissue in the central portion of the penis that allows for influx of blood during erection of the penis. (See Figure 3-21)

corpus epididymis. The body of the epididymis. (See Figures 3-15 and 3-18)

corpus hemorrhagicum. A small, blood clot that results from rupture of blood vessels during ovulation. (See Figures 9-2, 9-3, 9-4, and 9-6)

corpus luteum (CL) (pl. corpora lutea). An orange to yellow colored transient endocrine structure formed after ovulation from granulosal and thecal cells of the ovarian follicle. The corpus luteum is responsible for producing progesterone and oxytocin. (See Figures 2-11, 9-2, 9-3, 9-4, 9-6, and 9-8)

corpus prostate. The body of the prostate, located dorsal to the cranial pelvic urethra. (See Figure 3-4)

corpus spongiosum. The portion of erectile tissue in the penis that surrounds the penile urethra. (See Figure 3-21)

cortical reaction. A reaction following spermatozoal penetration of the oocyte in which the membrane surrounding the cortical granule in the oocyte cytoplasm fuses with the oocyte plasma membrane. Their contents are expelled into the perivitelline space. The cortical reaction is believed to prevent polyspermy. (See Figure 12-12)

corticoids. A class of steroid hormones secreted by the adrenal cortex.

cortisol (hydrocortisone). An anti-inflammatory steroid secreted by the adrenal cortex.

cotyledonary. A term referring to the presence of cotyledons (found in ruminants) as the functional unit of the placenta.

cotyledons. The points of attachment between the fetal and maternal placenta, consisting of a maternal cotyledon contributed by the caruncular areas of the uterus and the fetal cotyledon contributed by the chorion of the conceptus. (See Figure 14-3)

countercurrent heat exchanger. Network of the testicular artery and vein in which heat passively diffuses between vessels separating the two streams so that at the end the fluid leaving is the same temperature as the fluid entering the system. (See Figure 3-9)

cranial. Relating to the cranium or head; in the direction of the cranium.

cremaster muscle. A striated muscle continuous with the internal oblique muscle that partially surrounds the spermatic cord and attaches to the parietal vaginal tunic. (See Figures 3-2, 3-3, 3-4, 3-5 and 3-7)

crossing-over. When segments of one chromosome crossover and attach to a homologous chromosome during the pachytene stage of the first meiotic prophase. When the chromatids separate (during anaphase I) crossing-over results in a random assortment of different segments of each chromosome thus assuring genetic heterogeneity.

crus penis. The posterior attached portion of the corpus cavernosum penis. (See Figures 3-3, 3-4, 3-5, 3-6 and 3-7)

cryoprotectant. A material that protects the cell membrane against damage during cooling and freezing.

cryptorchid. An individual in which the testes have failed to descend into the scrotum and remain in the abdominal cavity.

Glossary

cycle of seminiferous epithelium. The progression through a complete series of cellular associations at one location along a seminiferous tubule. (See Figure 10-11)

cyclic AMP. Cyclic adenosine monophosphate; a cyclic nucleotide that serves as a "second messenger" for protein hormone action. (See Figure 5-14)

cyclic recruitment. Follicular recruitment after puberty that results from elevated FSH (follicle stimulating hormone).

cyclicity. The condition in which a female displays estrus (or menstrual) cycles with a predictable duration.

cyclopentanoperhydrophenanthrene. The common nucleus of steroid hormones consisting of three 6-membered rings (A, B and C) and one 5-membered ring (D). (See Figure 5-9)

cytokines. Messenger proteins released by immune cells that act as intercellular mediators of the immune response.

daily sperm production (DSP). The quantity of spermatozoa produced by both testicles in one day.

dartos muscle. See tunica dartos.

decapacitation. The exposure of spermatozoa to seminal plasma after capacitation has occurred, thus requiring additional capacitation time before fertility can again be acquired.

defeminization. Failure to promote the development of female appearance and/or behavior.

depolarization. A change in nerve cell electrical potential caused by sodium influx.

descendin. A material believed to be produced by the fetal testis that promotes rapid growth of the gubernaculum, thus promoting descent of the testis into the scrotum.

Desert Hedgehog Gene (DHH). A member of the hedgehog gene family that encodes for signaling molecules that play roles in tissue differentiation. Specifically, DHH plays a role in differentiation of fetal Leydig cells.

diastolic pressure. The minimum arterial blood pressure reached during the diastolic phase (relaxation) of the cardiac cycle.

dictyotene phase. A phase of meiosis unique to the primary oocyte in which the nuclear material is arrested or rendered inactive until final stages of oogenesis. Oocytes remain in the dictyotene phase in the fetal ovary until final folliculogenesis.

diestrus. The stage of the estrous cycle characterized by a dominance of progesterone from the corpora lutea and periods of relative quiescence of reproductive behavior.

differential-interference contrast microscope. A microscope that transforms differences in intracellular density into an image that gives the appearance of surface relief (See Figure 10-14; ruffled acrosome; knobbed acrosome) or cratering (See Figure 10-14; crater defect).

differentiation. The development of structure and function that is more specialized than the original cells or tissue.

differentiation phase. The final phase of spermatogenesis where a spermatid becomes a fully differentiated spermatozoon.

diffuse placenta. A placenta characterized by uniform distribution of chorionic villi across the surface of the chorion (e.g. pig, mare). (See Figure 14-1)

dimethyl sulfoxide (DMSO). A cryoprotectant used for protecting living cells against damage caused by freezing and thawing.

discoid. Placenta characterized by a regional disk that attaches to the endometrium. Primates have a discoid placenta. (See Figure 14-2)

disseminate prostate. Prostatic tissue diffusely distributed within the walls of the pelvic urethra.

distal cytoplasmic droplet. A remnant of cytoplasm located just posterior to the middle piece of the spermatozoon.

disulfide cross-linking. A covalent linkage between two cystein residues on two different proteins or on two different regions on the same protein. Disulfide cross-linking increases integrity and insolubility. The chromatin in the head of sperm and the structural components of the flagellum have high degrees of disulfide cross-linking. (See Figure 3-18)

diverticulum (pl. diverticula). A blind tube, or outpocketing that diverts from a main tubular organ or cavity.

dominance (follicular). The condition of a large antral follicle in the final stages of maturation. Dominant follicles become atretic when LH levels are low and ovulate when LH levels are high.

dominant follicle. The final maturational structure during folliculogenesis that produces relatively high concentrations of estradiol and inhibin. (See Figure 8-6)

donor female. A female that contributes (donates) oocytes or embyos for embryo transfer. (See Figure 13-19)

down-regulation. Reduced receptor density.

ductus deferens. The duct derived from the mesonephric duct that connects the tail of the epididymis to the ampulla and transports sperm into the pelvic urethra.

duplex uterus. A uterus containing two cervices (rabbit). (See Figure 2-15)

dystocia. Abnormal or difficult parturition.

ectoderm. The outer layer of cells in the embryo.

efferent ducts. Ducts that are embryologically derived from the mesonephric tubules connecting the rete testis to the head of the epididymis.

efferent neurons. Neurons originating in the central nervous system and travelling to effector organs. (See Figure 5-1)

ejaculation. The expulsion of semen from the pelvic and penile urethra. (See Figure 11-13)

electroejaculation. Electrical stimulation of the accessory sex glands and pelvic urethra resulting in ejaculation.

elongated blastocyst. A blastocyst that has undergone rapid growth after hatching from the zona pellucida but before attachment to the uterus to form a long, filamentous structure.

embryo. An animal in the early stages of development that has not taken an anatomical form that is recognizable as a member of a species.

embryo transfer. A procedure used to transfer embyos from a donor female to a group of recipient females generally used to amplify the genetic characteristics of the donor female. (See Figure 13-9)

embryogenesis. The formation and growth of an embryo.

emission. The discharge of accessory sex gland secretions into the pelvic urethra.

endocrine. Pertaining to the secretion of hormones by an internal gland that are secreted into the blood.

endocrine gland. Any of various glands such as thyroid, adrenal, pituitary, ovary, testis and placenta that secrete hormones directly into the blood.

endocrine system. The endocrine glands of the body and the internal secretion of hormones.

endoderm. The innermost layer of cells in the embryo.

endometrial cups. Discrete raised areas (ranging from a few millimeters to a few centimeters) found in the gravid uterine horn of the mare that produce equine chorionic gonadotropin (eCG). These structures slough from the endometrial surface at about day 100 of gestation.

endometrium. The mucosal lining of the uterus.

endotheliochorial placenta. A form of placenta found in dogs and cats in which the endometrial epithelium has completely eroded and the maternal capillaries are almost directly exposed to the chorionic epithelium. (See Figure 14-5)

enzyme-linked immunosorbent assay (ELISA). A method of detecting and quantifying hormones utilizing an enzyme-linked antibody that produces an identifying color in the presence of the appropriate substrates. (See Figure 5-19)

epididymal duct. See epididymis.

epididymal transit. The transport of spermatozoa from the proximal head of the epididymis to the distal tail.

epididymal transit time. The time required for spermatazoa to be transported from the proximal head of the epididymis to the distal tail of the epididymis. Epididymal transit time is relatively constant within species and cannot be significantly altered by high ejaculation frequencies. (See Table 3-1)

epididymis (ductus epididymis). A duct derived embryologically from the mesonephric duct that connects the efferent ducts to the ductus deferens. It serves as a transport, storage and maturation site for spermatozoa.

episodic. A pattern of secretion in which a hormone is released in bursts of varying duration and quantity.

epitheliochorial placenta. A form of placenta found in the sow and mare in which the endometrial epithelium is directly apposed to the epithelium of the chorion. (See Figure 14-5)

equine chorionic gonadotropin (eCG). A luteotropic hormone produced by the endometrial cups of the mare. It also has powerful FSH-like actions when administered to females of other species.

erectile dysfunction. The inability to achieve and maintain an penile erection.

erection. The rigid state of the penis caused when blood enters the cavernous tissue of the penis. (See Figure 11-9)

erotogenic stimuli. Stimuli capable of causing sexual excitement or arousal.

esterases. A generic classification of enzymes that catalyze the hydrolysis of esters.

estradiol. The predominant estrogen produced by the dominant follicles during the follicular phase of the estrus cycle.

estrogen. A class of steroid hormones (natural or synthetic) that exerts physiologic effects on the female reproductive and mammary systems.

estrous. Adjective used to describe phenomena associated with the estrous cycle.

estrous cycle. The reproductive cycle of nonprimate females, generally defined as the period from one estrus (heat) to the next. Ovulation can also signify the beginning and/or the end of the estrous cycle. The estrous cycle consists of the follicular phase and the luteal phase.

estrual. An adjective used to describe phenomena associated with estrus (heat).

estrus. The period of sexual receptivity in the female.

eutherian mammal. Mammals characterized by having a highly developed placenta; all mammals except marsupials and monotromes.

excitatory neurotransmitter. A neurotransmitter that causes increased sodium permeability in the membrane of postsynaptic neurons.

excurrent duct system (extragonadal duct system). The efferent ducts, the epididymal duct and the ductus deferens. These ducts (continuous with one another) transport spermatozoa from the efferent ducts into the pelvic urethra. (See Figure 3-15)

exocrine. A glandular secretion that is delivered to a surface, into a lumen or through a duct.

exocytosis. Process whereby secretory materials too large to diffuse through the cell membrane are released from the cell. During exocytosis the membrane surrounding the secretory product fuses with the plasma membrane of the cell and releases the contents to the exterior.

exogenous. Originating or produced outside the body.

extender. A medium added to semen to increase its volume and to extend the time of in-vitro viability.

external genitalia. Portion of the male or female reproductive tract that can be viewed externally.

external uterine bifurcation. The external point of separation (forking) of the two uterine horns.

extra-abdominal gubernaculum. The portion of the gubernaculum located outside of the body cavity.

extracellular domain. The portion of a hormone receptor that protrudes from the surface of the plasma membrane and binds the hormone. (See Figure 5-13)

extraembryonic membranes. Membranes formed by the embryo and that are outside of it. The three extraembryonic membranes are the amnion, the chorion and the allantois.

extragonadal spermatozoal reserves (EGR). The spermatozoa stored within the epididymis, ductus deferens and ampulla.

facilitated diffusion. A type of diffusion requiring a carrier molecule that moves materials across a plasma membrane from a region of high concentration to a region of low concentration.

fallopian tube. The oviduct.

false mount. A mount in which intromission is purposely prevented. (See Figure 11-6)

fascia. Sheets of fibrous connective tissue that connect and support other tissues.

feminization. The promotion of the development of female appearance and behavior.

fetal cortisol. A hormone secreted from the adrenal cortex of the fetus as a result of stress on the fetus near parturition. Fetal cortisol causes a dramatic cascade of events that change the endocrine status of the dam, thus initiating parturition.

fetal cotyledon. See cotyledon.

fetus. The unborn young of a eutherian mammal that has developed identifiable features of a given species.

fimbria (pl. fimbriae). A fringe-like structure at the distal end of the infundibulum of the oviduct.

first polar body. See polar body.

flagellum (pl. flagella). A whip-like appendage of the spermatozoa responsible for propelling it.

Flehmen response. A specific investigative behavior seen in both the male and the female cattle, sheep, goats and horses in which the upper lip is curled upward to restrict airflow through the nostrils creating a subatmospheric pressure in the nasopalantine duct. This reduced pressure allows fluids to be aspirated into the duct and onto the surface of the vomeronasal organ. (See Figure 11-5)

fluorochrome. A fluorescent dye used to stain specific subcellular components.

follicle. A spherical structure within the ovary that contains an oocyte. Follicles may be primordial, primary, secondary, antral or atretic. (See definitions for each follicle type) (See Figure 2-11)

follicle stimulating hormone (FSH). A glycoprotein hormone secreted by the anterior lobe of the pituitary in response to GnRH. FSH promotes follicular development in the female and Sertoli cell function in the male.

follicular aspiration. Aspiration of an oocyte by inserting a needle directly into an antral follicle. (See Figure 13-10)

follicular dynamics. The sum of the intraovarian processes involved in follicular development and degeneration.

follicular fluid. A fluid produced by the granulosal cells that fills the antrum of the follicle.

follicular phase. The phase of the estrous cycle characterized by the presence of a dominant follicle that produces estradiol. Females display behavioral estrus and ovulate during the follicular phase.

follicular selection. The emergence of ovulatory follicles from a cohort of previously recruited antral follicles. (See Figure 8-8)

folliculogenesis. The process whereby ovarian follicles develop from primary into secondary and eventually into antral follicles that become eligible for ovulation.

fornix vagina. The cranial portion of the vagina that forms a crypt extending cranially to the cervix.

freemartin. The sterile heifer twin to a bull. It has incomplete development of the reproductive tract and male-like behavior.

fructose. A naturally occurring D-isomer sugar ($C_6H_{12}O_6$) that is the result of sucrose hydrolysis. Fructose is a major substrate for sperm metabolism.

fusion protein. A protein believed to be located on the equatorial segment of a spermatozoon that allows the oocyte plasma membrane to fuse with the equatorial segment.

G-protein. A membrane-bound protein that responds to a hormone-receptor complex by activating membrane-bound adenylate cyclase. (See Figure 5-14)

gap junctions. The membrane specializations that provide continuity between two adjacent cells, allowing passage of small molecular weight materials from one cell to another.

Gartner's cysts (ducts). The remnants of the mesonephric ducts that can be found in the vagina as blind cysts or ducts.

genital ridge. The swellings in the dorsal body wall of the developing embryo into which primordial germ cells migrate; these form the gonad.

germ cells. Spermatozoa or oocytes.

germ layers. The ectoderm, mesoderm and endoderm. These are the earliest recognizable forms of tissue structure in the early embryo.

germinal epithelium. The epithelium of the seminiferous tubule that produces spermatozoa.

gestation. Pregnancy. The period that a female is pregnant between conception and parturition.

glans penis. The anatomically specialized, highly sensitive distal end of the penis.

glucose. A monosaccharide found widely in animal tissue; the main form of sugar that circulates in the blood. Glucose is also a major nutrient in sperm metabolism.

glucuronide. A metabolite of steroid hormones excreted in the urine. Glucuronic acid is attached to the steroid rendering it water soluble so that it can be excreted in the urine.

glycerol. A liquid that may be used as a solvent, antifreeze, plasticizer, and a sweetener. It is also a common cryoprotectant used in freezing mammalian spermatozoa.

glycoprotein. A type of protein characterized as having carbohydrate molecules attached to the main protein chain.

glycosylation. The process of attaching carbohydrate moieties to a protein. The degree of glycosylation of glycoprotein hormones is believed to influence the half-life of the hormone.

glycosylation sites. Regions along a protein hormone to which carbohydrate moieties attach. Attachment of carbohydrates to a protein changes it to a glycoprotein. (See Figure 5-8)

goitrogen. A substance that inhibits thyroid function.

Golgi phase. The phase of spermiogenesis in which the Golgi vesicles fuse to form larger vesicles that reside on one side of the nucleus. (See Figure 10-6)

gonadal hormones. Any hormone produced by the male or female gonad.

gonadotroph. A cell type in the anterior pituitary that produces gonadotropins.

gonadotropin. The hormones (FSH and LH) of anterior pituitary origin that stimulate gonadal function.

gonadotropin releasing hormone (GnRH). A decapeptide released from terminals of neurons in the surge and tonic centers of the hypothalamus that causes the release of gonadotropins from the anterior lobe of the pituitary.

Graafian follicle. A large, dominant preovulatory follicle.

granulosal cells. (Granulosal cell layer, or membrana granulosa). Cells that line the antrum of an antral follicle that play a major role in oocyte development, steroidogenesis and follicular fluid secretion. After ovulation granulosal cells give rise to large luteal cells of the corpus luteum. (See Figure 9-2)

growth hormone (somatotropin). A hormone produced by the anterior lobe of the pituitary. It promotes growth and lactogenesis.

gubernaculum. A connective tissue cord attaching the testes to the base of the scrotum. It governs testicular descent. (See Figure 4-8)

gynecology. A specialty of human medicine focusing on normal function and pathology of the female reproductive system.

half-life. The period of time required for one-half of a substance to be destroyed or removed from the body.

heat. See estrus.

hemochorial placenta. A placenta characterized as having the chorionic epithelium in direct apposition to pools of maternal blood. (See Figure 14-5)

hilus. A region housing blood and lymphatic vessels and nerves that enter and leave an organ. (See Figure 2-13)

histamine. A substance secreted by mast cells or basalphils to initiate/enhance the inflammatory response. Histamine plays a role in ovulation by causing hyperemia and edema that increases intrafollicular pressure in the preovulatory follicle.

hormone. A substance produced by one or more glands that is transported by the blood to exert a specific effect upon another organ.

hormone receptor. A highly specific molecule found in the plasma membrane or the nucleus of a target cell. A receptor has affinity for a specific hormone. When the hormone binds to its receptor, a response from the cell in the target tissue occurs. (See Figure 5-12)

human chorionic gonadotropin (hCG). A hormone produced by the human placenta that has strong luteotropic activity.

hyaluronidase. A group of enzymes that hydrolyze hyaluronic acid. One or more of these enzymes is present in the acrosome of the spermatozoa.

hyperemia. Excessive blood flow to an organ or region of the body.

hyperplasia. An increase in the number of cells in a tissue or organ.

hypertonic. Solutions containing solute concentrations greater than intracellular fluids. Cells in hypertonic solutions dehydrate and shrink.

hypertrophy. An increase in organ or gland size not related to elevated cell numbers, but due to increased individual cell size.

hypothalamic hormones. Hormones produced by neurons located in the hypothalamus.

hypothalamic nuclei. Anatomically specific groupings or clusters of nerve cell bodies in the hypothalamus.

hypothalamo-hypophyseal portal system. A unique circulatory network that delivers minute quantities of releasing hormones from the pituitary stalk directly to the anterior lobe of the pituitary without dilution by the systemic circulation. (See Figure 5-5)

hypotonic. Solutions containing solute concentrations less than intracellular fluids. Water diffuses into cells in hypotonic solutions and they swell and may lyse.

hysterectomy. Surgical removal of the uterus. (uterectomy)

immunostimulation. Stimulation of the immune system.

implantation. See attachment.

incisive duct. The duct that connects the oral cavity to the nasal cavity and receives the ducts of the vomeronasal organ. (See Figure 11-5)

induced ovulation. See reflex ovulation.

infrared thermography. A technique that enables the surface temperature of a physical body to be determined. (See Figure 3-12)

infundibulum. A hollow funnel-shaped structure or passage. (oviduct - See Figures 2-12, 2-13, 2-14, and 2-16 pituitary - See Figure 4-3)

inguinal. Of, relating to, or located in the groin.

inguinal hernia. An abnormal condition where abdominal contents pass through the inguinal canal and enter the vaginal cavity. (See Figure 4-11)

inguinal-scrotal phase. The second phase of testicular descent in which the testis moves through the inguinal canal into the scrotum. This phase is brought about by the rapid growth of the gubernaculum in the scrotum that "pulls" the scrotum through the inguinal canal and into the scrotum. This phase is androgen dependent.

inhibin. A glycoprotein hormone produced by Sertoli cells in the male and granulosal cells in the female that specifically inhibit the release of FSH from the anterior lobe of the pituitary.

inhibitory neuron. A neuron producing a neurotransmitter that causes hyperpolarization of a postsynaptic neuron.

inhibitory neurotransmitter. A specific chemical released by an inhibitory neuron causing the post synaptic membrane to become more permeable to potassium, thus lowering the resting membrane potential.

initial recruitment phase. The continuous recruitment of primordial follicles into a growing follicle pool that terminates in atresia. (See Figure 8-7)

inner cell mass. A cluster of cells located at one pole of the blastocyst from which the embryo will develop. (See Figure 13-4)

insulin. A polypeptide hormone secreted from the pancreas that promotes glucose utilization and protein synthesis.

intercellular bridges. The connections between adjacent developing male germ cells that form a cohort of cells of similar developmental type.

interception. Preventing implantation

interferons (IFN). Glycoproteins produced by a variety of cells that exert antiviral, antiproliferative and immunosuppressant effects. They are classified as α (from leukocytes), β (from fibroblasts), γ (from lymphocytes), and τ. IFN-τ is produced by the trophoblast of the ruminant embryo. It is antiluteolytic in addition to possessing characteristics of the other classes of IFNs.

interneurons. Neurons found in the central nervous system between afferent (sensory neuron) and efferent neurons (motor neuron). Interneurons can be either excitatory or inhibitory.

interstitial compartment. The compartment of the testicular parenchyma that surrounds the seminiferous tubules. (See Figure 3-16)

intracellular domain. The component of a hormone receptor located inside the cell that is attached to the transmembrane domain of the receptor. (See Figure 5-13)

intracervical insemination. Insemination in which the semen is deposited into the cervix (sow). (See Figure 12-3)

intracytoplasmic sperm injection (ICSI). A procedure whereby a spermatozoon is injected into the cytoplasm of an oocyte with the purpose of generating a zygote and eventual embryo. (See Figure 16-13).

intrauterine device (IUD). Usually a small molded plastice interceptive device that is inserted into the uterus by a physician that prevents implantation.

intravaginal insemination. Insemination in which the semen is deposited into the cranial vagina.

intromission. The insertion of one part into another. The insertion of the penis into the vagina.

involution, mammary. The process whereby alveolar cells stop secreting milk and become similar in structure to a nulliparous female. (See Figure 15-12)

involution, uterine. The process whereby the uterus returns to its normal nonpregnant size and function following parturition. (See Figure 15-1)

ipsilateral. On the same side.

ischemia. A local reduction in blood flow resulting in accumulation of metabolites in the tissue.

ischiocavernosus muscle(s). Paired, powerful, striated muscles originating on the medial surface of the ischium, covering the crura of the penis and inserting on the proximal shaft of the penis. (See Figures 3-4, 3-5, 3-6, 3-7, 3-8, 3-19 and 3-20)

isometric growth. Growth in which body components enlarge at the same rate.

isotonic. Solutions containing solute concentration similar to intracellular fluids. There is no net diffusion of water.

isthmus. A narrow passage connecting two larger cavities. The isthmus of the oviduct is of small diameter and connects the large diameter ampulla of the oviduct to the uterus.

junctional complexes. The specialized regions of cell-to-cell attachment consisting of tight junctions, intermediate junctions, gap junctions or desmosomes.

keratinization. The synthesis of an insoluble protein (keratin) containing a high degree of disulfide cross-links found in hair, feathers, nails, sperm heads and tails.

kisspeptin. A class of neuropeptides secreted by hypothalamic neurons that are known to have direct stimulatory action on GnRH neurons.

kisspeptin neurons. Neurons found in the periventricular, preoptic and arcuate nuclei in the hypothalamus. These neurons send dendritic arborizations into hypothalamic nuclei where GnRH neurons are abundant. Activity of kisspeptin neurons is known to influence GnRH secretion.

Kisspeptin-10. A neuropeptide secreted by kisspeptin neurons that are stimulated by long total periods. In the long-day breeder, kisspeptin-10 stimulates GnRH secretion and is thought to facilitate the onset of cyclicity in long-day breeders.

labia. The lip-shaped structures forming the lateral boundaries of the female external genitalia. (See Figures 2-23 and 2-24)

labial commissure. The point of junction between the two labia of the female external genitalia.

lactation. Formation and/or secretion of milk by the mammary glands.

lactational anestrus. A lack of cyclicity brought about by nursing and presence of the young. (See Figure 7-8)

lactiferous ducts. Ducts that produce, secrete or convey milk. (See Figure 15-13)

lactocrine signaling. Delivery of bioactive materials from the mother to the offspring as a specific consequence of suckling and consumption of colostrum and milk. Milk-born bioactive factors such as relaxin are absorbed into the neonatal blood from the gut and act on remote target tissues in the neonate.

lactogenic. Stimulation of lactation.

lateral ventricle. A cavity within the brain through which cerebral spinal fluid moves. Lateral ventricles are attached to the third ventricle. (See Figure 5-4)

leptin. Material produced by adipocytes that correlates directly with the amount of body fat. Leptin may influence GnRH secretion from the hypothalamus.

leukocyte. A white blood cell produced by myeloid or lymphoid tissue that fights infection and disease (neutrophils, basophils, eosinophils, lymphocytes and monocytes).

Leydig cells. Cells found in the interstitial compartment of the testis that produce testosterone. (See Figure 10-3)

libido. The behavioral drive associated with the desire to copulate.

ligand. A small molecule that binds to a larger molecule. For example, a hormone (ligand) binding to a receptor.

lobulation. Subdivided into lobules or lobes.

lobules. A small lobe or subdivision of a lobe.

lobulo-alveolar structures. Structures formed in the mammary gland during the final trimester of pregnancy that consist of ductules and apocrine glands that secrete milk. (See Figure 15-13)

lochia. Normal uterine discharge consisting of blood, necrotic tissue and mucus after parturition. (See Figures 15-5 and 15-6)

long-day breeder. A seasonal breeder in which reproductive activity and cyclicity peaks during long photoperiods (spring and summer). (See Figure 7-1)

lordosis. A condition in which the lumbar spine is flexed, forming a convex or hollowed-out appearance. The lumbar curvature is characteristic as a mating posture of females in estrus.

luteal phase. The phase of the estrous cycle characterized by progesterone dominance and the presence of a functional corpus luteum. The luteal phase begins immediately after ovulation and ends after lysis of the corpus luteum.

luteinization. The process whereby granulosal and thecal cells are transformed into luteal cells. Luteinization is brought about by the hormone LH.

luteinizing hormone (LH). A glycoprotein hormone secreted by the anterior lobe of the pituitary that causes ovulation and subsequent development and maintenance of the corpus luteum. In the male, it causes Leydig cells to produce testosterone.

luteolysis. The process whereby luteal tissue undergoes regression and cell death.

luteolytic. A material that promotes luteolysis.

lysin. A substance capable of causing destruction or dissolution of cellular elements.

lysis. The destruction of cells or tissue. In tissues/organs (like corpora lutea) "destruction" and loss of function. In blood cells usually associated with rupture of the cell.

lysosomes. Intracellular vesicles that contain digestive enzymes.

mammary ridges. Two longitudinal ridges of slightly thickened epithelium on the ventral surface of the conceptus that give rise to the mammary glands. (See Figure 15-10)

mammogenesis. Development of the mammary gland. (See Figure 15-10)

manchette. The specialized microtubules that appear in the cytoplasm of developing spermatids around the posterior portion of the nucleus. They become closely apposed to the nuclear membranes and contribute to the postnuclear cap region. (See Figure 15-7)

masculinization. A process that promotes the development of male appearance and behavior.

maternal cotyledon. The maternal contribution to a cotyledonary placenta derived from the uterine caruncles.

maternal recognition of pregnancy. The process whereby the female physiologically recognizes the presence of a conceptus and therefore luteolysis does not occur. (See Figures 13-5, 13-6)

maturation phase. The final phase of spermiogenesis in which the developing spermatid resembles a spermatozoon. During this phase the flagellum is completely formed and the mitochondria cluster around the flagellum to form a middle piece. (See Figure 10-7)

median eminence. The most ventral part of the hypothalamus that forms a stalk connecting the hypothalamus to the pituitary. Nerve terminals from neurons originating in various hypothalamic nuclei populate this region and secrete releasing hormone into the primary capillaries of the hypothalamo-hypophyseal portal system. (See Figure 5-5)

mediastinum. The connective tissue core of the testes that houses the rete tubules. (See Figure 3-15)

meiosis. The cell divisions occurring in developing germ cells in which the daughter cell nucleus receives half the number of chromosomes (haploid) found in somatic cells.

meiotic phase. The phase of spermatogenesis involving primary and secondary spermatocytes that produce haploid spermatids.

meiotic prophase. The first stage of meiosis in which the nuclear or chromosomal material duplicates. Meiotic prophase occurs in primary spermatocytes.

melatonin. A hormone secreted by the pineal gland predominantly during darkness that alters GnRH and gonadotropin secretion. (See Figure 7-7)

menopause. Permanent cessation of menses; termination of menstrual cycles brought about by depletion of ovarian follicles. (See Figure 16-13)

menses (menstruation). The periodic endometrial sloughing and hemorrhagic discharge to the exterior lasting 5-7 days in most women; the time of menstruation. (See Figure 9-15)

menstrual cycle. The reproductive cycle of the woman that consists of the physiologic events during and between menstrual periods (lasting about 28 days). There are three phases in the menstrual cycle; menses, the proliferative phase and secretory phase. (See Figure 7-10)

menstrual period. Time of menses.

mesoderm. The middle germ layer of the embryo. (See Figure 4-1 and Table 4-1)

mesometrium. The portion of the broad ligament that supports the uterus and is continuous with the peritoneum.

mesonephric ducts (Wolffian ducts). The ducts that provide an outlet for the fluid produced by the mesonephros in the developing embryo. They will be retained and form the epididymis and the ductus deferens in the male or will become vestigial in the female. (See Figures 4-7, 4-13)

mesonephric kidney (mesonephros). One of three renal systems appearing in the mammalian embryo. The mesonephros undergoes regression and does not serve an excretory function in the postnatal animal. (See Figure 4-5)

mesonephric tubules. The tubules of the mesonephric kidney that connect the capillary tufts of the mesonephros to the mesonephric duct. These tubules will be retained as the efferent ducts in the male. (See Figure 4-7)

mesosalpinx. A portion of the broad ligament that surrounds and supports the oviduct. (See Figures 2-13, 2-14)

mesovarium. A portion of the broad ligament that attaches the ovary to the mesometrium. (See Figures 2-13, 2-14)

metabolic hormones. Hormones that regulate metabolic function, e.g. thyroxin, adrenal corticoids and somatotropin.

metanephros kidney. The most advanced form of the three renal types found in the developing mammalian embryo that is retained and becomes the permanent and functional kidney. (See Figure 4-5)

metestrus. A stage of the estrous cycle between ovulation and formation of a functional corpus luteum. (See Figure 7-3)

microcotyledons. Unique forms of chorionic villi that characterize the mare placenta. (See Figure 14-1)

microtubules. Cylindrical cytoplasmic elements associated with mitosis and meiosis and related to the movement of chromosomes on the nuclear spindle during cell division.

middle piece (midpiece). A portion of the sperm flagellum around which the mitochondrial helix is entwined. (See Figure 10-9)

milk. A whitish liquid containing proteins, fats, lactose and various vitamins and minerals produced by the mammary glands of mammalian females after parturition.

milk ejection. The process whereby milk is moved from the alveolar lumen into the ducts so that it can easily be removed by the suckling neonate. The process is brought about by oxytocin induced contractions of myoepithelial cells. (See Figure 15-13)

mitochondrial helix. The helical arrangement of mitochondria around the flagellum of mammalian sperm. (See Figure 10-9)

monoestrus. Animals that display only one period of sexual receptivity (estrus) during a year.

monotocous. Mammals that typically give birth to a single offspring at a time.

morula. A stage of early embryonic development within the confines of the zona pellucida characterized by a round mass of blastomeres resulting from cleavage divisions of the zygote. (See Figures 13-1, 13-2)

motility. The ability to move or contract (sperm motility, swimming; uterine motility, contracting).

mucopolysaccharide. A protein-polysaccharide complex that functions as a protective coating.

mucosa. An epithelial lining or coating of a structure. (See Figure 2-1)

Müllerian ducts. See paramesonephric ducts.

multiparous. A female that has had at least one previously successful pregnancy and parturition.

muscularis. The smooth muscular layer covering a tubular or hollow organ. (See Figure 2-1)

myoepithelial cells. Cells within the mammary glands that have receptors for oxytocin and upon stimulation contract to cause milk ejection. (See FIgure 15-13)

myoid layer. A smooth muscle layer (e.g. surrounding the seminiferous tubule, epididymis or oviduct).

myometrium. The smooth muscle layer of the uterus consisting of an inner circular layer and an outer longitudinal layer. (See Figures 2-16, 2-17 and 2-18)

nasopalatine ducts. See incisive ducts.

neat semen. Unadulterated, unaltered semen.

necrosis. The death of cells, tissues or organs, usually resulting from damage to the tissue or from ischemia.

negative feedback. The set of conditions whereby a hormone exerts an inhibitory effect on another gland or organ suppressing the level of hormone secretion. For example, progesterone exerts a negative feedback on the hypothalamus and thus limits the release of GnRH.

nervous system. The system consisting of the brain, spinal cord and peripheral nerves that regulate the body's response to internal and external stimuli.

neuroendocrine reflex. A reflex initiated by stimulation of sensory neurons that causes the release of a neurohormone from neurosecretory cells. (See Figure 5-1)

neurohormone. A hormone that is synthesized and secreted by neurons.

neurohypophysis. The posterior lobe of the pituitary gland.

neuropeptides. A variety of regulatory molecules produced by neurons that exert specific effects on other neurons or tissues.

neurosecretory cell. A neuron that secretes a substance into the blood.

neurotransmitter. A specific chemical released from the terminal boutons of neurons that causes either excitation or inhibition of postsynaptic neurons. (See Figure 5-1)

nuclear receptors. The specialized molecules within the nucleus of the cell that combine with a drug, steroid hormone or chemical mediator to alter the metabolism of the cell. (See Figure 5-15)

nulliparous. A female that has not become pregnant.

obstetrics. A specialty of human and veterinary medicine focusing on the care of the female during pregnancy, parturition and the puerperium.

oestrous. British spelling of estrous.

oestrus. British spelling of estrus (heat).

olfactory. Relating to, or contributing to the sense of smell.

oocyte meiotic inhibitor (OMI). Substance implicated in controlling the resumption of meiosis in the oocyte just before or after ovulation.

ootid. The oocyte after the first meiotic division in which the first polar body is present. (See Figure 13-1)

ostium. A small opening in a tubular organ such as the cervix or oviduct.

ovarian cortex. The outer portion of the ovary that contains developing and atretic follicles as well as functional and regressing corpora lutea. (See Figure 2-11)

ovarian follicles. Spherical structures that contain an oocyte. Follicles are classified as primary, secondary or antral, depending on the number and type of cellular layers present. (See Figure 2-11)

ovarian medulla. The inner portion of the ovary that houses blood vessels, lymphatics and nerves. (See Figure 2-11)

ovarian stimulation. Procedures whereby exogenous FSH and hCG are used to promote development of multiple ovarian follicles with the goal of providing multiple oocytes for IVF.

ovariectomy. Surgical removal of one or both ovaries.

ovary. The female gonad.

oviducts. The small, usually convoluted ducts (Fallopian tubes or uterine tubes) originating embryologically from the paramesonephric ducts that transport ova and sperm. The oviduct consists of the ampullary and isthmic regions.

ovine interferon τ (oIFN-τ). A specific protein produced by the ovine trophoblast that is antiluteolytic. It contributes to maternal recognition of pregnancy in the ewe. (See Figure 13-5)

ovine placental lactogen. A placental lactogen produced by the ewe that has higher lactogenic effects than somatotrophic effects.

ovine trophoblastic protein 1. See ovine Interferon τ.

oviparous. Animals that produce eggs that are hatched outside the body of the ovulatory animal, as in birds.

ovulation fossa. A conspicuous depression in the ovarian surface that is the site of each ovulation in the mare.

oxytocin. A peptide synthesized by neurons in the hypothalamus and released by nerve terminals in the posterior lobe of the pituitary. It is also produced by the corpus luteum. It causes contractions in smooth muscle in the male and female reproductive tract and regulates luteolysis.

pampiniform plexus. A specialized venous plexus beginning in the spermatic cord and terminating on the dorsal pole of the testis. It consists of the testicular vein that elaborately intertwines around the testicular artery. The pampiniform plexus provides a countercurrent heat exchange mechanism for the testes. (See Figure 3-9)

paramesonephric ducts (Müllerian ducts). The ducts that originate lateral to the mesonephric ducts in the female embryo. They develop into the oviducts, uterus, cervix and portions of the cranial vagina. (See Figures 4-13, 4-17)

paraplacenta. The pigmented area at the distal borders of a zonary placenta that consists of hematomas (blood clots) that is thought to be involved in iron transport from the dam to the fetus. (See Figure 14-2)

parenchyma. The functional cells of a gland or organ supported by a connective tissue framework. (See Figure 3-15)

parietal vaginal tunic. The layer of peritoneum that defines the outermost (peripheral) boundary of the vaginal cavity in the male. (See Figure 3-15)

parturition. To give birth.

pelvic urethra. The region of the urethra within the pelvis that extends to the base of the penis. Surrounding the pelvic urethra is a specialized muscle known as the urethralis muscle. The accessory sex glands that secrete their products via ducts directly into the pelvic urethra. (See Figures 3-3, 3-4, 3-6, 3-7, 3-8, 3-19 and 3-20)

penile protrusion. The forward positioning or projection of the penis; protrusion of an erect penis is an indicator of sexual stimulation and is obligatory for intromission.

penile urethra. The portion of the urethra inside the penis.

penis. The male organ of copulation consisting of a shaft and the glans penis.

peptide. A compound of two or more amino acids in which a carboxyl group of one amino acid is united with an amino group of another, resulting in the elimination of a molecule of water and formation of a peptide bond.

perimetrium. The serous outer covering of the uterus that is continuous with the peritoneum.

perineum. The external surface surrounding the vulva and the anus in the female and between the scrotum and the anus in the male.

peritoneum. A thin, serous, semitransparent connective tissue that lines the abdominal cavity and surrounds most of the viscera. (See Figure 2-2, 4-8)

pheromone. A volatile material secreted externally that is recognized by the olfactory system. Pheromones stimulate or inhibit reproduction.

photoperiod. The period of time during the day when there is daylight. (See Figure 7-7)

pineal gland. A neural structure on the dorsal surface of the midbrain that secretes melatonin in response to changing photoperiods. (See Figure 7-7)

pinealocyte. The cells of the pineal gland that secretes melatonin. (See Figure 7-7)

pituitary hormone. Any hormone secreted into the blood from the anterior or posterior lobes of the pituitary. The primary reproductive hormones secreted from the anterior lobe are follicle stimulating hormone (FSH), luteinizing hormone (LH) and prolactin. Oxytocin is secreted from the posterior lobe of the pituitary.

placebo pills. Pills containing no hormone. While placebo pills are taken, progesterone drps and a new menstrual period is initiated.

placenta. The organ of metabolic exchange between the fetus and the dam consisting of a portion of embryonic origin (chorion) and a portion of maternal origin (endometrium). The placenta is also a temporary endocrine organ. Placentas are classified according to the distribution of chorionic villi or the intimacy of the maternal-fetal tissue interface.

placental lactogen (somatomammotropin). A hormone produced by the placenta that stimulates lactogenesis in the dam and fetal growth.

placentation. The structural organization and physical relationship of the fetal membranes to the endometrium that provides the site of metabolic exchange between the dam and the fetus.

placentome. The specific anatomical region or zone of attachment between the fetal and maternal placenta.

plasmin. An enzyme that converts fibrin to soluble products. It is thought to enhance the action of collagenase to promote follicle wall breakdown during ovulation.

plasminogen. An inactive precursor to plasmin found in blood plasma.

plasminogen activator. A substance that converts plasminogen into plasmin.

polar body. A small portion of oocyte cytoplasm containing one-half of the female genetic material. It is removed by exocytosis into the perivitelline space during the first (first polar body formation) and second (second polar body formation) meiotic divisions. (See Figure 8-16)

polyestrus. Animals that display estrous cycles uniformly distributed throughout the year without marked seasonal influence. (See Figure 7-1)

polyspermy. A condition in which more than one spermatozoon fertilizes the oocyte.

polytocous. Mammals that give birth to multiple offspring. (litter-bearers)

positive feedback. A condition whereby a hormone exerts a stimulatory effect on another gland or tissue.

postcopulatory stage. The third (last) stage of reproductive behavior consisting of a dismount, a refractory period and memory.

posterior lobe of the pituitary (neurohypophysis). The portion of the pituitary gland that originates from the infundibulum of the brain during embryogenesis. The posterior lobe of the pituitary is neural tissue that houses terminals from neurons located in specific hypothalamic nuclei.

postestrus. An interestrus period that follows behavioral estrus in the queen that has not been induced to ovulate by copulation. (See Figure 7-5)

postnuclear cap. The membranous portion surrounding the posterior one-half to one-third of the sperm cell. The postnuclear cap originates from the manchette during spermiogenesis. (Figure 10-7)

postpartum recovery. See puerperium.

postsynaptic neuron. A neuron onto which the terminals of presynaptic neurons synapse.

precopulatory stage. The first stage of reproductive behavior consisting of search, courtship, sexual arousal, erection and penile protrusion.

pregnancy. A condition of the female mammal in which the conceptus (future offspring) develops in the uterus. The duration of pregnancy (gestation) varies greatly among species. (See Table 14-1)

pregnancy maintenance hormones. A group of hormones responsible for the maintenance of pregnancy, e.g. progesterone, estradiol, bIFτ, oIFτ, hCG, eCG. (See Figure 14-4)

pregnancy specific protein B (PSPB). A protein unique to pregnancy in ruminants that is produced by binucleate giant cells in the chorion.

pregnant mare's serum gonadotropin (PMSG). See equine chorionic gonadotropin.

premenstrual syndrome (PMS). Temporary mood changes that occur in a high percentage of women during the late luteal phase prior to menstruation. Symptoms may include: elevated anxiety, tension, anger and irritability, and increased interpersonal conflicts.

prenatal. Preceding birth.

preoptic nucleus. Hypothalamic nucleus located rostral to the optic chiasm that is part of the GnRH surge center.

preovulatory GnRH center (surge center). A group of specific hypothalamic nuclei in the female that respond to high levels of estradiol by secreting high concentrations of GnRH during a relatively short period of time. (See Figure 8-3)

preovulatory GnRH surge. A series of high amplitude, high frequency episodes of GnRH released from the hypothalamic surge center that cause the preovulatory LH surge.

pressure atrophy. The build-up of pressure usually from secretory products within a secretory organ that results in the decrease or the cessation of secretion.

presynaptic neuron. A neuron that secretes neurotransmitters that cause excitation or inhibition in the postsynaptic neuron.

primary corpus luteum. The corpus luteum formed from the ovulatory follicle in the mare.

primary follicle. An ovarian follicle characterized as having a single layer of spindle shaped cells surrounding the oocyte. The nucleus of the oocyte contained within the primary follicle is arrested in the dictyate stage (dictyotene). (See Figure 2-11)

primary mammary bud. The primary embryonic stage of mammary gland development in which future mammary tissue pushes into the dermis. (See Figure 15-10)

primary portal plexus. The arterial capillary plexus of the hypothalamo-hypophyseal portal system into which releasing hormones are secreted. (See Figure 5-5)

primary spermatocyte. The daughter cells of spermatogonia that enter the first meiotic prophase and will give rise to a secondary spermatocyte. (See Figures 3-16, 10-5, 10-10 and 10-11)

primary zona binding region. One of the binding sites found on the sperm plasma membrane that is believed to be responsible for adherence of spermatozoa to the zona pellucida. (See Figure 12-10)

primiparous. Referring to the first parity or pregnancy of a female.

primitive endoderm. A tissue layer that is formed very early in development that lines the trophoblast and will eventually give rise to the yolk sac. (See Figure 13-4)

primitive gut. The embryonic precursor to the gastrointestinal tract. (See Figure 13-4)

primitive sex cords. Cords of cells that penetrate to the interior of the male embryonic gonad that incorporate primordial germ cells. These cords will give rise to the seminiferous tubules. (See Figure 4-4)

primordial follicles. The most primitive stage of the ovarian follicle. (See Figure 2-11)

principal piece. The portion of the sperm tail that extends from the middle piece to the terminal piece. (See Figure 10-9)

proacrosin. An inactive form of acrosin found in the acrosome of mammalian spermatozoa.

proceptivity. Female behaviors toward males that stimulate the male to copulate, e.g. headbutting and mounting the male.

proestrus. The stage of the estrus cycle between luteolysis and the onset of estrus.

progesterone. A steroid hormone produced by corpora lutea and the placenta that is required for the maintenance of pregnancy.

progesterone block. The inhibition (block) of myometrial contractions brought about by high levels of progesterone during pregnancy.

progestin. Any substance that produces an effect similar to progesterone.

prolactin. A hormone secreted by the anterior lobe of the pituitary that stimulates lactogenesis and initiates maternal behavior.

proliferation phase. (Spermatogenesis) The phase of spermatogenesis that consists of all spermatogonial mitotic divisions, resulting in increasing numbers of spermatogonia (proliferation). (See Figure 10-5)

proliferative phase. (Mentrual cycle) Phase of the menstrual cycle in which the endometrium begins to grow and increase in thickness in response to rising estrogen levels. (See Figure 9-15)

pronephros. The most primitive form of kidney found in developing mammalian embryos that degenerates and gives way to the mesonephros.

prostaglandin (PG). A class of physiologically active substances (designated as PGE, PGF, PGA and PGB) that are present in most tissues of the body. Prostaglandins are derived from arachidonic acid and have a wide variety of functions.

prostaglandin $F_{2\alpha}$. A hormone that causes luteolysis. It is secreted from the uterus in most animals, and secreted by the ovary and uterus in the human.

prostate gland. One of the accessory sex glands of the male consisting of a body (sometimes paired) that is outside of the pelvic urethra and/or a disseminate portion that forms a glandular layer in the wall of the pelvic urethra. (See Figures 3-3, 3-4, 3-5, 3-6, 3-19 and 3-20)

protein kinases. A class of control enzymes that phosphorylate proteins. (See Figure 5-14)

proximal cytoplasmic droplet. A cytoplasmic remnant in the neck region of a newly formed spermatozoon.

puberty. A developmental process in which endocrine and morphologic changes transform the animal into an individual capable of reproducing. Puberty is the acquisition of gonadotropin secretion, gametogenesis, gonadal steroid secretion, reproductive behavior and development of secondary sex characteristics.

puerperium. The period between parturition and return to the normal cycling state of the ovaries and uterus.

pulsatile secretion. A secretory pattern in which the secretions are released in a relatively predictable rhythmic fashion.

pulse pressure eliminator. The blood within the testicular artery has a very low pulse pressure (about 10mmHg) when compared to other systemic arteries (about 40mmHg). It is believed that the long torturous highly compliant testicular artery greatly reduces the pulse pressure. The physiological significance is not known.

R

radioimmunoassay (RIA). An immunologic assay that quantifies hormones or other immunogenic substances using radiolabeled hormones.

rapid transport phase. The short burst of spermatozoal transport activity during and soon after copulation brought about by muscular contractions of the female tract; functional importance not known.

Rathke's pocket (pouch). An invagination of the stomodeal ectoderm in the developing embryo that gives rise to the anterior lobe of the pituitary. (See Figure 4-3)

receptivity. Specific behavior in the female that promotes copulation, e.g. lordosis, tail deviation and backing toward males.

receptor domains. The regions of specific receptor proteins of the plasma membrane consisting of the extracellular, transmembrane and intracellular domains.

recipient female. A female into which embryos are transferred (generally into the uterus) from a donor female with the goal of generating a pregnancy that progresses to term.

recruitment (follicular). The process whereby a cohort of antral follicles are recruited and begin to grow from a pool of FSH sensitive antral follicles. (See Figure 8-7)

rectogenital pouch. The pouch (space) between the rectum and the reproductive organs.

rectus. Straight; lacking curvature.

reflex ovulation (induced). A condition whereby the female must experience cervical and/or vaginal stimulation (usually in the form of mating) before ovulation can occur.

refractory. Temporarily unresponsive to nervous or sexual stimuli.

refractory period (postcopulatory). The period of time after copulation where neither the male nor the female will engage in another copulation.

relaxin. A polypeptide hormone secreted by the placenta and/or the corpus luteum of pregnancy that causes the cervix to dilate and softens the ligaments in the pelvic region, thus tending to widen the birth canal during parturition. (See Figure 14-14)

releasing hormones. Small peptides produced by neurons in hypothalamic nuclei that cause the release of anterior pituitary hormones.

renewable stem cells. Cells in the seminiferous epithelium that provide a continual supply of stem cells so that spermatogenesis can continue indefinitely.

restraint, sexual. A maneuver used to prolong sexual stimulation by preventing a sexually stimulated male from mounting a stimulus animal or device.

rete fluid. Fluid located within the rete testis that contains spermatozoa and secretions from the seminiferous epithelium.

rete testis. A network of tubules housed within the mediastinum of the testis that are connected to the straight portions (tubuli recti) of the seminiferous tubules and merging into the efferent ducts. (See Figure 3-15)

rete tubules. The tubules found in the mediastinum of the testes that transport or allow spermatozoa and fluid from the seminiferous tubules to the efferent ducts. (See Figure 3-15)

retractor penis muscles. A pair of smooth muscles originating on the ventral surface of the first few caudal vertebrae. The muscle(s) circumvent the rectum and continue to their attachment on the lateral and urethral surfaces of the penis. Relaxation of this muscle is required for full penile protrusion and erection.

retrograde loss of sperm. The loss of sperm to the exterior of the female after insemination.

retroperitoneal. Located behind or outside of the peritoneum. The reproductive tracts of both the male and the female are retroperitoneal.

RFRP neurons. Hypothalamic neurons that secrete small amide related peptides.

RFRP-3. A neuropeptide secreted by RFRP neurons that inhibits kiss neurons in short-day breeders and stimulates kiss neurons in the long-day breeder.

salpinx. Oviduct.

scrotum. A sac consisting of skin, sweat glands, a layer of smooth muscle (tunica dartos) and connective tissue that houses the testis. (See Figures 3-11 and 3-12)

season. A term used in reference to the breeding season in females, or referring to estrus as, "in season".

seasonal anestrus. A period of anestrus induced by either long (ewe) or short (mare) photoperiods.

seasonal polyestrus. A condition in which females exhibit multiple estrous cycles during a specific season of the year. (See Figure 7-1)

second messenger. An intracellular material that responds to a hormone-receptor complex and initiates a specific set of intracellular reactions. (See Figure 5-14)

second polar body. See polar body.

secondary follicle. An ovarian follicle characterized by having two or more cell layers surrounding the oocyte but without an antrum. (See Figure 2-11)

secondary mammary bud. An early stage of embryonic mammary gland development in which the primary mammary bud begins to produce numerous additional buds that penetrate the dermis. (See Figure 15-10)

secondary spermatocyte. The daughter cells of primary spermatocytes that will complete the second meiotic division and give rise to spermatids. (See Figures 10-5, 10-10 and 10-11)

secretory phase. Phase of the menstrual cycle in which the endometrial glands gain full secretory activity in response to progesterone and estrogen. (See Figure 9-15)

selection (follicular). The process by which a cohort of antral follicles are selected from the previously recruited antral follicles. (See Figure 8-7)

sella turcica. A vault-like depression in the sphenoid bone that houses the anterior and posterior lobes of the pituitary. (See Figure 4-3)

seminal plasma. The noncellular liquid portion of semen produced by the accessory sex glands.

seminiferous epithelium. The epithelium between the basement membrane and the lumen of the seminiferous tubules consisting of developing germ cells and Sertoli cells.

seminiferous tubules. The highly tortuous tubules within the testes that produce spermatozoa. (See Figures 3-15 and 10-10)

serosa. A serous membrane making up the outermost covering of an organ or serving as a lining of a cavity. (See Figure 2-1)

Sertoli cells. Somatic cells in the seminiferous epithelium that are believed to govern spermatogenesis. Sertoli cells contain FSH receptors and produce a wide variety of materials and hormones. They are named after the famous Italian scientist Enrico Sertoli. (See Figure 10-3)

sexually indifferent stage. The stage of embryogenesis when the sex of the embryo cannot be determined based on morphologic features.

sexual promoters (estrogens, progesterone and androgens). Steroid hormones secreted by the gonads that regulate reproductive function.

sexual stimulation. A set of stimulus conditions in the male that will result in arousal, mounting and ejaculation.

shaft of penis. The portion of the penis between the base and the glans.

short-day breeders. Females that begin to exhibit estrous cycles during times of short photoperiods (short days). (See Figure 7-1)

short scrotumed bull. A bull whose scrotum has been artificially shortened to hold the testes next to the body resulting in elevated testicular temperature that inhibits spermatogenesis.

sialomucin. A mucus of low viscosity produced by the mucosa of the basal cervical crypts. (See Figure 12-5)

sigmoid flexure. The s-shaped curvature of the flaccid fibroelastic penis when it is retracted into the body. During sexual excitation and erection, the sigmoid flexure disappears when the penis straightens. (See Figure 3-4)

silent ovulation. A condition whereby ovulation occurs without behavioral estrus. Silent ovulation frequently occurs in the first postpartum estrous cycle of dairy cows and the first estrous cycle after seasonal anestrus in ewes. (See Figure 7-6)

simple diffusion. The movement of materials from high concentration to low concentration without active expenditure of energy.

simple neural reflex. The mechanism by which external stimuli trigger a response without cognition. The components are the afferent sensory neuron, an interneuron (located in the spinal cord) and an efferent neuron that leaves the spinal cord and innervates an effector organ. (See Figures 5-1, 5-2)

simplex uterus. A uterus found in primates consisting of a large uterine body without uterine horns. (See Figure 2-15)

sire-on-fetus-hypothesis. A theory that suggests that it may be possible for the sire to influence placental lactogen secretion by the placenta and thus enhance milk production of the dam.

slough. The separation of necrotic tissue from living tissue.

smooth muscle. A type of muscle without striations that surrounds most organs of the reproductive tract often referred to as the muscularis.

somatomammotropin. See placental lactogen.

somatostatin. A hormone secreted by the hypothalamus and pancreas that inhibits the secretion of somatotropin, insulin, gastrin and other hormones.

spay. The removal of the ovaries (ovariectomy).

spermatic cord. A cord-like collection of tissues containing the testicular artery and vein, lymphatics, the pampiniform plexus, nerves, the cremaster muscle, the ductus deferens and the vaginal tunics. (See Figures 3-2, 3-4, 3-5, 3-6, 3-7, and 3-8)

spermatids. Haploid male germ cells derived from secondary spermatocytes that undergo a transformation from a spherical cell to a fully specialized and differentiated spermatozoon with a head and a tail. (See Figures 10-5, 10-10, and 10-11)

spermatocytes. The male germ cells derived from the final mitotic division of spermatogonia (primary spermatocyte). They give rise to secondary spermatocytes. (See Figures 10-5, 10-10 and 10-11)

spermatogenesis. The process whereby spermatozoa are formed. It consists of proliferation (mitosis), meiosis and differentiation. (See Figure 10-5)

spermatogenic efficiency. The number of spermatozoa produced per gram of testicular parenchyma. (See Figures 10-1 and 10-2)

spermatogenic wave. A sequential ordering of the stages of the cycle of the seminiferous epithelium along the length of the seminiferous tubule.

spermatogonia. The most primitive of the adult male germ cells located in the basal compartment of the seminiferous tubule that give rise to primary spermatocytes after a series of mitotic divisions. Spermatogonia proliferate through a series of histologically definable types generally accepted to be A, I and B spermatogonia. (See Figures 10-5, 10-10, and 10-11)

spermatozoa. The male gamete consisting of a head (nucleus) and a tail (flagellum) that exhibits motility when exposed to the appropriate physiologic environment. (See Figure 10-9)

spermiation. The release of mature spermatozoa from Sertoli cells into the lumen of the seminiferous tubule. (See Figure 10-11)

spermiogenesis. A subcategory of spermatogenesis during which spermatids undergo morphologic transformation into highly specialized spermatozoa. Spermiogenesis consists of the Golgi phase, the cap phase, the acrosomal phase and the maturation phase. (See Figures 10-6 and 10-7)

sphenoid bone. A bone forming the floor of the cranium that houses the sella turcica into which the hypophysis fits. (See Figure 4-3)

spontaneous ovulation. A condition whereby ovulation is brought about by changing endocrine conditions without the need for cervical or vaginal stimulation.

SRY. Sex determining Region of the Y chromosome (SRY) that contains the SRY gene.

SRY gene. A gene present on the Y chromosome that directs the synthesis of SRY protein. SRY protein controls development of the male reproductive tract.

SRY protein. The protein synthesized by the primitive sex cords of the primitive gonad that stimultes development of the male reproductive tract.

standing estrus. A female behavioral characteristic of estrus in which the female remains immobile allowing the male to mount her.

stem cell renewal. The process during the proliferative phase of spermatogenesis whereby differentiation of spermatogonia into more mature spermatogonia does not occur.

steroid. A generic term referring to closely related compounds that contain a common ring structure. (See Figures 5-9 and 5-10)

steroidogenic. Producing or synthesizing steroid hormones.

stigma. The small protrusion at the apex of a follicle that represents a site of deterioration of the follicular wall prior to ovulation.

stomodeal ectoderm. A layer lining the stomodeum or embryonic mouth (oral cavity). (See Figure 4-3)

stomodeum. A depression in the oral region of the embryo that will form the mouth and become continuous with the gut. (See Figure 4-3)

stratified squamous epithelium. A type of epithelium characterized by irregular flattened cells in multiple layers lining portions of the vagina and covering the glans penis. (See Figure 2-22)

submucosa. A general region of tissue lying just beneath the mucosal layer housing the vasculature, nerve supply and lymphatics. (See Figures 2-1, 2-12, 2-16 and 2-22)

suburethral diverticulum. An outpocketing of tissue located just beneath the urethra that forms a blind pouch with probably no functional significance.

sulfate salt. An end product of the metabolism of testosterone that is excreted in urine. (See Figure 5-17)

sulfated glycoproteins 1 and 2. The products of Sertoli cells believed to be related to fertility acquisition (SGP-1) and provides a detergent effect that allows spermatozoa and fluids to move through the tubular network of the testis with ease (SPG-2).

sulfomucin. A type of mucus characterized as being highly viscous and produced by cells that line the lumen in the bovine cervix. (See Figure 12-5)

superfecundation. Fertilization of two or more ova during the same estrus by sperm from different males. For example, since the bitch has an estrus of several days, mating can occur during this time by several males. Thus, it is common for a bitch to deliver a litter containing offspring sired by several males.

superfetation. The presence of fetuses of different ages (not twins) resulting from fertilization of oocytes ovulated in successive periods of estrus.

superior cervical ganglion. The ganglion where neurons from the suprachiasmatic nucleus synapse with neurons that innervate the pineal gland to control melatonin release.

superior hypophyseal artery. The primary artery supplying the hypothalamo-hypophyseal portal system.

superovulation. Ovulation of abnormally high numbers of ova.

supplemental (accessory) corpora lutea. Corpora lutea that form as a result of eCG secretion from the endometrial cups in the mare. These corpora lutea produce progesterone that helps maintain pregnancy when the reduction in progesterone secretion by the primary corpus luteum occurs and before the onset of placental secretion of progesterone. (See Figure 14-7)

supplementary corpora lutea. The corpora lutea produced by the pregnant mare as a result of ovulation and/or luteinization induced by equine chorionic gonadotropin. (See Figure 14-7)

suprachiasmatic nucleus. A hypothalamic nucleus located just above the optic chiasm that is believed to be part of the GnRH surge center.

surge center. See preovulatory GnRH center.

sustained transport phase. Phase in which spermatozoa are transported to the ampulla of the oviducts in a "trickle-like" effect from the cervix and/or uterotubal junction.

synapse. The functional junction between two nerve cells characterized by close apposition of the membrane of the presynaptic terminal (teledendrite) with the postsynaptic membrane (dendrite). Nerve terminals can also synapse with blood vessels, in the case of the hypothalamic portal system, or in the case of oxytocin producing neurons in the posterior lobe of the pituitary.

synchronization of estrus (ovulation). Hormonal intervention designed to interrupt the luteal phases or to stimulate the onset of the follicular phase so that a group of females will display estrus and ovulate at similar times. (See Figures 9-19 and 9-20)

syncytiotrophoblast. Cells comprising the outer layer of the trophoblast that make contact with the endometrium of the uterus forming attachment with the endometrium.

syndesmochorial placenta. A type of epitheliochorial placenta in which the endometrial epithelium locally erodes, causing intermittent exposure of the maternal capillaries to the chorionic epithelium.

syndrome. A group of symptoms that occur together.

syngamy. The fusion of the male and female pronuclei within the cytoplasm of the newly fertilized oocyte, giving rise to the zygote.

systolic pressure. Blood pressure occurring during ventricular systole (contraction). Systolic pressure is the highest pressure during the cardiac cycle.

target tissue. A tissue containing receptors to a specific hormone or neurotransmitter.

teratogenic. Causing physical defects in the developing conceptus.

terminal piece. The terminal portion (end) of the flagellum of mammalian spermatozoa. (See Figure 10-9)

tertiary follicle. See antral follicle. (See Figure 2-11)

testicular artery. The vessel that provides the arterial blood supply to the testes. It originates from the abdominal aorta, passes through the inguinal canal and becomes quite torturous in the spermatic cord and provides the surface for the venous pampiniform plexus. In most species the testicular artery is highly convoluted on the surface of the testes and then enters the interior of it. (See Figures 3-2, 3-9 and 3-10)

testicular capsule. The tunica albuginea and visceral vaginal tunic. (See Figure 3-15)

testis (pl. testes). One of the two male gonads.

testis determining factor (TDF). A substance synthesized by the primitive sex cords of the male embryo that causes the development of the male gonad and the male reproductive tract. The absence of TDF results in the development of the female reproductive tract. (See Figure 4-6)

testosterone. The male sex hormone and the most potent naturally occurring androgen produced by the interstitial cells of Leydig. (See Figure 5-10)

theca externa. The outermost layer of an antral follicle that provides structural integrity and support for the follicle. (See Figure 9-2)

theca interna. The layer of flattened spindle-shaped cells just outside the basement membrane of an antral follicle with receptors to LH. (See Figures 2-11, 8-9)

theriogenology. A specialty of veterinary medicine focusing on the physiology and pathology of the reproductive system of animals.

third ventricle. One of the ventricles of the brain that is attached to the right and left lateral ventricles and to the cerebral aqueduct. It is surrounded by the hypothalamus. (See Figures 5-3, 5-4)

threshold. The minimal stimulus required to elicit a response.

thyroxin. Hormone produced by the thyroid gland that governs metabolic rate.

tight junctions. Specialized intracellular junctions that prevent materials from gaining access to the adluminal compartment of the seminiferous epithelium. (See Figures 3-16 and 10-3)

tonic GnRH center. A term used to describe the hypothalamic nuclei that control the tonic release of GnRH. The tonic center collectively consists of the ventromedial nucleus, the arcuate nucleus and the median eminence. (See Figures 5-3, 5-5 and 5-6)

totipotency. The ability of a single cell to differentiate and develop into a complete organism.

transabdominal phase. The phase of testicular descent in which the testicle moves from the level of the ribs to the inguinal region. The transabdominal phase takes place because of elongation of the body away from a stationary testicle and the rapid growth of the gubernaculum toward the scrotum. This phase is controlled by Insulin-like growth factor-3 (Insl-3).

transcervical insemination. Technique of artificial insemination in which the semen is deposited into the uterus using a pipette to penetrate and bypass the cervix (cow and mare). (See Figure 12-3)

transdermal patch. A patch that is applied to the skin (similar to a band-aid) that contains progestin that diffuses through the skin and enters the blood. Patches are replaced weekly for three weeks. During a "patch free week" progesterone drops and a new menstrual period begins.

transduce. To convert from one form of energy into another form of energy.

transferrin. A plasma globulin responsible for transporting iron. Some transferrin is produced by Sertoli cells. Relatively high concentrations are found in fluid of the seminiferous tubules and the rete tubules.

transgene. A cloned gene not normally found in the genone of the species that is introduced into the plant or animal. It is stably incorporated into the plant or animal and is passed on to successive generations.

transgenic. Referring to any plant or animal carrying a transgene.

translocating cytoplasmic droplet. The residual cytoplasm from spermiogenesis that is relocating from the neck to the distal middle piece of the spermatozoa. Sperm containing translocating droplets are characterized as having the flagellum bent back toward the head of the sperm forming a crook containing the droplet. (See Figure 3-18)

transmembrane domain. The portion of a hormone receptor within the plasma membrane that connects the extracellular and intracellular domains. (See Figure 5-13)

transuterine migration. The mechanism for maternal recognition of pregnancy in the mare via the movement of the conceptus through both uterine horns for a defined period of time. In other species, the migration of the conceptus from one uterine horn to the other. (See Figure 13-7)

transvaginal follicular aspiration. A non-surgical technique used to recover oocytes from mares and cows in which an ultrasound guided hypodermic needle is inserted through the vaginal wall into a dominant follicle and the follicular fluid containing the oocyte is aspirated. (See Figure 13-10)

trophectoderm. The cell layer from which the trophoblast differentiates. (See Figure 13-4)

trophoblast. The cell layer covering the blastocyst that will form the chorion. (See Figure 13-4)

-tropin. A suffix referring to nourishment or having an affinity for.

true anestrous. A condition where a female does not cycle due to insufficient hormonal stimuli.

tubular compartment. The compartment of the testicular parenchyma consisting of the seminiferous tubules.

tubulus contortus. The highly convoluted tortuous component of a seminiferous tubule contributing to the majority of its length. It is attached to a straight portion (tubulus rectus) that connects to the rete tubule. The tubulus contortus is the primary site of spermatogenesis. (See Figure 3-15)

tumescence. A swelling or enlarging as in penile erection.

tumor necrosis factor-alpha. A cytokine involved in systemic inflammation that is produced primarily by macrophages. It is thought to play a role in ovulation by destroying granulosal cells and facilitating the action of collagenase to promote follicular weakening during ovulation.

tunica albuginea. A dense, white connective tissue covering an organ (testis, ovary, penis). (See Figures 2-11, 3-14, 3-15 and 11-9)

tunica dartos. The layer of smooth muscle that is a component of the scrotum that controls contraction and relaxation of the scrotum. (See Figure 3-15)

tunica vasculosa. A layer well supplied with blood vessels. The vascular lining of the connective tissue septa within the testes. (See Figure 3-15)

umbilical cord. A cord-like structure that connects the developing fetus to the placenta. It contains two arteries and one vein that bring nutrients to the fetus and transports fetal wastes to the dam. (See Figure 14-2)

up-regulate. An increase in receptor density.

urethral gland. See disseminate prostate.

urethral tubercle. An elevated nodule located dorsal to the urethra in the vagina of the bitch. (See Figure 2-9)

urethralis muscle. The striated, circular muscle surrounding the pelvic urethra, the contractions of which cause semen to move into the penile urethra. (See Figures 3-2, 3-3, 3-4, 3-6, 3-7, 3-8, 3-19 and 3-20)

urogenital sinus. An embryonic cavity in the caudal portion of the animal that will give rise to the bladder, the pelvic urethra (male), the vagina (female) and the external genitalia of both the male and female. (See Figure 4-14)

uterectomy. Complete removal of the uterus; also known as a hysterectomy. (See Figure 9-10)

uterine horns (cornua). The portions of the uterus that are the result of the incomplete fusion of paramesonephric ducts. (See Figures 2-2, 2-3, 2-4, 2-7, 2-8, 2-9, and 2-10)

uterine involution. The acquisition of normal uterine size and function in the postpartum female. (See Figure 15-1)

utero-ovarian ligament. A portion of the broad ligament that attaches the ovary to the uterus. (See Figure 2-13)

uterotubal junction. The site where the oviduct joins the uterus.

uterus. A hollow, tubular organ surrounded by smooth muscle and lined with epithelium that connects the cervix to the oviducts. It is responsible for sperm transport, early embryonic development, formation of maternal placenta, housing the fetus throughout gestation and parturition. The uterus produces prostaglandin $F_{2\alpha}$.

vagina. The female copulatory organ that connects the external genitalia to the cervix. (See Figures 2-4, 2-5, 2-6, 2-7, 2-8, 2-9, and 2-10b)

vaginal cavity. The space that separates the visceral vaginal tunic from the parietal vaginal tunic of the descended testicle. (See Figure 4-8)

vaginal process. The space (cavity) formed between the visceral and parietal vaginal tunics during descent of the testes. (See Figure 4-8)

vaginal ring. A small, flexible ring inserted into the vagina that steadily releases uniform concentrations of progestin for a period of three weeks. Removal of the ring initiates a menstrual period.

vas deferens. (See ductus deferens).

vascular countercurrent exchange. A process whereby exchange of substances and/or heat occurs between an artery and a vein that are intimately associated. (See Figures 3-9, 9-11)

ventromedial nucleus. A hypothalamic nucleus located in the medial floor of the hypothalamus that contributes to the tonic GnRH center.

vesicular glands. Paired accessory sex glands located lateral to the ductus deferens and dorsal to the pelvic urethra. They secrete a portion of the seminal plasma into the pelvic urethra. (See Figures 3-4, 3-5, 3-6, 3-19, and 3-20)

vesiculation. A process whereby membrane vesicles are formed. Vesiculation occurs during the acrosome reaction when the plasma membrane of the sperm fuses with the outer acrosomal membrane, forming many small vesicles. (See Figure 12-11)

vestibular glands. Mucous secreting glands located in the wall of the vestibule. The secretion from these glands lubricates the vestibule at copulation and at parturition. The odor of the secretions has a sexually stimulating effect on the male in some species.

vestibule. The portion of the vagina cranial to the clitoris extending to and including the urethral opening. It is common to both the urinary and reproductive systems. (See Figures 2-5, 2-7, and 2-9)

visceral vaginal tunic. The layer of peritoneum that defines the inside boundary of the vaginal cavity in the male. This layer is tightly adherent to the tunica albuginea of the testis. (See Figure 3-15)

vital dye. Staining material for living cells that does not result in cell death.

vitelline block. A phenomenon that prevents polyspermy by rendering the plasma membrane of the oocyte incapable of further binding with the sperm membrane.

vomeronasal organ. An accessory olfactory organ consisting of a pair of blind ducts located ventral to the nasal cavity. The ducts open into the oral cavity through the incisive duct. They are believed to be associated with identification of nonvolatile pheromones. (See Figure 11-5)

vulva. The external genitalia of the female. (See Figures 2-23 and 2-24)

Wolffian duct. See mesonephric duct.

X chromosome. Female somatic chromosome.

Y chromosome. Male somatic chromosome.

yolk sac. An extraembryonic structure that develops from the primitive endoderm and regresses in size as the conceptus develops. In mammals the yolk sac does not contain yolk. However, it does contribute primitive germ cells that migrate to the genital ridge, and also produces erythrocytes and alpha fetoprotein. (See Figures 4-4, 13-4)

zona block. A mechanism to prevent polyspermy that renders the zona pellucida incapable of binding additional spermatozoa.

zona lysin. An enzyme in the acrosome that aids in penetration of the zona pellucida.

zona pellucida. A thick, translucent mucoprotein surrounding the oocyte and early embryo. (See Figures 2-11, 12-10, 12-12 and 12-13)

zona proteins (ZP). Specific proteins of the zona pellucida that provide structure (ZP1 and ZP2) and bind spermatozoa (ZP3). (See Figure 12-10)

zonary placenta. A placenta of dogs and cats in which chorionic villi attach to the uterus in a well defined zone or band. (See Figure 14-2)

zygote. The diploid cell resulting from the fusion of the male and female pronuclei. (See Figure 13-1)

INDEX

F = Figure; S = Specimen Photo; T = Table

F = Figure; S = Specimen Photo; T = Table

F = Figure; S = Specimen Photo; T = Table

F = Figure; S = Specimen Photo; T = Table

R

F = Figure; S = Specimen Photo; T = Table

F = Figure; S = Specimen Photo; T = Table

F = Figure; S = Specimen Photo; T = Table